PEARSON ALWAYS LEARNING

Finite Mathematics and its Applications

Fourth Custom Edition for the University of Victoria

Taken from:
Finite Mathematics and its Applications, Twelfth Edition
by Larry J. Goldstein, David I. Schneider, Martha J. Siegel,
and Steven M. Hair

Finite Mathematics for Business, Economics, Life Sciences, and Social Sciences, Fourteenth Edition
by Raymond A. Barnett, Michael R. Ziegler, Karl E. Byleen,
and Christopher J. Stocker

Cover Art: Courtesy of Jill Simmons.

Taken/Excerpts taken from:

Finite Mathematics and its Applications, Twelfth Edition
by Larry J. Goldstein, David I. Schneider, Martha J. Siegel, and Steven M. Hair

New York, New York 10013

Finite Mathematics for Business, Economics, Life Sciences, and Social Sciences, Fourteenth Edition
by Raymond A. Barnett, Michael R. Ziegler, Karl E. Byleen, and Christopher J. Stocker

New York, New York 10013

Pearson Custom Edition.

Pearson Education, Inc., 330 Hudson Street, New York, New York 10013
A Pearson Education Company
www.pearsoned.com

Printed in the United States of America

10 2021

000200010272198387

EJ

ISBN 10: 0-135-88995-2
ISBN 13: 978-0-135-88995-4

Contents

Chapters 1–4 are taken from *Finite Mathematics and its Applications*, Twelfth Edition, by Larry J. Goldstein, David I. Schneider, Martha J. Siegel, and Steven M. Hair

Chapters 3 and 5–6 are taken from *Finite Mathematics for Business, Economics, Life Sciences, and Social Sciences*, Fourteenth Edition, by Raymond A. Barnett, Michael R. Ziegler, Karl E. Byleen, and Christopher J. Stocker

CHAPTER

1

Sets and Counting

In this chapter, we introduce some ideas useful in the study of probability (Chapter 2). Our first topic, the theory of sets, will provide a convenient language and notation in which to discuss probability. Using set theory, we develop a number of counting principles that can also be applied to computing probabilities.

1.1 Sets

In many applied problems, one must consider collections of various sorts of objects. For example, a survey of unemployment trends might consider the collection of all U.S. cities with current unemployment greater than 9 percent. A study of birthrates might consider the collection of countries with a current birthrate less than 20 per 1000 population. Such collections are examples of sets. A **set** is any collection of objects. The objects, which may be countries, cities, years, numbers, letters, or anything else, are called the **elements** of the set. A set is often specified by listing its elements inside a pair of braces. For example, the set whose elements are the first six letters of the alphabet is written

$$\{a, b, c, d, e, f\}.$$

Similarly, the set whose elements are the even numbers between 1 and 11 is written

$$\{2, 4, 6, 8, 10\}.$$

We can also specify a set by giving a description of its elements (without actually listing the elements). For example, the set $\{a, b, c, d, e, f\}$ can also be written

$$\{\text{the first six letters of the alphabet}\},$$

and the set $\{2, 4, 6, 8, 10\}$ can be written

$$\{\text{all even numbers between 1 and 11}\}.$$

For convenience, we usually denote sets by capital letters, A, B, C, and so on.

Two sets A and B are said to be **equal** if every element of A is also in B, and every element of B is also in A. For example,

$$\{a, b, c, d, e, f\} = \{f, e, d, b, c, a\}$$

and

$$\{2, 4, 6, 8\} = \{2, 2, 4, 4, 4, 6, 6, 8\}.$$

The great diversity of sets is illustrated by the following examples:

1. Let $C = \{\text{possible sequences of outcomes of tossing a coin three times}\}$. If we let H denote "heads" and T denote "tails," the various sequences can be easily described:

$$C = \{\text{HHH, THH, HTH, HHT, TTH, THT, HTT, TTT}\},$$

where, for instance, THH means "first toss tails, second toss heads, third toss heads."

2. Let $B = \{\text{license plate numbers consisting of three letters followed by three digits}\}$. Some elements of B are

SBG 602, GXZ 179, YHJ 006.

The number of elements in B is sufficiently large so that listing all of them is impractical. However, in this chapter, we develop a technique that allows us to calculate the number of elements of B.

3. The graph of the equation $y = x^2$ is the set of all points (a, b) in the plane for which $b = a^2$. This set has infinitely many elements.

Sets arise in many practical contexts, as the next example shows.

EXAMPLE 1 **Listing the Elements of a Set** Table 1 gives the rate of inflation, as measured by the percentage change in the consumer price index, for the years from 1996 to 2015. Let

$$A = \{\text{years from 1996 to 2015 in which inflation was above 3\%}\}$$
$$B = \{\text{years from 1996 to 2015 in which inflation was below 2\%}\}.$$

Determine the elements of A and B.

Table 1 U.S. Inflation Rates

Year	Inflation (%)	Year	Inflation (%)
1996	3.0	2006	3.2
1997	2.3	2007	2.8
1998	1.6	2008	3.8
1999	2.2	2009	−0.4
2000	3.4	2010	1.6
2001	2.8	2011	3.2
2002	1.6	2012	2.1
2003	2.3	2013	1.5
2004	2.7	2014	1.6
2005	3.4	2015	0.1

(Source: www.bls.gov)

SOLUTION By reading Table 1, we see that

$$A = \{2000, 2005, 2006, 2008, 2011\}$$
$$B = \{1998, 2002, 2009, 2010, 2013, 2014, 2015\}.$$

» ***Now Try Exercises 9(a) and (b)***

Suppose that we are given two sets, A and B. Then it is possible to form new sets from A and B.

DEFINITIONS Union and Intersection of Two Sets The **union** of A and B, written $A \cup B$ and pronounced "A union B," is defined as follows:

$A \cup B$ is the set of all elements that belong to either A or B (or both).

The **intersection** of A and B, written $A \cap B$ and pronounced "A intersection B," is defined as follows:

$A \cap B$ is the set of all elements that belong to both A and B.

For example, let $A = \{1, 2, 3, 4\}$ and $B = \{1, 3, 5, 7, 11\}$. Then,

$$A \cup B = \{1, 2, 3, 4, 5, 7, 11\}$$
$$A \cap B = \{1, 3\}.$$

EXAMPLE 2 **The Intersection and Union of Sets** Table 2 gives the rates of unemployment and inflation for the years from 2001 to 2015. Let

$$A = \{\text{years from 2001 to 2015 in which unemployment is at least 5\%}\}$$
$$B = \{\text{years from 2001 to 2015 in which the inflation rate is at least 3\%}\}.$$

(a) Describe the sets $A \cap B$ and $A \cup B$.
(b) Determine the elements of A, B, $A \cap B$, and $A \cup B$.

Table 2 U.S. Unemployment and Inflation Rates

Year	Unemployment (%)	Inflation (%)
2001	4.7	2.8
2002	5.8	1.6
2003	6.0	2.3
2004	5.5	2.7
2005	5.1	3.4
2006	4.6	3.2
2007	4.6	2.8
2008	5.8	3.8
2009	9.3	−0.4
2010	9.6	1.6
2011	8.9	3.2
2012	8.1	2.1
2013	7.4	1.5
2014	6.2	1.6
2015	5.3	0.1

(Source: www.bls.gov)

SOLUTION **(a)** From the descriptions of A and B, we have

$$A \cap B = \{\text{years from 2001 to 2015 in which unemployment is at least 5\% and inflation is at least 3\%}\}$$

$$A \cup B = \{\text{years from 2001 to 2015 in which either unemployment is at least 5\% or inflation is at least 3\% (or both)}\}.$$

(b) From the table, we see that

$$A = \{2002, 2003, 2004, 2005, 2008, 2009, 2010, 2011, 2012, 2013, 2014, 2015\}$$

$$B = \{2005, 2006, 2008, 2011\}$$

$$A \cap B = \{2005, 2008, 2011\}$$

$$A \cup B = \{2002, 2003, 2004, 2005, 2006, 2008, 2009, 2010, 2011, 2012, 2013, 2014, 2015\}.$$

>> Now Try Exercises 9(c) and (d)

We have defined the union and the intersection of two sets. In a similar manner, we can define the union and intersection of any number of sets. For example, if A, B, and C are three sets, then their union, denoted $A \cup B \cup C$, is the set whose elements are precisely those that belong to at least one of the sets A, B, and C. Similarly, the intersection of A, B, and C, denoted $A \cap B \cap C$, is the set consisting of those elements that belong to all of the sets A, B, and C. In a similar way, we may define the union and intersection of more than three sets.

Suppose that we are given a set A. We may form new sets by selecting elements from A. Sets formed in this way are called *subsets* of A.

> DEFINITION **Subset of a Set** The set B is a **subset** of the set A, written $B \subseteq A$ and pronounced "B is a subset of A," provided that every element of B is an element of A.

For example, $\{1, 3\} \subseteq \{1, 2, 3\}$.

One set that is considered very often is the set that contains no elements at all. This set is called the **empty set** (or *null set*) and is written $\varnothing$ or $\{\ \}$. The empty set is a subset of every set. (Here is why: Let A be any set. Every element of $\varnothing$ also belongs to A. If you do not agree, then you must produce an element of $\varnothing$ that does not belong to A. But you cannot, since $\varnothing$ has no elements. So $\varnothing \subseteq A$.)

> DEFINITION **Disjoint Sets** Two sets A and B are **disjoint** if they have no elements in common, that is, if $A \cap B = \varnothing$.

EXAMPLE 3 **Listing the Subsets of a Set** Let $A = \{a, b, c\}$. Find all subsets of A.

SOLUTION Since A contains three elements, every subset of A has at most three elements. We look for subsets according to the number of elements:

Number of Elements in Subset	Possible Subsets
0	$\varnothing$
1	$\{a\}, \{b\}, \{c\}$
2	$\{a, b\}, \{a, c\}, \{b, c\}$
3	$\{a, b, c\}$

Thus, we see that A has eight subsets, namely, those listed on the right. (Note that we count A as a subset of itself.)

>> Now Try Exercise 5

In general, if a set A contains n elements, then A will have 2^n subsets.

It is usually convenient to regard all sets involved in a particular discussion as subsets of a single larger set. Thus, for example, if a problem involves the sets $\{a, b, c\}$, $\{e, f\}$, $\{g\}$, $\{b, x, y\}$, then we can regard all of these as subsets of the set

$$U = \{\text{all letters of the alphabet}\}.$$

Since U contains all elements being discussed, it is called a **universal set** (for the particular problem). In this book, we shall specify the particular universal set that we have in mind or it will be clearly defined by the context.

The set A contained in the universal set U has a counterpart, called its *complement*.

DEFINITION Complement of a Set The **complement** of A, written A' and pronounced "A complement," is defined as follows:

A' is the set of all elements in the universal set U that do not belong to A.

For example, let $U = \{1, 2, 3, 4, 5, 6, 7, 8, 9\}$ and $A = \{2, 4, 6, 8\}$. Then,

$$A' = \{1, 3, 5, 7, 9\}.$$

EXAMPLE 4 **Finding the Complement of a Set** Let $U = \{a, b, c, d, e, f, g\}$, $S = \{a, b, c\}$, and $T = \{a, c, d\}$. List the elements of the following sets:

(a) S' **(b)** T' **(c)** $(S \cap T)'$ **(d)** $S' \cap T'$ **(e)** $S' \cup T'$

SOLUTION

(a) S' consists of those elements of U that are not in S, so $S' = \{d, e, f, g\}$.

(b) Similarly, $T' = \{b, e, f, g\}$.

(c) As is the case in arithmetic, we perform the operation in parentheses first. To determine $(S \cap T)'$, we must first determine $S \cap T$:

$$S \cap T = \{a, c\}.$$

Then, we determine the complement of this set:

$$(S \cap T)' = \{b, d, e, f, g\}.$$

(d) We determined S' and T' in parts (a) and (b). The set $S' \cap T'$ consists of the elements that belong to both S' and T'. Therefore, referring to parts (a) and (b), we have

$$S' \cap T' = \{e, f, g\}.$$

(e) Since $S' \cup T'$ consists of the elements that belong to S' or T' (or both),

$$S' \cup T' = \{b, d, e, f, g\}.$$

» Now Try Exercises 9(e) and (f)

NOTE The results of parts (c) and (d) show that in general $(S \cap T)'$ *is not* the same as $S' \cap T'$. In the next section, we show that $(S \cap T)'$ *is* the same as $S' \cup T'$. «

EXAMPLE 5 **College Students** Let $U = $ {students at Gotham College}, $E = $ {students at Gotham College who are at most 18 years old}, and $S = $ {STEM majors at Gotham College}.

(a) Use set-theoretic notation (that is, union, intersection, and complement symbols) to describe {students at Gotham College who are at most 18 years old or are not STEM majors}.

(b) Use set-theoretic notation to describe {students at Gotham College who are older than 18 and are STEM majors}.

(c) Describe in words the set $E' \cap S'$.

(d) Describe in words the set $E' \cup S$.

SOLUTION (a) $E \cup S'$
(b) $E' \cap S$
(c) {students at Gotham College who are older than 18 and are not STEM majors}
(d) {students at Gotham College who are older than 18 or are STEM majors}

» Now Try Exercises 21 and 33

The symbol $\in$ is commonly used with sets as a shorthand for "is an element of." For instance, if $S = \{H, T\}$, then $H \in S$. The symbol $\in$ should not be confused with the symbol $\subseteq$. For instance, $H \in S$, but $\{H\} \subseteq S$. The symbol $\notin$ is shorthand for "is not an element of." The symbol $\in$ can be used when defining union, intersection, complement, and subset.

DEFINITIONS

Union	$A \cup B$ is the set of all x such that $x \in A$ or $x \in B$.
Intersection	$A \cap B$ is the set of all x such that $x \in A$ and $x \in B$.
Complement	A' is the set of all $x \in U$ such that $x \notin A$.
Subset	$B \subseteq A$ if $x \in A$ whenever $x \in B$.

Check Your Understanding 1.1

Solutions can be found following the section exercises.

1. Let $U = \{a, b, c, d, e, f, g\}$, $R = \{a, b, c, d\}$, $S = \{c, d, e\}$, and $T = \{c, e, g\}$. List the elements of the following sets:
   (a) R' (b) $R \cap S$
   (c) $(R \cap S) \cap T$ (d) $R \cap (S \cap T)$
2. Let $U =$ {all Nobel winners}, $W =$ {women who have received Nobel Prizes}, $A =$ {Americans who have received Nobel Prizes}, $L =$ {Nobel winners in literature}. Describe the following sets:
   (a) W' (b) $A \cap L'$ (c) $W \cap A \cap L'$
3. Refer to Problem 2. Use set-theoretic notation to describe {Nobel winners who are American men or recipients of the Nobel Prize in literature}.

EXERCISES 1.1

1. Let $U = \{1, 2, 3, 4, 5, 6, 7\}$, $S = \{1, 2, 3, 4\}$, and $T = \{1, 3, 5, 7\}$. List the elements of the following sets:
   (a) S' (b) $S \cup T$ (c) $S \cap T$ (d) $S' \cap T$
2. Let $U = \{1, 2, 3, 4, 5\}$, $S = \{1, 2, 3\}$, and $T = \{5\}$. List the elements of the following sets:
   (a) S' (b) $S \cup T$ (c) $S \cap T$ (d) $S' \cap T$
3. Let $U =$ {all letters of the alphabet}, $R = \{a, b, c\}$, $S = \{a, e, i, o, u\}$, and $T = \{x, y, z\}$. List the elements of the following sets:
   (a) $R \cup S$ (b) $R \cap S$ (c) $S \cap T$ (d) $S' \cap R$
4. Let $U = \{a, b, c, d, e, f, g\}$, $R = \{a\}$, $S = \{a, b\}$, and $T = \{b, d, e, f, g\}$. List the elements of the following sets:
   (a) $R \cup S$ (b) $R \cap S$ (c) T' (d) $T' \cup S$
5. List all subsets of the set $\{1, 2\}$.
6. List all subsets of the set $\{1, 2, 3, 4\}$.
7. **College Students** Let $U =$ {all college students}, $F =$ {all freshman college students), and $B =$ {all college students who like basketball}. Describe the elements of the following sets:
   (a) $F \cap B$ (b) B' (c) $F' \cap B'$ (d) $F \cup B$
8. **Corporations** Let $U =$ {all corporations}, $S =$ {all corporations with headquarters in New York City}, and $T =$ {all privately owned corporations}. Describe the elements of the following sets:
   (a) S' (b) T' (c) $S \cap T$ (d) $S \cap T'$
9. **S&P Index** The Standard and Poor's Index measures the price of a certain collection of 500 stocks. Table 3 on the next page compares the percentage change in the index during the first 5 business days of certain years with the percentage change for the entire year. Let $U =$ {all years from 1996 to 2015}, $S =$ {all years during which the index increased by 2% or more during the first 5 business days}, and $T =$ {all years for which the index increased by 16% or more during the entire year}. List the elements of the following sets:
   (a) S (b) T (c) $S \cap T$
   (d) $S \cup T$ (e) $S' \cap T$ (f) $S \cap T'$
10. **S&P Index** Refer to Table 3 on the next page. Let $U =$ {all years from 1996 to 2015}, $A =$ {all years during which the index declined during the first 5 business days}, and $B =$ {all years during which the index declined for the entire year}. List the elements of the following sets:
    (a) A (b) B (c) $A \cap B$
    (d) $A' \cap B$ (e) $A \cap B'$
11. **S&P Index** Refer to Exercise 9. Describe in words the fact that $S \cap T'$ has two elements.
12. **S&P Index** Refer to Exercise 10. Describe in words the fact that $A' \cap B$ has two elements.
13. Let $U = \{a, b, c, d, e, f\}$, $R = \{a, b, c\}$, $S = \{a, b, d\}$, and $T = \{e, f\}$. List the elements of the following sets:
    (a) $(R \cup S)'$ (b) $R \cup S \cup T$
    (c) $R \cap S \cap T$ (d) $R \cap S \cap T'$
    (e) $R' \cap S \cap T$ (f) $S \cup T$
    (g) $(R \cup S) \cap (R \cup T)$ (h) $(R \cap S) \cup (R \cap T)$
    (i) $R' \cap T'$

Table 3 Percentage Change in the Standard and Poor's Index

Year	Percent Change for First 5 Days	Percent Change for Year	Year	Percent Change for First 5 Days	Percent Change for Year
2015	0.0	−0.7	2005	−2.1	3.0
2014	−0.5	11.4	2004	1.8	9.0
2013	2.2	29.6	2003	3.4	26.4
2012	1.7	13.4	2002	1.1	−23.4
2011	1.1	0.0	2001	−1.9	−13.0
2010	2.7	12.8	2000	−1.9	−10.1
2009	0.7	23.5	1999	3.7	19.5
2008	−5.3	−38.5	1998	−1.5	26.7
2007	−0.4	4.8	1997	1.0	31.0
2006	3.0	13.6	1996	0.4	20.3

(Source: www.forecast-chart.com, www.investing.com)

14. Let $U = \{1, 2, 3, 4, 5\}$, $R = \{1, 3, 5\}$, $S = \{3, 4, 5\}$, and $T = \{2, 4\}$. List the elements of the following sets:
(a) $R \cap S \cap T$ **(b)** $R \cap S \cap T'$ **(c)** $R \cap S' \cap T$
(d) $R' \cap T$ **(e)** $R \cup S$ **(f)** $R' \cup R$
(g) $(S \cap T)'$ **(h)** $S' \cup T'$

In Exercises 15–20, simplify each given expression.

15. $(S')'$ **16.** $S \cap S'$ **17.** $S \cup S'$
18. $S \cap \varnothing$ **19.** $T \cap S \cap T'$ **20.** $S \cup \varnothing$

Corporation A large corporation classifies its many divisions by their performance in the preceding year. Let P = {divisions that made a profit}, L = {divisions that had an increase in labor costs}, and T = {divisions whose total revenue increased}. Describe the sets in Exercises 21–26 by using set-theoretic notation.

21. {divisions that had increases in labor costs or total revenue}

22. {divisions that did not make a profit}

23. {divisions that made a profit despite an increase in labor costs}

24. {divisions that had an increase in labor costs and either were unprofitable or did not increase their total revenue}

25. {profitable divisions with increases in labor costs and total revenue}

26. {divisions that were unprofitable or did not have increases in either labor costs or total revenue}

Automobile Insurance An automobile insurance company classifies applicants by their driving records for the previous three years. Let S = {applicants who have received speeding tickets}, A = {applicants who have caused accidents}, and D = {applicants who have been arrested for driving while intoxicated}. Describe the sets in Exercises 27–32 by using set-theoretic notation.

27. {applicants who have not received speeding tickets}

28. {applicants who have caused accidents and been arrested for drunk driving}

29. {applicants who have received speeding tickets, caused accidents, or been arrested for drunk driving}

30. {applicants who have not been arrested for drunk driving, but have received speeding tickets or have caused accidents}

31. {applicants who have not both caused accidents and received speeding tickets but who have been arrested for drunk driving}

32. {applicants who have not caused accidents or have not been arrested for drunk driving}

College Teachers and Students Let U = {people at Mount College}, A = {students at Mount College}, B = {teachers at Mount College}, C = {people at Mount College who are older than 35}, and D = {people at Mount College who are younger than 35}. Describe verbally the sets in Exercises 33–40.

33. $A \cap D$ **34.** $B \cap C$ **35.** $A \cap B$ **36.** $B \cup C$
37. $A \cup C'$ **38.** $(A \cap D)'$ **39.** D' **40.** $D \cap U$

Ice Cream Preferences Let U = {all people}, S = {people who like strawberry ice cream}, V = {people who like vanilla ice cream}, and C = {people who like chocolate ice cream}. Describe the sets in Exercises 41–46 by using set-theoretic notation.

41. {people who don't like vanilla ice cream}

42. {people who like vanilla but not chocolate ice cream}

43. {people who like vanilla but not chocolate or strawberry ice cream}

44. {people who don't like any of the three flavors of ice cream}

45. {people who like neither chocolate nor vanilla ice cream}

46. {people who like only strawberry and chocolate ice cream}

47. Let U be the set of vertices in Fig. 1. Let R = {vertices (x, y) with $x > 0$}, S = {vertices (x, y) with $y > 0$}, and T = {vertices (x, y) with $x \leq y$}. List the elements of the following sets:
(a) R **(b)** S **(c)** T
(d) $R' \cup S$ **(e)** $R' \cap T$ **(f)** $R \cap S \cap T$

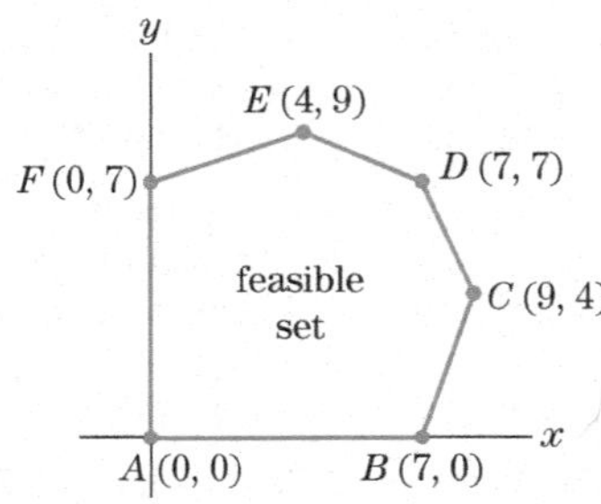

Figure 1

48. Let U be the set of vertices in Fig. 2. Let $R = \{\text{vertices } (x, y) \text{ with } x \geq 150\}$, $S = \{\text{vertices } (x, y) \text{ with } y \leq 100\}$, and $T = \{\text{vertices } (x, y) \text{ with } x + y \leq 400\}$. List the elements of the following sets.
(a) R (b) S (c) T
(d) $R \cap S'$ (e) $R' \cup T$ (f) $R' \cap S' \cap T'$

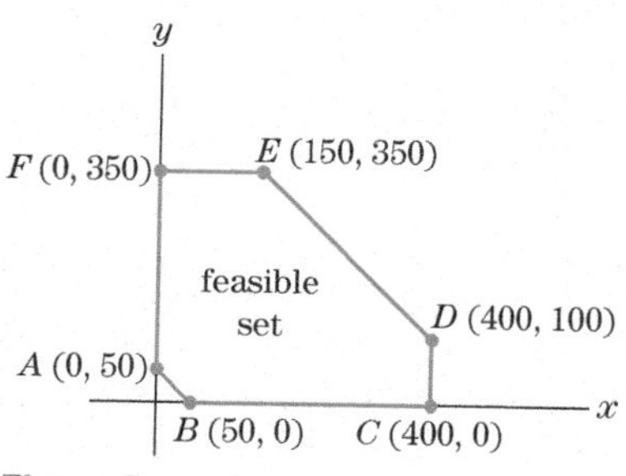

Figure 2

49. **Sandwich Toppings** Ed's Cheesesteaks offers any combination of three toppings on his sandwiches: peppers, onions, and mushrooms. How many different ways can you order a sandwich from Ed? List them.

50. **Toppings Choices** Amy ordered a baked potato at a restaurant. The server offered her butter, cheese, chives, and bacon as toppings. How many different ways could she have her potato? List them.

51. Let $S = \{1, 3, 5, 7\}$ and $T = \{2, 5, 7\}$. Give an example of a subset of T that is not a subset of S.

52. Suppose that S and T are subsets of the set U. Under what circumstance will $S \cap T = T$?

53. Suppose that S and T are subsets of the set U. Under what circumstance will $S \cup T = T$?

54. Find three subsets of the set of integers from 1 through 10, R, S, and T, such that $R \cup (S \cap T)$ is different from $(R \cup S) \cap T$.

In Exercises 55–62, determine whether the statement is true or false.

55. $5 \in \{3, 5, 7\}$
56. $\{1, 3\} \subseteq \{1, 2, 3\}$
57. $\{b\} \subseteq \{b, c\}$
58. $0 \in \{1, 2, 3\}$
59. $0 \in \varnothing$
60. $\varnothing \subseteq \{a, b, c\}$
61. $\{b, c\} \subseteq \{b, c\}$
62. $1 \notin \{1\}$

Solutions to Check Your Understanding 1.1

1. (a) $\{e, f, g\}$ (b) $\{c, d\}$
(c) $\{c\}$. This problem asks for the intersection of two sets. The first set is $R \cap S = \{c, d\}$, and the second set is $T = \{c, e, g\}$. The intersection of these sets is $\{c\}$.
(d) $\{c\}$. Here again, the problem asks for the intersection of two sets. However, now the first set is $R = \{a, b, c, d\}$ and the second set is $S \cap T = \{c, e\}$. The intersection of these sets is $\{c\}$.

Note: It should be expected that the set $(R \cap S) \cap T$ is the same as the set $R \cap (S \cap T)$, for each set consists of those elements that are in all three sets. Therefore, each of these sets equals the set $R \cap S \cap T$.

2. (a) $W' = \{$men who have received Nobel Prizes$\}$. This is so, since W' consists of those elements of U that are not in W—that is, those Nobel winners who are not women.
(b) $A \cap L' = \{$Americans who have received Nobel Prizes in fields other than literature$\}$
(c) $W \cap A \cap L' = \{$American women who have received Nobel Prizes in fields other than literature$\}$. This is so, since to qualify for $W \cap A \cap L'$, a Nobel winner must simultaneously be in W, in A, and in L'—that is, a woman, an American, and not a Nobel winner in literature.

3. $(A \cap W') \cup L$

1.2 A Fundamental Principle of Counting

A counting problem is one that requires us to determine the number of elements in a set S. Counting problems arise in many applications of mathematics and comprise the mathematical field of combinatorics. We shall study a number of different sorts of counting problems in the remainder of this chapter.

If S is any set, we will denote the number of elements in S by $n(S)$. For example, if $S = \{1, 7, 11\}$, then $n(S) = 3$, and if $S = \{a, b, c, d, e, f, g, h, i\}$, then $n(S) = 9$. Of course, if $S = \varnothing$, the empty set, then $n(S) = 0$.

Let us begin by stating one of the fundamental principles of counting, the **inclusion–exclusion principle**.

Inclusion–Exclusion Principle Let S and T be sets. Then,

$$n(S \cup T) = n(S) + n(T) - n(S \cap T). \tag{1}$$

Notice that formula (1) connects the four quantities $n(S \cup T)$, $n(S)$, $n(T)$, and $n(S \cap T)$. Given any three, the remaining quantity can be determined by using this formula.

To test the plausibility of the inclusion–exclusion principle, consider this example. Let $S = \{a, b, c, d, e\}$ and $T = \{a, c, g, h\}$. Then,

$$S \cup T = \{a, b, c, d, e, g, h\} \qquad n(S \cup T) = 7$$
$$S \cap T = \{a, c\} \qquad n(S \cap T) = 2.$$

In this case, the inclusion–exclusion principle reads

$$\begin{aligned} n(S \cup T) &= n(S) + n(T) - n(S \cap T) \\ 7 \quad &= \quad 5 \;\; + \;\; 4 \;\; - \;\; 2, \end{aligned}$$

which is correct.

Here is the reason for the validity of the inclusion–exclusion principle: The left side of formula (1) is $n(S \cup T)$, the number of elements in either S or T (or both). As a first approximation to this number, add the number of elements in S to the number of elements in T, obtaining $n(S) + n(T)$. However, if an element lies in both S and T, it is counted twice—once in $n(S)$ and again in $n(T)$. To make up for this double counting, we must subtract the number of elements counted twice, namely, $n(S \cap T)$. So doing gives us $n(S) + n(T) - n(S \cap T)$ as the number of elements in $S \cup T$.

When S and T are disjoint, the inclusion–exclusion principle reduces to a simple sum.

Inclusion-Exclusion Principle for 2 Sets If $S \cap T = \varnothing$, then

$$n(S \cup T) = n(S) + n(T).$$

The next example illustrates a typical use of the inclusion–exclusion principle in an applied problem.

EXAMPLE 1 **Using the Inclusion–Exclusion Principle** In the year 2016, *Executive* magazine surveyed the presidents of the 500 largest corporations in the United States. Of these 500 people, 310 had degrees (of any sort) in business, 238 had undergraduate degrees in business, and 184 had graduate degrees in business. How many presidents had both undergraduate and graduate degrees in business?

SOLUTION Let

$$S = \{\text{presidents with an undergraduate degree in business}\}$$
$$T = \{\text{presidents with a graduate degree in business}\}.$$

Then,

$$S \cup T = \{\text{presidents with at least one degree in business}\}$$
$$S \cap T = \{\text{presidents with both undergraduate and graduate degrees in business}\}.$$

From the data given, we have

$$n(S) = 238 \qquad n(T) = 184 \qquad n(S \cup T) = 310.$$

The problem asks for $n(S \cap T)$. By the inclusion–exclusion principle, we have

$$\begin{aligned} n(S \cup T) &= n(S) + n(T) - n(S \cap T) \\ 310 &= 238 + 184 - n(S \cap T) \\ n(S \cap T) &= 112. \end{aligned}$$

That is, exactly 112 of the presidents had both undergraduate and graduate degrees in business.

» Now Try Exercise 9

Venn Diagrams

It is possible to visualize sets geometrically by means of drawings known as **Venn diagrams**. Such graphical representations of sets are very useful tools in solving counting problems. In order to describe Venn diagrams, let us begin with a single set S contained in a universal set U. Draw a rectangle, and view its points as the elements of U [Fig. 1(a)]. To show that S is a subset of U, we draw a circle inside the rectangle and view S as the set of points in the circle [Fig. 1(b)]. The resulting diagram is called a Venn diagram of S. It illustrates the proper relationship between S and U. Since S' consists of those elements of U that are not in S, we may view the portion of the rectangle that is outside of the circle as representing S' [Fig. 1(c)].

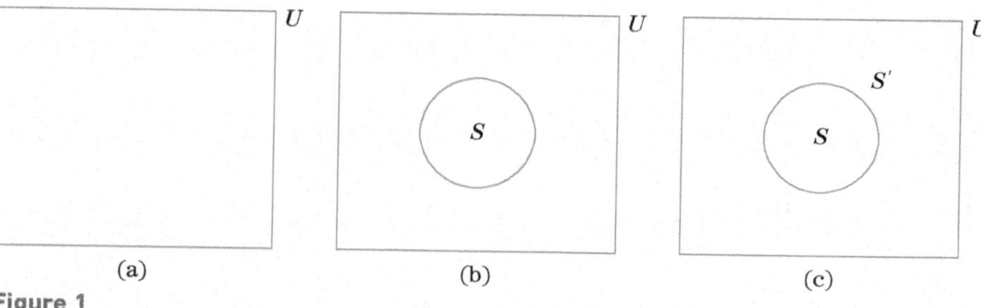

Figure 1

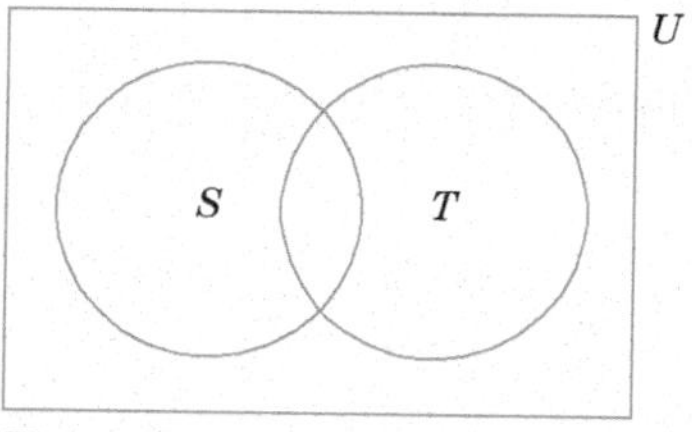

Figure 2

Venn diagrams are particularly useful for visualizing the relationship between two or three sets. Suppose that we are given two sets S and T in a universal set U. As before, we represent each of the sets by means of a circle inside the rectangle (Fig. 2).

We can now illustrate a number of sets by shading in appropriate regions of the rectangle. For instance, in Fig. 3(a), (b), and (c), we have shaded the regions corresponding to T, $S \cup T$, and $S \cap T$, respectively.

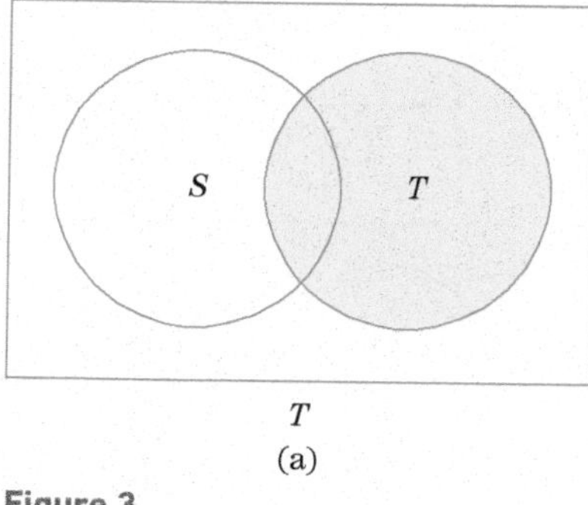

T
(a)

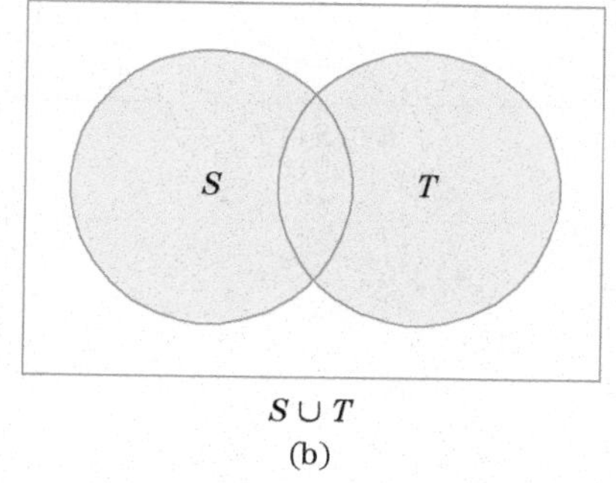
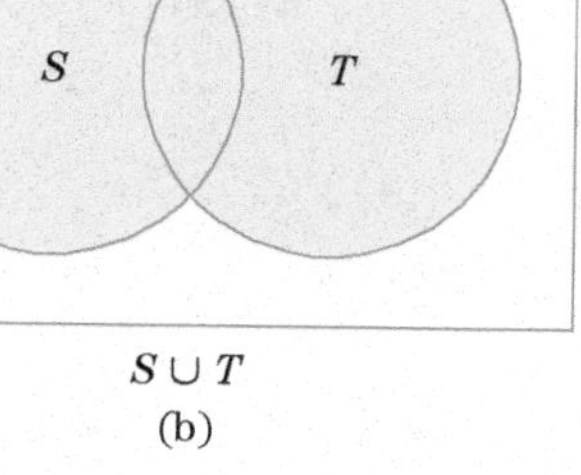

$S \cup T$
(b)

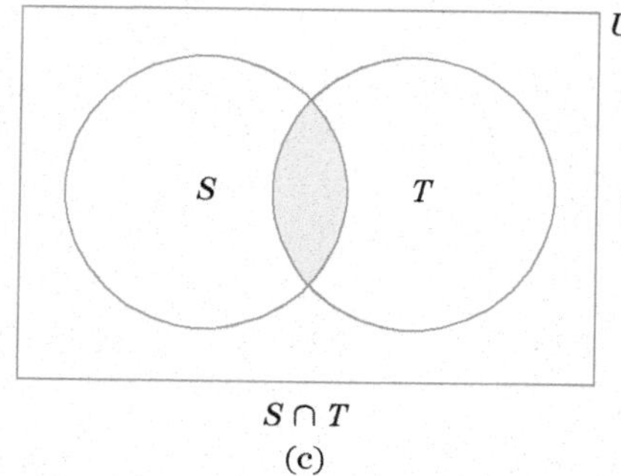

$S \cap T$
(c)

Figure 3

EXAMPLE 2 **Shading Portions of a Venn Diagram** Shade the portions of the rectangle corresponding to the sets
(a) $S \cap T'$ **(b)** $(S \cap T')'$.

SOLUTION
(a) $S \cap T'$ consists of the points in S and in T'—that is, the points in S and not in T [Figs. 4(a), 4(b) on the next page]. So we shade the points that are in the circle S but are not in the circle T [Fig. 4(c)].
(b) $(S \cap T')'$ is the complement of the set $S \cap T'$. Therefore, it consists of exactly those points not shaded in Fig. 4(c). [See Fig. 4(d).]

» Now Try Exercises 15 and 19

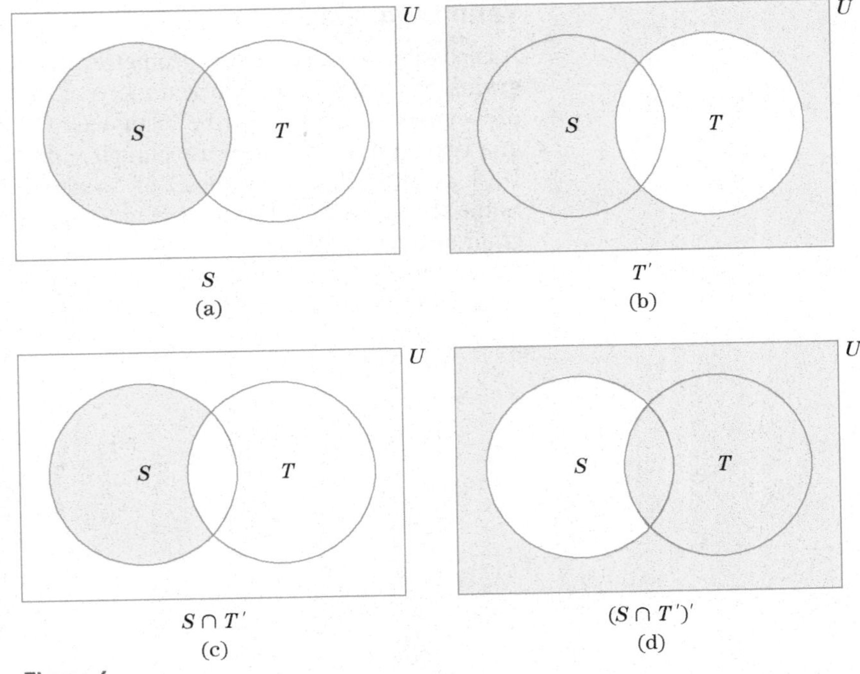

Figure 4

In a similar manner, Venn diagrams can illustrate intersections and unions of three sets. Some representative regions are shaded in Fig. 5.

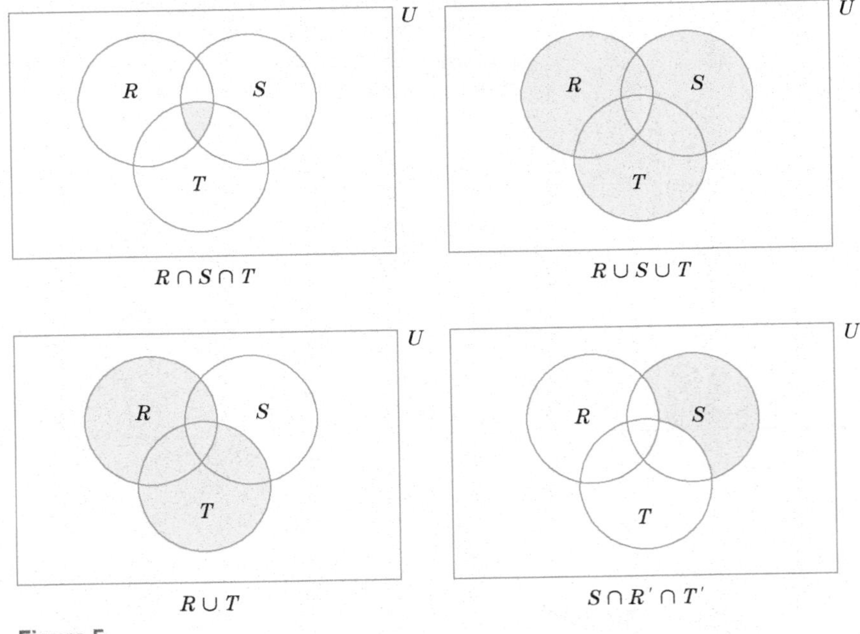

Figure 5

There are many formulas expressing relationships between intersections and unions of sets. Possibly the most fundamental are the two formulas known as *De Morgan's laws*.

De Morgan's Laws Let S and T be sets. Then,

$$(S \cup T)' = S' \cap T' \quad \text{and} \quad (S \cap T)' = S' \cup T'.$$

In other words, De Morgan's laws state that, to form the complement of a union (or intersection), form the complements of the individual sets and change unions to intersections (or intersections to unions).

Verification of De Morgan's Laws

Let us use Venn diagrams to describe $(S \cup T)'$. In Fig. 6(a), we have shaded the region corresponding to $S \cup T$. In Fig. 6(b), we have shaded the region corresponding to $(S \cup T)'$. In Figs. 6(c) and 4(d), we have shaded the regions corresponding to S' and T'. By considering the common shaded regions of Figs. 6(c) and (d), we arrive at the shaded region corresponding to $S' \cap T'$ [Fig. 6(e)]. Note that this is the same region as shaded in Fig. 6(b). Therefore,

$$(S \cup T)' = S' \cap T'.$$

This verifies the first of De Morgan's laws. The proof of the second law is similar.

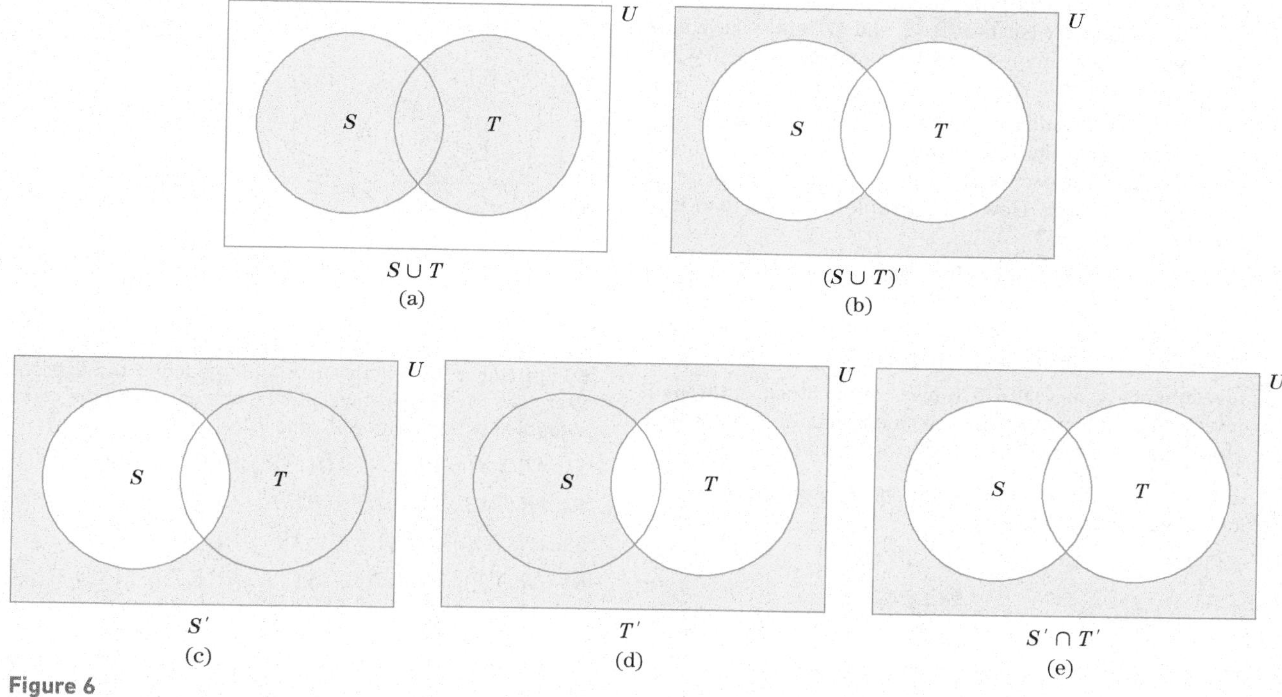

Figure 6

INCORPORATING TECHNOLOGY

WolframAlpha Venn diagrams can be displayed with instructions containing the words **intersect**, **union**, and **complement**. For instance, the instruction

S intersect (complement R) intersect (complement T)

produces the fourth Venn diagram of Fig. 5.

Check Your Understanding 1.2

Solutions can be found following the section exercises.

1. Draw a two-circle Venn diagram, and shade the portion corresponding to the set $(S \cap T') \cup (S \cap T)$.
2. What does the inclusion–exclusion principle conclude when T is a subset of S?

EXERCISES 1.2

1. Find $n(S \cup T)$, given that $n(S) = 4$, $n(T) = 4$, and $n(S \cap T) = 2$.
2. Find $n(S \cup T)$, given that $n(S) = 17$, $n(T) = 13$, and $n(S \cap T) = 0$.
3. Find $n(S \cap T)$, given that $n(S) = 6$, $n(T) = 9$, and $n(S \cup T) = 15$.
4. Find $n(S \cap T)$, given that $n(S) = 4$, $n(T) = 12$, and $n(S \cup T) = 15$.

5. Find $n(S)$, given that $n(T) = 7$, $n(S \cap T) = 5$, and $n(S \cup T) = 10$.

6. Find $n(T)$, given that $n(S) = 14$, $n(S \cap T) = 6$, and $n(S \cup T) = 14$.

7. If $n(S) = n(S \cap T)$, what can you conclude about S and T?

8. If $n(T) = n(S \cup T)$, what can you conclude about S and T?

9. **Languages** Suppose that each of the 314 million adults in South America is fluent in Portuguese or Spanish. If 170 million are fluent in Portuguese and 155 million are fluent in Spanish, how many are fluent in both languages?

10. **Course Enrollments** Suppose that all of the 1000 first-year students at a certain college are enrolled in a math or an English course. Suppose that 400 are taking both math and English and 600 are taking English. How many are taking a math course?

11. **Symmetry of Letters** Of the 26 capital letters of the alphabet, 11 have vertical symmetry (for instance, A, M, and T), 9 have horizontal symmetry (such as B, C, and D), and 4 have both (H, I, O, X). How many letters have neither horizontal nor vertical symmetry?

12. **Streaming Subscriptions** A survey of employees in a certain company revealed that 250 people subscribe to a streaming video service, 75 subscribe to a streaming music service, and 25 subscribe to both. How many people subscribe to at least one of these services?

13. **Automobile Options** Motors Inc. manufactured 325 cars with navigation systems, 216 with push-button start, and 89 with both of these options. How many cars were manufactured with at least one of the two options?

14. **Investments** A survey of 120 investors in stocks and bonds revealed that 90 investors owned stocks and 70 owned bonds. How many investors owned both stocks and bonds?

In Exercises 15–26, draw a two-circle Venn diagram and shade the portion corresponding to the set.

15. $S \cap T'$
16. $S' \cap T'$
17. $S' \cup T$
18. $S' \cup T'$
19. $(S \cap T')'$
20. $(S \cap T)'$
21. $(S \cap T') \cup (S' \cap T)$
22. $(S \cap T) \cup (S' \cap T')$
23. $S \cup (S \cap T)$
24. $S \cup (T' \cup S)$
25. $S \cup S'$
26. $S \cap S'$

In Exercises 27–38, draw a three-circle Venn diagram and shade the portion corresponding to the set.

27. $R \cap S \cap T'$
28. $R' \cap S' \cap T$
29. $R \cup (S \cap T)$
30. $R \cap (S \cup T)$
31. $R \cap (S' \cup T)$
32. $R' \cup (S \cap T')$
33. $R \cap T$
34. $S \cap T'$
35. $R' \cup S' \cup T'$
36. $(R \cap S \cap T)'$
37. $(R \cap T) \cup (S \cap T')$
38. $(R \cup S') \cap (R \cup T')$

In Exercises 39–44, use De Morgan's laws to simplify each given expression.

39. $S' \cup (S \cap T)'$
40. $S \cap (S \cup T)'$
41. $(S' \cup T)'$
42. $(S' \cap T')'$
43. $T \cup (S \cap T)'$
44. $(S' \cap T)' \cup S$

In Exercises 45–50, give a set-theoretic expression that describes the shaded portion of each Venn diagram.

45.
46.
47.
48.

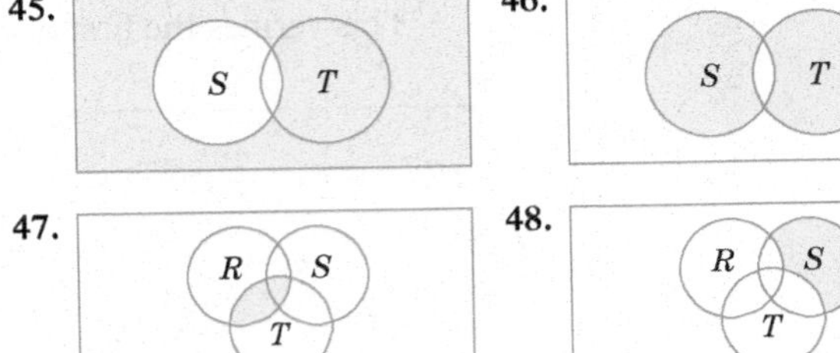

49.
50.

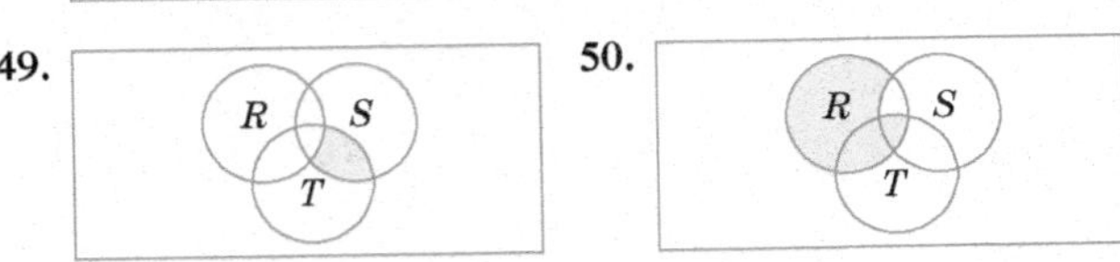

By drawing a Venn diagram, simplify each of the expressions in Exercises 51–54 to involve at most one union and the complement symbol applied only to R, S, and T.

51. $(T \cap S) \cup (T \cap R) \cup (R \cap S') \cup (T \cap R' \cap S')$

52. $(R \cap S) \cup (S \cap T) \cup (R \cap S' \cap T')$

53. $((R \cap S') \cup (S \cap T') \cup (T \cap R'))'$

54. $(R \cap T) \cup (R \cap S) \cup (S \cap T') \cup (R \cap S' \cap T')$

Citizenship Assume that the universal set U is the set of all people living in the United States. Let A be the set of all U.S. citizens, let B be the set of all children under 5 years of age, let C be the set of children from 5 to 18 years of age, let D be the set of everyone over the age of 18, and let E be the set of all people who are employed. Describe in words each set in Exercises 55–60.

55. $A' \cup (D \cap E)$
56. $A \cap C \cap E$
57. $D \cap E'$
58. $A \cap (D \cup E)$
59. $A' \cap B'$
60. $B \cap E$

Solutions to Check Your Understanding 1.2

1. $(S \cap T') \cup (S \cap T)$ is given as a union of two sets, $S \cap T'$ and $S \cap T$. The Venn diagrams for these two sets are given in Figs. 7(a) and (b). The desired set consists of the elements that are in one or the other (or both) of the two sets. Therefore, its Venn diagram is obtained by shading everything that is shaded in either Fig. 7(a) or (b). [See Fig. 7(c).] *Note:* Looking at Fig. 7(c) reveals that $(S \cap T') \cup (S \cap T)$ and S are the same set. Often, Venn diagrams can be used to simplify complicated set-theoretic expressions.

2. When $T \subseteq S$, $S \cup T = S$ *and* $S \cap T = T$; the inclusion–exclusion principle becomes

$$n(S \cup T) = n(S) + n(T) - n(S \cap T)$$
$$n(S) = n(S) + n(T) - n(T)$$
$$n(S) = n(S).$$

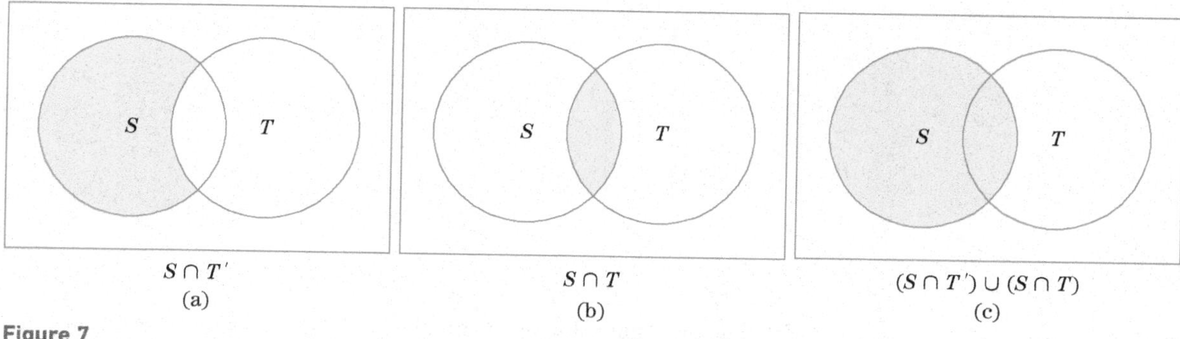

$S \cap T'$
(a)

$S \cap T$
(b)

$(S \cap T') \cup (S \cap T)$
(c)

Figure 7

1.3 Venn Diagrams and Counting

In this section, we discuss the use of Venn diagrams in solving counting problems. The techniques developed are especially useful in analyzing survey data.

Each Venn diagram divides the universal set U into a certain number of regions. For example, the Venn diagram for a single set divides U into two regions—the inside and outside of the circle [Fig. 1(a)]. The Venn diagram for two sets divides U into four regions [Fig. 1(b)]. The Venn diagram for three sets divides U into eight regions [Fig. 1(c)]. Each of the regions is called a **basic region** for the Venn diagram. Knowing the number of elements in each basic region is of great use in many applied problems. As an illustration, consider the next example.

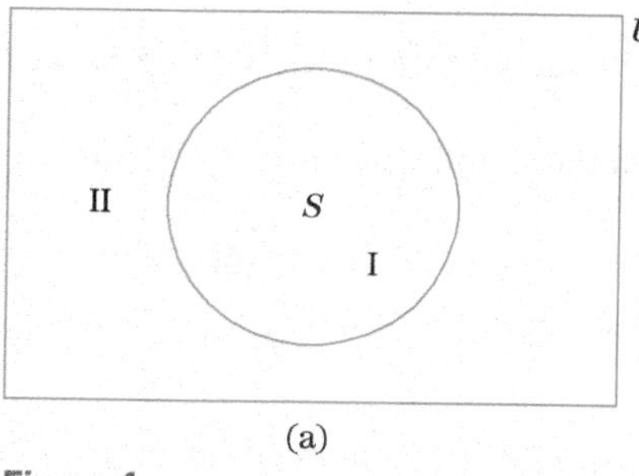

(a)

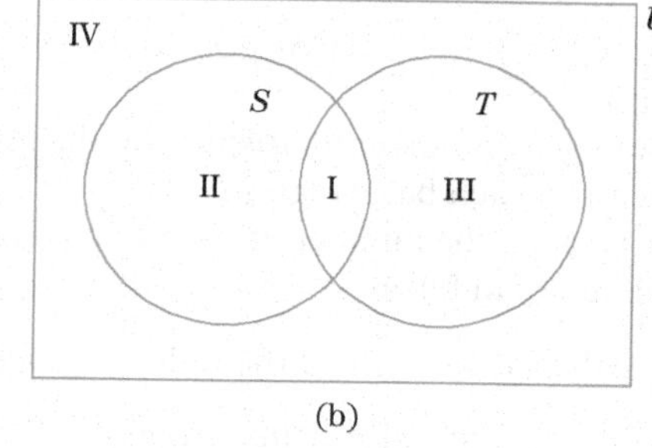

(b)

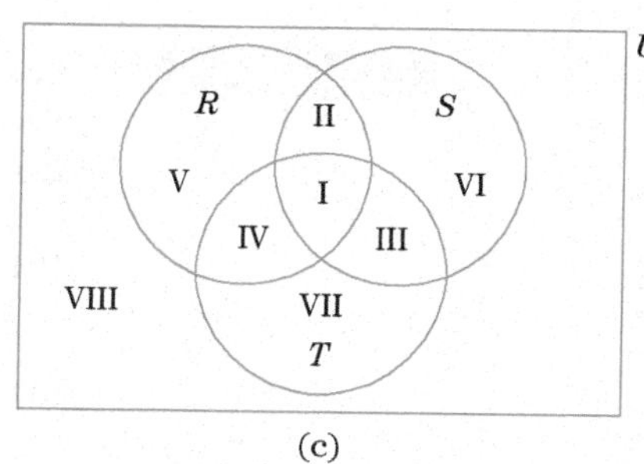

(c)

Figure 1

EXAMPLE 1 **Nobel Prize Winners** Let

$U =$ {Nobel winners during the period 1901–2015}

$A =$ {American Nobel winners during the period 1901–2015}

$C =$ {Chemistry Nobel winners during the period 1901–2015}

$P =$ {Nobel Peace Prize winners during the period 1901–2015}.

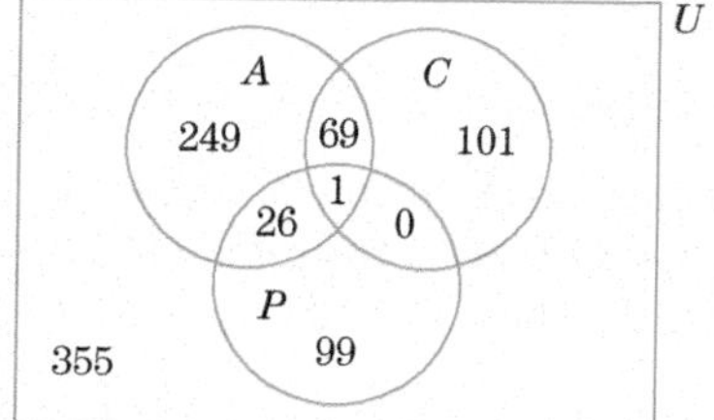

Figure 2

These sets are illustrated in the Venn diagram of Fig. 2, in which each basic region has been labeled with the number of elements in it.

(a) How many Americans received a Nobel Prize during this period 1901–2015?

(b) How many Americans received Nobel Prizes in fields other than chemistry and peace during this period?

(c) How many Americans received the Nobel Peace Prize during this period?

(d) How many Nobel Prize winners were there during this period?

SOLUTION (a) The number of Americans who received a Nobel Prize is the total contained in the circle A [Fig. 3(a) on the next page], which is

$$249 + 26 + 1 + 69 = 345.$$

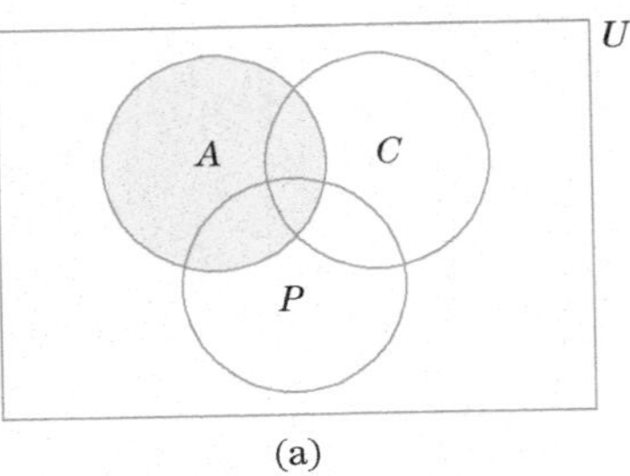

(a)

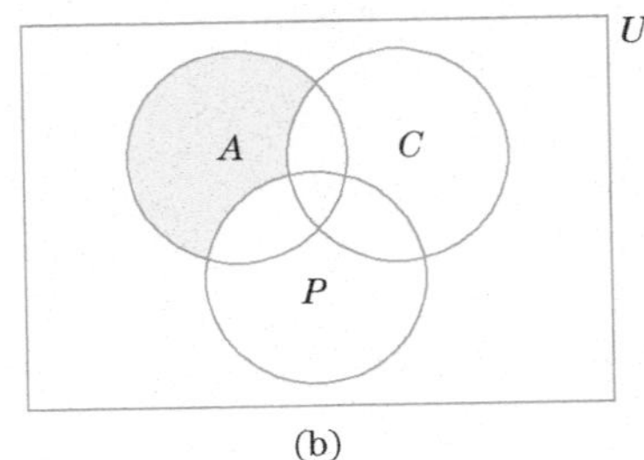

(b)

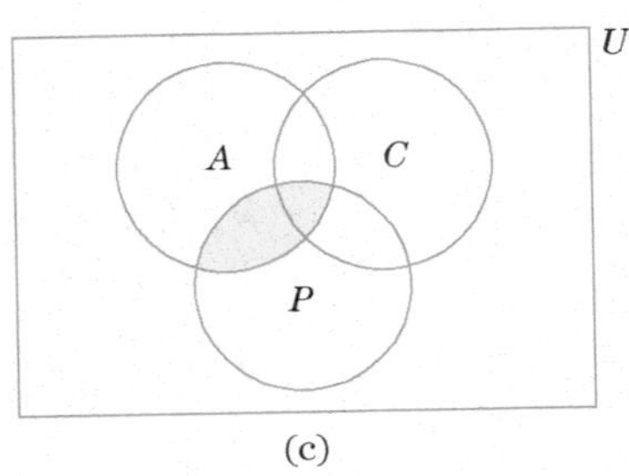

(c)

Figure 3

(b) The question asks for the number of Nobel winners in A but not in C and not in P. So start with the A circle, and eliminate those basic regions belonging to C or P [Fig. 3(b)]. There remains a single basic region with 249. Nobel winners. Note that this region corresponds to $A \cap C' \cap P'$.

(c) The question asks for the number of elements in both A and P—that is, $n(A \cap P)$. But $A \cap P$ comprises two basic regions [Fig. 3(c)]. Thus, to compute $n(A \cap P)$, we add the numbers in these basic regions to obtain $26 + 1 = 27$ Americans who have received the Nobel Peace Prize.

(d) The number of recipients is just $n(U)$, and we obtain it by adding together the numbers corresponding to the basic regions. We obtain

$$355 + 249 + 69 + 1 + 26 + 101 + 0 + 99 = 900.$$

>> Now Try Exercises 1–4

One need not always be given the number of elements in each of the basic regions of a Venn diagram. Very often, this data can be deduced from given information.

EXAMPLE 2 **Corporate Presidents** Consider the set of 500 corporate presidents of Example 1, Section 1.2.

(a) Draw a Venn diagram displaying the given data, and determine the number of elements in each basic region.

(b) Determine the number of presidents having exactly one degree (graduate or undergraduate) in business.

SOLUTION **(a)** Recall that we defined the following sets:

$$S = \{\text{presidents with an undergraduate degree in business}\}.$$
$$T = \{\text{presidents with a graduate degree in business}\}.$$

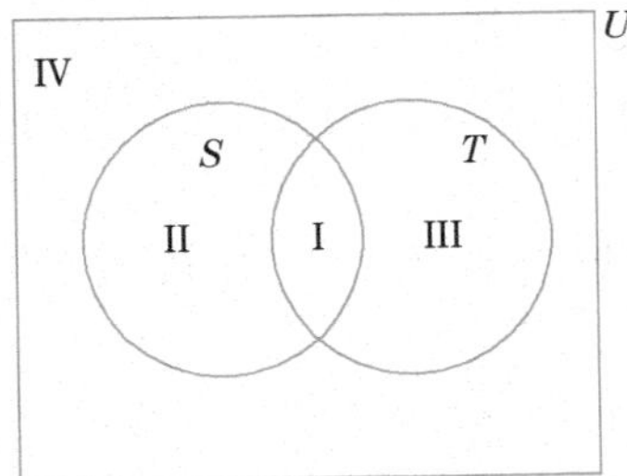

Figure 4

We were given the following data:

$$n(U) = 500 \qquad n(S) = 238 \qquad n(T) = 184 \qquad n(S \cup T) = 310.$$

We draw a Venn diagram corresponding to S and T (Fig. 4). Notice that none of the given information corresponds to a basic region of the Venn diagram. So we must use our wits to determine the number of presidents in each of the regions I–IV. Region IV is the complement of $S \cup T$, so it contains

$$n(U) - n(S \cup T) = 500 - 310 = 190$$

presidents. Region I is just $S \cap T$. By using the inclusion–exclusion principle, in Example 1, Section 1.2, we determined that $n(S \cap T) = 112$. Now, the total number of presidents in I and II combined equals $n(S)$, or 238. Therefore, the number of presidents in II is

$$n(S) - n(S \cap T) = 238 - 112 = 126.$$

Similarly, the number of presidents in III is

$$n(T) - n(S \cap T) = 184 - 112 = 72.$$

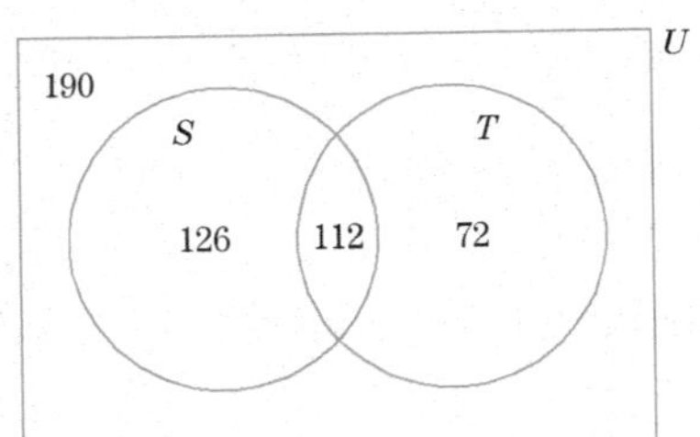

Figure 5

Thus, we may fill in the data to obtain a completed Venn diagram (Fig. 5).

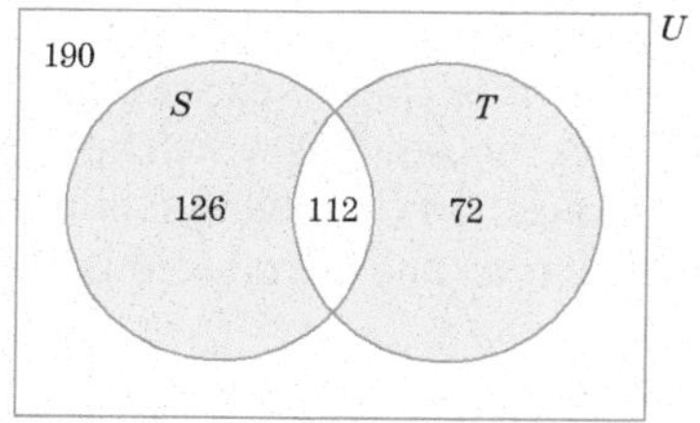

Figure 6

(b) The number of people with exactly one business degree corresponds to the shaded region in Fig. 6. Adding together the number of presidents in each of these regions gives $126 + 72 = 198$ presidents with exactly one business degree.

» ***Now Try Exercise 23***

Here is another example illustrating the procedure for determining the number of elements in each of the basic regions of a Venn diagram.

EXAMPLE 3 **Advertising Media** An advertising agency finds that the media use of its 170 clients is as follows:

115 use television (T)
100 use the Internet (I)
130 use mobile apps (M)
75 use television and the Internet
95 use the Internet and mobile apps
85 use television and mobile apps
70 use all three.

Use this data to complete the Venn diagram in Fig. 7 to display the clients' use of mass media.

$n(U) = 170$

Figure 7

SOLUTION Of the various data given, only the last item corresponds to one of the eight basic regions of the Venn diagram—namely, the "70" corresponding to the use of all three media. So we begin by entering this number in the diagram [Fig. 8(a)]. We can fill in the rest of the Venn diagram by working with the remaining information one piece at a time in the reverse order that it is given. Since 85 clients advertise in television and mobile apps, $85 - 70 = 15$ advertise in television and mobile apps but not on the Internet. The appropriate region is labeled in Fig. 8(b). In Fig. 8(c), the next two pieces of information have been used in the same way to fill in two more basic regions. In Fig. 8(c), we observe that three of the four basic regions comprising M have been filled in. Since $n(M) = 130$, we deduce that the number of clients advertising only in

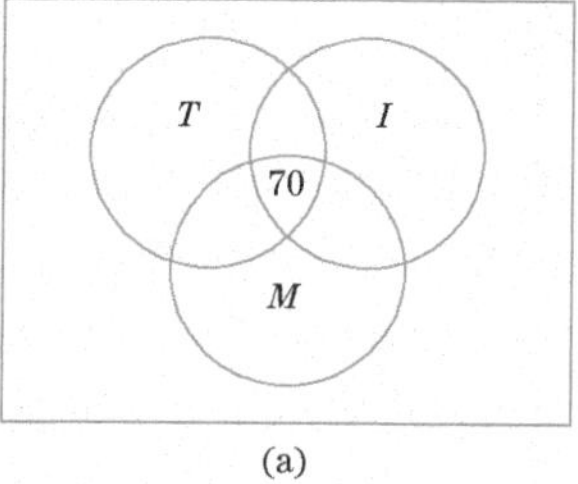

(a)

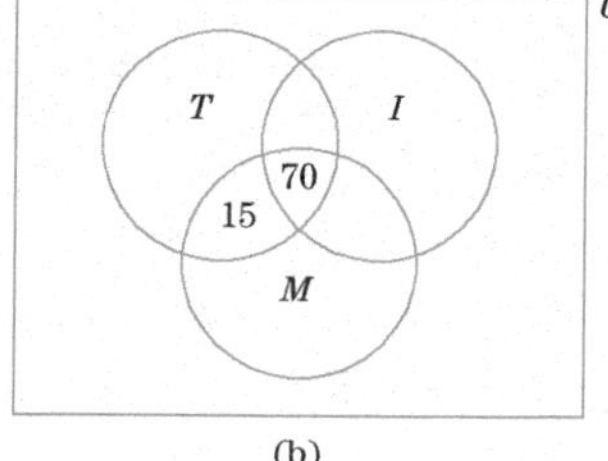

(b)

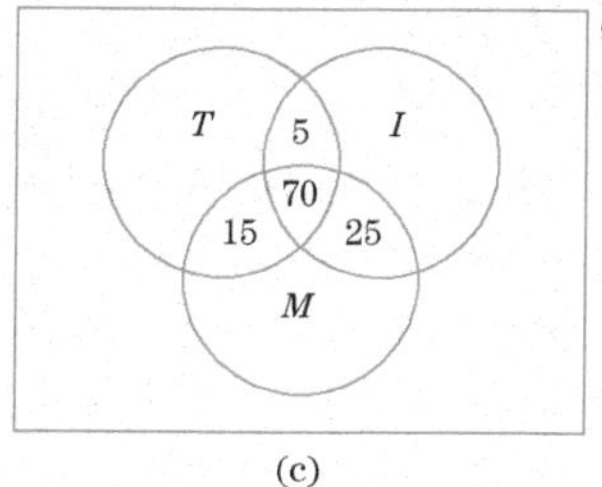

(c)

Figure 8

mobile apps is $130 - (15 + 70 + 25) = 130 - 110 = 20$ [Fig. 9(a)]. By similar reasoning, the number of clients using only Internet advertising and the number using only television advertising can be determined [Fig. 9(b)]. Adding together the numbers in the three circles gives the number of clients utilizing television, Internet, or mobile apps as $25 + 5 + 0 + 15 + 70 + 25 + 20 = 160$. Since there were 170 clients in total, the remainder—or $170 - 160 = 10$ clients—use none of these media. Figure 9(c) gives a complete display of the data.

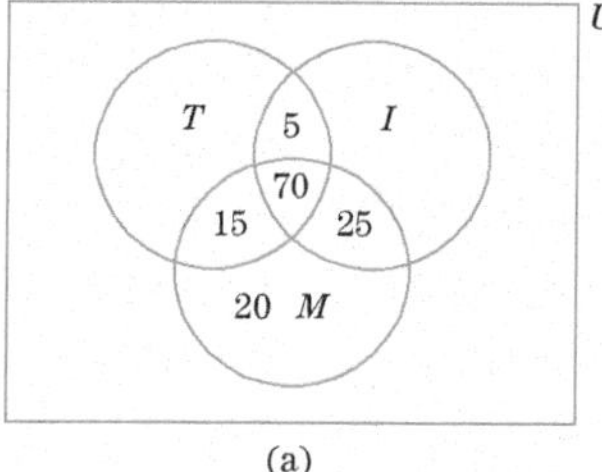

(a)

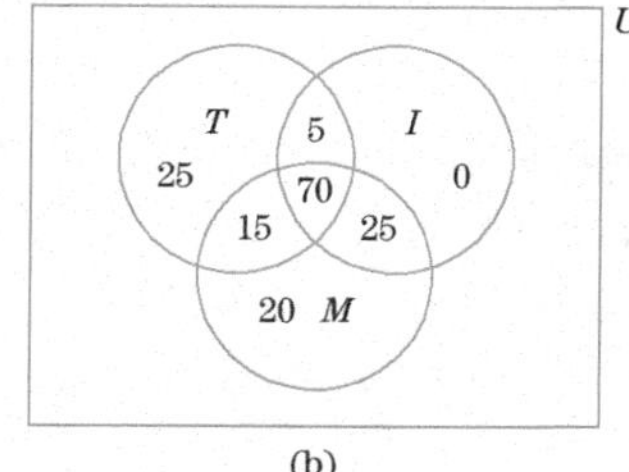

(b)

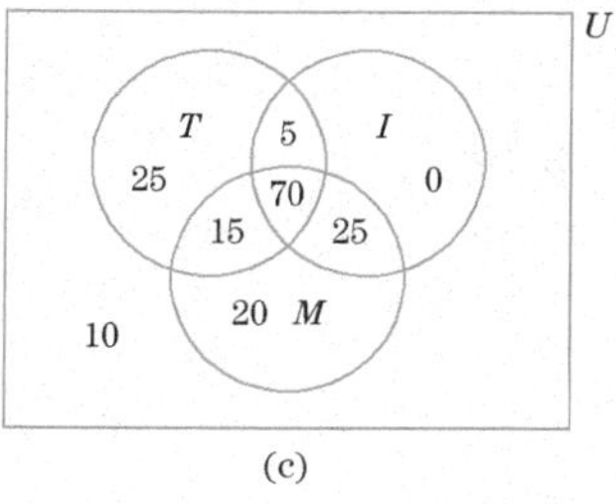

(c)

Figure 9

» ***Now Try Exercise 31(a)***

In Example 3, it was determined that the number of clients who use at least one of the three types of media is 160. Using set theory notation this can be expressed as $n(T \cup R \cup M) = 160$. While a Venn diagram can be a very useful tool, it is worth noting that it is not always necessary to draw one in order to solve questions involving sets, and in fact $n(T \cup R \cup M)$ can be calculated using a formula similar to one introduced in the previous section.

In Section 1.2, the Inclusion-Exclusion Principle for 2 Sets was given. An analogous result holds for three sets (and in fact for any finite number of sets):

Inclusion-Exclusion Principle for 3 Sets Let R, S, and T be sets. Then

$$n(R \cup S \cup T) = n(R) + n(S) + n(T) - n(R \cap S) - n(R \cap T) - n(S \cap T) + n(R \cap S \cap T).$$

NOTE In Example 3, the Inclusion-Exclusion Principle can be used with the information given to directly calculate

$$\begin{aligned} n(T \cup R \cup M) &= n(T) + n(R) + n(M) - n(T \cap R) - n(T \cap M) - n(R \cap M) \\ &\quad + n(T \cap R \cap M) \\ &= 115 + 100 + 130 - 75 - 85 - 95 + 70 \\ &= 160. \end{aligned}$$

Check Your Understanding 1.3

Solutions can be found following the section exercises.

1. Of the 1000 first-year students at a certain college, 700 take mathematics courses, 300 take mathematics and economics courses, and 200 do not take any mathematics or economics courses. Represent this data in a Venn diagram.

2. Refer to the Venn diagram from Problem 1.
   (a) How many of the first-year students take an economics course?
   (b) How many take an economics course but not a mathematics course?

EXERCISES 1.3

Family Library The Venn diagram in Fig. 10 classifies the 100 books in a family's library as hardback (H), fiction (F), and children's (C). Exercises 1–10 refer to this Venn diagram.

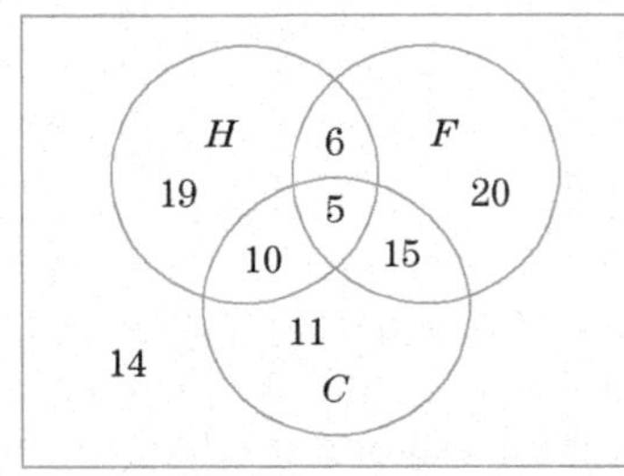

Figure 10

1. How many books are hardback fiction?
2. How many books are paperback fiction?
3. How many books are fiction?
4. How many books are nonfiction?
5. How many books are paperback nonfiction children's books?
6. How many books are adult hardback nonfiction?
7. How many books are either hardback or fiction?
8. How many hardback books are either fiction or children's books?
9. How many children's books are either hardback or fiction?
10. How many books are either hardback, fiction, or children's books?

In Exercises 11–22, let R, S, and T be subsets of the universal set U. Draw an appropriate Venn diagram, and use the given data to determine the number of elements in each basic region.

11. $n(U) = 17, n(S) = 12, n(T) = 7, n(S \cap T) = 5$
12. $n(U) = 20, n(S) = 11, n(T) = 7, n(S \cap T) = 7$
13. $n(U) = 20, n(S) = 12, n(T) = 14, n(S \cup T) = 18$
14. $n(S') = 4, n(S \cup T) = 12, n(S \cap T) = 5, n(T) = 9$
15. $n(U) = 75, n(S) = 15, n(T) = 25, n(S' \cap T') = 40$
16. $n(S) = 10, n(T) = 10, n(S \cap T) = 5, n(S') = 13$
17. $n(S) = 3, n(S \cup T) = 6, n(T) = 4, n(S' \cup T') = 9$
18. $n(U) = 15, n(S) = 8, n(T) = 9, n(S \cup T) = 14$
19. $n(U) = 28, n(R) = 12, n(S) = 12, n(T) = 9, n(R \cap S) = 5, n(S \cap T) = 3, n(R \cap T) = 7, n(R \cap S \cap T) = 2$
20. $n(U) = 29, n(R) = 10, n(S) = 12, n(T) = 10, n(R \cap S) = 1, n(R \cap T) = 5, n(S \cap T) = 4, n(R \cap S \cap T) = 1$
21. $n(R') = 22, n(R \cup S) = 21, n(S) = 14, n(T) = 22, n(R \cap S) = 7, n(S \cap T) = 9, n(R \cap T) = 11, n(R \cap S \cap T) = 5$
22. $n(U) = 64, n(R \cup S \cup T) = 45, n(R) = 22, n(T) = 26, n(R \cap S) = 4, n(S \cap T) = 6, n(R \cap T) = 8, n(R \cap S \cap T) = 1$
23. **Music Preferences** A survey of 70 high school students revealed that 35 like rock music, 15 like hip-hop music, and 5 like both. How many of the students surveyed do not like either rock or hip-hop music?

24. **Nobel Winners** A total of 900 Nobel Prizes had been awarded by 2015. Fourteen of the 112 prizes in literature were awarded to Scandinavians. Scandinavians received a total of 57 awards. How many Nobel Prizes outside of literature have been awarded to non-Scandinavians?

25. **Analysis of Sonnet** One of Shakespeare's sonnets has a verb in 11 of its 14 lines, an adjective in 9 lines, and both in 7 lines. How many lines have a verb but no adjective? An adjective but no verb? Neither an adjective nor a verb?

Exam Performance The results from an exam taken by 150 students were as follows:

90 students correctly answered the first question,
71 students correctly answered the second question,
66 students correctly answered both questions.

Exercises 26–30 refer to these students.

26. How many students correctly answered either the first or second question?

27. How many students did not answer either of the two questions correctly?

28. How many students answered either the first or the second question correctly, but not both?

29. How many students answered the second question correctly, but not the first?

30. How many students missed the second question?

31. **Class Enrollment** Out of 35 students in a finite math class, 22 are male, 19 are business majors, 27 are first-year students, 14 are male business majors, 17 are male first-year students, 15 are first-year business majors, and 11 are male first-year business majors.
   (a) Use this data to complete a Venn diagram displaying the characteristics of the students.
   (b) How many students in the class are neither first-year, nor male, nor business majors?
   (c) How many non-male business majors are in the class?

32. **Exercise Preferences** A survey of 100 college faculty who exercise regularly found that 45 jog, 30 swim, 20 cycle, 6 jog and swim, 1 jogs and cycles, 5 swim and cycle, and 1 does all three. How many of the faculty members do not do any of these activities? How many just jog?

Flag Colors The three most common colors in the 193 flags of the member nations of the United Nations are red, white, and blue:

52 flags contain all three colors
103 flags contain both red and white
66 flags contain both red and blue
73 flags contain both white and blue
145 flags contain red
132 flags contain white
104 flags contain blue.

Exercises 33–38 refer to the 193 flags.

33. How many flags contain red, but not white or blue?

34. How many flags contain exactly one of the three colors?

35. How many flags contain none of the three colors?

36. How many flags contain exactly two of the three colors?

37. How many flags contain red and white, but not blue?

38. How many flags contain red or white, but not both?

News Dissemination A merchant surveyed 400 people to determine from what source they found out about an upcoming sale. The results of the survey follow:

180 from the Internet
190 from television
190 from newspapers
80 from the Internet and television
90 from the Internet and newspapers
50 from television and newspapers
30 from all three sources.

Exercises 39–44 refer to the people in this survey.

39. How many people learned of the sale from newspapers or the Internet but not from both?

40. How many people learned of the sale only from newspapers?

41. How many people learned of the sale from the Internet or television but not from newspapers?

42. How many people learned of the sale from at least two of the three media?

43. How many people learned of the sale from exactly one of the three media?

44. How many people learned of the sale from the Internet and television but not from newspapers?

45. **Course Enrollments** Table 1 shows the number of students enrolled in each of three science courses at Gotham College. Although no students are enrolled in all three courses, 15 are enrolled in both chemistry and physics, 10 are enrolled in both physics and biology, and 5 are enrolled in both biology and chemistry. How many students are enrolled in at least one of these science courses?

Table 1

Course	Enrollment
Chemistry	60
Physics	40
Biology	30

Foreign Language Courses A survey in a local high school shows that, of the 4000 students in the school,

2000 take French (F)
3000 take Spanish (S)
500 take Latin (L)
1500 take both French and Spanish
300 take both French and Latin
200 take Spanish and Latin
50 take all three languages.

Use a Venn diagram to find the number of people in the sets given in Exercises 46–50.

46. $L \cap (F \cup S)$
47. $(L \cup F \cup S)'$
48. L'
49. $L \cup S \cup F'$
50. $F \cap S' \cap L'$

51. **Voting Preferences** One hundred college students were surveyed after voting in an election involving a Democrat and a Republican. There were 50 first-year students, 55 voted Democratic, and 25 were non-first-year students who voted Republican. How many first-year students voted Democratic?

52. **Union Membership and Education Status** A group of 100 workers were asked whether they were college graduates and whether they belonged to a union. According to their responses, 60 were not college graduates, 20 were nonunion college graduates, and 30 were union members. How many of the workers were neither college graduates nor union members?

53. **Diagnostic Test Results** A class of 30 students was given a diagnostic test on the first day of a mathematics course. At the end of the semester, only 2 of the 21 students who had passed the diagnostic test failed the course. A total of 23 students passed the course. How many students managed to pass the course even though they failed the diagnostic test?

54. **Air-Traffic Controllers** A group of applicants for training as air-traffic controllers consists of 35 pilots, 20 veterans, 30 pilots who were not veterans, and 50 people who were neither veterans nor pilots. How large was the group?

College Majors A group of 61 students has the following characteristics:

6 are biology majors and seniors
17 are biology majors and not seniors
12 are not seniors and are majoring in a field other than biology.

Exercises 55–60 refer to these students.

55. How many of the students are either seniors or biology majors?

56. How many of the students are seniors?

57. How many of the students are not seniors?

58. How many of the students are biology majors?

59. How many of the seniors are not biology majors?

60. How many of the students are not biology majors?

Music Preferences A campus radio station surveyed 190 students to determine the genres of music they liked. The survey results follow:

114 like rock
50 like country
15 like rock and rap
11 like rap and country
20 like rap only
10 like rock and rap, but not country
9 like rock and country, but not rap
20 don't like any of the three types of music.

Exercises 61–68 refer to the students in this survey.

61. How many students like rock only?

62. How many students like country but not rock?

63. How many students like rap and country but not rock?

64. How many students like rap or country but not rock?

65. How many students like exactly one of the genres?

66. How many students like all three genres?

67. How many students like at least two of the three genres?

68. How many students do not like either rock or country?

69. **Website Preferences** One hundred and sixty business executives were surveyed to determine whether they regularly visit the *CNN Money*, *Bloomberg*, or *The Wall Street Journal* websites. The survey showed that 70 visit *CNN Money*, 60 visit *Bloomberg*, 55 visit *The Wall Street Journal*, 45 visit exactly two of the three websites, 20 visit *CNN Money* and *Bloomberg*, 20 visit *Bloomberg* and *The Wall Street Journal*, and 5 visit all three websites. How many do not visit any of the three websites?

70. **Small Businesses** A survey of the characteristics of 100 small businesses that had failed revealed that 95 of them either were undercapitalized, had inexperienced management, or had a poor location. Four of the businesses had all three of these characteristics. Forty businesses were undercapitalized but had experienced management and good location. Fifteen businesses had inexperienced management but sufficient capitalization and good location. Seven were undercapitalized and had inexperienced management. Nine were undercapitalized and had poor location. Ten had inexperienced management and poor location. How many of the businesses had poor location? Which of the three characteristics was most prevalent in the failed businesses?

71. **Music** Each of the 100 students attending a conservatory of music plays at least one of three instruments: piano, violin, and clarinet. Of the students, 65 play the piano, 42 play the violin, 28 play the clarinet, 20 play the piano and the violin, 10 play the violin and the clarinet, and 8 play the piano and the clarinet. How many play all three instruments? *Hint:* Let x represent the number of students who play all three instruments.

72. **Courses** Students living in a certain dormitory were asked about their enrollment in mathematics and history courses. Ten percent were taking both types of courses, and twenty percent were taking neither type of course. One hundred sixty students were taking a mathematics course but not a history course, and one hundred twenty students were taking a history course but not a mathematics course. How many students were taking a mathematics course? *Hint:* Let x be the total number of students living in the dormitory.

Solutions to Check Your Understanding 1.3

1. Draw a Venn diagram with two circles, one for mathematics (M) and one for economics (E) [Fig. 11(a)]. This Venn diagram has four basic regions, and our goal is to label each basic region with the proper number of students. The numbers for two of the basic regions are given directly. Since "300 take mathematics and economics," $n(M \cap E) = 300$. Since "200 do not take any mathematics or economics courses," $n((M \cup E)') = 200$ [Fig. 11(b)]. Now, "700 take mathematics courses." Since M is made up of two basic regions and one region has 300 elements, the other basic region of M must contain 400 elements [Fig. 11(c)]. At this point, all but one of the basic regions have been labeled and $400 + 300 + 200 = 900$ students have been accounted for. Since there is a total of 1000 students, the remaining basic region has 100 students [Fig. 11(d)].

2. (a) 400. "Economics" refers to the entire circle E, which is made up of two basic regions, one having 300 elements and the other 100. (A common error is to interpret the question as asking for the number of first-year students who take economics exclusively and therefore give the answer 100. To say that a person takes an economics course does not imply anything about the person's enrollment in mathematics courses.)

   (b) 100

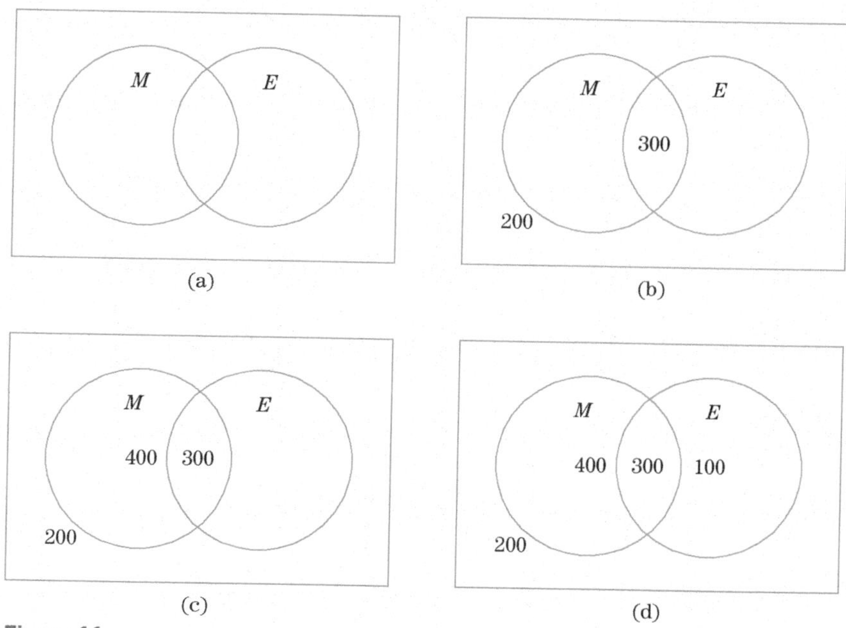

Figure 11

1.4 The Multiplication Principle

In this section, we introduce a second fundamental principle of counting, the *multiplication principle*. By way of motivation, consider the following example:

EXAMPLE 1 **Counting Paths through a Maze** A medical researcher wishes to test the effect of a drug on a rat's perception by studying the rat's ability to run a maze while under the influence of the drug. The maze is constructed so that, to arrive at the exit point C, the rat must pass through a central point B. There are five paths from the entry point A to B, and three paths from B to C. In how many different ways can the rat run the maze from A to C? (See Fig. 1.)

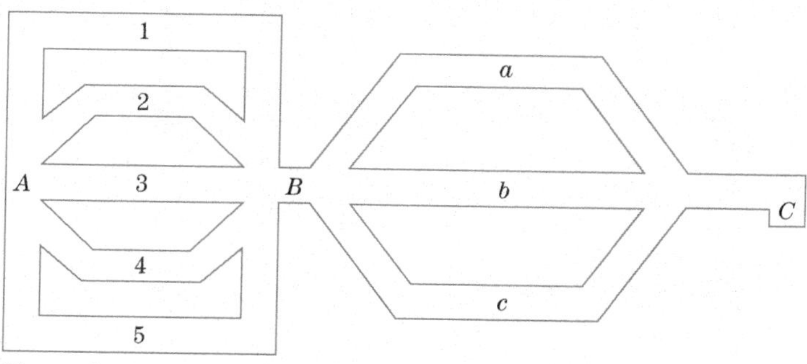

Figure 1

SOLUTION The paths from A to B have been labeled 1 through 5, and the paths from B to C have been labeled a through c. The various paths through the maze can be schematically represented as in Fig. 2 on the next page. The diagram shows that there are five ways to go from A to B. For each of these five ways, there are three ways to go from B to C. So there are five groups of three paths each and therefore $5 \cdot 3 = 15$ possible paths from A to C. (A diagram such as Fig. 2, called a **tree diagram**, is useful in enumerating the various possibilities in counting problems.)

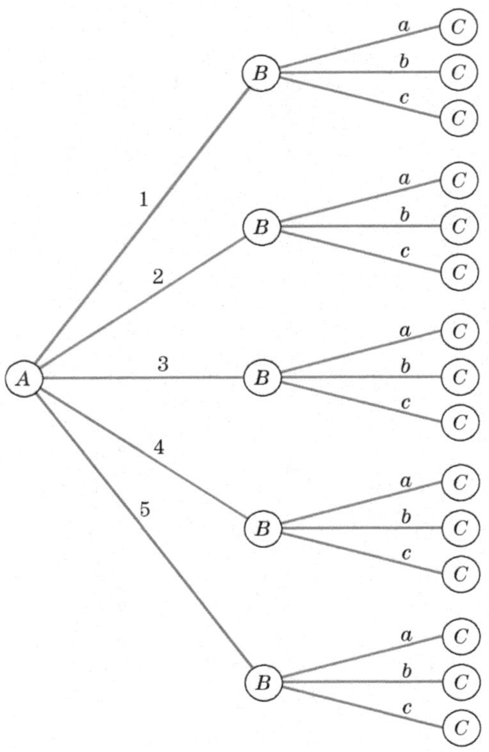

Figure 2

» Now Try Exercise 1

In the preceding problem, selecting a path is a task that can be broken up into two consecutive choices.

Choose path from A to B	Choose path from B to C
Choice 1	Choice 2

The first choice can be performed in five ways, and after the first choice has been carried out, the second can be performed in three ways. And we determined that the entire task can be performed in $5 \cdot 3 = 15$ ways. The same reasoning as just used yields the following useful counting principle.

Multiplication Principle Suppose that a task is composed of two consecutive choices. If choice 1 can be performed in m ways and, for each of these, choice 2 can be performed in n ways, then the complete task can be performed in $m \cdot n$ ways.

EXAMPLE 2 **Counting Routes for a Trip** An airline passenger must fly from New York to Frankfurt via London. There are 8 flights leaving New York for London. All of these provide connections on any one of 19 flights from London to Frankfurt. In how many different ways can the passenger book reservations?

SOLUTION The task *Fly from New York to Frankfurt* is composed of two consecutive choices:

Select a flight from New York to London	Select a flight from London to Frankfurt
Choice 1	Choice 2

From the data given, the multiplication principle implies that the task can be accomplished in $8 \cdot 19 = 152$ ways.

» Now Try Exercise 3

It is possible to generalize the multiplication principle to tasks consisting of more than two choices.

Generalized Multiplication Principle Suppose that a task consists of t choices performed consecutively. Suppose that choice 1 can be performed in m_1 ways; for each of these, choice 2 in m_2 ways; for each of these, choice 3 in m_3 ways; and so forth. Then the task can be performed in

$$m_1 \cdot m_2 \cdot m_3 \cdot \cdots \cdot m_t \quad \text{ways.}$$

EXAMPLE 3 **Officers for a Board of Directors** A corporation has a board of directors consisting of 10 members. The board must select from among its members a chairperson, vice chairperson, and secretary. In how many ways can this be done?

SOLUTION The task *Select the three officers* can be divided into three consecutive choices:

Select chairperson	Select vice chairperson	Select secretary

Since there are 10 directors, choice 1 can be performed in 10 ways. After the chairperson has been selected, there are 9 directors left as possible candidates for vice chairperson so that for each way of performing choice 1, choice 2 can be performed in 9 ways. After this has been done, there are 8 directors who are possible candidates for secretary, so choice 3 can be performed in 8 ways. By the generalized multiplication principle, the number of possible ways to perform the sequence of three choices equals $10 \cdot 9 \cdot 8$, or 720. So the officers of the board can be selected in 720 ways.

» Now Try Exercise 7

In Example 3, we made important use of the phrase "for each of these" in the generalized multiplication principle. The choice *Select a vice chairperson* can be performed in 10 ways, since any member of the board is eligible. However, when we view the selection process as a sequence of choices of which *Select a vice chairperson* is the second choice, the situation has changed. *For each way* that the first choice is performed, one person will have been used up; hence, there will be only 9 possibilities for choosing the vice chairperson.

Note that the order of the choices doesn't matter. For example, we could choose the vice chairman first, then the secretary, then the chairperson, and we would arrive at the same result.

EXAMPLE 4 **Posing for a Group Picture** In how many ways can a baseball team of nine players arrange themselves in a line for a group picture?

SOLUTION Choose the players by their place in the picture—say, from left to right. The first can be chosen in nine ways; for each of these outcomes, the second can be chosen in eight ways; for each of these outcomes, the third can be chosen in seven ways; and so forth. So the number of possible arrangements is

$$9 \cdot 8 \cdot 7 \cdot 6 \cdot 5 \cdot 4 \cdot 3 \cdot 2 \cdot 1 = 362{,}880.$$

» Now Try Exercise 11

We can write the product $9 \cdot 8 \cdot 7 \cdot 6 \cdot 5 \cdot 4 \cdot 3 \cdot 2 \cdot 1$ from the previous example in a condensed way by using **factorial** notation:

DEFINITION Factorial If n is a positive integer, the number n **factorial**, denoted $n!$, is defined to be the product

$$n! = n(n-1)(n-2)\cdots(2)(1).$$

In addition, we define $0! = 1$.

EXAMPLE 5 **License Plates** A certain state uses automobile license plates that consist of three letters followed by three digits. How many such license plates are there?

SOLUTION The task in this case, *Form a license plate*, consists of a sequence of six choices: three for choosing letters and three for choosing digits. Each letter can be chosen in 26 ways and each digit in 10 ways. So the number of license plates is

$$26 \cdot 26 \cdot 26 \cdot 10 \cdot 10 \cdot 10 = 17{,}576{,}000.$$

>> Now Try Exercise 17

Check Your Understanding 1.4

Solutions can be found following the section exercises.

1. There are five seats available in a sedan. In how many ways can five people be seated if only three can drive?
2. A multiple-choice exam contains 10 questions, each having 3 possible answers. Assuming you answer each question, how many different ways are there of completing the exam?

EXERCISES 1.4

1. Jolene wants to drive from her house to the grocery store and then to the library. If her GPS suggests four routes from her house to the grocery store, and two routes from the grocery store to the library, how many total ways are there for Jolene to do this? (See Fig. 3.)

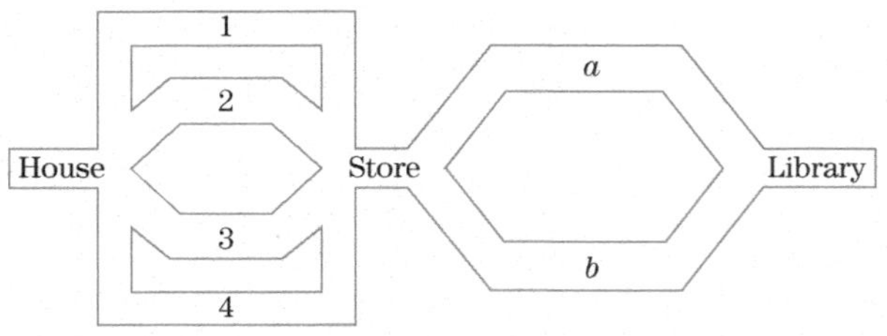

Figure 3

2. There are three bridges from the west shore of a river to an island in the center, and three bridges from the island to the east shore. How many different ways are there to cross from the west shore to the east shore? (See Fig. 4.)

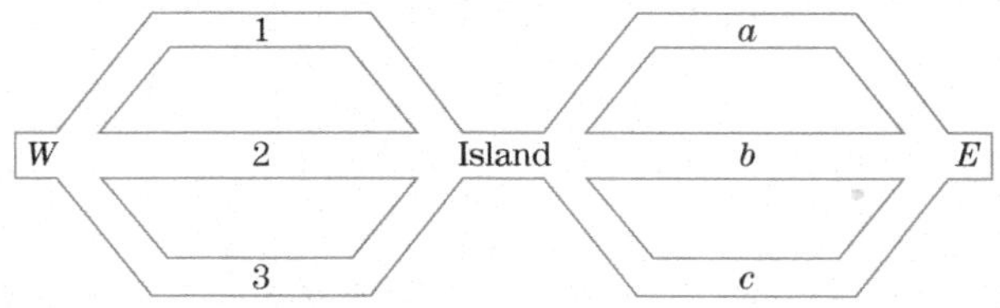

Figure 4

3. **Travel Options** If you can travel from Frederick, Maryland, to Baltimore, Maryland, by car, bus, or train and from Baltimore to London by airplane or ship, how many different ways are there to go from Frederick to London via Baltimore?
4. **Travel Options** Suppose that Maria wants to go from Florida to Maine via New York and can travel each leg of the journey by bus, car, train, or airplane. How many different ways can Maria make the trip?
5. **Daytona 500** Forty-four race cars competed in the 2016 Daytona 500. Assuming no ties, how many possibilities were there for the first-, second-, and third-place finishers?
6. **Kentucky Derby** Twenty horses competed in the 2016 Kentucky Derby. Assuming no ties, how many possibilities were there for the first, second, and third place finishers?
7. **Winners** Twenty athletes enter an Olympic event. Assuming no ties, how many different possibilities are there for winning the Gold Medal, Silver Medal, and Bronze Medal?
8. **Ranking Teams** A sportswriter is asked to rank six teams. How many different orderings are possible?
9. **Electing Captains** A football squad can elect a captain and an assistant captain in 870 possible ways. How many members does the squad have?
10. **Club Officers** A club can elect a president and a treasurer in 600 different ways. How many members does the club have?
11. **Group Picture** A group of five boys and three girls is to be photographed.
    (a) How many ways can they be arranged in one row?
    (b) How many ways can they be arranged with the girls in the front row and the boys in the back row?
12. **Arranging Books** Three history books and six novels are to be arranged on a bookshelf.
    (a) How many ways can they be arranged?
    (b) How many ways can they be arranged with the history books to the left of the novels?
13. **Rearranging Letters** How many different words (including nonsense words) can be formed by using the four letters of the word "MATH"?
14. **Three-Letter Words** How many different three-letter words (including nonsense words) are there in which successive letters are different?
15. **Selecting an Outfit** How many different outfits consisting of a coat and a hat can be selected from two coats and three hats?
16. **Selecting an Outfit** How many different outfits can be selected from two coats, four hats, and two scarves?
17. **Serial Numbers** A computer manufacturer assigns serial numbers to its computers. The first symbol of a serial number is either A, B, or C, indicating the manufacturing plant. The second and third symbols taken together are one of the numbers 01, 02, . . . , 12, indicating the month of manufacture. The final four symbols are digits. How many possible serial numbers are there?
18. **License Plates** Suppose that a license plate consists of a nonzero digit followed by three letters and then three nonzero digits. How many such license plates are there?

19. **Social Security Numbers** How many Social Security numbers are available if the only restriction is that the number 000-00-0000 cannot be assigned?

20. **Call Letters** In 1923, the Federal Communications Commission directed that all new radio stations east of the Mississippi River have call letters beginning with the letter W. How many different three- or four-letter call letters are possible?

21. **Area Codes** Before 1995, three-digit area codes for the United States had the following restrictions:
    (i) Neither 0 nor 1 could be used as the first digit.
    (ii) 0 or 1 had to be used for the second digit.
    (iii) There were no restrictions on the third digit.
    How many different area codes were possible?

22. **Area Codes** Refer to Exercise 21. Beginning in 1995, restriction (ii) was lifted and any digit could be used in the second position. How many different area codes were then possible?

Palindromes A number or word is said to be a *palindrome* if it reads the same backward as forward (e.g., 58485 or radar).

23. How many 5-digit numbers are palindromes?

24. How many 6-digit numbers are palindromes?

25. How many 4-letter words (including nonsense words) are palindromes?

26. How many 3-letter words (including nonsense words) are palindromes?

27. **World Series** The World Series of Baseball is played between the American League and National League champions, in which each league consists of 15 teams. How many different possible matchups are there for the World Series?

28. **Super Bowl** The Super Bowl is a game played between the National Football Conference and American Football Conference champions. Each conference consists of 16 teams. How many different possible matchups are there for the Super Bowl?

29. **Bridge Games** There are 3200 duplicate bridge clubs sanctioned by the American Contract Bridge Association. If each club holds two games per week and each duplicate game consists of 24 deals, how many deals are played in club games each year?

30. **Ice Cream Selections** An ice cream parlor offers 25 flavors of ice cream. Assuming that order matters, how many different two-scoop cones can be made? What if no flavor can be repeated?

31. **Internet Accounts** A college of 20,000 students provides each student with an Internet account. Explain why letting each student have his or her initials as the username cannot possibly work. Assume that each person has a first name, middle name, and last name and therefore that each person's initials consist of three letters.

32. **Pairs of Initials** A company has 700 employees. Explain why there must be two people with the same first and last initials.

33. **Game Outcomes** The final score in a soccer game is 6 to 4. How many different halftime scores are possible?

34. **Selecting an Outfit** Each day, Gloria dresses in a blouse, a skirt, and shoes. She wants to wear a different combination on every day of the year. If she has the same number of blouses, skirts, and pairs of shoes, how many of each article would she need to have a different combination every day?

35. **Mismatched Gloves** A man has five different pairs of gloves. In how many ways can he select a right-hand glove and a left-hand glove that do not match?

36. **Mismatched Shoes** Fred has 11 different pairs of shoes. In how many ways can he put on a pair of shoes that do not match?

37. **Coin Tosses** Toss a coin six times, and observe the sequence of heads and tails that results. How many different sequences are possible?

38. **Coin Tosses** Refer to Exercise 37. In how many of the sequences are the first and last tosses identical?

39. **Exam Questions** An exam contains five true-or-false questions. In how many different ways can the exam be completed? Assume that every question must be answered.

40. **Exam Questions** An exam contains five true-or-false questions. In how many ways can the exam be completed if leaving the answer blank is also an option?

41. **Exam Questions** Each of the 10 questions on a multiple-choice exam has four possible answers. How many different ways are there for a student to answer the questions? Assume that every question must be answered.

42. **Exam Questions** Rework Exercise 41 under the assumption that not every question must be answered.

ZIP Codes ZIP (Zone Improvement Plan) codes, sequences of five digits, were introduced by the United States Post Office Department in 1963.

43. How many ZIP codes are possible?

44. ZIP codes for Delaware, New York, and Pennsylvania begin with the digit 1. How many such ZIP codes are possible?

45. **Group Pictures** How many ways can eight people stand in a line for a group picture? If you took a picture every 15 seconds (day and night with no breaks), how long would it take to photograph every possible arrangement?

46. **License Plates** A company is manufacturing license plates with the pattern LL#-##LL, where L represents a letter and # represents a digit from 1 through 9. If a letter can be any letter from A to Z except O, how many different license plates are possible? If the company produces 500,000 license plates per week, how many years will be required to make every possible license plate?

47. **Menu Selections** A college student eats all of their meals at a restaurant offering six breakfast specials, seven lunch specials, and four dinner specials. How many days can they go without repeating an entire day's menu selections?

48. **Menu Selections** A restaurant menu lists 7 appetizers, 10 entrées, and 4 desserts. How many ways can a diner select a three-course meal?

49. **Gift Wrapping** The gift-wrap desk at a large department store offers 5 box sizes, 10 wrapping papers, 7 colors of ribbon in 2 widths, and 9 special items to be added on the box. How many different ways are there to package a gift, assuming that the customer must choose at least a box but need not choose any of the other offerings?

50. **Selecting Fruit** José was told to create a gift basket containing one dozen oranges, eight apples, and a half-pound of grapes. When he gets to the store, he finds five varieties of oranges, five varieties of apples, and two varieties of grapes. Assuming

that he selects only one variety of each type of fruit, how many different gift baskets of fruit could he bring home?

51. **Shading of Venn Diagrams** How many different ways can a Venn diagram with two circles be shaded?

52. **Shading of Venn Diagrams** How many different ways can a Venn diagram with three circles be shaded?

Roulette An American roulette wheel consists of 38 numbered pockets. Two of them (numbered 0 and 00) are colored green, 18 are colored red, and 18 are colored black. Gamblers bet on which numbered pocket a ball will fall into when the wheel is spun. For Exercises 53 and 54, assume the wheel is spun three times.

53. How many outcomes are possible if the first number is green?

54. How many outcomes are possible if all three numbers are red and no number repeats?

55. **Batting Orders** The manager of a Little League baseball team has picked the nine starting players for a game. How many different batting orders are possible under each of the following conditions?
    (a) There are no restrictions.
    (b) The pitcher must bat last.
    (c) The pitcher must bat last, the catcher eighth, and the shortstop first.

56. **Test Volunteers** A physiologist wants to test the effects of exercise and meditation on blood pressure. She devises four different exercise programs and three different meditation programs. If she wants 10 subjects for each combination of exercise and meditation program, how many volunteers must she recruit?

57. **Handshakes** Two 10-member basketball teams play a game. After the game, each of the members of the winning team shakes hands once with each member of both teams. How many handshakes take place?

58. **Band Selections** In how many ways can a band play a set of three waltzes and three tangos without repeating any song, such that the first, third, and fifth songs are waltzes?

59. **Colored Houses** Six houses in a row are each to be painted with one of the colors red, blue, green, and yellow. In how many different ways can the houses be painted so that no two adjacent houses are of the same color?

60. **Chair Varieties** A furniture manufacturer makes three types of upholstered chairs and offers 20 fabrics. How many different chairs are available?

61. **Ballots** Seven candidates for mayor, four candidates for city council president, and six propositions are being put before the electorate. How many different ballots could be cast, assuming that every voter votes on each of the items? If voters can choose to leave any item blank, how many different ballots are possible?

62. **College Applications** Allison is preparing her applications for college. She will apply to three community colleges and has to fill out six parts in each of those applications. She will apply to three four-year schools, each of which has a seven-part application. How many application segments must she complete?

63. **Paths to Texas** Consider the triangular display of letters below. Start with the letter T at the top and move down the triangle to a letter S at the bottom. From any given letter, move only to one of the letters directly below it on the left or right. How many different paths spell *TEXAS*?

$$\begin{array}{ccccccccc} & & & & T & & & & \\ & & & E & & E & & & \\ & & X & & X & & X & & \\ & A & & A & & A & & A & \\ S & & S & & S & & S & & S \end{array}$$

64. **Railroad Tickets** A railway has 20 stations. If the names of the point of departure and the destination are printed on each ticket, how many different kinds of single tickets must be printed? How many different kinds of tickets are needed if each ticket may be used in either direction between two stations?

Solutions to Check Your Understanding 1.4

1. 72. Pretend that you are given the task of seating the five people. This task consists of five choices performed consecutively, as shown in Table 1. After you have performed choice 1, four people will remain, and any one of these four can be seated in the right front seat. After choice 2, three people remain, and so on. By the generalized multiplication principle, the task can be performed in $3 \cdot 4 \cdot 3 \cdot 2 \cdot 1 = 72$ ways.

2. 3^{10}. The task of answering the questions consists of 10 consecutive choices, each of which can be performed in three ways. Therefore, by the generalized multiplication principle, the task can be performed in

$$\underbrace{3 \cdot 3 \cdot 3 \cdot \cdots \cdot 3}_{10 \text{ terms}} \text{ ways.}$$

Note: The answer can be left as 3^{10} or can be multiplied out to 59,049.

Table 1

Choice	Number of Ways Choice Can Be Performed
1: Select person to drive.	3
2: Select person for right front seat.	4
3: Select person for left rear seat.	3
4: Select person for middle rear seat.	2
5: Select person for right rear seat.	1

1.5 Permutations and Combinations

In preceding sections, we have solved a variety of counting problems by using Venn diagrams and the generalized multiplication principle. Let us now turn our attention to two types of counting problems that occur very frequently and that can be solved by using formulas derived from the generalized multiplication principle. These problems involve what are called *permutations* and *combinations*, which are particular types of arrangements of elements of a set. The sorts of arrangements that we have in mind are illustrated in two problems:

Problem A How many words (by which we mean *strings of letters*) of two distinct letters can be formed from the letters $\{a, b, c\}$?

Problem B A construction crew has three members. A team of two must be chosen for a particular job. In how many ways can the team be chosen?

Each of the two problems can be solved by enumerating all possibilities.

Solution of Problem A There are six possible words, namely,

$$ab \quad ac \quad ba \quad bc \quad ca \quad cb.$$

Solution of Problem B Designate the three crew members by a, b, and c. Then there are three possible two-person teams, namely,

$$\{a, b\} \quad \{a, c\} \quad \{b, c\}.$$

Note that $\{b, a\}$, the team consisting of b and a, is the same as the team $\{a, b\}$.

We deliberately set up both problems with the same letters in order to facilitate comparison. Both problems are concerned with counting the numbers of arrangements of the elements of the set $\{a, b, c\}$, taken two at a time, without allowing repetition. (For example, aa was not allowed.) However, in Problem A, the order of the arrangement mattered, whereas in Problem B it did not. Arrangements of the sort considered in Problem A are called *permutations*, whereas those in Problem B are called *combinations*.

More precisely, suppose that we are given a set of n distinguishable objects.

Permutations **A permutation of n objects taken r at a time** is an arrangement of r of the n objects in a specific order.

So, for example, Problem A was concerned with permutations of the three objects a, b, c $(n = 3)$ taken two at a time $(r = 2)$.

Combinations **A combination of n objects taken r at a time** is a selection of r objects from among the n, with order disregarded.

Thus, for example, in Problem B, we considered combinations of the three objects a, b, c $(n = 3)$ taken two at a time $(r = 2)$.

It is convenient to introduce the notation that follows for counting permutations and combinations. Let

$$P(n, r) = \text{the number of permutations of } n \text{ objects taken } r \text{ at a time}$$
$$C(n, r) = \text{the number of combinations of } n \text{ objects taken } r \text{ at a time.}$$

Thus, for example, from our solutions to Problems A and B, we have

$$P(3, 2) = 6 \qquad C(3, 2) = 3.$$

Very simple formulas for $P(n, r)$ and $C(n, r)$ allow us to calculate these quantities for any n and r. Let us begin by stating the formula for $P(n, r)$. For $r = 1, 2, 3$, respectively,

$$P(n, 1) = n$$
$$P(n, 2) = n(n-1) \qquad \text{(two factors)},$$
$$P(n, 3) = n(n-1)(n-2) \qquad \text{(three factors)}.$$

Continuing, we obtain the following formula:

Permutation Formula The number of permutations of n objects taken r at a time, $P(n, r)$, is the product of the r whole numbers counting down by 1 from n. That is,

$$P(n, r) = n(n-1)(n-2)\cdots(n-r+1) \qquad (r \text{ factors}), \tag{1}$$

or

$$P(n, r) = \frac{n!}{(n-r)!} \tag{2}$$

This formula is verified at the end of the section.

EXAMPLE 1 **Applying the Permutation Formula** Compute the following numbers:
(a) $P(100, 2)$ **(b)** $P(6, 4)$ **(c)** $P(5, 5)$

SOLUTION **(a)** Here, $n = 100$, $r = 2$. So we take the product of two factors, beginning with 100:

$$P(100, 2) = 100 \cdot 99 = 9900.$$

(b) $P(6, 4) = 6 \cdot 5 \cdot 4 \cdot 3 = 360$
(c) $P(5, 5) = 5 \cdot 4 \cdot 3 \cdot 2 \cdot 1 = 120$

>> Now Try Exercise 1

Combination Formula The number of combinations of n objects taken r at a time, is

$$C(n, r) = \frac{P(n, r)}{r!} = \frac{n(n-1)\cdot\cdots\cdot(n-r+1)}{r(r-1)\cdot\cdots\cdot 1} = \frac{n!}{r!\,(n-r)!}$$

This formula is verified at the end of this section.

EXAMPLE 2 **Applying the Combination Formula** Compute the following numbers:
(a) $C(100, 2)$ **(b)** $C(6, 4)$ **(c)** $C(5, 5)$

SOLUTION **(a)** $C(100, 2) = \dfrac{P(100, 2)}{2!} = \dfrac{100 \cdot 99}{2 \cdot 1} = 4950$

(b) $C(6, 4) = \dfrac{P(6, 4)}{4!} = \dfrac{6 \cdot 5 \cdot 4 \cdot 3}{4 \cdot 3 \cdot 2 \cdot 1} = 15$

(c) $C(5, 5) = \dfrac{P(5, 5)}{5!} = \dfrac{5 \cdot 4 \cdot 3 \cdot 2 \cdot 1}{5 \cdot 4 \cdot 3 \cdot 2 \cdot 1} = 1$

>> Now Try Exercise 5

EXAMPLE 3 **Applying the Permutation and Combination Formulas** Solve Problems A and B, using formulas (1) and (3).

SOLUTION The number of two-letter words that can be formed from the three letters a, b, and c is equal to $P(3, 2) = 3 \cdot 2 = 6$, in agreement with our previous solution.

The number of two-worker teams that can be formed from three individuals is equal to $C(3, 2)$, and

$$C(3, 2) = \frac{P(3, 2)}{2!} = \frac{3 \cdot 2}{2 \cdot 1} = 3,$$

in agreement with our previous result.

>> Now Try Exercises 27 and 29

EXAMPLE 4 **Selecting a Committee** The board of directors of a corporation has 10 members. In how many ways can they choose a committee of three board members to negotiate a merger?

SOLUTION Since the committee of three involves no ordering of its members, we are concerned here with combinations. The number of combinations of 10 people taken 3 at a time is $C(10, 3)$, which is

$$C(10, 3) = \frac{10 \cdot 9 \cdot 8}{3 \cdot 2 \cdot 1} = 120.$$

Thus, there are 120 possibilities for the committee.

>> Now Try Exercise 31

EXAMPLE 5 **Selecting Club Officers** A club has 10 members. In how many ways can they choose a slate of four officers, consisting of a president, vice president, secretary, and treasurer?

SOLUTION In this problem, we are dealing with an ordering of four members. (The first is the president, the second the vice president, and so on.) So we are dealing with permutations, and the number of ways of choosing the officers is

$$P(10, 4) = 10 \cdot 9 \cdot 8 \cdot 7 = 5040.$$

>> Now Try Exercise 33

EXAMPLE 6 **Outcomes of a Horse Race** Eight horses are entered in a race in which a first, second, and third prize will be awarded. Assuming no ties, how many different outcomes are possible?

SOLUTION In this example, we are considering ordered arrangements of three horses, so we are dealing with permutations. The number of permutations of eight horses taken three at a time is

$$P(8, 3) = 8 \cdot 7 \cdot 6 = 336,$$

so the number of possible outcomes of the race is 336.

>> Now Try Exercise 39

EXAMPLE 7 **Polling Sample** A political pollster wishes to survey 1500 individuals chosen from a sample of 5,000,000 adults. In how many ways can the 1500 individuals be chosen?

SOLUTION No ordering of the 1500 individuals is involved, so we are dealing with combinations. So the number in question is $C(5{,}000{,}000, 1500)$, a number too large to be written down in digit form. (It has several thousand digits!) But it could be calculated with the aid of a computer.

>> Now Try Exercise 29

EXAMPLE 8 **Seating Arrangements** Three couples go on a movie date. In how many ways can they be seated in a row of six seats so that each couple is seated together?

SOLUTION A seating arrangement can be composed of four consecutive choices:

Select an order in which to seat the couples	Seat the left-most couple	Seat the middle couple	Seat the right-most couple
Choice 1	Choice 2	Choice 3	Choice 4

Since there are three couples, choice 1 can be performed in 3! ways. After the order of the three couples has been chosen, there are 2! ways to seat the two members of the leftmost couple. Similarly, there are 2! ways to perform choice 3 and 2! ways to perform choice 4.

By the generalized multiplication principle, the number of possible arrangements is $3! \cdot 2! \cdot 2! \cdot 2! = 48$. **>> Now Try Exercise 59**

EXAMPLE 9 **Arranging Books** If you have six books, in how many ways can you select four books and arrange them on a shelf?

SOLUTION Arrange four of the six books in order. This can be done in $P(6, 4) = 360$ ways.

As is often the case in counting problems, there are multiple ways to arrive at a solution.

ALTERNATIVE SOLUTION First, select the four books from the group of six. Since order does not matter at this point, this can be done in $C(6, 4)$ ways. Next, arrange the selection of four books on the shelf, which can be done in 4! ways. By the multiplication principle, the number of possible arrangements is $C(6, 4) \cdot 4! = 15 \cdot 24 = 360$. **>> Now Try Exercise 58**

Example 9 shows that $P(n, r) = C(n, r) \cdot r!$ when $n = 6$ and $r = 4$. The discussion that follows shows that this formula holds for all values of n and r.

Verification of the Formulas for $P(n, r)$ and $C(n, r)$

Let us first derive the formula for $P(n, r)$, the number of permutations of n objects taken r at a time. The task of choosing r objects (in a given order) consists of r consecutive choices (Fig. 1). The first choice can be performed in n ways. For each way that the first choice is performed, one object will have been used up so that we can perform the second choice in $n - 1$ ways, and so on. For each way of performing the sequence of choices $1, 2, 3, \ldots, r - 1$, the rth choice can be performed in $n - (r - 1) = n - r + 1$ ways. By the generalized multiplication principle, the task of choosing the r objects from among the n can be performed in

$$n(n-1) \cdot \cdots \cdot (n-r+1) \quad \text{ways.}$$

That is,

$$P(n, r) = n(n-1) \cdot \cdots \cdot (n-r+1),$$

which is formula (1).

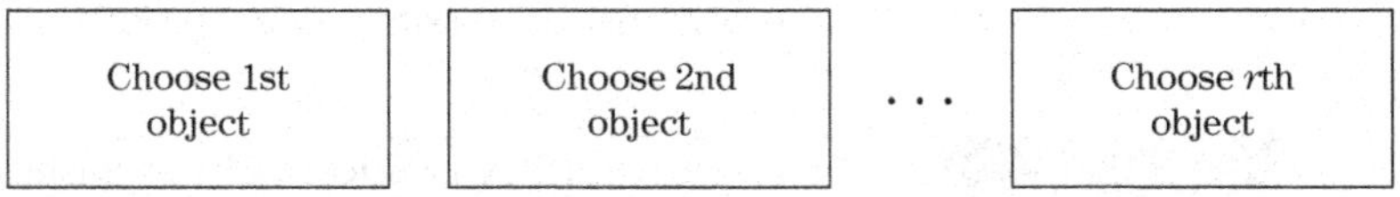

Choose 1st object	Choose 2nd object	. . .	Choose rth object

Figure 1

Let us now verify the formula for $C(n, r)$, the number of combinations of n objects taken r at a time. Each such combination is a set of r objects and, therefore, can be ordered in

$$P(r, r) = r(r-1) \cdot \cdots \cdot 2 \cdot 1 = r!$$

ways by formula (1). In other words, each different combination of r objects gives rise to $r!$ permutations of the same r objects. On the other hand, each permutation of n objects taken r at a time gives rise to a combination of n objects taken r at a time, by simply ignoring the order of the permutation. Thus, if we start with the $P(n, r)$ permutations, we will have all of the combinations of n objects taken r at a time, with each combination repeated $r!$ times. Thus,

$$P(n, r) = r!\, C(n, r).$$

On dividing both sides of the equation by $r!$, we obtain formula (3).

Check Your Understanding 1.5

Solutions can be found following the section exercises.

1. Calculate the following values:
   (a) $5!$ (b) $P(5, 5)$ (c) $P(7, 3)$ (d) $C(7, 3)$

2. A newborn child is to be given a first name and a middle name from a selection of 10 names. How many different possibilities are there?

EXERCISES 1.5

For Exercises 1–20, calculate the values.

1. $P(4, 2)$
2. $P(5, 1)$
3. $P(6, 3)$
4. $P(5, 4)$
5. $C(10, 3)$
6. $C(12, 2)$
7. $C(5, 4)$
8. $C(6, 3)$
9. $P(7, 1)$
10. $P(5, 5)$
11. $P(n, 1)$
12. $P(n, 2)$
13. $C(4, 4)$
14. $C(n, 2)$
15. $C(n, n - 2)$
16. $C(n, 1)$
17. $6!$
18. $\frac{10!}{4!}$
19. $\frac{9!}{7!}$
20. $7!$

In Exercises 21–26, determine whether the computation involves a permutation, a combination, or neither.

21. **Stock Abbreviations** The number of different stock abbreviations for which each abbreviation consists of four letters, none repeated.
22. **Airport Codes** The number of different airport codes in which each code consists of three letters, none repeated.
23. **Ice Cream Flavors** The selection of three different flavors of ice cream (out of 29 flavors) for the three scoops of ice cream in a sundae.
24. **Ice Cream Flavors** The selection of three different flavors of ice cream (out of 29 flavors) for the three scoops of ice cream on an ice cream cone, where order matters.
25. **Rolling Dice** The number of possible sums when two dice are rolled and the numbers displayed are added.
26. **Meal Choices** The number of possible meals consisting of an appetizer, a main course, and a dessert from a restaurant that offers 5 different appetizers, 10 main courses, and 4 desserts.
27. **Group Picture** In how many ways can four people line up in a row for a group picture?
28. **Waiting in Line** In how many ways can six people line up at a single counter to order food at a fast-food restaurant?
29. **Book Selection** How many different selections of seven books can be made from nine books?
30. **Pizza Varieties** A pizzeria offers five toppings for the plain cheese base of the pizzas. How many pizzas can be made that use three different toppings?
31. **Selecting Colleges** A high school student decides to apply to four of the eight Ivy League colleges. In how many possible ways can the four colleges be selected?
32. **Senate Committees** In how many different ways can a committee of 5 senators be selected from the 100 members of the U.S. Senate?
33. **Ranking Teams** A sportswriter makes a preseason guess of the top five football teams (in order) from among the 65 Power Five conference teams. How many different possibilities are there?
34. **CD Changer** Suppose that you have 36 CDs and your CD player has five slots numbered 1 through 5. How many ways can you fill your CD player?
35. **Guest Lists** How many ways can you choose five out of 10 friends to invite to a dinner party?
36. **Choosing Exam Questions** A student is required to work exactly four problems from an eight-problem exam. In how many ways can the problems be chosen?
37. **DVDs** In a batch of 100 DVDs, seven are defective. A sample of three DVDs is to be selected from the batch. How many samples are possible? How many of the samples consist of all defective DVDs?
38. **Debates** There are 17 candidates for an elected office. If 10 candidates are selected to participate in a debate, determine the total number of possible debate groups.
39. **Race Winners** Theoretically, assuming no ties, how many possibilities are there for first, second, and third places in a marathon race with 150 entries?
40. **Player Introductions** The five starting players of a basketball team are introduced one at a time. In how many different ways can they be introduced?

Poker Hands Exercises 41–44 refer to poker hands. A poker hand consists of 5 cards selected from a standard deck of 52 cards.

41. How many different poker hands are there?
42. How many different poker hands consist entirely of aces and kings?
43. How many different poker hands consist entirely of clubs?
44. How many different poker hands consist entirely of red cards?
45. **Distributing Sandwiches** Five students order different sandwiches at a campus eatery. The waiter forgets who ordered what and gives out the sandwiches at random. In how many different ways can the sandwiches be distributed?

46. **Nautical Signals** A nautical signal consists of three flags arranged vertically on a flagpole. If a sailor has six flags, each of a different color, how many different signals are possible?

47. **Selecting Sweaters** Suppose that you own 10 sweaters.
   (a) How many ways can you select four of them to take on a trip?
   (b) How many ways can you select six of the sweaters to leave at home?
   (c) Explain why the answers to parts (a) and (b) are the same.

48. **Distributing Books** Fred has 12 different books.
   (a) Suppose that Fred first gives three books to Jill and then gives four of the remaining books to Jack. How many different outcomes are possible?
   (b) Suppose that Fred first gives four books to Jack and then gives three of the remaining books to Jill. How many different outcomes are possible?
   (c) Explain why the answers to parts (a) and (b) are the same.

49. **Conference Games** In an eight-team football conference, each team plays every other team exactly once. How many games must be played?

50. **League Games** In a six-team softball league, each team plays every other team three times during the season. How many games must be scheduled?

51. **Powerball** In the Powerball lottery, five white balls are drawn out of a drum with 69 numbered white balls and then one red ball is drawn out of a drum with 26 numbered red balls. The jackpot is won by guessing all five white balls in any order and the red Powerball. Determine the number of possible outcomes.

52. **Baseball Lineup** On a children's baseball team, there are four players who can play at any of the following infield positions: catcher, first base, third base, and shortstop. There are five possible pitchers, none of whom plays any other position. And there are four players who can play any of the three outfield positions (right, left, and center) or second base. In how many ways can the coach assign players to positions?

Lotto Exercises 53 and 54 refer to the New York State lottery (Lotto). When it was first established, a contestant had to select six numbers from 1 to 49. A few years later, the numbers 50 through 54 were added. In March 2007, the numbers 55 through 59 were added.

53. The number of possible combinations of six numbers selected from 1 to 59 is approximately _____ times the number of combinations selected from 1 through 49.
   (a) 2 (b) 3 (c) 10 (d) 100

54. Drawings for Lotto are held twice per week. Suppose that you decide to purchase 110 tickets for each drawing and never use the same combination twice. Approximately how many years would be required before you would have bet on every possible combination?
   (a) 100 (b) 1000 (c) 2000 (d) 4000

55. **Choosing Candy** Two children, Moe and Joe, are allowed to select candy from a plate of nine pieces of candy. Moe, being younger, is allowed to choose first but can take only two candies. Joe is then allowed to take four of the remaining candies. Joe complains that he has fewer options than Moe. Is Joe correct? How many options will each child have?

56. **Committee Selection** The 12 members of the Gotham City Council consists of four members from each of the city's three wards. In how many ways can a committee of six council members be selected if the committee must contain at least one council member from each ward?

57. **Group Picture** The student council at Gotham College is made up of four freshmen, five sophomores, six juniors, and seven seniors. A yearbook photographer would like to line up three council members from each class for a picture. How many different pictures are possible if each group of classmates stands together?

58. **Arranging Books** George has three books by each of his five favorite authors. In how many ways can the books be placed on a shelf if books by the same author must be together?

59. **Seating Arrangements** In the quiz show *It's Academic*, three-person teams from three high schools are seated in a row, with each team seated together. How many different seating arrangements are possible?

60. **Displaying Paintings** An art gallery has four paintings, by each of three artists, hanging in a row, with paintings by the same artist grouped together. How many different arrangements are possible?

61. **Handshakes** At a party, everyone shakes hands with everyone else. If 45 handshakes take place, how many people are at the party?

62. **Football Games** In a football league, each team plays one game against each other team in the league. If 55 games are played, how many teams are in the league?

63. **Side Dishes** A restaurant offers its customers a choice of three side dishes with each meal. The side dishes can be chosen from a list of 15 possibilities, with duplications allowed. For instance, a customer can order two sides of mashed potatoes and one side of string beans. Show that there are 680 possible options for the three side dishes.

64. **Ice Cream Specials** An ice cream parlor offers a special consisting of three scoops of ice cream chosen from 16 different flavors. Duplication of flavors is allowed. For instance, one possibility is two scoops of chocolate and one scoop of vanilla. Show that there are 816 different possible options for the special.

65. **Determine Position** There are $6! = 720$ six-letter words (that is, strings of letters) that can be made from the letters C, N, O, S, T, and U. If these 720 words are listed in alphabetical order, what position in the list will be occupied by TUCSON? *Hint:* Count the number of words that follow TUCSON in the list. They must each be of the form TUNxxx or Uxxxxx.

66. **Detour-Prone ZIP Codes** A five-digit ZIP code is said to be detour prone if it looks like a valid and different ZIP code when read upside down (Fig. 4). For instance, 68901 and 88111 are detour prone, whereas 32145 and 10801 are not. How many of the 10^5 possible ZIP code numbers are detour prone?

Figure 4

TECHNOLOGY EXERCISES

67. **Lottery**
(a) Calculate the number of possible lottery tickets if the player must choose five distinct numbers from 0 to 44, inclusive, where the order does not matter. The winner must match all five.
(b) Calculate the number of lottery tickets if the player must choose four distinct numbers from 0 to 99, inclusive, where the order does not matter. The winner must match all four.
(c) In which lottery does the player have a better chance of choosing the randomly selected winning numbers?

68. **Bridge** A bridge hand contains 13 cards.
(a) What percent of bridge hands contain all four aces?
(b) What percent of bridge hands contain the two red kings, the two red queens, and no other kings or queens?
(c) Which is more likely—a bridge hand with four aces or one with the two red kings, the two red queens, and no other kings or queens?

69. **Cards versus Atoms** Are there more ways to order a deck of 52 cards than there are atoms on Earth? *Note:* There are about 10^{50} atoms on Earth.

70. **Alphabet versus Atoms** Are there more ways to rearrange the 26 letters of the alphabet than there are atoms on Earth?

Solutions to Check Your Understanding 1.5

1. (a) $5! = 5 \cdot 4 \cdot 3 \cdot 2 \cdot 1 = 120$

(b) $P(5, 5) = 5 \cdot 4 \cdot 3 \cdot 2 \cdot 1 = 120$
[$P(n, n)$ is the same as $n!$]

(c) $P(7, 3) = \underbrace{7 \cdot 6 \cdot 5}_{3 \text{ factors}} = 210$

[$P(7, 3)$ is the product of the 3 whole numbers, counting down by 1 from 7.]

(d) $C(7, 3) = \dfrac{7 \cdot 6 \cdot 5}{3 \cdot 2 \cdot 1} = \dfrac{7 \cdot \cancel{6} \cdot 5}{\cancel{3} \cdot \cancel{2} \cdot 1} = 35$

[A convenient procedure to follow when calculating $C(n, r)$ is first to write the product expansion of $r!$ in the denominator and then to write in the numerator a whole number above each integer in the denominator. The whole numbers should begin with n and successively decrease by 1.]

2. 90. The first question to be asked here is whether permutations or combinations are involved. Two names are to be selected, and the order of the names is important. (The name Amanda Beth is different from the name Beth Amanda.) Since the problem asks for arrangements of 10 names taken 2 at a time in a *specific order*, the number of arrangements is $P(10, 2) = 10 \cdot 9 = 90$. In general, order is important if a different outcome results when two items in the selection are interchanged.

1.6 Further Counting Techniques

In Section 1.5, we introduced permutations and combinations and developed formulas for counting all permutations (or combinations) of a given type. Many counting problems can be formulated in terms of permutations or combinations. But to use the formulas of Section 1.5 successfully, we must be able to recognize these problems when they occur and to translate them into a form in which the formulas may be applied. In this section, we practice doing that. We consider several interesting applications giving rise to permutations or combinations. At first glance, the first two applications may seem to have little practical significance. However, they suggest a common way to "model" outcomes of real-life situations having two equally likely results.

As our first application, consider a coin-tossing experiment in which we toss a coin a fixed number of times. We can describe the outcome of the experiment as a sequence of "heads" and "tails." For instance, if a coin is tossed three times, then one possible outcome is "heads on the first toss, tails on the second toss, and tails on the third toss." This outcome can be abbreviated as HTT. We can use the methods of the preceding sections to count the number of possible outcomes having various prescribed properties.

EXAMPLE 1

Tossing a Coin Ten Times Suppose that an experiment consists of tossing a coin 10 times and observing the sequence of heads and tails.
(a) How many different outcomes are possible?
(b) How many different outcomes have exactly four heads?

SOLUTION (a) Visualize each outcome of the experiment as a sequence of 10 boxes, where each box contains one letter, H or T, with the first box recording the result of the first toss, the second box recording the result of the second toss, and so forth.

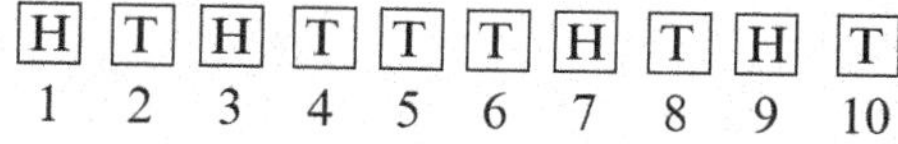

Each box can be filled in two ways. So by the generalized multiplication principle, the sequence of 10 boxes can be filled in

$$\underbrace{2 \cdot 2 \cdot \cdots \cdot 2}_{10 \text{ factors}} = 2^{10}$$

ways. So there are $2^{10} = 1024$ different possible outcomes.

(b) An outcome with 4 heads corresponds to filling the boxes with 4 H's and 6 T's. A particular outcome is determined as soon as we decide where to place the H's. The 4 boxes to receive H's can be selected from the 10 boxes in $C(10, 4)$ ways. So the number of outcomes with 4 heads is

$$C(10, 4) = \frac{10 \cdot 9 \cdot 8 \cdot 7}{4 \cdot 3 \cdot 2 \cdot 1} = 210.$$

» ***Now Try Exercise 1***

Ideas similar to those applied in Example 1 are useful in counting even more complicated sets of outcomes of coin-tossing experiments. The second part of our next example highlights a technique that can often save time and effort.

EXAMPLE 2 **Tossing a Coin Ten Times** Consider the coin-tossing experiment of Example 1.

(a) How many different outcomes have at most two heads?

(b) How many different outcomes have at least three heads?

SOLUTION **(a)** The outcomes with at most two heads are those having 0, 1, or 2 heads. Let us count the number of these outcomes separately:

0 heads: There is 1 outcome, namely, T T T T T T T T T T.

1 head: To determine such an outcome, we just select the box in which to put the single H. And this can be done in $C(10, 1) = 10$ ways.

2 heads: To determine such an outcome, we just select the boxes in which to put the two H's. And this can be done in $C(10, 2) = (10 \cdot 9)/(2 \cdot 1) = 45$ ways.

Adding up all the possible outcomes, we see that the number of outcomes with at most two heads is $1 + 10 + 45 = 56$.

(b) "At least three heads" refers to an outcome with either 3, 4, 5, 6, 7, 8, 9, or 10 heads. The total number of such outcomes is

$$C(10, 3) + C(10, 4) + \cdots + C(10, 10).$$

This sum can, of course, be calculated, but there is a less tedious way to solve the problem. Just start with all outcomes [1024 of them by Example 1(a)], and subtract those with at most two heads [56 of them by part (a)]. So the number of outcomes with at least three heads is $1024 - 56 = 968$. **»** ***Now Try Exercise 3***

The solution to part (b) of Example 2 employs a useful counting technique.

Complement Rule for Counting If U is the set of all possible outcomes and S is a subset of U, then S' is the set of all outcomes for which S does *not* occur, and

$$n(S') = n(U) - n(S).$$

Let us now turn to a different sort of counting problem, namely, one that involves counting the number of paths between two points.

EXAMPLE 3 **Routes through a City** In Fig. 1, we have drawn a partial map of the streets in New York City. A tourist wishes to walk from Times Square to Grand Central Station. We have drawn two possible routes. What is the total number of routes (with no back-tracking) from Times Square to Grand Central Station?

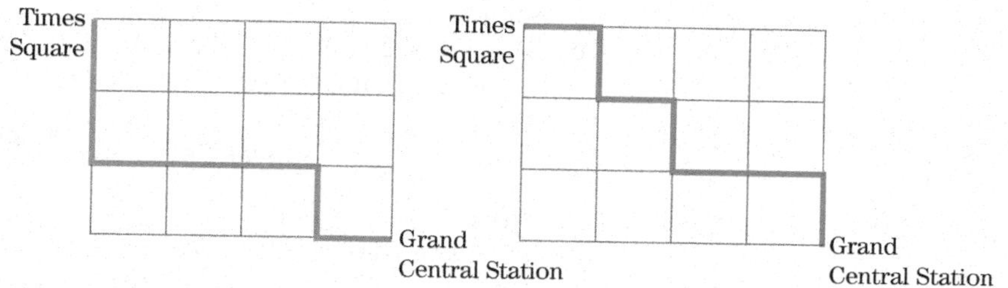

Figure 1

SOLUTION Any particular route can be described by giving the directions of each block walked in the appropriate order. For instance, the route on the left of Fig. 1 is described as "a block south, a block south, a block east, a block east, a block east, a block south, a block east." Using S for south and E for east, this route can be designated by the string of letters SSEEESE. Similarly, the route on the right is ESESEES. Note that each route is then described by a string of seven letters, of which three are S's (we must go three blocks south) and four are E's (we must go four blocks east). Selecting a route is thus the same as placing three S's in a string of seven boxes:

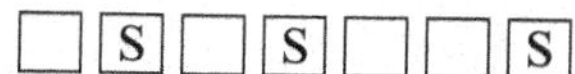

The three boxes to receive S's can be selected in $C(7, 3) = 35$ ways. So the number of paths from Times Square to Grand Central Station is 35. **»** ***Now Try Exercise 11***

EXAMPLE 4 **Routes through a City** Refer to the street map of Example 3. In how many of the routes does the tourist never walk south for two consecutive blocks?

SOLUTION Each route is a string of letters containing three S's and four E's. We are asked to count the number of such strings in which two S's are never adjacent to each other. One way to construct such a string is to write down four E's and then decide where to insert the three S's. The arrows below show the five places that the S's can be inserted:

The three insertion points can be selected in $C(5, 3) = 10$ ways. Therefore, there are 10 routes without consecutive souths. **»** ***Now Try Exercise 15***

Let us now move on to a third type of counting problem. Suppose that we have an urn in which there are a certain number of red balls and a certain number of white balls. We perform an experiment that consists of selecting a number of balls from the urn and observing the color distribution of the sample selected. (This model may be used, for example, to describe the process of selecting people to be polled in a survey. The different colors would correspond to different opinions.) By using familiar counting techniques, we can calculate the number of possible samples having a given color distribution. The next example illustrates a typical computation.

EXAMPLE 5 **Selecting Balls from an Urn** An urn contains 25 numbered balls, of which 15 are red and 10 are white. A sample of 5 balls is to be selected.

(a) How many different samples are possible?
(b) How many samples contain all red balls?
(c) How many samples contain 3 red balls and 2 white balls?
(d) How many samples contain at least 4 red balls?

SOLUTION

(a) A sample is just an unordered selection of 5 balls out of 25. There are $C(25, 5)$ such samples. Numerically, we have

$$C(25, 5) = \frac{25 \cdot 24 \cdot 23 \cdot 22 \cdot 21}{5 \cdot 4 \cdot 3 \cdot 2 \cdot 1} = 53{,}130$$

samples.

(b) To form a sample of all red balls, we must select 5 balls from the 15 red ones. This can be done in $C(15, 5)$ ways—that is, in

$$C(15, 5) = \frac{15 \cdot 14 \cdot 13 \cdot 12 \cdot 11}{5 \cdot 4 \cdot 3 \cdot 2 \cdot 1} = 3003$$

ways.

(c) To answer this question, we use both the multiplication principle and the formula for $C(n, r)$. We form a sample of 3 red balls and 2 white balls, using a sequence of two choices:

Select 3 red balls	Select 2 white balls
Choice 1	Choice 2

The first choice can be performed in $C(15, 3)$ ways and the second in $C(10, 2)$ ways. Thus, the total number of samples having 3 red and 2 white balls is $C(15, 3) \cdot C(10, 2)$. That is,

$$C(15, 3) = \frac{15 \cdot 14 \cdot 13}{3 \cdot 2 \cdot 1} = 455$$

$$C(10, 2) = \frac{10 \cdot 9}{2 \cdot 1} = 45$$

$$C(15, 3) \cdot C(10, 2) = 455 \cdot 45 = 20{,}475.$$

So the number of possible samples is 20,475.

(d) A sample with at least 4 red balls has either 4 or 5 red balls. By part (b), the number of samples with 5 red balls is 3003. Using the same reasoning as in part (c), the number of samples with 4 red balls is $C(15, 4) \cdot C(10, 1) = 1365 \cdot 10 = 13{,}650$. Thus, the total number of samples having at least 4 red balls is $13{,}650 + 3003 = 16{,}653$.

>> Now Try Exercise 25

EXAMPLE 6 **Photo Session** The nine justices of the United States Supreme Court can be seated in a row for a photo session in 9! different ways. In how many of the choices will Justice Elena Kagan be seated to the left of, but not necessarily beside, Justice John Roberts?

FIRST SOLUTION A possible seating for the justices can be obtained as follows:

1. Select the set of two chairs for Justices Kagan and Roberts. — $C(9, 2)$ possibilities
2. Seat Justice Kagan in the left chair and Justice Roberts in the right chair. — 1 possibility
3. Seat the remaining justices in the unoccupied seven chairs. — 7! possibilities

Therefore, by the multiplication principle, the number of such seatings are

$$C(9, 2) \cdot 1 \cdot 7! = 36 \cdot 1 \cdot 5040 = 181{,}440.$$

SECOND SOLUTION There are a total of $9! = 362{,}880$ possible seatings of the nine justices. In half of them, Justice Kagan will be seated to the left of Justice Roberts. Therefore, the answer to the question is $\frac{1}{2} \cdot 362{,}880 = 181{,}440$.

>> Now Try Exercise 37

EXAMPLE 7 **Numbers** How many six-digit numbers are there in which the digits strictly decrease when read from left to right? (Two examples are 865,421 and 976,532.)

SOLUTION One way to obtain a six-digit number is to start with the ten-digit number 9876543210 and remove four digits. Since the four digits can be selected in $C(10, 4) = 210$ different ways, there are 210 six-digit numbers whose digits are strictly decreasing.

»» *Now Try Exercise 39*

NOTE In counting problems, we often compute permutations or combinations as an intermediate step, then add, subtract, or multiply to solve the problem. A useful guideline to determine when to perform which arithmetic operation is:

- **Addition** If a set of outcomes can be expressed as the union of disjoint subsets of outcomes, then we may calculate the number of outcomes in each subset and add [see Example 2(a)].
- **Subtraction** If a set of outcomes can be expressed as the complement of another set, then we may use the complement rule [see Example 2(b)].
- **Multiplication** If a set of outcomes can be expressed as a sequence of choices, then we may use the multiplication principle (see Example 5). «

NOTE In Example 1, the number of different outcomes that result in exactly 4 heads when a coin is tossed 10 times was calculated to be $C(10, 4) = 210$. Notice that each of these 210 outcomes corresponds to a linear arrangement of the letters H, H, H, H, T, T, T, T, T, T. In Section 1.5, the number of linear arrangements of n distinguishable objects was given to be $n!$. However, the 10 objects H, H, H, H, T, T, T, T, T, T are not all distinguishable and so the number of linear arrangements of them is not simply 10!. You can however verify that 210 is equal to $\frac{10!}{4!6!}$. Why?

If we initially treat the 10 letters as distinguishable and look at the 10! possible permutations, many of them will look identical. For example, in the arrangement H T H T T T H T H T, if we switch the H in the first position with the H in the third position, the resulting arrangement is identical. In fact, for the arrangement H T H T T T H T H T (and in fact for any arrangement), there are 4! ways to arrange the Hs so that the Hs remain in precisely the same 4 positions. Similarly, there are 6! ways to arrange the Ts so that the Ts remain in precisely the same 6 positions. This means that each linear arrangement of the 10 letters is counted precisely 4!6! times by 10!, and hence the number of distinguishable linear arrangements is $\frac{10!}{4!6!} = 210$. «

NOTE A similar observation can be made in Example 3, where each of the routes from A to B corresponds to a linear arrangement of the letters S, S, S, E, E, E, E. The answer to the stated problem was $C(7,3) = 35$. You can verify that $\frac{7!}{3!5!} = 35$. «

The idea described in the two previous notes can be generalized to find a method that is useful for counting linear arrangements of objects when not all of the objects are distinguishable. Just before that method is given, let us look at one new example for which we have not already found a solution.

EXAMPLE 8 **Arranging the Letters in a Word** How many distinguishable linear arrangements are there of the 11 letters in the 'word' O N E T W O T H R E E?

SOLUTION Previous counting methods can be used to solve this problem using the following reasoning.

First, there are $C(11, 2)$ ways to decide where to position the two Os. An example of a choice of 2 positions for the Os is - - O - O - - - - - - .

For each such selection of positions for the Os, there are 9 positions left in which to place the remaining letters. As a second step, there are now $C(9, 3)$ ways to decide where to position the three Es. An example of a choice of 3 positions for the Es (leaving the Os in the positions previously chosen) is E - O - O - - E E - -.

Once the positions for the Os and Es has been determined, 6 empty positions remain. Hence there are $C(6, 2)$ ways to decide where to place the two Ts. An example of a choice of 2 positions for the Ts is E - O - O T - E E - T.

There are now four empty positions remaining in which to arrange the remaining letters N, W, H, and R. There are 4! ways to do this since the four remaining letters are distinguishable. Therefore the answer to the problem is

$$C(11, 2) \cdot C(9, 3) \cdot C(6, 2) \cdot 4!.$$

Rather than simply enter this solution into a calculator to get an answer, let us first simplify it using the Combinations Formula so that we can observe something interesting:

$$\begin{aligned} C(11, 2) \cdot C(9, 3) \cdot C(6, 2) \cdot 4! &= \frac{11!}{2!9!} \cdot \frac{9!}{3!6!} \cdot \frac{6!}{2!4!} \cdot 4! \\ &= \frac{11!}{2!3!2!} \\ &= 1,663,200 \end{aligned}$$

«

The simplified answer of $\frac{11!}{2!3!2!}$ in the solution to Example 8 hints at the possibility of an alternative (simpler) solution method! The method comes from the following result.

> **Linear Arrangements Formula** The number of linear arrangements of n objects, where n_1 are identical of Type 1, n_2 are identical of Type 2, ... , n_r are identical of Type r, and $n_1 + n_2 + \cdots + n_r = n$, is
>
> $$\frac{n!}{n_1!n_2!\cdots n_r!}$$

NOTE

We can use the Linear Arrangements Formula to directly answer Example 8 quickly. The 11 letters that are being arranged consist of 2 of Type E, 3 of Type O, 2 of Type T, and 1 each of Types N, W, H, and R. Therefore the formula immediately gives the solution

$$\frac{11!}{2!3!2!1!1!1!1!} = \frac{11!}{2!3!2!} = 1,663,200.$$ «

There are many applications in which the Linear Arrangements Formula is useful. Sometimes the formula will need to be used along with other counting methods, as can be seen in the following example.

EXAMPLE 9

Flag Patterns At a summer camp the girls in two of the neighbouring cabins have come up with a plan to communicate messages to each other without leaving their cabins by hanging a pattern of 8 coloured flags on a rope hung across their doorways. Each message is to consist of a linear pattern made from 1 black, 2 red, 3 green, and 2 white flags.

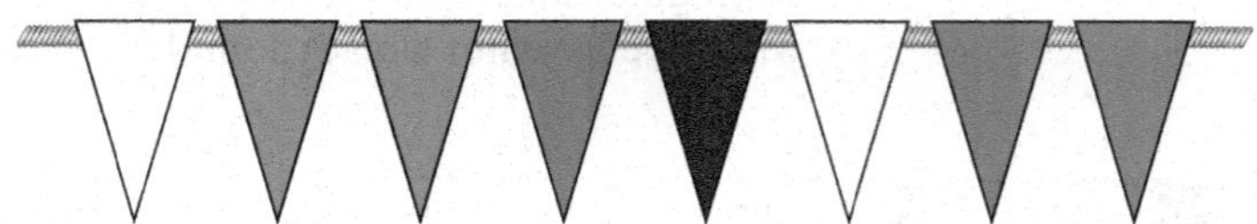

(a) How many different messages are possible?

(b) How many of the messages have the three green flags appearing directly next to each other?

(c) How many of the messages do not have any of the green flags occurring consecutively?

(d) How many of the messages start and end with flags of the same colour?

SOLUTION (a) Let B represent a black flag, R represent a red flag, G represent a green flag, and W represent a white flag. Then each message can be represented by a linear arrangement of the letters B, R, R, G, G, G, W, W. Using the Linear Arrangements Formula, the number of possible messages is simply

$$\frac{8!}{2!3!2!} = 1680.$$

Unless the girls have an awful lot of secret messages that they want to be able to communicate, they likely will not need to use all 1680 possible patterns!

(b) In order to make sure all three green flags occur consecutively, consider the three green flags as one unit. You can visualize this as stitching the three green flags together in a row so that they can't be separated. That is, what needs to be counted are the arrangements of the 6 objects: B, R, R, (GGG), W, W. The number of such arrangements is

$$\frac{6!}{2!2!} = 180.$$

Notice that the 2!2! in the denominator results from the duplicate Rs and duplicate Ws. There is no 3! in the denominator since GGG is a single object.

(c) This problem may sound simple at a glance, but it can pose quite a challenge. It would be a good exercise to try to solve this question before reading the solution. You may get the correct answer in an entirely different way that you can compare to the following new idea.

First consider all of the different ways to arrange only the flags B, R, R, W, W. There are $\frac{5!}{2!2!} = 30$ ways to do this. One example of an arrangement of these five flags (corresponding to the arrangement R W R B W) is shown:

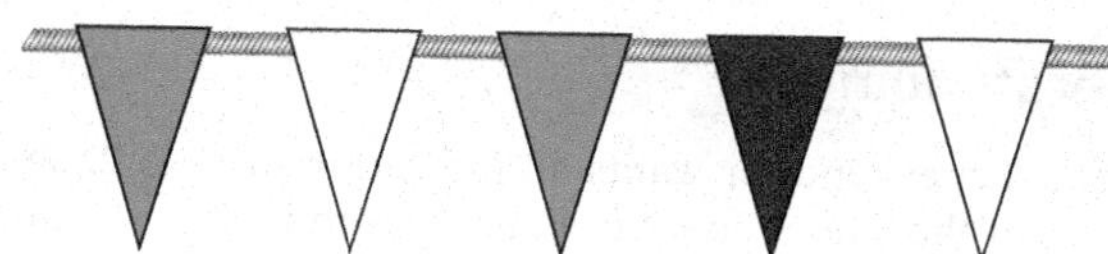

For each pattern of the five non-green flags, there are many ways to insert the three green flags amongst them to form a pattern with all eight flags. However, to ensure that no two green flags are placed consecutively, 3 of the 6 spaces created by the five non-green flags can be selected as positions for the green flags:

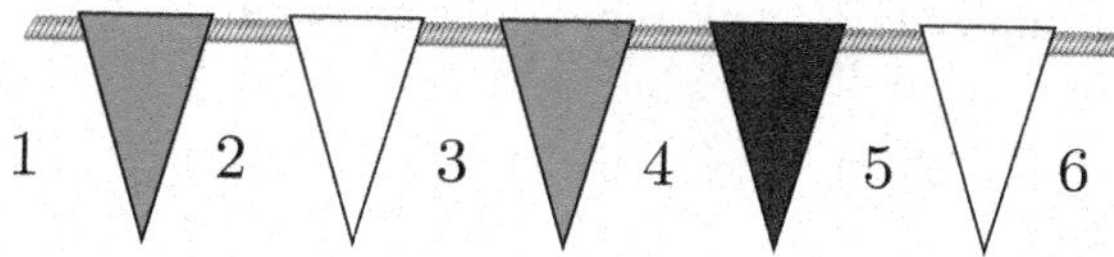

For example, if spaces 1, 3, and 4 are chosen, the resulting pattern of flags would be G R W G R G B W.

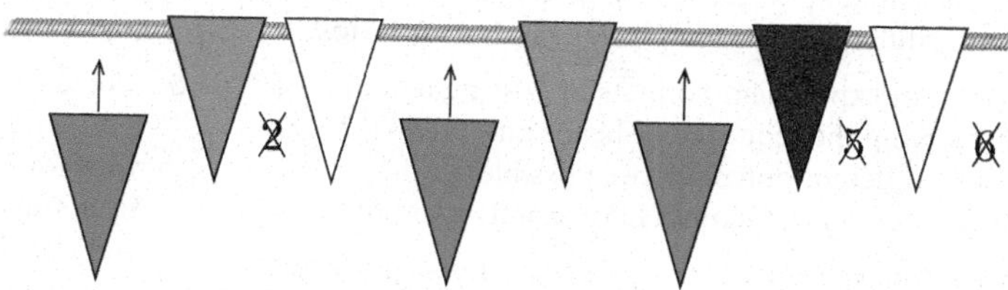

Since there are $C(6, 3)$ ways to choose three spaces for the three green flags, the solution is

$$\frac{5!}{2!2!} \cdot C(6, 3) = 600.$$

(d) There are three cases to consider: the first and last flags are both red, they are both white, or they are both black.

If the first and last flags are red, the number of ways to arrange the other 6 flags between the 2 red flags is the number of arrangements of B, G, G, G, W, W. There are $\frac{6!}{3!2!} = 60$ such arrangements.

Similarly, there are 60 arrangements in which the first and last flags are both white.

In the last case, the number of arrangements is the number of arrangements of B, R, R, G, W, W between two green flags, which is $\frac{6!}{2!2!} = 180$.

Therefore the solution is $60 + 60 + 180 = 300$. «

It is hoped that from the given examples it is apparent how many unique types of problems can be tackled with very few fundamental methods. A lot of practice is critical for becoming skilled at identifying when and how to apply each of the methods shown. Some seemingly simple problems can have quite challenging solutions, while other problems that may sound complicated at first can have very simple solutions.

Example 7 is an example of a problem that has a simple solution that may not have been immediately obvious. It is tempting in a problem like that one to try to break the problem into cases, such as based on the first digit. You could observe that none of the numbers of interest start with 0, 1, 2, 3, 4, or 5, because it would not then be possible to have six distinct and decreasing digits. However, in each of the remaining cases that are actually possible, there are a different number of possible 6-digit numbers based on the value of the first digit. For example, there is only one such number that has 6 as the first digit, but there will be many that have 9 as the first digit. You can try this method to see how hard it is! Fortunately, the solution provided in Example 7 answers the question very quickly.

Check Your Understanding 1.6

Solutions can be found following the section exercises.

1. **School Board** A newspaper reporter wants an indication of how the 15 members of the school board feel about a certain proposal. She decides to question a sample of 6 of the board members.
   (a) How many different samples are possible?
   (b) Suppose that 10 of the board members support the proposal, and 5 oppose it. How many of the samples reflect the distribution of the board? That is, in how many of the samples do 4 people support the proposal and 2 oppose it?

2. **Free Throws** A basketball player shoots eight free throws and lists the sequence of results of each trial in order. Let S represent *success* and F represent *failure*. Then, for instance, FFSSSSSS represents the outcome of missing the first two shots and hitting the rest.
   (a) How many different outcomes are possible?
   (b) How many of the outcomes have six successes?

EXERCISES 1.6

1. **Tossing a Coin** An experiment consists of tossing a coin eight times and observing the sequence of heads and tails.
   (a) How many different outcomes are possible?
   (b) How many different outcomes have exactly four heads?

2. **Tossing a Coin** An experiment consists of tossing a coin nine times and observing the sequence of heads and tails.
   (a) How many different outcomes are possible?
   (b) How many different outcomes have exactly two tails?

3. **Tossing a Coin** An experiment consists of tossing a coin seven times and observing the sequence of heads and tails.
   (a) How many different outcomes have at least five heads?
   (b) How many different outcomes have at most four heads?

4. **Tossing a Coin** An experiment consists of tossing a coin six times and observing the sequence of heads and tails.
   (a) How many different outcomes have at most three heads?
   (b) How many different outcomes have four or more heads?

5. **World Series** In the World Series, the American League team ("A") and the National League team ("N") play until one team wins four games. Each sequence of winners can be designated by a sequence of As and Ns. For instance, NAAAA means the National League won the first game and lost the next four games. In how many ways can a series end in seven games? Six games?

6. **World Series** Refer to Exercise 5. How many different sequences are possible?

7. **Game Outcomes** A football team plays 11 games. In how many ways can these games result in five wins, five losses, and one tie?

8. **Game Outcomes** A chess master plays 15 games. In how many ways can these games result in 10 wins, 2 losses, and 3 draws?

Bytes Exercises 9 and 10 refer to computer bytes. A computer *byte* is a string of eight digits, where each digit is either a zero or a one. Two examples are 01001001 and 11001101.

9. How many bytes have exactly five ones?

10. In how many of the bytes with exactly five ones are no two zeroes next to each other?

11. **Routes through City Streets** Refer to the map in Fig. 2. How many shortest routes are there from A to B?

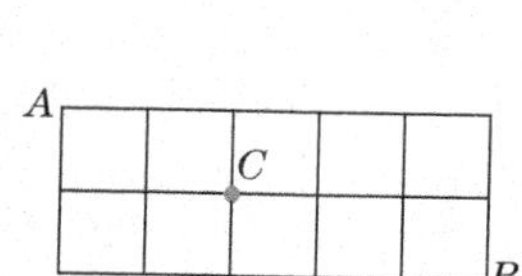

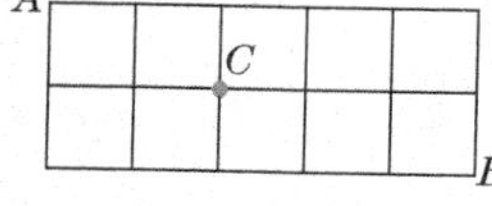

Figure 2

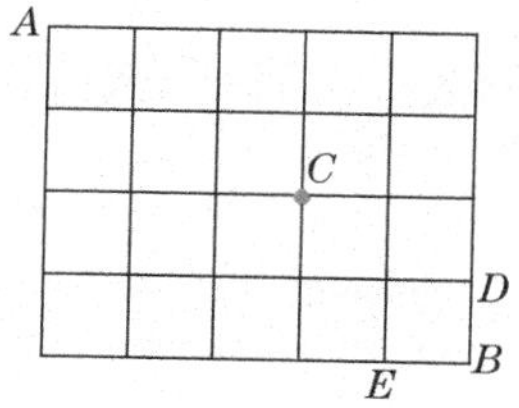

Figure 3

12. **Routes through City Streets** Refer to the map in Fig. 3. How many shortest routes are there from A to B?

13. **Routes through City Streets** Refer to the map in Fig. 3. How many shortest routes are there from A to B that pass through the point C?

14. **Routes through City Streets** Refer to the map in Fig. 2. How many shortest routes are there from A to B that pass through the point C?

15. **Routes through City Streets** Refer to the map in Fig. 2. How many shortest routes are there from A to B that do not have two consecutive souths?

16. **Routes through City Streets** Refer to the map in Fig. 3. How many shortest routes are there from A to B that do not have two consecutive souths?

17. **Routes through City Streets** Refer to the map in Fig. 3. The number of shortest routes from A to B is $C(9, 4)$.
   (a) Observe that the number of shortest routes from A to D is $C(8, 3)$.
   (b) Observe that the number of shortest routes from A to E is $C(8, 4)$.
   (c) By looking at Fig. 3, explain why $C(8, 3) + C(8, 4)$ should equal $C(9, 4)$.
   (d) Calculate the values in part (c) to verify the equality.

18. **Routes through City Streets** Imagine a street map similar to the map in Fig. 3 but having r streets vertically and $n - r$ street horizontally. Then, the number of shortest routes from A to B would be $C(n, r)$.
   (a) Explain why the number of shortest routes A to D, the intersection directly north of B, would be $C(n - 1, r - 1)$.
   (b) Explain why the number of shortest routes A to E, the intersection directly west of B, would be $C(n - 1, r)$.
   (c) Explain why $C(n - 1, r - 1) + C(n + 1, r) = C(n, r)$.

19. **Tossing a Coin** A coin is tossed 10 times, and the sequence of heads and tails is observed. How many of the possible outcomes contain three heads, with no two heads adjacent to each other?

20. **Arranging Books** Four mathematics books and seven history books are arranged on a bookshelf. In how many of the possible arrangements are no two mathematics books next to each other?

21. **Seating Arrangements** In how many ways can six people be seated in a row of ten chairs so that at least two adjacent chairs are vacant? (*Hint*: First use the reasoning in Example 4 to count the number of ways they can be seated so that no two adjacent chairs are empty.)

22. **Photo Session** In 2015, there were three women and six men on the United States Supreme Court. In how many ways could the justices be seated in a row for a group picture where no women sat next to each other?

23. **Selecting Balls from an Urn** An urn contains 12 numbered balls, of which 7 are red and 5 are white. A sample of 5 balls is to be selected.
   (a) How many different samples are possible?
   (b) How many samples contain all red balls?
   (c) How many samples contain two red balls and three white balls?
   (d) How many samples contain at least four red balls?

24. **Selecting Balls from an Urn** An urn contains 15 numbered balls, of which 6 are red and 9 are white. A sample of six balls is to be selected.
   (a) How many different samples are possible?
   (b) How many samples contain all white balls?
   (c) How many samples contain two red balls and four white balls?
   (d) How many samples contain at least two red balls?

25. **Selecting Apples** A bag of 10 apples contains 2 rotten apples and 8 good apples. A shopper selects a sample of three apples from the bag.
   (a) How many different samples are possible?
   (b) How many samples contain all good apples?
   (c) How many samples contain at least one rotten apple?

26. **Selecting Light Bulbs** A package contains 100 LED light bulbs, of which 10 are defective. A sample of five bulbs is selected at random.
   (a) How many different samples are there?
   (b) How many of the samples contain two defective bulbs?
   (c) How many of the samples contain at least one defective bulb?

27. **Subcommittee Selection** A committee has four male and six female members. In how many ways can a subcommittee consisting of two males and two females be selected?

28. **Investment Portfolio** In how many ways can an investor put together a portfolio of five stocks and six bonds selected from her favorite nine stocks and seven bonds?

Poker Hands Exercises 29–32 refer to poker hands. A poker hand consists of 5 cards selected from a standard deck of 52 cards.

29. How many poker hands consist of three aces and two kings?

30. How many poker hands consist of two aces, two cards of another rank, and one card of a third rank?

31. How many poker hands consist of three cards of one rank and two cards of another rank? (Such a poker hand is called a "full house.")

32. How many poker hands consist of two cards of one rank, two cards of another (different) rank, and one card of a third rank? (Such a poker hand is called "two pairs.")

In Exercises 33–36, a "word" is interpreted to be a sequence of letters.

33. **SEQUOIA** How many seven-letter words with no repeated letters contain all five vowels?

34. **FACETIOUS** How many nine-letter words with no repeated letters contain the five vowels in alphabetical order?

35. **ABSTEMIOUS** How many 10-letter words with no repeated letters contain the five vowels in alphabetical order?

36. **DIALOGUE** How many eight-letter words with no repeated letters contain all five vowels?

37. **Photo Session** In 2015, there were three women and six men on the United States Supreme Court. In how many ways could the justices be seated in a row for a group picture in which the three women sat next to each other?

38. **Seating Arrangements** You, a friend, and four other people are to be seated in a row of six chairs. How many arrangements are there in which you and your friend are seated next to each other?

39. **Numbers** In how many five-digit numbers (without zeros) are the digits strictly increasing when read from left to right?

40. **Alphabetical Order** In how many four-letter words (including nonsense words) using four different letters from *A* through *J* are the letters in alphabetical order?

41. **License Plates** Suppose that license plates from a certain state consist of four different letters followed by three different digits. In how many license plates are the letters in alphabetical order and the digits in increasing order?

42. **License Plates** Suppose that license plates from a certain state consist of two different letters followed by four different digits. In how many license plates are the letters in alphabetical order and the digits in increasing order?

43. **Seating Arrangements** A family has 12 members. In how many ways can six family members be seated in a row so that their ages increase from left to right?

44. **Arranging Books** In how many ways can five books out of eight be selected and lined up on a bookshelf so that their page counts increase from left to right? *Note:* Assume that no two books have the same page count.

TECHNOLOGY EXERCISES

45. **Tossing a Coin** What percent of the possible outcomes resulting from tossing a coin 100 times contain exactly 50 heads?

46. **Tossing a Coin** What percent of the possible outcomes resulting from tossing a coin 200 times contain exactly 100 heads?

47. **Selecting Balls from an Urn** Suppose that a sample of 20 balls is selected from an urn containing 50 white balls and 50 red balls. What percent of the possible outcomes contains 10 white balls and 10 red balls?

48. **Selecting Balls from an Urn** Suppose that a sample of 20 balls is selected from an urn containing 100 white balls and 100 red balls. What percent of the possible outcomes contains 10 white balls and 10 red balls?

Solutions to Check Your Understanding 1.6

1. (a) $C(15, 6)$. Each sample is an unordered selection of 15 objects taken 6 at a time.

   (b) $C(10, 4) \cdot C(5, 2)$. Asking for the number of samples of a certain type is the same as asking for the number of ways that the task of forming such a sample can be performed. This task is composed of two consecutive choices. Choice 1, selecting 4 people from among the 10 who support the proposal, can be performed in $C(10, 4)$ ways. Choice 2, selecting two people from among the five people who oppose the proposal, can be performed in $C(5, 2)$ ways. Therefore, by the multiplication principle, the complete task can be performed in $C(10, 4) \cdot C(5, 2)$ ways.

   Note: $C(15, 6) = 5005$ and $C(10, 4) \cdot C(5, 2) = 2100$. Therefore, less than half of the possible samples reflect the true distribution of the school board.

2. (a) 2^8, or 256. Apply the generalized multiplication principle.

   (b) $C(8, 6)$, or 28. Each outcome having six successes corresponds to a sequence of eight letters of which six are S's and two are F's. Such an outcome is specified by selecting the six locations for the S's from among the eight locations, and this has $C(8, 6)$ possibilities.

CHAPTER

2

Probability

Probability is the mathematics of chance. A probability is a numerical measure of the likelihood that a specific event will occur. In this chapter, we consider the basic concepts that allow us to associate realistic probabilities to random events in many diverse fields.

2.1 Experiments, Outcomes, Sample Spaces, and Events

The events whose probabilities we wish to compute all arise as outcomes of experiments. So as our first step in developing probability theory, let us define *experiments*, *outcomes*, *events*, and the associated concept *sample spaces*.

DEFINITIONS An **experiment** is an activity with an observable result. Each possible result is called an **outcome** of the experiment. The set of all possible outcomes is called the **sample space** of the experiment. An **event** is a subset of the sample space. (We say that the event E has occurred when the outcome of the experiment is an element of E.)

EXAMPLE 1 **Rolling a Die** Illustrate the preceding definitions for the experiment of rolling a die and observing the number on the uppermost face.

SOLUTION (a) The possible outcomes are the numbers 1, 2, 3, 4, 5, and 6.
(b) The sample space is $\{1, 2, 3, 4, 5, 6\}$.
(c) One possible event is $\{2, 4, 6\}$. This event also can be described as "the event that the outcome is an even number." «

EXAMPLE 2 **Rolling a Pair of Dice** Illustrate the preceding definitions for the experiment of rolling two dice, one red and one green, and observing the number on the uppermost face of each.

SOLUTION (a) Each outcome of the experiment can be regarded as an ordered pair of numbers, the first representing the number on the red die and the second the number on the green die. Thus, for example, the pair of numbers (3, 5) represents the outcome "3 on the red die, 5 on the green die." That is, each outcome is an ordered pair of numbers (r, g), where r and g are each one of the numbers 1, 2, 3, 4, 5, 6.
(b) The sample space, which has 36 elements, is as follows:

$$\begin{gathered}\{(1,1),(1,2),(1,3),(1,4),(1,5),(1,6),\\(2,1),(2,2),(2,3),(2,4),(2,5),(2,6),\\(3,1),(3,2),(3,3),(3,4),(3,5),(3,6),\\(4,1),(4,2),(4,3),(4,4),(4,5),(4,6),\\(5,1),(5,2),(5,3),(5,4),(5,5),(5,6),\\(6,1),(6,2),(6,3),(6,4),(6,5),(6,6)\}.\end{gathered}$$

(c) One possible event is $\{(1, 4), (2, 3), (3, 2), (4, 1)\}$. This event also can be described as "the event that the sum of the two numbers is 5." » *Now Try Exercise 3(a)*

EXAMPLE 3 **Number of People in a Queue** Once every hour, a supermarket manager observes the number of people standing in a checkout line. The store has space for at most 30 customers to wait in line. Illustrate the preceding definitions for this situation.

SOLUTION (a) The possible outcomes are the numbers 0, 1, 2, 3, . . . , 30.
(b) The sample space is $\{0, 1, 2, 3, \ldots, 30\}$.
(c) One possible event is $\{0, 1, 2, 3, 4, 5\}$. This event also can be described as "the event that there are at most five people standing in the line." «

EXAMPLE 4 **Sample Space for Pollutant Levels** The Environmental Protection Agency ordered Middle States Edison Corporation to install "scrubbers" to remove the pollutants from its smokestacks. To monitor the effectiveness of the scrubbers, the corporation installed monitoring devices to record the levels of sulfur dioxide, particulate matter, and oxides of nitrogen in the smokestack emissions. Consider the monitoring operation as an experiment. Describe the associated sample space.

SOLUTION Each reading of the instruments consists of an ordered triple of numbers (x, y, z), where $x =$ level of sulfur dioxide, $y =$ level of particulate matter, and $z =$ level of oxides of nitrogen. The sample space thus consists of all possible triples (x, y, z), where $x \geq 0$, $y \geq 0$, and $z \geq 0$. » *Now Try Exercise 7(a)*

The sample spaces in Examples 1, 2, and 3 are **finite**. That is, the associated experiments have only a finite number of possible outcomes. However, the sample space of Example 4 is **infinite**, since there are infinitely many triples (x, y, z), where $x \geq 0$, $y \geq 0$, and $z \geq 0$.

EXAMPLE 5

Tossing a Coin Three Times Suppose that an experiment consists of tossing a coin three times and observing the sequence of heads and tails. (Order counts.)

(a) Determine the sample space S.

(b) Determine the event $E =$ "exactly two heads."

SOLUTION

(a) Denote "heads" by H and "tails" by T. Then a typical outcome of the experiment is a sequence of Hs and Ts. So, for instance, the sequence HTT would stand for a head followed by two tails. We exhibit all such sequences and arrive at the sample space S:

$$S = \{\text{HHH, HHT, HTH, THH, HTT, THT, TTH, TTT}\}.$$

(b) Here are the outcomes in which exactly two heads occur: HHT, HTH, THH. Therefore, event E is

$$E = \{\text{HHT, HTH, THH}\}.$$

» Now Try Exercise 3(b)

EXAMPLE 6

Political Poll A political poll surveys a group of people to determine their income levels and political affiliations. People are classified as either low-, middle-, or upper-level income and as either Democrat, Republican, or Independent.

(a) Find the sample space corresponding to the poll.

(b) Determine the event $E_1 =$ "Independent."

(c) Determine the event $E_2 =$ "low income and not Independent."

(d) Determine the event $E_3 =$ "neither upper income nor Independent."

SOLUTION

(a) Let us abbreviate low, middle, and upper income by the letters L, M, and U, respectively. And let us abbreviate Democrat, Republican, and Independent by the letters D, R, and I, respectively. Then a response to the poll can be represented as a pair of letters. For example, the pair (L, D) refers to a low-income-level Democrat. The sample space S is then given by

$$S = \{(\text{L, D}), (\text{L, R}), (\text{L, I}), (\text{M, D}), (\text{M, R}), (\text{M, I}), (\text{U, D}), (\text{U, R}), (\text{U, I})\}.$$

(b) For event E_1, the income level may be anything, but the political affiliation is Independent. Thus,

$$E_1 = \{(\text{L, I}), (\text{M, I}), (\text{U, I})\}.$$

(c) For event E_2, the income level is low and the political affiliation may be either Democrat or Republican. In this case,

$$E_2 = \{(\text{L, D}), (\text{L, R})\}.$$

(d) For event E_3, the income level may be either low or middle and the political affiliation may be Democrat or Republican. Thus,

$$E_3 = \{(\text{L, D}), (\text{L, R}), (\text{M, D}), (\text{M, R})\}.$$

» Now Try Exercise 9

As we have seen, an event is a subset of a sample space. Two events are worthy of special mention. The first is the event corresponding to the empty set, $\varnothing$. This is called the **impossible event**, since it can never occur. The second special event is the set S, the sample space itself. Every outcome is an element of S, so S always occurs. For this reason, S is called the **certain event**.

One particular advantage of defining experiments and events in terms of sets is that it allows us to define new events from given ones by applying the operations of set theory. When so doing, we always let the sample space S play the role of universal set. (All outcomes belong to the universal set.)

If E and F are events, then so are $E \cup F$, $E \cap F$, and E'. For example, consider the die-rolling experiment of Example 1. Then

$$S = \{1, 2, 3, 4, 5, 6\}.$$

Let E and F be the events given by

$$E = \{3, 4, 5, 6\} \qquad F = \{1, 4, 6\}.$$

Then we have

$$E \cup F = \{1, 3, 4, 5, 6\}$$
$$E \cap F = \{4, 6\}$$
$$E' = \{1, 2\}.$$

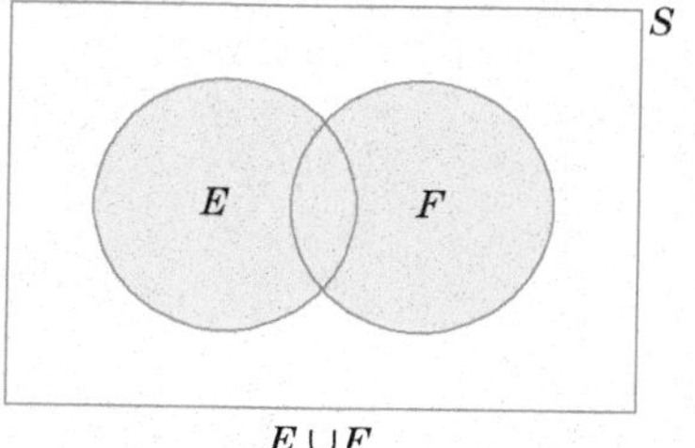

$E \cup F$

Figure 1

Let us interpret the events $E \cup F$, $E \cap F$, and E' by using Venn diagrams. In Fig. 1, we have drawn a Venn diagram for $E \cup F$. Note that $E \cup F$ occurs precisely when the experimental outcome belongs to the shaded region—that is, to E or F. Thus, we have the following result:

> **DEFINITION Union of Two Events** The event $E \cup F$ occurs precisely when either E or F (or both) occurs.

Similarly, we can interpret the event $E \cap F$. This event occurs when the experimental outcome belongs to the shaded region of Fig. 2—that is, to both E and F. Thus, we have an interpretation for $E \cap F$:

> **DEFINITION Intersection of Two Events** The event $E \cap F$ occurs precisely when both E and F occur.

Finally, the event E' consists of all of those outcomes not in E (Fig. 3). Therefore, we have the following:

> **DEFINITION Complement of an Event** The event E' occurs precisely when E does not occur.

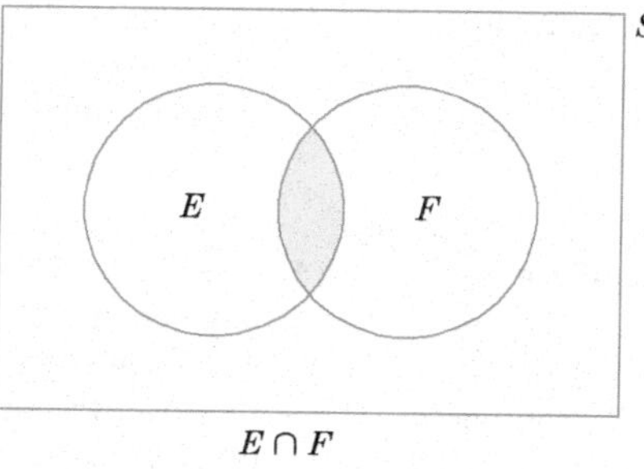

$E \cap F$

Figure 2

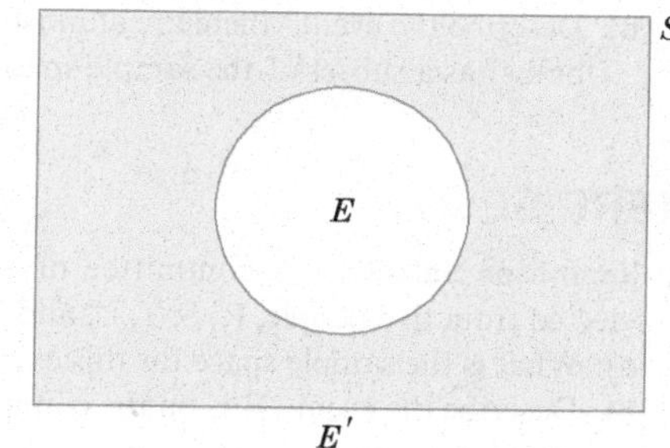

E'

Figure 3

EXAMPLE 7 **Events Related to Pollution Control** Consider the pollution monitoring described in Example 4. Let E, F, and G be the events

$$E = \text{“level of sulfur dioxide} \geq 100\text{”}$$
$$F = \text{“level of particulate matter} \leq 50\text{”}$$
$$G = \text{“level of oxides of nitrogen} \leq 30.\text{”}$$

Describe the following events:

(a) $E \cap F$ **(b)** E' **(c)** $E \cup G$ **(d)** $E' \cap F \cap G$

SOLUTION

(a) $E \cap F =$ "level of sulfur dioxide ≥ 100 *and* level of particulate matter ≤ 50."
(b) $E' =$ "level of sulfur dioxide < 100."
(c) $E \cup G =$ "level of sulfur dioxide ≥ 100 *or* level of oxides of nitrogen ≤ 30."
(d) $E' \cap F \cap G =$ "level of sulfur dioxide < 100 *and* level of particulate matter ≤ 50 *and* level of oxides of nitrogen ≤ 30."

» ***Now Try Exercise 7(b)***

Suppose that E and F are events in a sample space S. We say that E and F are **mutually exclusive** (or *disjoint*) provided that $E \cap F = \varnothing$. In terms of Venn diagrams, we may represent a pair of mutually exclusive events as a pair of circles with no points in common (Fig. 4). If the events E and F are mutually exclusive, then E and F cannot simultaneously occur; if E occurs, then F does not; and if F occurs, then E does not.

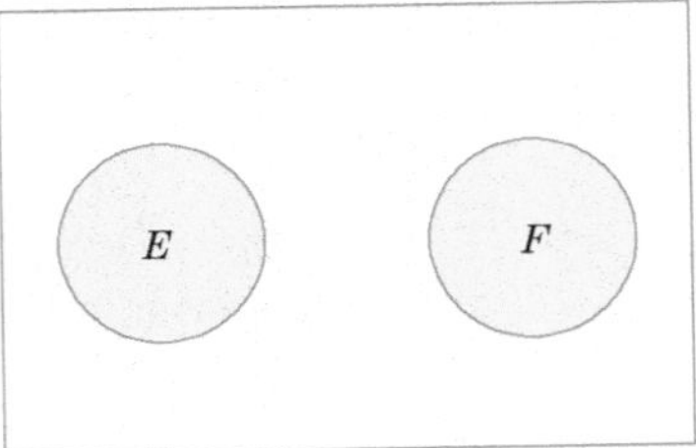

Figure 4 E and F are mutually exclusive.

EXAMPLE 8 **Determining Whether Events Are Mutually Exclusive** Let $S = \{a, b, c, d, e, f, g\}$ be a sample space, and let $E = \{a, b, c\}$, $F = \{e, f, g\}$, and $G = \{c, d, f\}$.
(a) Are E and F mutually exclusive?
(b) Are F and G mutually exclusive?

SOLUTION

(a) $E \cap F = \varnothing$, so E and F are mutually exclusive.
(b) $F \cap G = \{f\}$, so F and G are *not* mutually exclusive.

» ***Now Try Exercise 11***

Check Your Understanding 2.1

Solutions can be found following the section exercises.

1. **Lightbulbs** A machine produces lightbulbs. As part of a quality control procedure, a sample of five lightbulbs is collected each hour and the number of defective lightbulbs among these is observed.
   (a) What is the sample space for this experiment?
   (b) Describe the event "there are at most two defective lightbulbs" as a subset of the sample space.
2. **Citrus Fruit** Suppose that there are two crates of citrus fruit and each crate contains oranges, grapefruit, and tangelos. An experiment consists of selecting a crate and then selecting a piece of fruit from that crate. Both the crate and the type of fruit are noted. Refer to the crates as crate I and crate II.
   (a) What is the sample space for this experiment?
   (b) Describe the event "a tangelo is selected" as a subset of the sample space.

EXERCISES 2.1

1. **Committee Selection** A committee of two people is to be selected from five people, R, S, T, U, and V.
   (a) What is the sample space for this experiment?
   (b) Describe the event "R is on the committee" as a subset of the sample space.
   (c) Describe the event "neither R nor S is on the committee" as a subset of the sample space.
2. **Selecting Letters** A letter is selected at random from the word "MISSISSIPPI."
   (a) What is the sample space for this experiment?
   (b) Describe the event "the letter chosen is a vowel" as a subset of the sample space.
3. **Heads and Tails** An experiment consists of tossing a coin two times and observing the sequence of heads and tails.
   (a) What is the sample space of this experiment?
   (b) Describe the event "the first toss is a head" as a subset of the sample space.
4. **Four-Sided Dice** A pair of four-sided dice—each with the numbers from 1 to 4 on their sides—are rolled, and the numbers facing down are observed. (*Note:* A four-sided die is similar to a pyramid with a triangular base.)
   (a) List the sample space.
   (b) Describe each of the following events as a subset of the sample space:
      (i) Both numbers are even.
      (ii) At least one number is odd.
      (iii) Neither number is less than or equal to 2.
      (iv) The sum of the numbers is 7.
      (v) The sum of the numbers is greater than or equal to 6.
      (vi) The numbers are the same.
      (vii) A 2 or 3 occurs, but not both 2 and 3.
      (viii) No 4 appears.
5. **Selecting from Urns** Suppose that we have two urns—call them urn I and urn II—each containing red balls and white

balls. An experiment consists of selecting an urn and then selecting a ball from that urn and noting its color.
(a) What is a suitable sample space for this experiment?
(b) Describe the event "urn I is selected" as a subset of the sample space.

6. **Coin Tosses** An experiment consists of tossing a coin four times and observing the sequence of heads and tails.
(a) What is the sample space of this experiment?
(b) Determine the event E_1 = "more heads than tails occur."
(c) Determine the event E_2 = "the first toss is a head."
(d) Determine the event $E_1 \cap E_2$.

7. **Efficiency Studies** An efficiency expert records the time it takes an assembly line worker to perform a particular task. Let E be the event "more than 5 minutes," F the event "less than 8 minutes," and G the event "less than 4 minutes."
(a) Describe the sample space for this experiment.
(b) Describe the events $E \cap F$, $E \cap G$, E', F', $E' \cap F$, $E' \cap F \cap G$, and $E \cup F$.

8. **Census Data** A census taker records the annual income of each household they visit. Let E be the event "more than \$50,000" and F be the event "less than \$75,000." Describe the events $E \cap F$, E', and F'.

9. **Student Poll** A campus survey is taken to correlate the number of years that students have been on campus with their political leanings. Students are classified as first-year, sophomore, junior, or senior and as conservative or liberal.
(a) Find the sample space corresponding to the poll.
(b) Determine the event E_1 = "conservative."
(c) Determine the event E_2 = "junior and liberal."
(d) Determine the event E_3 = "neither first-year nor conservative."

10. **Automobiles** An experiment consists of selecting a car at random from a college parking lot and observing the color and make. Let E be the event "the car is red," F be the event "the car is a Chevrolet," G be the event "the car is a green Ford," and H be the event "the car is black or a Chrysler."
(a) Which of the following pairs of events are mutually exclusive?

(i) E and F	(ii) E and G
(iii) F and G	(iv) E and H
(v) F and H	(vi) G and H
(vii) E' and G	(viii) F' and H'

(b) Describe each of the following events:

(i) $E \cap F$	(ii) $E \cup F$
(iii) E'	(iv) F'
(v) G'	(vi) H'
(vii) $E \cup G$	(viii) $E \cap G$
(ix) $E \cap H$	(x) $E \cup H$
(xi) $G \cap H$	(xii) $E' \cap F'$
(xiii) $E' \cup G'$	

11. Let $S = \{1, 2, 3, 4, 5, 6\}$ be a sample space,

$$E = \{1, 2\} \qquad F = \{2, 3\} \qquad G = \{1, 5, 6\}.$$

(a) Are E and F mutually exclusive?
(b) Are F and G mutually exclusive?

12. Draw the events E and E' on two separate Venn diagrams. Are E and E' mutually exclusive?

13. Let $S = \{a, b, c\}$ be a sample space. Determine all possible events associated with S.

14. Let S be a sample space with n outcomes. How many events are associated with S?

15. Let $S = \{1, 2, 3, 4\}$ be a sample space, $E = \{1\}$, and $F = \{2, 3\}$. Are the events $E \cup F$ and $E' \cap F'$ mutually exclusive?

16. Let S be any sample space, and E, F any events associated with S. Are the events $E \cup F$ and $E' \cap F'$ mutually exclusive? (*Hint:* Apply De Morgan's laws.)

17. **Coin Tosses** Suppose that 10 coins are tossed and the number of heads observed.
(a) Describe the sample space for this experiment.
(b) Describe the event "more heads than tails" in terms of the sample space.

18. **Three-Digit Numbers** An experiment consists of forming a three-digit number by using the digits 1, 7, and 8 without repetition.
(a) Describe the sample space for this experiment.
(b) Describe the event "the number is greater than 300" as a subset of the sample space.

19. **Genetic Traits** An experiment consists of observing the eye color and age of all United States citizens. Let E be the event "blue eyes," F the event "at least 18 years old," and G the event "brown eyes and younger than 18."
(a) Are E and F mutually exclusive?
(b) Are E and G mutually exclusive?
(c) Are F and G mutually exclusive?

20. **Genetic Traits** Consider the experiment and events of Exercise 19. Describe the following events:

(a) $E \cup F$	**(b)** $E \cap G$
(c) E'	**(d)** F'
(e) $(G \cup F) \cap E$	**(f)** $G' \cap E$

21. **Shuttle Bus** Suppose that you observe the number of passengers arriving at a metro station on a shuttle bus that holds up to eight passengers. Describe the sample space.

22. **Dice** A pair of dice is rolled, and the sum of the numbers on the two uppermost faces is observed. What is the sample space of this experiment?

23. **Selecting Balls from an Urn** An urn contains balls numbered 1 through 9. Suppose that you draw a ball from the urn, observe its number, replace the ball, draw a ball again, and observe its number. Give an example of an outcome of the experiment. How large is the sample space?

24. **Selecting Balls from an Urn** Repeat Exercise 23 in the case that the first ball is not replaced.

25. **NBA Draft Lottery** In the NBA, the 14 basketball teams that did not make the playoffs participate in the draft lottery. Ping-pong balls numbered 1 through 14 are placed in a lottery machine, and a sample of four balls is drawn randomly to determine which team will have the first overall draft pick. The order in which the numbers are drawn does not matter. The combination $\{11, 12, 13, 14\}$ is ignored if it is drawn. (*Note:* Each team is assigned between 5 and 250 combinations prior to the drawing in the order of their regular season record.) Give an example of an outcome of the draw. In 2015, the Minnesota Timberwolves, who had the worst record in the NBA and were assigned 250 combinations, won the first overall pick. What percentage of the combinations were assigned to the Minnesota Timberwolves?

26. **Coin & Die** Suppose that a coin is tossed and a die is rolled, and the face and number appearing are observed. How many outcomes are in the sample space?

27. **The Game of Clue** *Clue* is a board game in which players are given the opportunity to solve a murder that has six suspects, six possible weapons, and nine possible rooms where the murder may have occurred. The six suspects are Colonel Mustard, Miss Scarlet, Professor Plum, Mrs. White, Mr. Green, and Mrs. Peacock. Determine a sample space for the choice of murderer. Discuss how to form a sample space with the entire solution to the murder, giving murderer, weapon, and site.
    (a) How many outcomes would the sample space for the entire solution have?

    Let E be the event that the murder occurred in the library. Let F be the event that the weapon was a gun.
    (b) Describe $E \cap F$.
    (c) Describe $E \cup F$.

Solutions to Check Your Understanding 2.1

1. **(a)** $\{0, 1, 2, 3, 4, 5\}$. The sample space is the set of all outcomes of the experiment. At first glance, it might seem that each outcome is a set of five lightbulbs. What is observed, however, is not the specific sample but rather the number of defective bulbs in the sample. Therefore, the outcome must be a number.
   (b) $\{0, 1, 2\}$. "At most 2" means "2 or less."

2. **(a)** {(crate I, orange), (crate I, grapefruit), (crate I, tangelo), (crate II, orange), (crate II, grapefruit), (crate II, tangelo)}. Two selections are being made, and both should be recorded.
   (b) {(crate I, tangelo), (crate II, tangelo)}. This set consists of those outcomes in which a tangelo is selected.

2.2 Assignment of Probabilities

A **probability** is a numerical measure of the likelihood that a specific event will occur. The number is between 0 and 1 and is called the *probability of the event.* It is written Pr(*event*). The larger the number, the more confident we are that the event will occur.

There are three types of probabilities.

1. A **logical probability** is obtained by mathematical reasoning—often, by the use of the counting techniques of the previous chapter. Some examples are as follows.
   - Pr(coin toss showing heads)
   - Pr(obtaining a full house in poker)
   - Pr(winning the Powerball Lottery)
2. An **empirical probability** is obtained by sampling or observation and is calculated by dividing the number of times the event occurs by the total number of observations. This value is also called the **relative frequency**. Some examples are as follows.
   - Pr(a certain brand of lightbulb will last more than 1000 hours)
   - Pr(a person selected at random will be a smoker)
   - Pr(taking small amounts of aspirin daily will lower your risk of having a stroke)
3. A **judgmental probability** is obtained by an educated guess. Also known as a **subjective probability**, it describes an individual's personal judgment about how likely a particular event is to occur. Some examples are as follows.
   - Pr(New England Patriots will win next year's Super Bowl)
   - Pr(a Democrat will be elected president in 2024)
   - Pr(you will get an A on your next mathematics exam)

EXAMPLE 1 **Forecasting Rain** Classify the following probability as *logical*, *empirical*, or *judgmental*:

$$\text{Pr(it will rain tomorrow)} = 30\%.$$

SOLUTION Empirical. Weather probabilities are widely misunderstood. Some people think that the statement means that it will rain in 30% of the area. Others think that it will rain 30% of the time. Actually, what the weather person means is that, based on past observations when weather conditions were similar to today's weather conditions, 30% of the time it rained the next day.

>> Now Try Exercise 1

In this chapter, we develop techniques for calculating logical probabilities and use tables acquired by sampling to obtain empirical probabilities. We will not explore judgmental probabilities.

In the previous section, we introduced the sample space of an experiment and used it to describe events. We complete our description of experiments by introducing probabilities associated with events. For the remainder of this chapter, we limit our discussion to experiments with only a finite number of outcomes. This restriction will remain in effect until our discussion of the normal distribution in the next chapter.

Suppose that an experiment has a sample space S consisting of a finite number of outcomes $s_1, s_2, \ldots, s_N$. To each outcome we associate a number, called the *probability* of the outcome, which represents the likelihood that the outcome will occur. Suppose that to the outcome s_1 we associate the probability p_1, to the outcome s_2 the probability p_2, and so forth. We can summarize this data in a chart of the following sort:

Outcome	Probability
s_1	p_1
s_2	p_2
$\vdots$	$\vdots$
s_N	p_N

Such a chart is called the **probability distribution** for the experiment.

We require that probabilities obey two fundamental properties:

Fundamental Property 1 Each of the numbers $p_1, p_2, \ldots, p_N$ is between 0 and 1.

Fundamental Property 2 $p_1 + p_2 + \cdots + p_n = 1$.

Fundamental Property 1 says that the likelihood of each outcome lies between 0% and 100%, whereas Fundamental Property 2 says that there is a 100% chance that one of the outcomes $s_1, s_2, \ldots, s_N$ will occur.

In the experiments associated with many common applications, all outcomes are **equally likely**—that is, they all have the same probability. This is the case, for example, if we toss an unbiased coin or select a person at random from the population. If a sample space has N equally likely outcomes, then the probability of each outcome is $1/N$ (since the probabilities must add up to 1).

The next three examples illustrate some methods for determining probability distributions.

EXAMPLE 2 **Probability Distributions** Determine the probability distributions for the following experiments.

(a) Toss an unbiased coin and observe the side that faces upward.

(b) Roll a die and observe the side that faces upward.

SOLUTION **(a)** Since the coin is unbiased, we expect each of the outcomes "heads" and "tails" to be equally likely. We assign the two outcomes equal probabilities, namely, $\frac{1}{2}$. The probability distribution is as follows:

Outcome	Probability
Heads	$\frac{1}{2}$
Tails	$\frac{1}{2}$

(b) There are six possible outcomes, namely, 1, 2, 3, 4, 5, and 6. Assuming that the die is unbiased, these outcomes are equally likely. So we assign to each outcome the probability $\frac{1}{6}$. Here is the probability distribution for the experiment:

Outcome	Probability	Outcome	Probability
1	$\frac{1}{6}$	4	$\frac{1}{6}$
2	$\frac{1}{6}$	5	$\frac{1}{6}$
3	$\frac{1}{6}$	6	$\frac{1}{6}$

» Now Try Exercise 5

Probabilities may be assigned to the elements of a sample space by using common sense about the physical nature of the experiment. The fair coin has two sides, both equally likely to be face up. The unbiased die has six equally probable faces. However, in general, it may not be possible to use intuition alone to decide on a realistic probability to assign to individual sample elements. Sometimes it is necessary to use experimental data to determine the relative frequency with which events occur. The following example demonstrates this technique:

EXAMPLE 3

College Majors A group of 141,000 college freshmen were asked the question, "What is your intended major?" Table 1 shows the results of this question. (The data was obtained from *The American Freshman: National Norms Fall 2015*.) Consider the experiment of selecting a student at random from the group surveyed and observing their answer.

(a) Determine the probability distribution for this experiment.

(b) Verify that the probabilities satisfy Fundamental Properties 1 and 2.

Table 1 Intended Majors

Intended Major	Number of Freshmen
Arts and humanities	14,241
Biological science	21,009
Business	18,894
Engineering	18,471
Health professions	15,933
Math, computer science, and physical science	11,421
Social science	15,228
Other and undecided	25,803

(Source: www.heri.ucla.edu)

SOLUTION

(a) For each of the eight possible outcomes, we use the data to compute its relative frequency. For example, of the 141,000 freshmen sampled, 18,471 intended to

Table 2 Probability Distribution of Intended Majors

Outcome	Probability
Arts and humanities	.101
Biological science	.149
Business	.134
Engineering	.131
Health professions	.113
Math, computer science, and physical science	.081
Social science	.108
Other and undecided	.183

major in engineering. So the outcome "Engineering" occurred in $\frac{18{,}471}{141{,}000} = 13.1\%$ of the answers. Therefore, we assign to the outcome "Engineering" the probability .131. Similarly, we assign probabilities to the other outcomes on the basis of the fraction of times that they occurred.

(b) The probabilities are .101, .149, .134, .131, .113, .081, .108, and .183. Clearly, each is between 0 and 1, so Fundamental Property 1 is satisfied. Adding the probabilities shows that their sum is 1, satisfying Fundamental Property 2.

>> Now Try Exercise 15

Unlike in Example 2, we cannot always rely on intuition to assign a value to a logical probability. Instead, we must use our knowledge of sets and counting to construct a theoretical model of the experiment along with associated probabilities. This allows us to determine the probability for *events* rather than just single *outcomes*, and we can construct probability distributions for events that satisfy Fundamental Properties 1 and 2. We can observe this in the following probability distribution for the number of heads in four tosses of a fair coin:

Events	Probability
0 heads	$\frac{1}{16}$
1 heads	$\frac{4}{16} = \frac{1}{4}$
2 heads	$\frac{6}{16} = \frac{3}{8}$
3 heads	$\frac{4}{16} = \frac{1}{4}$
4 heads	$\frac{1}{16}$
Total	1

Note that the column labeled "Events" contains all possible outcomes in the sample space. Also, all of the entries in the probability column are nonnegative numbers between 0 and 1. Furthermore, the sum of the probabilities is 1.

The Addition and Inclusion–Exclusion Principles

Suppose that we are given an experiment with a finite number of outcomes. Let us now assign to each event E a probability, which we denote by $\Pr(E)$. If E consists of a single outcome, say, $E = \{s\}$, then E is called an **elementary event**. In this case, we associate with E the probability of the outcome s. If E consists of more than one outcome, we may compute $\Pr(E)$ via the **addition principle**.

Addition Principle Suppose that an event E consists of the finite number of outcomes $s, t, u, \ldots, z$. That is,

$$E = \{s, t, u, \ldots, z\}.$$

Then

$$\Pr(E) = \Pr(s) + \Pr(t) + \Pr(u) + \cdots + \Pr(z).$$

We supplement the addition principle with the convention that the probability of the impossible event $\varnothing$ is 0. This is certainly reasonable, since the impossible event never occurs.

EXAMPLE 4 **Probability Associated with a Die** Suppose that we roll a die and observe the side that faces upward. What is the probability that an odd number will occur?

SOLUTION The event "odd number occurs" corresponds to the subset of the sample space given by

$$E = \{1, 3, 5\}.$$

That is, the event occurs if a 1, 3, or 5 appears on the side that faces upward. By the addition principle,

$$\Pr(E) = \Pr(1) + \Pr(3) + \Pr(5).$$

As we observed in Example 2(b), each of the outcomes in the die-rolling experiment has probability $\frac{1}{6}$. Therefore,

$$\Pr(E) = \tfrac{1}{6} + \tfrac{1}{6} + \tfrac{1}{6} = \tfrac{1}{2}.$$

So we expect an odd number to occur approximately half of the time.

» Now Try Exercise 7

EXAMPLE 5 **Probability Distribution for the Number of Boys in Two-Child Families** Observe the genders and birth orders in two-child families, and calculate the probabilities of 0, 1, and 2 boys.

SOLUTION The sample space $S = \{\text{GG, GB, BG, BB}\}$ describes the gender and birth order in two-child families. (Here, for instance, GB denotes the birth sequence "first child is a girl, second child is a boy.") If we assume that each of the four outcomes in S is equally likely to occur, we should assign probability $\frac{1}{4}$ to each outcome. Then

$$\Pr(\text{no boys}) = \Pr(\text{GG}) = \tfrac{1}{4}$$
$$\Pr(\text{one boy}) = \Pr(\text{GB}) + \Pr(\text{BG}) = \tfrac{1}{4} + \tfrac{1}{4} = \tfrac{1}{2}$$
$$\Pr(\text{two boys}) = \Pr(\text{BB}) = \tfrac{1}{4}.$$

«

EXAMPLE 6 **Probability Associated with College Majors** Consider the college major survey of Example 3. What is the probability that a student selected at random from the group surveyed intends to major in one of the three most popular fields outside the "other and undecided" choice?

SOLUTION The event "top three most popular fields" is the same as

$$\{\text{biological science, business, engineering}\}.$$

Thus, the probability of the event is

$$\Pr(\text{biological science}) + \Pr(\text{business}) + \Pr(\text{engineering}) = .149 + .134 + .131 = .414.$$

» Now Try Exercise 17

EXAMPLE 7 **Probability Associated with the Roll of a Pair of Dice** Suppose that we roll a red die and a green die and observe the numbers on the sides that face upward.

(a) Calculate the probabilities of the elementary events.

(b) Calculate the probability that the two dice show the same number.

SOLUTION

(a) As shown in Example 2 of the previous section, the sample space consists of 36 pairs of numbers:

$$S = \{(1, 1), (1, 2), \ldots, (6, 5), (6, 6)\}.$$

Each of these pairs is equally likely to occur. (How could the dice show favoritism to a particular pair?) Therefore, each outcome is expected to occur about $\frac{1}{36}$ of the time, and the probability of each elementary event is $\frac{1}{36}$.

(b) The event

$$E = \text{"both dice show the same number"}$$

consists of six outcomes:

$$E = \{(1, 1), (2, 2), (3, 3), (4, 4), (5, 5), (6, 6)\}.$$

Thus, by the addition principle,

$$\Pr(E) = \tfrac{1}{36} + \tfrac{1}{36} + \tfrac{1}{36} + \tfrac{1}{36} + \tfrac{1}{36} + \tfrac{1}{36} = \tfrac{6}{36} = \tfrac{1}{6}.$$

» Now Try Exercise 13

EXAMPLE 8

Probability Associated with a Scratch-Off Ticket A person playing a certain scratch-off ticket can win \$100, \$10, or \$1; can break even; or can lose \$10. These five outcomes with their corresponding probabilities are given by the probability distribution in Table 3.

(a) Which outcome has the greatest probability?
(b) Which outcome has the least probability?
(c) What is the probability that the person will win some money?

Table 3

Winnings	Probability
100	.02
10	.05
1	.40
0	.03
−10	.50

SOLUTION

(a) Table 3 reveals that the outcome −10 has the greatest probability, .50. (A person playing the lottery repeatedly can expect to lose \$10 about 50% of the time.) This outcome is just as likely to occur as not.
(b) The outcome 100 has the least probability, .02. A person playing the lottery can expect to win \$100 about 2% of the time. (This outcome is quite unlikely to occur.)
(c) We are asked to determine the probability that the event E occurs, where $E = \{100, 10, 1\}$. By the addition principle,

$$\begin{aligned}\Pr(E) &= \Pr(100) + \Pr(10) + \Pr(1)\\ &= .02 + .05 + .40\\ &= .47.\end{aligned}$$

«

Here is a useful formula that relates $\Pr(E \cup F)$ to $\Pr(E \cap F)$:

Inclusion–Exclusion Principle Let E and F be any events. Then

$$\Pr(E \cup F) = \Pr(E) + \Pr(F) - \Pr(E \cap F).$$

In particular, if E and F are mutually exclusive, then

$$\Pr(E \cup F) = \Pr(E) + \Pr(F).$$

Note the similarity of this principle to the principle of the same name that was used in Section 1.2 to count the elements in a set.

EXAMPLE 9

Resource Availability A factory needs two raw materials in order to operate. The probability of not having an adequate supply of material A is .05, whereas the probability of not having an adequate supply of material B is .03. A study determines that the probability of a shortage of both A and B is .01. What proportion of the time can the factory operate?

SOLUTION

Let E be the event "shortage of A" and F the event "shortage of B." We are given that

$$\Pr(E) = .05 \qquad \Pr(F) = .03 \qquad \Pr(E \cap F) = .01.$$

The factory can operate only if it has both raw materials. Therefore, we must calculate the proportion of the time in which there is no shortage of material A or material B. A shortage of A or B is the event $E \cup F$. By the inclusion–exclusion principle,

$$\begin{aligned}\Pr(E \cup F) &= \Pr(E) + \Pr(F) - \Pr(E \cap F)\\ &= .05 + .03 - .01\\ &= .07.\end{aligned}$$

Thus, the factory is likely to be short of one raw material or the other 7% of the time. Therefore, the factory can expect to operate 93% of the time.

» Now Try Exercise 37

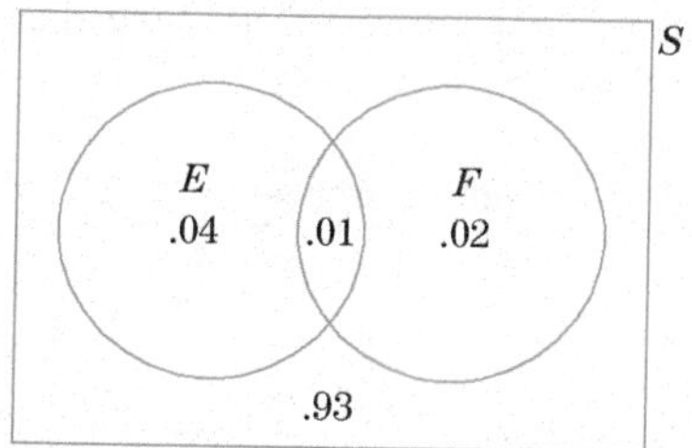

Figure 1

Probabilities involving unions and intersections of events are often conveniently displayed in a Venn diagram, similar to counting problems. Figure 1 displays the probabilities from Example 9.

Check Your Understanding 2.2

Solutions can be found following the section exercises.

1. **T-Maze** A mouse is put into a T-maze (a maze shaped like a "T") (Fig. 2). If it turns to the left, it receives cheese, and if it turns to the right, it receives a mild shock. This trial is done twice with the same mouse and the directions of the turns recorded.
   (a) What is the sample space for this experiment?
   (b) Why would it not be reasonable to assign each outcome the same probability?

2. The New York State lottery (Lotto) requires a contestant to select six numbers from 1 to 59. The probability of the same combination of six numbers occurring twice in one year is exceptionally low. Lotto system books advise people to avoid number combinations that have been drawn before. What is your assessment of this advice?

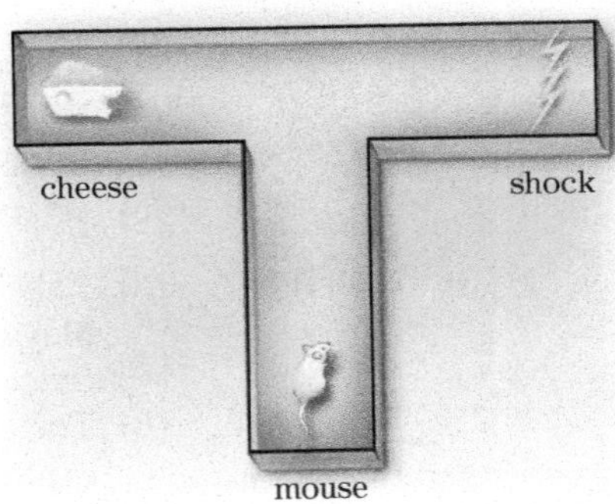

Figure 2

EXERCISES 2.2

In Exercises 1–4, classify the type of probability as logical, empirical, or judgmental.

1. Pr(China will win the most gold medals in the 2020 Olympics)
2. Pr(a person who smokes two packs of cigarettes each day has an increased risk of lung cancer)
3. Pr(obtaining a sum of 7 when rolling a pair of dice)
4. Pr(NASDAQ will increase by more than 10% in the next 12 months)

In Exercises 5 and 6, determine the probability distribution for the given experiment.

5. **Coin Tossing** Toss an unbiased coin twice, and count the number of heads.
6. **Selecting a Letter** A box contains seven slips of paper: one with a letter A printed on it, one with a B, three with a C, and two with a D. Draw a slip of paper and observe which letter is selected.
7. **Roulette** The modern American roulette wheel has 38 slots, which are labeled with 36 numbers evenly divided between red and black, plus two green numbers 0 and 00. What is the probability that the ball will land on a green number?
8. **U.S. States** A state is selected at random from the 50 states of the United States. What is the probability that it is one of the six New England states?
9. **Word Frequencies** There are 4487 words in the U.S. Constitution. The word "shall" occurs 191 times, and the word "States" occurs 81 times. Suppose that a word is selected at random from the U.S. Constitution.
   (a) What is the probability that the word is "shall"?
   (b) What is the probability that the word is "shall" or "States"?
   (c) What is the probability that the word is neither "shall" nor "States"?
10. **United Nations** Of the 193 member countries of the United Nations, 54 are in the African Group and 23 are in the Eastern European Group. Suppose that a country is selected at random from the members of the United Nations.
    (a) What is the probability that the country is in the African Group?
    (b) What is the probability that the country is in the African Group or the Eastern European Group?
    (c) What is the probability that the country is in neither the African Group nor the Eastern European Group?
11. **Selecting a Letter** An experiment consists of selecting a letter at random from the alphabet. Find the probability that the letter selected
    (a) precedes G alphabetically.
    (b) is a vowel (A, E, I, O, or U).
    (c) precedes G alphabetically or is a vowel.
12. **Selecting a Number** An experiment consists of selecting a number at random from the set of numbers $\{1, 2, 3, 4, 5, 6, 7, 8, 9\}$. Find the probability that the number selected is
    (a) less than 4. (b) odd. (c) less than 4 or odd.
13. **Dice** Suppose that a red die and a green die are rolled and the numbers on the sides that face upward are observed. (See Example 7 of this section and Example 2 of the first section.)
    (a) What is the probability that the numbers add up to 9?
    (b) What is the probability that the sum of the numbers is less than 5?
14. **Children** An experiment consists of observing the genders and birth orders in three-child families. Assume all eight outcomes have the same probability of occurring.
    (a) What is the probability that a family has at least two boys?
    (b) What is the probability that the oldest child is a girl?
15. **Kind of High School** The given table shows the results from *The American Freshman: National Norms Fall 2015* when the question "From what kind of high school did you graduate?" was posed to 141,000 college freshmen. Consider the experiment of selecting a student at random from the group surveyed and observing his or her answer. Determine the probability distribution for this experiment.

Kind of High School	Number of Freshmen
Public	115,620
Private	24,252
Home school	1128

Source: www.heri.ucla.edu

16. **Highest Degree Planned** The next table shows the results from *The American Freshman: National Norms Fall 2015* of a question posed to 141,000 college freshmen. Consider the experiment of selecting a student at random from the group surveyed and observing his or her answer. Determine the probability distribution for this experiment.

Highest Academic Degree Planned	Number of Freshmen
Master's	59,361
Bachelor's	29,751
Ph.D. or Ed.D.	26,931
M.D., D.O., D.D.S., D.V.M.	15,792
Other	9,165

Source: www.heri.ucla.edu

17. **Grade Distributions** The following table shows the probability distributions of letter grades from a mathematics class. What is the probability that a randomly chosen student received a letter grade higher than F but lower than A?

Letter Grade	Probability
A	.29
B	.34
C	.21
D	.09
F	.07

18. **Candy Colors** The colors in a bag of candy-coated milk chocolate candies have the probability distribution in the table that follows. What is the probability of randomly selecting a brown, orange, or red candy?

Color	Probability
Brown	.13
Yellow	.14
Red	.13
Orange	.20
Blue	.24
Green	.16

19. An experiment with outcomes s_1, s_2, s_3, s_4 has the following probability distribution:

Outcome	Probability
s_1	.1
s_2	.5
s_3	.2
s_4	.2

Let $E = \{s_1, s_2\}$ and $F = \{s_2, s_4\}$.
(a) Determine $\Pr(E)$ and determine $\Pr(F)$.
(b) Determine $\Pr(E')$.
(c) Determine $\Pr(E \cap F)$.
(d) Determine $\Pr(E \cup F)$.

20. An experiment with outcomes $s_1, s_2, s_3, s_4, s_5, s_6$ has the following probability distribution:

Outcome	Probability
s_1	.05
s_2	.25
s_3	.05
s_4	.01
s_5	.63
s_6	.01

Let $E = \{s_1, s_2\}$ and $F = \{s_3, s_5, s_6\}$.
(a) Determine $\Pr(E)$ and determine $\Pr(F)$.
(b) Determine $\Pr(E')$.
(c) Determine $\Pr(E \cap F)$.
(d) Determine $\Pr(E \cup F)$.

21. **College Applications** The table that follows was derived from a survey of college freshmen in 2015. Each probability is the likelihood that a randomly selected freshman applied to the specified number of colleges. For instance, 10% of the freshmen applied to just one college, and therefore, the probability that a student selected at random applied to just one college is .10.
(a) Convert these data into a probability distribution with outcomes 1, 2, 3, 4, and ≥ 5.
(b) What is the probability that a student applied to three or more colleges?

Number of Colleges Applied To	Probability
1	.10
2 or fewer	.17
3 or fewer	.27
4 or fewer	.40
20 or fewer	1

Source: www.heri.ucla.edu

22. **Employees' Ages** The next table summarizes the age distribution for a company's employees. Each probability is the likelihood that a randomly selected employee is in the specified age group.
(a) Convert this data into a probability distribution with outcomes 20–34 years, 35–49 years, 50–64 years, and 65–79 years.
(b) What is the probability that an employee selected at random is at least 50 years old?

Age (years)	Probability
20–34	.15
20–49	.70
20–64	.90
20–79	1

23. Which of the following probabilities are feasible for an experiment having sample space $\{s_1, s_2, s_3\}$? Explain your answer.
(a) $\Pr(s_1) = .4, \Pr(s_2) = .4, \Pr(s_3) = .4$
(b) $\Pr(s_1) = .5, \Pr(s_2) = .7, \Pr(s_3) = -.2$
(c) $\Pr(s_1) = \frac{1}{5}, \Pr(s_2) = \frac{2}{5}, \Pr(s_3) = \frac{1}{5}$

24. Which of the following probabilities are feasible for an experiment having sample space $\{s_1, s_2, s_3\}$? Explain your answer.
 (a) $\Pr(s_1) = .25, \Pr(s_2) = .25, \Pr(s_3) = .4$
 (b) $\Pr(s_1) = .7, \Pr(s_2) = .8, \Pr(s_3) = -.5$
 (c) $\Pr(s_1) = .2, \Pr(s_2) = .3, \Pr(s_3) = \frac{1}{2}$

25. **Car Race** Three cars, a Mazda, a Honda, and a Ford, are in a quarter-mile race. The probability that the Mazda will win the race is 2/3, and the probability that the Honda will win is 1/4. Assuming no ties are possible, what is the probability that the Ford will win the race?

26. **Hair Color** In a study, the residents of Edinburgh, Scotland, were classified as having either black hair, brown hair, blonde hair, or red hair. The probabilities of a randomly selected resident having black, brown, or blonde hair are .17, .47, and .20 respectively. Assuming each resident has one of these four hair colors,
 (a) what is the probability that a randomly selected resident has red hair?
 (b) what is the probability that a randomly selected resident has brown or black hair?
 (c) what is the probability that a randomly selected resident does not have blonde hair?

27. **Political Views** On a certain campus, the probability that a student selected at random has liberal political views is .28. The probability of having middle-of-the-road political views is twice the probability of having conservative political views. What is the probability that a student selected at random has conservative political views?

28. **Tennis** The probability that Alice beats Ben in a game of tennis is twice the probability that Ben beats Alice. Determine the two probabilities.

29. **Pair of Dice** Suppose that a pair of dice is rolled. Find Pr(sum of the two numbers is odd) + Pr(sum of the two numbers is even).

30. **Coin Tossing** An experiment consists of tossing a coin five times and observing the sequence of heads and tails. Find Pr(an even number of heads occurs) + Pr(an odd number of heads occurs).

31. Suppose that $\Pr(E) = .4$ and $\Pr(F) = .5$, where E and F are mutually exclusive. Find $\Pr(E \cup F)$.

32. Suppose that $\Pr(E) = .3$ and $\Pr(E \cup F) = .7$, where E and F are mutually exclusive. Find $\Pr(F)$.

In Exercises 33–36, consider the probabilities shown in the Venn diagram in Figure 3.

33. Determine the probability that the event E occurs.

34. Determine the probability that exactly one of the events E or F occurs.

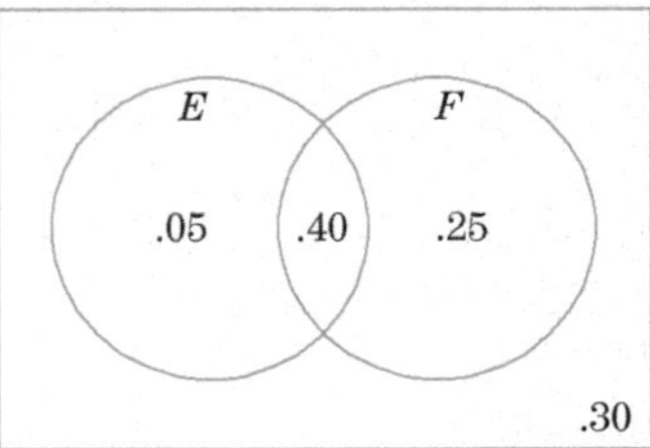

Figure 3

35. Determine the probability that F occurs, but E does not occur.

36. Determine the probability that E does not occur.

In Exercises 37–40, use a Venn diagram similar to the one in Fig. 1 to solve the problem.

37. Suppose that $\Pr(E) = .6$, $\Pr(F) = .5$, and $\Pr(E \cap F) = .4$. Find (a) $\Pr(E \cup F)$ (b) $\Pr(E \cap F')$.

38. Suppose that $\Pr(E) = .6$, $\Pr(F) = .5$, and $\Pr(E' \cup F') = .6$. Find (a) $\Pr(E \cap F)$ (b) $\Pr(E \cup F')$.

39. **Grades** Joe feels that the probability of his getting an A in history is .7, the probability of getting an A in psychology is .8, and the probability of getting an A in history or psychology is .9. What is the probability that he will get an A in both subjects?

40. **Courses** At a certain engineering college, the probability that a student selected at random is taking a mathematics course is 1/2, the probability that they are taking a computer science course is 3/8, and the probability they are taking either a mathematics course or a computer science course is 3/4. What is the probability that a student selected at random is taking both types of courses?

Exercises 41 and 42 can be answered without any computations.

41. **Zodiac Signs** A high school astrology club has 13 members. What is the probability that two or more members have the same zodiac sign? *Note:* There are 12 zodiac signs.

42. **Absent-Minded Attendant** Six people check their coats at a restaurant's coat-check counter. If the attendant returns the coats to the people at random, what is the probability that exactly five of the people receive the correct coat?

Solutions to Check Your Understanding 2.2

1. (a) {LL, LR, RR, RL}. Here, LL means that the mouse turned left both times, LR means that the mouse turned left the first time and right the second, and so on.
 (b) The mouse will learn something from the first trial. If it turned left the first time and got rewarded, then it is more likely to turn left again on the second trial. Hence, LL should have a greater probability than LR. Similarly, RL should be more likely than RR.

2. The ping-pong balls don't remember what combinations they produced in the past. Any combination of six numbers is just as likely to occur as any other combination.

2.3 Calculating Probabilities of Events

As mentioned in Section 2.2, there are several ways to assign probabilities to the events of a sample space. One way is to perform the experiment many times and assign probabilities based on empirical data. Sometimes, our intuition about situations suffices, as in simple coin-tossing experiments. But we frequently are faced with forming a model of an experiment to assign probabilities consistent with Fundamental Properties 1 and 2. This section shows how the counting techniques of Chapter 1 may be used to extend these ideas to more complex situations. In addition, the exceptionally wide range of applications that make use of probability theory is illustrated.

Experiments with Equally Likely Outcomes

In Section 2.2, we saw that, if a sample space has N equally likely outcomes, then the probability of each outcome is $1/N$. If we use this fact, the probability of any event is easy to compute. For instance, suppose that E is an event consisting of M outcomes. Then, by the addition principle,

$$\Pr(E) = \underbrace{\frac{1}{N} + \frac{1}{N} + \cdots + \frac{1}{N}}_{M \text{ terms}} = \frac{M}{N}.$$

We can restate this fundamental result as follows:

Probability with Equally Likely Outcomes Let S be a sample space consisting of N equally likely outcomes. Let E be any event. Then, if $n(E)$ is the number of outcomes in E,

$$\Pr(E) = \frac{n(E)}{N} = \frac{[\text{number of outcomes in } E]}{[\text{number of outcomes in } S]}. \tag{1}$$

In order to apply formula (1) in particular examples, it is necessary to compute N, the number of equally likely outcomes in the sample space, and $n(E)$. Often, these quantities can be determined by using the counting techniques of Chapter 1. Some illustrative computations are provided in Examples 1 through 6 here.

We should mention that, although the urn and dice problems considered in this section and the next might seem artificial and removed from applications, many applied problems can be described in mathematical terms as urn or dice experiments. We begin our discussion with two examples involving abstract urn problems. Then in two more examples, we show the utility of urn models by applying them to quality control and medical screening problems (Examples 2 and 4, respectively).

EXAMPLE 1 **Selecting Balls from an Urn** An urn contains eight white balls and two green balls. A sample of three balls is selected at random.

(a) What is the probability that the sample contains only white balls?

(b) What is the probability that the sample contains at least one green ball?

SOLUTION **(a)** The experiment consists of selecting 3 balls from the 10. Since the order in which the 3 balls are selected does not matter, the samples are combinations of 10 balls taken 3 at a time. The total number of samples is therefore $C(10, 3)$, and this is N, the number of elements in the sample space. Since the selection of the sample is random, all samples are equally likely, and thus we can use formula (1) to compute the probability of any event. The problem asks us to compute the probability of the event E = "all three balls selected are white." Since there are 8 white balls, the number of different samples in which all are white is $C(8, 3)$. Thus,

$$\Pr(E) = \frac{n(E)}{N} = \frac{C(8,3)}{C(10,3)} = \frac{56}{120} = \frac{7}{15}.$$

(b) As in Part (a), there are $N = C(10, 3)$ equally likely outcomes. Let F be the event "at least one green ball is selected." Let us determine the number of different outcomes in F. These outcomes contain either one or two green balls. There are $C(2, 1)$ ways to select one green ball from two; and for each of these, there are $C(8, 2)$ ways to select two white balls from eight. By the multiplication principle, the number of samples containing one green ball equals $C(2, 1) \cdot C(8, 2)$. Similarly, the number of samples containing two green balls equals $C(2, 2) \cdot C(8, 1)$. Note that, although the sample size is three, there are only two green balls in the urn. Since the sampling is done without replacement, no sample can have more than two greens. Therefore, the number of outcomes in F—namely, the number of samples having at least one green ball—equals

$$\underbrace{C(2, 1) \cdot C(8, 2)}_{\substack{\text{number of samples}\\ \text{containing}\\ \text{one green ball}}} + \underbrace{C(2, 2) \cdot C(8, 1)}_{\substack{\text{number of samples}\\ \text{containing}\\ \text{two green balls}}} = 2 \cdot 28 + 1 \cdot 8 = 64,$$

so

$$\Pr(F) = \frac{n(F)}{N} = \frac{64}{C(10, 3)} = \frac{64}{120} = \frac{8}{15}.$$

» Now Try Exercise 3

EXAMPLE 2

Quality Control A toy manufacturer inspects boxes of toys before shipment. Each box contains 10 toys. The inspection procedure consists of randomly selecting three toys from the box. If any are defective, the box is not shipped. Suppose that a given box has two defective toys. What is the probability that it will be shipped?

SOLUTION This problem is not really new! We solved it in disguise as Example 1(a). The urn can be regarded as a box of toys, and the balls as individual toys. The white balls are nondefective toys and the green balls defective toys. The random selection of three balls from the urn is just the inspection procedure. And the event "all three balls selected are white" corresponds to the box being shipped. As we calculated previously, the probability of this event is $\frac{7}{15}$. (Since $\frac{7}{15} \approx .47$, there is approximately a 47% chance of shipping a box with two defective toys. This inspection procedure is not particularly effective!)

» Now Try Exercise 11

EXAMPLE 3

Selecting Students A professor is randomly choosing a group of three students to do an oral presentation. In her class of 10 students, 2 are on the debate team. What is the chance that the professor chooses at least one of the debaters for the group?

SOLUTION This is the same as Example 1(b). Just think of the debate team members as the green balls and the others in the class as white balls. The chance of getting at least one debate team member in the group is $\frac{8}{15} \approx .53$.

» Now Try Exercise 9

EXAMPLE 4

Medical Screening Suppose that a cruise ship returns to the United States from the Far East. Unknown to anyone, 4 of its 600 passengers have contracted a rare disease. Suppose that the Public Health Service screens 20 passengers, selected at random, to see whether the disease is present aboard ship. What is the probability that the presence of the disease will escape detection?

SOLUTION The sample space consists of samples of 20 drawn from among the 600 passengers. There are $C(600, 20)$ such samples. The number of samples containing none of the sick passengers is $C(596, 20)$. Therefore, the probability of not detecting the disease is

$$\frac{C(596, 20)}{C(600, 20)} \approx .87.$$

So there is approximately an 87% chance that the disease will escape detection.

» Now Try Exercise 13

EXAMPLE 5 **Rolling a Die Five Times** A die is rolled five times. What is the probability of obtaining exactly three 4s?

SOLUTION Think of each of the 6^5 possible outcomes as a sequence of five digits from 1 through 6. To obtain an outcome containing three 4s, select the three positions to fill with 4s [$C(5, 3)$ possibilities], and then select digits other than 4 for the remaining two positions ($5 \cdot 5$ possibilities). Therefore, the probability of obtaining three 4s is

$$\frac{C(5, 3) \cdot 5 \cdot 5}{6^5} = \frac{10 \cdot 5 \cdot 5}{7776} \approx .03.$$

Thus, there is about a 3% chance of obtaining three 4s in five rolls of a die.

» Now Try Exercise 25

The Complement Rule

The **complement rule** relates the probability of an event E to the probability of its complement E'. When applied together with counting techniques, it often simplifies computation of probabilities.

> **Complement Rule** Let E be any event and E' its complement. Then
>
> $$\Pr(E) = 1 - \Pr(E').$$

For example, recall Example 1(a). We determined the probability of the event

$$E = \text{"all three balls selected are white"}$$

associated with the experiment of selecting three balls from an urn containing eight white balls and two green balls. We found that $\Pr(E) = \frac{7}{15}$. On the other hand, in Example 1(b), we determined the probability of the event

$$F = \text{"at least one green ball is selected."}$$

The event E is the complement of F:

$$E = F'.$$

So, by the complement rule,

$$\Pr(F) = 1 - \Pr(F') = 1 - \Pr(E) = 1 - \tfrac{7}{15} = \tfrac{8}{15},$$

in agreement with the calculations of Example 1(b).

The complement rule is especially useful in situations where $\Pr(E')$ is easier to compute than $\Pr(E)$. One of these situations arises in the celebrated *birthday problem.*

EXAMPLE 6 **The Famous "Birthday Problem"** A group of five people is to be selected at random. What is the probability that two or more of them have the same birthday?

SOLUTION For simplicity, we ignore February 29. Furthermore, we assume that each of the 365 days in a year is an equally likely birthday (not an unreasonable assumption). The experiment we have in mind is this. Pick out five people, and observe their birthdays. The outcomes of this experiment are strings of five dates, corresponding to the birthdays. For example, one outcome of the experiment is

(June 2, April 6, Dec. 20, Feb.12, Aug. 5).

Each birth date has 365 different possibilities. So, by the generalized multiplication principle, the total number N of possible outcomes of the experiment is

$$N = 365 \cdot 365 \cdot 365 \cdot 365 \cdot 365 = 365^5.$$

Let E be the event "at least two people have the same birthday." It is very difficult to calculate directly the number of outcomes in E. However, it is comparatively simple to compute the number of outcomes in E' and hence to compute $\Pr(E')$. This is because E' is the event "all five birthdays are different." An outcome in E' can be selected in a sequence of five steps:

① Select a day	② Select a different day	③ Select yet a different day	④ Select yet a different day	⑤ Select yet a different day

These five steps will result in a sequence of five different birthdays. The first step can be performed in 365 ways; for each of these, the next step in 364; for each of these, the next step in 363; for each of these, the next step in 362; and for each of these, the last step in 361 ways. Therefore, E' contains $365 \cdot 364 \cdot 363 \cdot 362 \cdot 361$ [or $P(365, 5)$] outcomes, and

$$\Pr(E') = \frac{365 \cdot 364 \cdot 363 \cdot 362 \cdot 361}{365^5} \approx .973.$$

By the complement rule,

$$\Pr(E) = 1 - \Pr(E') \approx 1 - .973 = .027.$$

So the likelihood is about 2.7% that two or more of the five people will have the same birthday.

» Now Try Exercise 17

The experiment of Example 6 can be repeated by using samples of 8, 10, 20, or any number of people. As before, let E be the event "at least two people have the same birthday," so that E' = "all the birthdays are different." If a sample of r people is used, then the same reasoning as used previously yields

$$\Pr(E') = \frac{365 \cdot 364 \cdot \cdots \cdot (365 - r + 1)}{365^r}.$$

Table 1 gives the values of $\Pr(E) = 1 - \Pr(E')$ for various values of r. You may be surprised by the numbers in the table. Even with as few as 23 people, it is more likely than not that at least two people have the same birthday. With a sample of 50 people, we are almost certain to have two with the same birthday. (Try this experiment in your class.)

Table 1 Probability That, in a Randomly Selected Group of *r* People, at Least Two People Will Have the Same Birthday

r	5	10	15	20	22	23	25	30	40	50
$\Pr(E)$	.027	.117	.253	.411	.476	.507	.569	.706	.891	.970

Verification of the Complement Rule If S is the sample space, then $\Pr(S) = 1$, $E \cup E' = S$, and $E \cap E' = \varnothing$. Therefore, by the inclusion–exclusion principle,

$$\Pr(S) = \Pr(E \cup E') = \Pr(E) + \Pr(E').$$

So we have

$$1 = \Pr(E) + \Pr(E') \quad \text{and} \quad \Pr(E) = 1 - \Pr(E').$$

«

Check Your Understanding 2.3

Solutions can be found following the section exercises.

1. **Children** A couple decides to have four children. What is the probability that among the children, there will be at least one boy and at least one girl?

2. **Roulette** Find the probability that all of the numbers are different in three spins of an American roulette wheel. [*Note:* An American roulette wheel has 38 numbers.]

EXERCISES 2.3

1. A number is chosen at random from the whole numbers between 1 and 17, inclusive.
   (a) What is the probability that the number is odd?
   (b) What is the probability that the number is even?
   (c) What is the probability that the number is a multiple of 3?
   (d) What is the probability that the number is odd or a multiple of 3?

2. A number is chosen at random from the whole numbers between 1 and 100, inclusive.
   (a) What is the probability that the number ends in a zero?
   (b) What is the probability that the number is odd?
   (c) What is the probability that the number is odd or ends in a zero?

3. **Balls in an Urn** An urn contains five red balls and six white balls. A sample of two balls is selected at random from the urn. Find the probability that
   (a) only red balls are selected.
   (b) at least one white ball is selected.

4. **Balls in an Urn** An urn contains seven green balls and five white balls. A sample of three balls is selected at random from the urn. Find the probability that
   (a) only green balls are selected.
   (b) at least one white ball is selected.

5. **Balls in an Urn** An urn contains six green balls and seven white balls. A sample of four balls is selected at random from the urn. Find the probability that
   (a) the four balls have the same color.
   (b) the sample contains more green balls than white balls.

6. **Balls in an Urn** An urn contains eight red balls and six white balls. A sample of three balls is selected at random from the urn. Find the probability that
   (a) the three balls have the same color.
   (b) the sample contains more white balls than red balls.

7. **Opinion Polling** Two out of the seven members of a school board feel that all high school students should be required to take a course in coding. A pollster selects three members of the board at random and asks them for their opinion on requiring a coding course. What is the probability that at least one of the members polled favors requiring the course?

8. **Opinion Polling** Of the 15 members on a Senate committee, 10 plan to vote "yes" and 5 plan to vote "no" on an important issue. A reporter attempts to predict the outcome of the vote by questioning six of the senators. Find the probability that this sample is precisely representative of the final vote. That is, find the probability that four of the six senators questioned plan to vote "yes."

9. **Committee Selection** In the 114th United States Congress, the House Committee on Rules consisted of nine Republicans and four Democrats. If a subcommittee of three committee members was selected at random, what is the probability that at least one Democrat was on the committee?

10. **Committee Selection** The U.S. Senate consists of two senators from each of the 50 states. Five senators are to be selected at random to form a committee. What is the probability that no two members of the committee are from the same state?

11. **Quality Control** A factory produces LCD panels, which are packaged in boxes of 10. Three panels are selected at random from each box for inspection. The box is rejected if at least one of these three panels is defective. What is the probability that a box containing six defective panels will be rejected?

12. **Rotten Tomato** A bag contains nine tomatoes, of which one is rotten. A sample of three tomatoes is selected at random. What is the probability that the sample contains the rotten tomato?

Selecting Students Exercises 13–16 refer to a classroom of children (12 boys and 10 girls) in which seven students are chosen to go to the blackboard.

13. What is the probability that no boys are chosen?

14. What is the probability that the first three children chosen are boys?

15. What is the probability that at least two girls are chosen?

16. What is the probability that at least three boys are chosen?

17. **Birthday** Three people are chosen at random. What is the probability that at least two of them were born on the same day of the week?

18. **Birthday** Four people are chosen at random. What is the probability that at least two of them were born in the same month? Assume that each month is as likely as any other.

19. **Date Conflict** Without consultation with each other, each of four organizations announces a one-day convention to be held during June. Find the probability that at least two organizations specify the same day for their convention.

20. **Presidential Choices** There were 16 presidents of the Continental Congress from 1774 to 1788. Each of the five students in a seminar in American history chooses one of these presidents on whom to do a report. If all presidents are equally likely to be chosen, calculate the probability that at least two students choose the same president.

21. **Name Badges** Eight workers need an employee number to be printed on a name badge. The company's security office uses a random-number generator to assign each employee a number between 81 and 100, inclusive. What is the probability that at least two workers receive the same number?

22. **Random Selection** Each person in a group of 10 people randomly selects a number from 1 to 100, inclusive. What is the probability that at least two people select the same number?

23. **Birthday Problem** What is the probability that, in a group of 25 people, at least one person has a birthday on June 13? Why is your answer different from the probability displayed in Table 1 for $r = 25$?

24. **Birthday Problem** Johnny Carson, host of *The Tonight Show* from 1962–1992, discussed the birthday problem during one of his monologues. To test the hypothesis, he asked the audience

whether any of them were born on his birthday, October 23. Carson was surprised that no one in the audience of 100 people shared his birthday. What was wrong with Carson's reasoning? What is the probability that one or more people in the audience were born on October 23?

25. **Dice** A die is rolled twice. What is the probability that the two numbers are different?

26. **Dice** A die is rolled three times. What is the probability of obtaining three different numbers?

27. **Dice** A die is rolled four times. What is the probability of obtaining only even numbers?

28. **Dice** A die is rolled three times. What is the probability that the number 1 does not appear?

29. **Coin Tosses** A coin is tossed 10 times. What is the probability of obtaining four heads and six tails?

30. **Coin Tosses** A coin is tossed seven times. What is the probability of obtaining five heads and two tails?

31. **Orientation Teams** A university admissions office randomly assigns each student from a group of four incoming freshmen to an orientation team. If there are seven orientation teams, what is the probability that two or more of these students are assigned to the same team?

32. **Elevator** An elevator has six buttons: *L, 1, 2, 3, 4,* and *5*. Suppose that five people get on the elevator at the Lobby. What is the probability that they are each going to a different floor? Assume that each of the floors 1 through 5 is equally likely.

33. **Street Routs** Figure 1 shows a partial map of the streets in New York City. (Such maps are discussed in Chapter 1.) A tourist starts at point A and selects at random a shortest path to point B. That is, they walk only south and east. Find the probability that
(a) they pass through point C.
(b) they pass through point D.
(c) they pass through point C and point D.
(d) they pass through point C or point D.

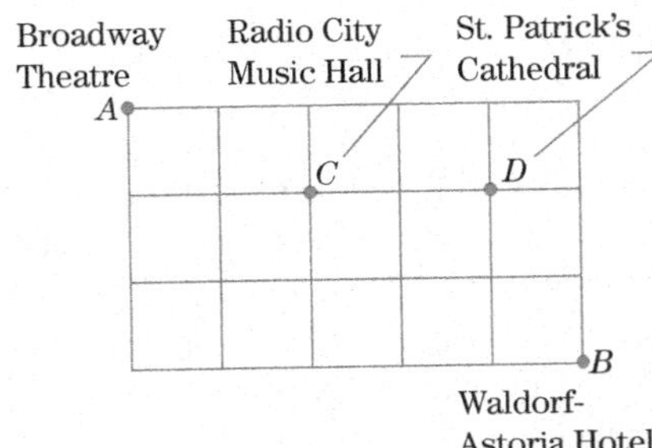

Figure 1

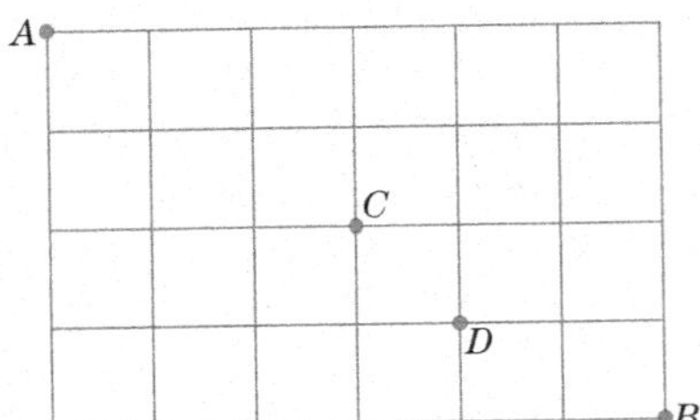

Figure 2

34. **Street Routes** Repeat Exercise 33 for Fig. 2.

35. **Baseball Predictions** In the American League, the East, Central, and West divisions each consists of five teams. A sportswriter predicts the winner of each of the three divisions by choosing a team completely at random in each division. What is the probability that the sportswriter will predict at least one winner correctly?

36. **Baseball Predictions** Suppose that the sportswriter in Exercise 35 eliminates from each division one team that clearly has no chance of winning and predicts a winner at random from the remaining teams. Assuming that the eliminated teams don't end up surprising anyone, what is the writer's chance of predicting at least one winner?

37. **Baseball Predictions** Suppose that the sportswriter in Exercise 35 simply puts the 15 team names in a hat and draws 3 completely at random. Does this increase or decrease the writer's chance of picking at least one winner?

38. **Baseball Predictions** Suppose that the sportswriter in Exercise 36 simply puts the 12 team names in a hat and draws 3 completely at random. Does this increase or decrease the writer's chance of picking at least one winner?

39. **Place Settings** Fred has five place settings consisting of a dinner plate, a salad plate, and a bowl. Each setting is a different color. If Fred randomly selects a dinner plate, a salad plate, and a bowl, what is the probability that they will all have different colors?

40. **Track Positions** Michael and Christopher are among seven contestants in a race to be run on a seven-lane track. If the runners are assigned to the lanes at random, what is the probability that Michael will be assigned to the inside lane and Christopher will be assigned to the outside lane?

41. **Group Picture** A man, a woman, and their three children randomly stand in a row for a family picture. What is the probability that the parents will be standing next to each other?

42. **Letter Positions** What is the probability that a random arrangement of the letters in the word GEESE has all the E's adjacent to one another?

Poker A poker hand consists of five cards drawn from a deck of 52 cards. Each card has one of 13 ranks (2, 3, 4, . . . , 10, jack, queen, king, ace) and one of four suits (spades, hearts, diamonds, clubs). In Exercises 43–46, determine the probability of the specified type of poker hand.

43. Full house (three cards of one rank and two cards of another rank)

44. Three of a kind (three cards of one rank and two cards of distinct rank, both different from the rank of the triple)

45. Two pairs (two cards of one rank, two cards of a different rank, and one card of a rank other than those two ranks)

46. One pair (two cards of one rank and three cards of distinct ranks, where each of the three cards has a different rank from the rank of the pair)

47. **Bridge** A bridge hand consists of thirteen cards drawn from a deck of 52 cards. Each card has one of 13 ranks (2, 3, 4, . . . , 10, jack, queen, king, ace) and one of four suits (spades, hearts, diamonds, clubs). What is the probability of each of the following suit distributions in a bridge hand?

(a) 4-3-3-3. That is, four cards of one suit and three cards of each of the other three suits. *Hint:* The number of hands having this distribution is $4 \cdot C(13, 4) \cdot C(13, 3) \cdot C(13, 3) \cdot C(13, 3)$.

(b) 4-4-3-2. That is, four cards of each of two suits, three cards of another suit, and two cards of the remaining suit.

48. **Powerball Lottery** The winner of the Powerball lottery must correctly pick a set of 5 numbers from 1 through 69 and then correctly pick one number (called the Powerball) from 1 through 26.

(a) What is the probability of winning the Powerball lottery?

Illinois Lotto Exercises 49 and 50 refer to the Illinois Lottery Lotto game. (The data for these exercises were taken from Allan J. Gottlieb's "Puzzle Corner" in *Technology Review*, February/March 1985.) In this game, the player chooses six different integers from 1 to 40. If the six match (in any order) the six different integers drawn by the lottery, the player wins the grand prize jackpot, which starts at \$1 million and grows weekly until won. Multiple winners split the pot equally. For each \$1 bet, the player must pick two (presumably different) sets of six integers.

49. What is the probability of winning the Illinois Lottery Lotto with a \$1 bet?

50. In the game week ending June 18, 1983, a total of 2 million people bought \$1 tickets, and 78 people matched all six winning integers and split the jackpot. If all numbers were selected randomly, the likelihood of having so many joint winners would be about 10^{-115}. Can you think of any reason that such an unlikely event would have occurred? (*Note:* The winning numbers were 7, 13, 14, 21, 28, and 35.) What would be the best strategy in selecting the numbers to ensure that in the event that you won, you would probably not have to share the jackpot with too many people?

51. **California Lottery** In the California Fantasy 5 lottery, a player pays \$1 for a ticket and selects 5 numbers from the numbers 1 through 39. If they match exactly three of the five numbers drawn, they receive \$15. What is the probability of selecting exactly three of the five numbers drawn?

52. **Florida Lottery** The winning combination in the Florida lottery consists of six numbers drawn from the numbers 1 through 53. What is the probability that a single ticket has no matches?

53. **License Plate Game** Johnny and Doyle are driving on a lightly traveled road. Johnny proposes the following game: They will look at the license plates of oncoming cars and focus on the last two digits. For instance, the license plates ABC512 and 7412BG would yield 12, and the license plate XY406T would yield the number 6. Johnny bets Doyle that at least 2 of the next 15 cars will yield the same number. What is the probability that Johnny wins? Assume that each of the 100 possible numbers is equally likely to occur.

54. **Parking Spaces** Ten people randomly park their cars in a row of fourteen parking spaces. Then Mr. Jones arrives in a wide camper that requires two adjacent parking spaces. What is the probability that Mr. Jones will be able to park his camper? *Hint*: Use the complement rule and the counting principle from Example 4 of Section 1.6.

TECHNOLOGY EXERCISES

55. **Pick a Card** Find the probability that at least two people in a group of size $n = 5$ select the same card when drawing from a 52-card deck with replacement. Determine the group size n for which the probability of such a match first exceeds 50%.

56. **Term Papers** A political science class has 20 students, each of whom chooses a topic from a list for a term paper. How big a pool of topics is necessary for the probability of at least one duplicate to drop below 50%?

57. **Birthday Problem** Refer to Exercise 24. How large would the audience have to have been so that the probability that someone in the audience had the same birthday as Carson was at least 50%?

58. **Birthday Problem** A year on planet Ork has 100 days. Find the smallest number of Orkians for which the probability that at least two of them have the same birthday is 50% or more.

59. **Lottery** In many state lotteries, six numbers are selected from a set of numbers. Quite often, the winning selection contains two consecutive numbers. When six numbers are selected from the numbers 1 through n, the probability that there will be two consecutive integers in the selection is .5771 when n is 40 and the probability is .4209 when n is 60. Determine the largest value of n for which the probability of having two consecutive numbers is greater than .5. *Note:* There are $C(n - k + 1, k)$ ways that k numbers selected from the numbers 1 through n will have no two consecutive numbers.

60. **The de Méré Problem** How many times must you roll two dice so that the probability of rolling a pair of 6s at least once is greater than or equal to .5? *Note:* This question was posed in 1654 by the French writer and gambler Chevalier de Méré.

Solutions to Check Your Understanding 2.3

1. Each possible outcome is a string of four letters composed of Bs and Gs. By the generalized multiplication principle, there are 2^4, or 16, possible outcomes. Let E be the event "children of both genders." Then $E' = \{\text{BBBB, GGGG}\}$, and

$$\Pr(E') = \frac{n(E')}{N} = \frac{2}{16} = \frac{1}{8}.$$

Therefore,

$$\Pr(E) = 1 - \Pr(E') = 1 - \frac{1}{8} = \frac{7}{8}.$$

So the probability is 87.5% that they will have children of both genders.

2. Each sequence of three numbers is just as likely to occur as any other. Therefore,

$$\Pr(\text{numbers different}) = \frac{[\text{number of outcomes with numbers different}]}{[\text{number of possible outcomes}]} = \frac{38 \cdot 37 \cdot 36}{38^3} \approx .92.$$

2.4 Conditional Probability and Independence

The probability of an event depends, often in a critical way, on the sample space in question. In this section, we explore this dependence in some detail by introducing what are called *conditional probabilities*.

To illustrate the dependence of probabilities on the sample space, consider the following example:

EXAMPLE 1 **College Students** Suppose that a certain mathematics class contains 26 students. Of these, 14 are economics majors, 15 are first-year students, and 7 are neither. Suppose that a person is selected at random from the class.

(a) What is the probability that the person is both an economics major and a first-year student?

(b) Suppose that we are given the additional information that the person selected is a first-year student. What is the probability that they are also an economics major?

SOLUTION Let E denote the set of economics majors and F the set of first-year students. A complete Venn diagram of the class can be obtained with the techniques of Section 1.3. See Fig. 1.

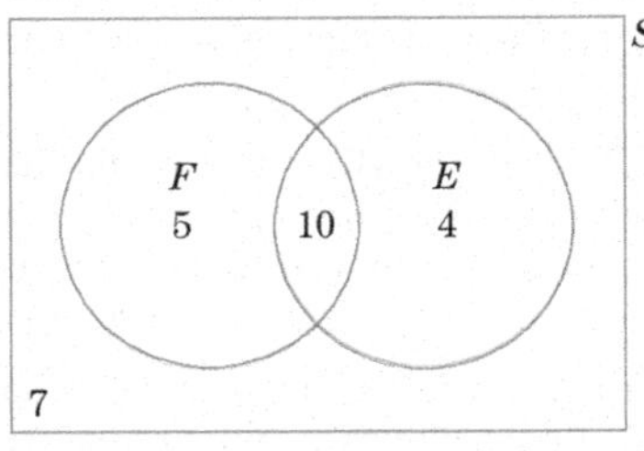

Figure 1

(a) In selecting a student from the class, the sample space consists of all 26 students. Since the choice is random, all students are equally likely to be selected. The event "economics major and first-year student" corresponds to the set $E \cap F$ of the Venn diagram. Therefore,

$$\Pr(E \cap F) = \frac{n(E \cap F)}{N} = \frac{10}{26} = \frac{5}{13}.$$

So the probability of selecting a first-year economics major is $\frac{5}{13}$.

(b) If we know that the student selected is a first-year student, then the possible outcomes of the experiment are restricted. They must belong to F. In other words, given the additional information, we must alter the sample space from "all students" to "first-year students." Since each of the 15 first-year students is equally likely to be selected, and since 10 of the 15 first-year students are economics majors, the probability of choosing an economics major under these circumstances is equal to $\frac{10}{15} = \frac{2}{3}$. «

Let us consider Example 1 more carefully. In part (a), the sample space is the set of all students in the mathematics class, E is the event "student is an economics major," and F is the event "student is a first-year student." On the other hand, part (b) poses a condition, "student is a first-year student." The condition is satisfied by every element of F. We are being asked to find the **conditional probability** of E given F, written $\Pr(E|F)$; this is the probability of E, assuming that F has occurred. To do this, we shall restrict our attention to the new (restricted) sample space, now just the elements of F.

Thus, we consider only first-year students and ask, of these, what is the probability of choosing an economics major? We assign a value to $\Pr(E|F)$ via the following formula:

DEFINITION Conditional Probability

$$\Pr(E|F) = \frac{\Pr(E \cap F)}{\Pr(F)}, \quad \text{provided that } \Pr(F) \neq 0. \tag{1}$$

We will provide an intuitive justification of this formula shortly. However, we first give an application.

EXAMPLE 2 **Earnings and Education** Twenty percent of the employees of Acme Steel Company are college graduates. Of all of its employees, 25% earn more than \$50,000 per year and 15% are college graduates earning more than \$50,000. What is the probability that an employee selected at random earns more than \$50,000 per year, given that they are a college graduate?

SOLUTION Let H and C be the events

$$H = \text{“earns more than \$50,000 per year”}$$
$$C = \text{“college graduate.”}$$

We are asked to calculate $\Pr(H|C)$. The given data is

$$\Pr(H) = .25 \qquad \Pr(C) = .20 \qquad \Pr(H \cap C) = .15.$$

By formula (1), we have

$$\Pr(H|C) = \frac{\Pr(H \cap C)}{\Pr(C)} = \frac{.15}{.20} = \frac{3}{4}.$$

Thus $\frac{3}{4}$ of all college graduates at Acme Steel earn more than \$50,000 per year.

» Now Try Exercise 15

Suppose that an experiment has N equally likely outcomes. Then we may apply the following formula to calculate $\Pr(E|F)$:

Conditional Probability in Case of Equally Likely Outcomes

$$\Pr(E|F) = \frac{n(E \cap F)}{n(F)}, \tag{2}$$

provided that $n(F) \neq 0$.

This formula was actually used in Example 1(b) to compute $\Pr(E|F)$. In that example, each student had the same likelihood of being selected.

Let us now justify formulas (1) and (2).

Justification of Formula (1) Formula (1) is a definition of conditional probability and as such does not really need any justification. (We can make whatever definitions we choose!) However, let us proceed intuitively and show that the definition is reasonable, in the sense that formula (1) gives the expected long-run proportion of occurrences of E, given that F occurs. Assume that our experiment is performed repeatedly, say, for 10,000 trials. We would expect F to occur in approximately 10,000 $\Pr(F)$ trials. Among these, the trials for which E also occurs are exactly those for which both E and F occur. In other words, the trials for which E also occurs are exactly those for which the event $E \cap F$ occurs; and this event has probability $\Pr(E \cap F)$. Therefore, out of the original 10,000 trials, there should be approximately 10,000 $\Pr(E \cap F)$ in which E and F both occur. Thus, considering only those trials in which F occurs, the proportion in which E also occurs is

$$\frac{10{,}000 \Pr(E \cap F)}{10{,}000 \Pr(F)} = \frac{\Pr(E \cap F)}{\Pr(F)}.$$

Thus, at least intuitively, it seems reasonable to define $\Pr(E|F)$ by formula (1). «

Justification of Formula (2) Suppose that the number of outcomes of the experiment is N. Then

$$\Pr(F) = \frac{n(F)}{N}$$
$$\Pr(E \cap F) = \frac{n(E \cap F)}{N}$$

Therefore, using formula (1), we have

$$\Pr(E|F) = \frac{\Pr(E \cap F)}{\Pr(F)} = \frac{\frac{n(E \cap F)}{N}}{\frac{n(F)}{N}} = \frac{n(E \cap F)}{n(F)}.$$

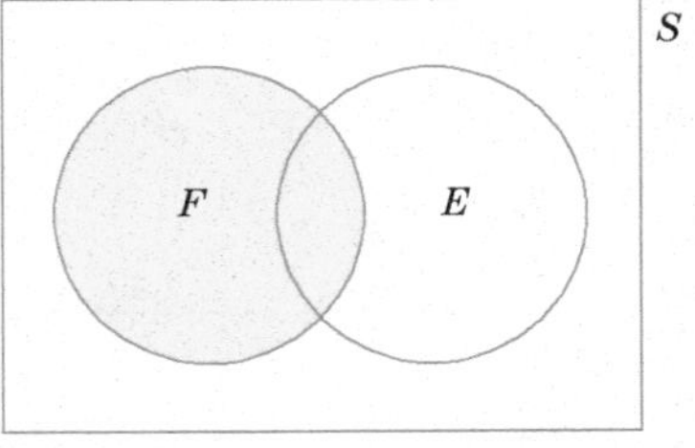

Figure 2

Alternatively, consider the Venn Diagram in Fig. 2. If we assume that the event F occurs, we are restricted to only the outcomes in the shaded region; that is, we consider F to be the sample space. Then, E occurs exactly when $E \cap F$ occurs, so the conditional probability is

$$\Pr(E|F) = \frac{n(E \cap F)}{n(F)}.$$

«

From formula (1), multiplying both sides of the equation by $\Pr(F)$, we can deduce the following useful fact:

Product Rule If $\Pr(F) \neq 0$,

$$\Pr(E \cap F) = \Pr(F) \cdot \Pr(E|F).$$

The next example illustrates the use of this rule.

EXAMPLE 3 **Color-Blind Males** Assume that a certain school contains an equal number of female and male students and that 5% of the male population is color blind. Find the probability that a randomly selected student is a color-blind male.

SOLUTION Let $M =$ "male" and $B =$ "color blind." We wish to calculate $\Pr(B \cap M)$. From the given data,

$$\Pr(M) = .5 \quad \text{and} \quad \Pr(B|M) = .05.$$

Therefore, by the product rule,

$$\Pr(B \cap M) = \Pr(M) \cdot \Pr(B|M) = (.5)(.05) = .025.$$

» Now Try Exercise 29

Often, an event G can be described as a sequence of two other events E and F. That is, G occurs if F occurs and then E occurs. The product rule allows us to compute the probability of G as the probability of F times the conditional probability $\Pr(E|F)$. The next example illustrates this point.

EXAMPLE 4 **Cards** A sequence of two playing cards is drawn at random (without replacement) from a standard deck of 52 cards. What is the probability that the first card is red and the second is black?

SOLUTION The event in question is a sequence of two events, namely,

$$F = \text{"the first card is red"}$$
$$E = \text{"the second card is black."}$$

Since half of the deck consists of red cards, $\Pr(F) = 1/2$. If we are given that F occurs, then there are only 51 cards left in the deck, of which 26 are black, so

$$\Pr(E|F) = \tfrac{26}{51}.$$

By the product rule,

$$\Pr(E \cap F) = \Pr(F) \cdot \Pr(E|F) = \tfrac{1}{2} \cdot \tfrac{26}{51} = \tfrac{13}{51}.$$

» Now Try Exercise 25

The product rule may be generalized to sequences of three events, E_1, E_2, and E_3.

$$\Pr(E_1 \cap E_2 \cap E_3) = \Pr(E_1) \cdot \Pr(E_2|E_1) \cdot \Pr(E_3|E_1 \cap E_2).$$

Similar formulas hold for sequences of four or more events.

One of the most important applications of conditional probability is in the discussion of independent events. Intuitively, two events are **independent** of each other if the occurrence of one has no effect on the likelihood that the other will occur. For example, suppose that we roll a die twice. Let the events E and F be

$$F = \text{"first roll is a 6"}$$
$$E = \text{"second roll is a 3."}$$

Then intuitively, we conclude that these events are independent of one another. Rolling a 6 on the first roll has no effect whatsoever on the outcome of the second roll. On the other hand, suppose that we draw a sequence of two cards at random (without replacement) from a deck. Then we know that the events

$$F = \text{"first card is red"}$$
$$E = \text{"second card is black"}$$

are not independent of one another, at least intuitively. Indeed, whether or not we draw a red on the first card affects the likelihood of drawing a black on the second.

The notion of independence of events is easily formulated. If E and F are events in a sample space and $\Pr(F) \neq 0$, then the product rule states that $\Pr(E \cap F) = \Pr(E|F) \cdot \Pr(F)$. However, if the occurrence of event F does not affect the likelihood of the occurrence of event E, we would expect that $\Pr(E|F) = \Pr(E)$. Substitution then shows that $\Pr(E \cap F) = \Pr(E) \cdot \Pr(F)$.

DEFINITION Let E and F be events. We say that E and F are **independent**, provided that

$$\Pr(E \cap F) = \Pr(E) \cdot \Pr(F).$$

If $\Pr(E) \neq 0$ and $\Pr(F) \neq 0$, then our definition is equivalent to the intuitive statement of independence stated in terms of conditional probability. The two may be used interchangeably.

> **DEFINITION** Let E and F be events with nonzero probability. E and F are **independent**, provided that
>
> $$\Pr(E|F) = \Pr(E) \quad \text{and} \quad \Pr(F|E) = \Pr(F).$$

EXAMPLE 5 **Determining Whether Probabilities Are Independent** For each pair of probabilities, determine whether E and F are independent.

(a) An experiment consists of observing the outcome of two consecutive rolls of a die. Let E and F be the events

$$E = \text{"the first roll is a 3"}$$
$$F = \text{"the second roll is a 6"}$$

(b) An experiment consists of observing the results of drawing two consecutive cards from a 52-card deck. Let E and F be the events

$$E = \text{"the second card is black"}$$
$$F = \text{"the first card is red"}$$

SOLUTION **(a)** Clearly, $\Pr(E) = \Pr(F) = \frac{1}{6}$. To compute $\Pr(E|F)$, assume that F occurs. Then there are six possible outcomes:

$$F = \{(1,6), (2,6), (3,6), (4,6), (5,6), (6,6)\},$$

and all outcomes are equally likely. Moreover.

$$E \cap F = \{(3,6)\},$$

so that

$$\Pr(E|F) = \frac{n(E \cap F)}{n(F)} = \frac{1}{6} = \Pr(E).$$

Similarly, $\Pr(E|F) = \Pr(F)$. So E and F are independent events, in agreement with our intuition.

(b) There are the same number of outcomes with the second card red as with the second card black, so $\Pr(E) = \frac{1}{2}$. To compute $\Pr(E|F)$, note that if F occurs, then there are 51 equally likely choices for the second card, of which 26 are black, so that $\Pr(E|F) = \frac{26}{51}$. Note that $\Pr(E|F) \neq \Pr(E)$, so E and F are not independent, in agreement with our intuition.

>> Now Try Exercise 45

EXAMPLE 6 **Determining Whether Probabilities Are Independent** For each pair of probabilities, determine whether E and F are independent.

(a) We toss a coin three times and record the sequence of heads and tails. Let E be the event "at most one head occurs" and F the event "both heads and tails occur."

(b) A family has four children. Let E be the event "at most one boy" and F the event "at least one child of each gender."

SOLUTION **(a)** Using the abbreviations H for "heads" and T for "tails," we have

$$E = \{\text{TTT, HTT, THT, TTH}\}$$
$$F = \{\text{HTT, HTH, HHT, THH, THT, TTH}\}$$
$$E \cap F = \{\text{HTT, THT, TTH}\}.$$

The sample space contains eight equally likely outcomes so that

$$\Pr(E) = \tfrac{1}{2} \qquad \Pr(F) = \tfrac{3}{4} \qquad \Pr(E \cap F) = \tfrac{3}{8}.$$

Moreover,

$$\Pr(E) \cdot \Pr(F) = \tfrac{1}{2} \cdot \tfrac{3}{4} = \tfrac{3}{8},$$

which equals $\Pr(E \cap F)$. So E and F are independent.

(b) Let B stand for "boy" and G for "girl." Then

$$\begin{aligned} E &= \{\text{GGGG, GGGB, GGBG, GBGG, BGGG}\} \\ F &= \{\text{GGGB, GGBG, GBGG, BGGG, BBBG, BBGB, BGBB,} \\ &\quad \text{GBBB, BBGG, BGBG, BGGB, GBBG, GBGB, GGBB}\}, \end{aligned}$$

and the sample space consists of 16 equally likely outcomes. Furthermore,

$$E \cap F = \{\text{GGGB, GGBG, GBGG, BGGG}\}.$$

Therefore,

$$\Pr(E) = \tfrac{5}{16} \qquad \Pr(F) = \tfrac{7}{8} \qquad \Pr(E \cap F) = \tfrac{1}{4}.$$

In this example,

$$\Pr(E) \cdot \Pr(F) = \tfrac{5}{16} \cdot \tfrac{7}{8} \neq \Pr(E \cap F).$$

So E and F are *not* independent events. ***>> Now Try Exercise 43***

Examples 6(a) and 6(b) are similar, yet the events they describe are independent in one case and not the other. Although intuition is frequently a big help, in complex problems we shall need to use the definition of independence to verify that our intuition is correct.

EXAMPLE 7 **Reliability of a Calculator** A new calculator is designed to be extra reliable by having two independent calculating units. The probability that a given calculating unit fails within the first 1000 hours of operation is .001. What is the probability that at least one calculating unit will operate without failure for the first 1000 hours of operation?

SOLUTION Let

$$\begin{aligned} E &= \text{"calculating unit 1 fails in first 1000 hours"} \\ F &= \text{"calculating unit 2 fails in first 1000 hours."} \end{aligned}$$

Then E and F are independent events, since the calculating units are independent of one another. Therefore,

$$\begin{aligned} \Pr(E \cap F) &= \Pr(E) \cdot \Pr(F) = (.001)^2 = .000001 \\ \Pr[(E \cap F)'] &= 1 - .000001 = .999999. \end{aligned}$$

Since $(E \cap F)' =$ "not both calculating units fail in first 1000 hours," the desired probability is .999999. <<

The concept of independent events can be extended to more than two events:

> **DEFINITION** A set of events is said to be **independent** if, for each collection of events chosen from them, say, $E_1, E_2, \ldots, E_n$, we have
>
> $$\Pr(E_1 \cap E_2 \cap \cdots \cap E_n) = \Pr(E_1) \cdot \Pr(E_2) \cdot \cdots \cdot \Pr(E_n).$$

EXAMPLE 8 **Probabilities Associated with Independent Events** Three events A, B, and C are independent: $\Pr(A) = .5$, $\Pr(B) = .3$, and $\Pr(C) = .2$.
(a) Calculate $\Pr(A \cap B \cap C)$. (b) Calculate $\Pr(A \cap C)$.

SOLUTION (a) $\Pr(A \cap B \cap C) = \Pr(A) \cdot \Pr(B) \cdot \Pr(C) = (.5)(.3)(.2) = .03$.
(b) $\Pr(A \cap C) = \Pr(A) \cdot \Pr(C) = (.5)(.2) = .1$.

» Now Try Exercise 41

We shall leave as an exercise the intuitively reasonable result that if E and F are independent events, so are E and F', E' and F, and E' and F'. This result also generalizes to any collection of independent events.

EXAMPLE 9 **Quality Control** A company manufactures stereo components. Experience shows that defects in manufacture are independent of one another. Quality-control studies reveal that

2% of CD players are defective,
3% of amplifiers are defective,
7% of speakers are defective.

A system consists of a CD player, an amplifier, and two speakers. What is the probability that the system is not defective?

SOLUTION Let C, A, S_1, and S_2 be events corresponding to defective CD player, amplifier, speaker 1, and speaker 2, respectively. Then

$$\Pr(C) = .02 \qquad \Pr(A) = .03 \qquad \Pr(S_1) = \Pr(S_2) = .07.$$

We wish to calculate $\Pr(C' \cap A' \cap S_1' \cap S_2')$. By the complement rule, we have

$$\Pr(C') = .98 \qquad \Pr(A') = .97 \qquad \Pr(S_1') = \Pr(S_2') = .93.$$

Since we have assumed that C, A, S_1, and S_2 are independent, so are C', A', S_1', and S_2'. Therefore,

$$\begin{aligned}\Pr(C' \cap A' \cap S_1' \cap S_2') &= \Pr(C') \cdot \Pr(A') \cdot \Pr(S_1') \cdot \Pr(S_2') \\ &= (.98)(.97)(.93)^2 \approx .822.\end{aligned}$$

Thus, there is an 82.2% chance that the system is not defective.

» Now Try Exercise 53

Check Your Understanding 2.4

Solutions can be found following the section exercises.

1. **Cards** Suppose that there are three cards: one red on both sides; one white on both sides; and one having a side of each color. A card is selected at random and placed on a table. If the up side is red, what is the probability that the down side is red? (Try guessing at the answer before working it by using the formula for conditional probability.)

2. Show that if events E and F are independent of each other, then so are E and F'. [*Hint:* Since $E \cap F$ and $E \cap F'$ are mutually exclusive, we have

$$\Pr(E) = \Pr(E \cap F) + \Pr(E \cap F').]$$

EXERCISES 2.4

1. The Venn diagram in Fig. 3 shows the probabilities for its four basic regions. Find
(a) $\Pr(E)$ **(b)** $\Pr(F)$ **(c)** $\Pr(E|F)$ **(d)** $\Pr(F|E)$.

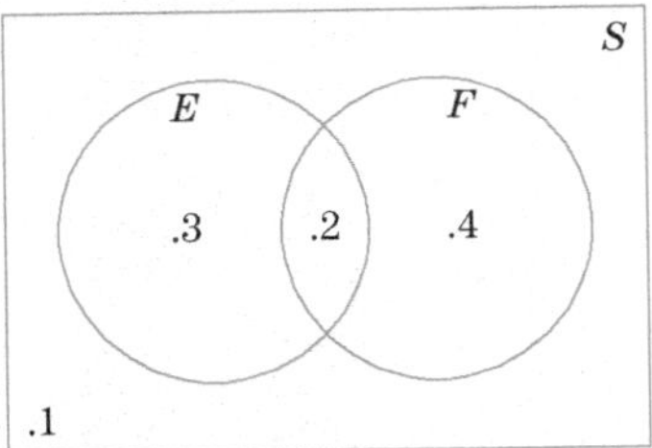

Figure 3

2. The Venn diagram in Fig. 4 shows the probabilities for its four basic regions. Find
(a) $\Pr(E)$ **(b)** $\Pr(F)$ **(c)** $\Pr(E|F)$ **(d)** $\Pr(F|E)$.

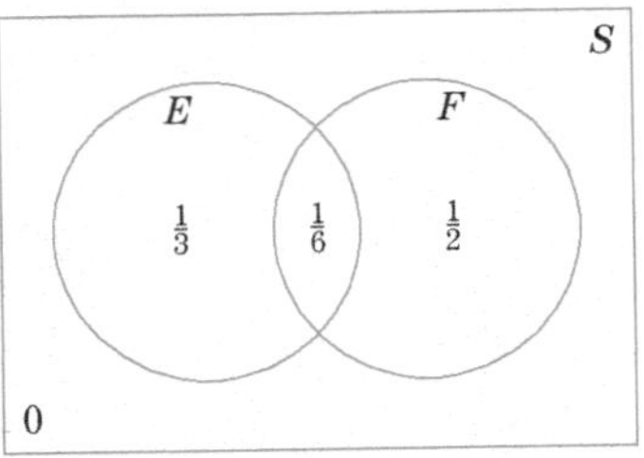

Figure 4

3. Let S be a sample space and E and F be events associated with S. Suppose that $\Pr(E) = .5$, $\Pr(F) = .4$, and $\Pr(E \cap F) = .1$. Calculate
   (a) $\Pr(E \mid F)$ (b) $\Pr(F \mid E)$
   (c) $\Pr(E \mid F')$ (d) $\Pr(E' \mid F')$.
4. Let S be a sample space and E and F be events associated with S. Suppose that $\Pr(E) = .6$, $\Pr(F) = .3$, and $\Pr(E \cap F) = .2$. Calculate
   (a) $\Pr(E \mid F)$ (b) $\Pr(F \mid E)$
   (c) $\Pr(E \mid F')$ (d) $\Pr(E' \mid F')$.
5. Let S be a sample space and E and F be events associated with S. Suppose that $\Pr(E) = \frac{1}{3}$, $\Pr(F) = \frac{5}{12}$, and $\Pr(E \cup F) = \frac{2}{3}$. Calculate
   (a) $\Pr(E \cap F)$ (b) $\Pr(E \mid F)$ (c) $\Pr(F \mid E)$.
6. Let S be a sample space and E and F be events associated with S. Suppose that $\Pr(E) = \frac{1}{2}$, $\Pr(F) = \frac{1}{3}$, and $\Pr(E \cup F) = \frac{7}{12}$. Calculate
   (a) $\Pr(E \cap F)$ (b) $\Pr(E \mid F)$ (c) $\Pr(F \mid E)$.
7. Let S be a sample space and E and F be events associated with S. Suppose that $\Pr(E) = .4$, $\Pr(F \mid E) = .25$, and $\Pr(F) = .3$. Calculate
   (a) $\Pr(E \cap F)$ (b) $\Pr(E \cup F)$
   (c) $\Pr(E \mid F)$ (d) $\Pr(E' \cap F)$.
8. Let S be a sample space and E and F be events associated with S. Suppose that $\Pr(E) = .5$, $\Pr(F \mid E) = .4$, and $\Pr(F) = .3$. Calculate
   (a) $\Pr(E \cap F)$ (b) $\Pr(E \cup F)$
   (c) $\Pr(E \mid F)$ (d) $\Pr(E \cap F')$.
9. **Dice** When a pair of dice is rolled, what is the probability that the sum of the dice is 8, given that the outcome is not 7?
10. **Dice** When a pair of dice is rolled, what is the probability that the sum of the dice is 5, given that exactly one of the dice shows a 3?
11. **Coins** A coin is tossed three times. What is the probability that the outcome is three heads, given that exactly one of the coins shows a head?
12. **Coins** A coin is tossed three times. What is the probability that the outcome contains no heads, given that exactly one of the coins shows a tail?
13. **Bag of Marbles** A bag contains five red marbles and seven white marbles. If a sample of four marbles contains at least one white marble, what is the probability that all the marbles in the sample are white?
14. **Balls in an Urn** Two balls are selected at random from an urn containing two white balls and three red balls. What is the conditional probability that both balls are white, given that at least one of them is white?
15. **Children** Suppose a family has two children and the youngest is a girl. What is the probability that both children are girls?
16. **Children** Suppose a family has two children and at least one is a girl. What is the probability that both children are girls?
17. **Value of College** Twenty-five percent of individuals in a certain city earn more than \$45,000 per year. The percentage of individuals earning more than \$45,000 and having a college degree is 10. Suppose that a person is randomly chosen and turns out to be earning more than \$45,000. What is the probability that they are a college graduate?
18. **Advanced Degrees** Sixty percent of the teachers at a certain high school are female. Forty percent of the teachers are females with a master's degree. What is the probability that a randomly selected teacher has a master's degree, given that the teacher is female?
19. **Advanced Degrees** Table 1 shows the projected number of advanced degrees (in thousands) earned in the United States in 2016 by gender and type of degree. Find the probability that a person selected at random who received an advanced degree
   (a) received a master's degree.
   (b) is male.
   (c) is female, given that the person received a master's degree.
   (d) received a doctor's degree, given that the person is female.

Table 1

	Bachelor's	Master's	Doctor's	Total
Male	779	329	93	1201
Female	1082	522	93	1697
Total	1861	851	186	2898

Source: www.nces.ed.gov

20. **Voting** Table 2 shows the number of registered voting-age U.S. citizens (in millions) by gender and their reported participation in the 2014 congressional election. Find the probability that a voting-age citizen selected at random
   (a) voted.
   (b) is male.
   (c) is female, given that the citizen voted.
   (d) voted, given that the citizen is male.

Table 2

	Voted	Did Not Vote	Total
Male	43.0	45.5	88.5
Female	49.2	47.6	96.8
Total	92.2	93.1	185.3

Source: www.nces.ed.gov

21. **Military Personnel** Table 3 shows the numbers (in thousands) of officers and enlisted persons on active military duty on December 31, 2015. Find the probability that a person in the military selected at random is
   (a) an officer.
   (b) a Marine.
   (c) an officer in the Marines.
   (d) an officer, given that they are a Marine.
   (e) a Marine, given that they are an officer.

Table 3

	Army	Navy	Marine Corps	Air Force	Total
Officer	93.6	54.0	20.7	60.3	228.6
Enlisted	384.3	269.7	162.5	246.7	1063.2
Total	477.9	323.7	183.2	307.0	1291.8

Source: www.dmdc.osd.mil

22. **College Majors** Table 4 shows the probable field of study for 1500 freshman males and 1000 freshman females. Find the probability that a freshman selected at random
(a) intends to major in business.
(b) is female.
(c) is a female intending to major in business.
(d) is male, given that the freshman intends to major in social science.
(e) intends to major in social science, given that the freshman is female.

Table 4

	Business	Social Science	Other	Total
Male	260	122	1118	1500
Female	102	130	768	1000
Total	362	252	1886	2500

Source: www.heri.ucla.edu

23. **Bills in Envelopes** Each of three sealed opaque envelopes contains two bills. One envelope contains two $1 bills, another contains two $5 bills, and the third contains a $1 bill and a $5 bill. An envelope is selected at random, and a bill is taken from the envelope at random. If it is a $5 bill, what is the probability that the other bill in the envelope is also a $5 bill?

24. **Gold and Silver Coins** Consider three boxes. One box contains two gold coins, one box contains two silver coins, and one box contains a gold coin and a silver coin. Suppose that you select a box at random and then select a coin at random from that box. If the coin is gold, what is the probability that the other coin in the box is gold?

25. **Cards** A sequence of two playing cards is drawn at random (without replacement) from a standard deck of 52 cards. What is the probability that both cards are kings?

26. **Cards** A sequence of two playing cards is drawn at random (without replacement) from a standard deck of 52 cards. What is the probability that both cards are diamonds?

27. **Coin Tosses** A coin is tossed five times. What is the probability that heads appears on every toss, given that heads appears on the first four tosses?

28. **Coin Tosses** A coin is tossed twice. What is the probability that heads appeared on the first toss, given that tails appeared on the second toss?

29. **Exit Polling** According to exit polling for the 2016 Missouri Republican primary election, 48% of the primary voters were women. Nine percent of the women polled voted for John Kasich. What is the probability that a randomly selected voter from the poll is a woman who voted for John Kasich?

30. **Population** Twenty percent of the world's population live in China. The residents of Shanghai constitute 1.6% of China's population. If a person is selected at random from the entire world, what is the probability that they live in Shanghai?

31. **Basketball** Suppose that your team is behind by two points and you have the ball on your opponent's court with a few seconds left in the game. You can try a two-point shot (probability of success is .48) or a three-point shot (probability of success is .29). Which choice gives your team the greater probability of winning the game? Assume that your shot will be taken just before the buzzer sounds and that each team has the same chance of winning in overtime.

32. **Password** Fred remembers all but the last character of the password for his e-mail account. However, he knows that it is a digit. He tries to log into his account by guessing the digit. What is the probability that Fred will be successful within two attempts?

33. Let E and F be events with $\mathrm{P}(E) = .4$, $\Pr(F) = .5$, and $\Pr(E \cup F) = .7$. Are E and F independent events?

34. Let E and F be events with $\mathrm{P}(E) = .2$, $\Pr(F) = .5$, and $\Pr(E \cup F) = .6$. Are E and F independent events?

35. Let E and F be independent events with $P(E) = .5$ and $\Pr(F) = .6$. Find $\Pr(E \cup F)$.

36. Let E and F be independent events with $P(E) = .25$ and $\Pr(F) = .4$. Find $\Pr(E \cup F)$.

In Exercises 37–40, assume that E and F are independent events. Use the given information to find $\Pr(F)$.

37. $\Pr(E) = .7$ and $\Pr(F \mid E) = .6$.

38. $\Pr(E) = .4$ and $\Pr(F' \mid E') = .3$.

39. $\Pr(E') = .6$. and $\Pr(E \cap F) = .1$.

40. $\Pr(E) = .8$ and $\Pr(E \cap F) = .4$.

41. Let A, B, and C be independent events with $\Pr(A) = .4$, $\Pr(B) = .1$, and $\Pr(C) = .2$. Calculate $\Pr[(A \cap B \cap C)']$.

42. Let A, B, and C be independent events with $\Pr(A) = .2$, $\Pr(A \cap B) = .12$, and $\Pr(A \cap C) = .06$. Calculate $\Pr(B \cap C)$.

43. **Balls in an Urn** A sample of two balls is drawn from an urn containing two white balls and three red balls. Are the events "the sample contains at least one white ball" and "the sample contains balls of both colors" independent?

44. **Balls in an Urn** An urn contains two white balls and three red balls. A ball is withdrawn at random (without being replaced), and then a second ball is drawn. Are the events "the first ball is red" and "the second ball is white" independent?

45. **Roll a Die** Roll a die, and consider the following two events: $E = \{2, 4, 6\}$, $F = \{3, 6\}$. Are the events E and F independent?

46. **Roll a Die** Roll a die, and consider the following two events: $E = \{2, 4, 6\}$, $F = \{3, 4, 6\}$. Are the events E and F independent?

47. **Rolling Dice** Roll a pair of dice, and consider the sum of the two numbers. Are the events "the sum is an odd number" and "the sum is 4, 5, or 6" independent?

48. **Rolling Dice** Roll a pair of dice, and consider the sum of the two numbers. Are the events "the sum is an odd number" and "the sum is 5, 6, or 7" independent?

49. **Epidemiology** A doctor studies the known cancer patients in a certain town. The probability that a randomly chosen resident has cancer is found to be .001. It is found that 30% of

the town works for Ajax Chemical Company. The probability that an employee of Ajax has cancer is equal to .003. Are the events "has cancer" and "works for Ajax" independent of one another?

50. **Blood Tests** A hospital uses two tests to classify blood. Every blood sample is subjected to both tests. The first test correctly identifies blood type with probability .7, and the second test correctly identifies blood type with probability .8. The probability that at least one of the tests correctly identifies the blood type is .9.
   (a) Find the probability that the second test is correct, given that the first test is correct.
   (b) Are the events "test I correctly identifies the blood type" and "test II correctly identifies the blood type" independent?

51. **Medical Screening** A medical screening program administers three independent tests. Of the persons taking the tests, 80% pass test I, 75% pass test II, and 60% pass test III. A participant is chosen at random.
   (a) What is the probability that they will pass all three tests?
   (b) What is the probability that they will pass at least two of the three tests?

52. **Guessing on an Exam** A "true–false" exam has 10 questions. Assuming that the questions are independent and that a student is guessing, find the probability that they get 100%.

53. **System Reliability** A TV set contains five circuit boards of type A, five of type B, and three of type C. The probability of failing in its first 5000 hours of use is .01 for a type A circuit board, .02 for a type B circuit board, and .025 for a type C circuit board. Assuming that the failures of the various circuit boards are independent of one another, compute the probability that no circuit board fails in the first 5000 hours of use.

54. **System Reliability** In November 2015, Intel announced the release of a business desktop computer with 72 processor cores. Suppose the probability that a given processor core will crash in 120 hours of use is .003, and that the failures of the various processor cores are independent of one another. What is the probability that no processor core will crash during the first 120 hours of use?

55. **Smartphones** Suppose that in Sleepy Valley, 70% of those over 50 years old own smartphones. Find the probability that among four randomly chosen people in that age group, none owns a smartphone.

56. **Fishing** The probability that a fisherman catches a tuna in any one excursion is .15. What is the probability that he catches a tuna on each of three excursions? On at least one of three excursions?

57. **Baseball** A baseball player's batting average changes every time he goes to bat and therefore should not be used as the probability of his getting a hit. However, we can still make a subjective assessment of his ability.
   (a) If a player with .3 probability of getting a hit bats four times in a game and each at-bat is an independent event, what is the probability of the player getting at least one hit in the game?
   (b) What is the probability of the player in part (a) starting off the season with at least one hit in each of the first 10 games?
   (c) If there are 20 players with .3 probability of getting a hit, what is the probability that at least one of them will start the season with a 10-game hitting streak?

58. **Roulette** If you bet on the number 7 in roulette, the probability of winning on a single spin of the wheel is $\frac{1}{38}$. Suppose that you bet on 7 for 38 consecutive spins.
   (a) Which of the following numbers do you think is closest to the probability of winning at least once: 1, .64, or .5?
   (b) Calculate the probability of winning at least once.

59. **Free-Throws** A basketball player makes each free-throw with a probability of .6 and is on the line for a one-and-one free throw. (That is, a second throw is allowed only if the first is successful.) Assume that the two throws are independent. What do you think is the most likely result: scoring 0 points, 1 point, or 2 points? After making a guess, calculate the three probabilities.

60. **Free-Throws** Rework Exercise 59 with a probability of .7.

61. **Free-Throws** Consider Exercise 59, but let the probability of success be p, where $0 < p < 1$. Explain why the probability of scoring 0 points is always greater than the probability of scoring 1 point.

62. **Free-Throws** Consider Exercise 59, but let the probability of success be p, where $0 < p < 1$. For what value of p will the probability of scoring 1 point be the same as the probability of scoring 2 points?

63. **Coin Toss** A biased coin shows heads with probability .6. What is the probability of obtaining the sequence HT in two tosses of the coin? TH? Explain how this coin can be used at the start of a football game to fairly determine which team is to kick off.

64. **Coin Toss** A coin is tossed five times. Is the outcome HTHHT more likely to occur than the outcome HHHHH?

65. Show that, if events E and F are independent of each other, then so are E' and F'.

66. Show that, if E and F are independent events, then $\Pr(E \cup F) = 1 - \Pr(E') \cdot \Pr(F')$.

67. Let $\Pr(F) > 0$.
   (a) Show that $\Pr(E' \mid F) = 1 - \Pr(E \mid F)$.
   (b) Find an example for which $\Pr(E \mid F') \neq 1 - \Pr(E \mid F)$.

68. Use the inclusion–exclusion principle for (nonconditional) probabilities to show that, if E, F, and G are events in S, then $\Pr(E \cup F \mid G) = \Pr(E \mid G) + \Pr(F \mid G) - \Pr(E \cap F \mid G)$.

Solutions to Check Your Understanding 2.4

1. $\frac{2}{3}$. Let F be the event that the up side is red and E be the event that the down side is red. $\Pr(F) = \frac{1}{2}$, since half of the faces are red. $F \cap E$ is the event that both sides of the card are red—that is, that the card that is red on both sides was selected, an event with probability $\frac{1}{3}$. By formula (1),

$$\Pr(E \mid F) = \frac{\Pr(E \cap F)}{\Pr(F)} = \frac{\frac{1}{3}}{\frac{1}{2}} = \frac{2}{3}.$$

(A common error is to conclude that the answer is $\frac{1}{2}$, since the card must be either the red/red card or the red/white card, and each of them is equally likely to have been selected. The correct probability is intuitively evident when you realize that two-thirds of the time, the card will have the same color on the bottom as on the top.)

2. By the hint,

$$\begin{aligned}\Pr(E \cap F') &= \Pr(E) - \Pr(E \cap F)\\ &= \Pr(E) - \Pr(E) \cdot \Pr(F)\\ &\text{(since } E \text{ and } F \text{ are independent)}\\ &= \Pr(E)[1 - \Pr(F)]\\ &= \Pr(E) \cdot \Pr(F')\\ &\text{(by the complement rule).}\end{aligned}$$

Therefore, E and F' are independent events.

2.5 Tree Diagrams

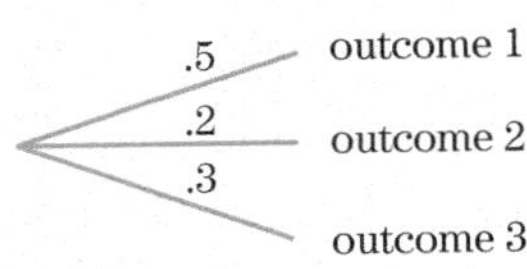

Figure 1

In solving many probability problems, it is helpful to represent the various events and their associated probabilities by a **tree diagram**. To explain this useful tool, suppose that we wish to compute the probability of an event that results from performing a sequence of experiments. The various outcomes of each experiment are represented as branches emanating from a point. For example, Fig. 1 represents an experiment with three outcomes. Notice that each branch has been labeled with the probability of the associated outcome. For example, the probability of outcome 1 is .5.

We represent experiments performed one after another by stringing together diagrams of the sort shown in Fig. 1, proceeding from left to right. For example, the diagram in Fig. 2 indicates that first we perform experiment A, having three outcomes, labeled 1–3. If the outcome is 1 or 2, we perform experiment B. If the outcome is 3, we perform experiment C. The probabilities on the right are conditional probabilities. For example, the top probability is the probability of outcome a (of B), given outcome 1 (of A). The probability of a sequence of outcomes may then be computed by multiplying the probabilities along a path. For example, to calculate the probability of outcome 2 followed by outcome b, we must calculate $\Pr(2 \text{ and } b) = \Pr(2) \cdot \Pr(b \mid 2)$. To carry out this calculation, trace out the sequence of outcomes. Multiplying the probabilities along the path gives $(.2)(.6) = .12$ —the probability of outcome 2 followed by outcome b.

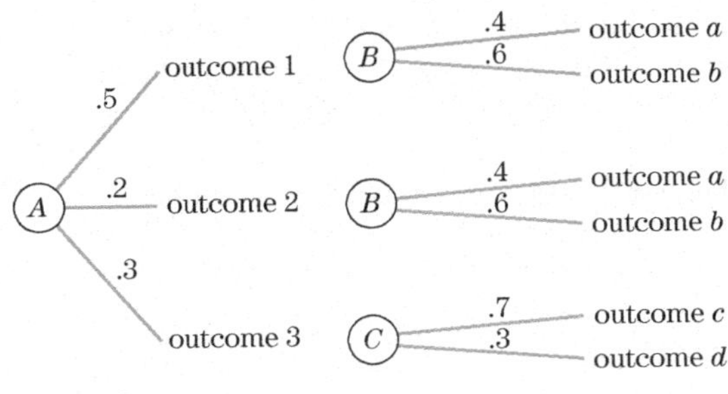

Figure 2

Tree diagrams come in all shapes and sizes. Some trees may not have the symmetry of the tree in Fig. 2. Tree diagrams arise whenever an activity can be thought of as a sequence of simpler activities.

EXAMPLE 1

Quality Control A box contains five good lightbulbs and two defective ones. Bulbs are selected one at a time (without replacement) until a good bulb is found. Find the probability that the number of bulbs selected is **(i)** one, **(ii)** two, **(iii)** three.

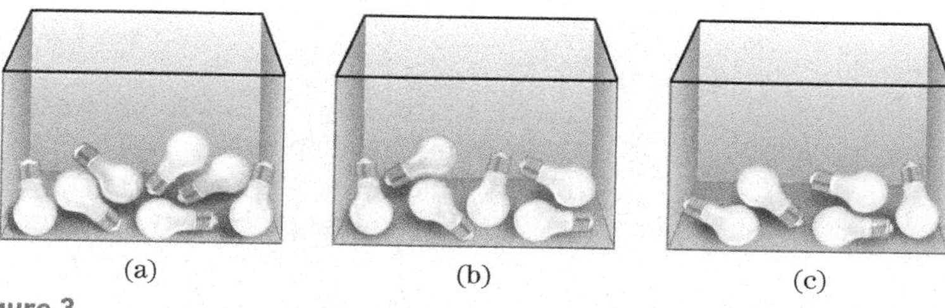

Figure 3

SOLUTION The initial situation in the box is shown in Fig. 3(a). A bulb selected at random will be good (G) with probability $\frac{5}{7}$ and defective (D) with probability $\frac{2}{7}$. If a good bulb is selected, the activity stops. Otherwise, the situation is as shown in Fig. 3(b), and a bulb selected at random has probability $\frac{5}{6}$ of being good and probability $\frac{1}{6}$ of being defective. If the second bulb is good, the activity stops. If the second bulb is defective, then the situation is as shown in Fig. 3(c). At this point, a bulb has probability 1 of being good.

The tree diagram corresponding to the sequence of activities is given in Fig. 4. Each of the three paths leading to a G has a different length. The probability associated with the length of each path has been computed by multiplying the probabilities for its branches. The first path corresponds to the situation in which only one bulb is selected, the second path corresponds to two bulbs, and the third path to three bulbs. Therefore,

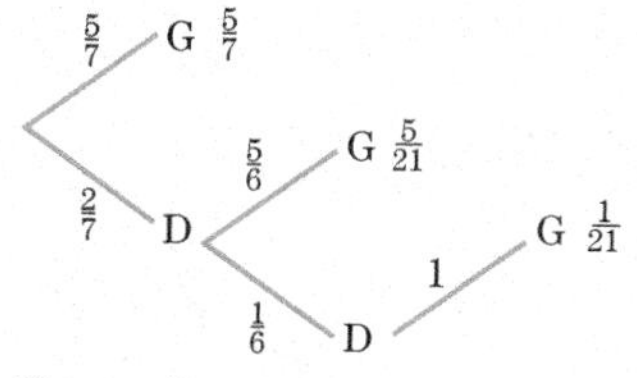

Figure 4

$$\textbf{(i)}\ \Pr(1) = \tfrac{5}{7} \qquad \textbf{(ii)}\ \Pr(2) = \tfrac{5}{21} \qquad \textbf{(iii)}\ \Pr(3) = \tfrac{1}{21}.$$

>> Now Try Exercise 11

EXAMPLE 2

Political Polling A presidential candidate uses a phone bank to determine their support among the voters of Pennsylvania's two big cities: Philadelphia and Pittsburgh. Each phone bank worker has an auto-dialer that selects one of the cities at random and calls a random voter from that city. Suppose that, in Philadelphia, two-fifths of the voters favor the Republican candidate and three-fifths favor the Democratic candidate. Suppose that, in Pittsburgh, two-thirds of the voters favor the Republican candidate and one-third favor the Democratic candidate.

(a) Draw a tree diagram describing the survey.

(b) Find the probability that the voter polled is from Philadelphia and favors the Republican candidate.

(c) Find the probability that the voter favors the Republican candidate.

(d) Find the probability that the voter is from Philadelphia, given that they favor the Republican candidate.

SOLUTION **(a)** The survey proceeds in two steps: First, select a city, and second, select and poll a voter. Figure 5(a) shows the possible outcomes of the first step and the associated probabilities. For each outcome of the first step, there are two possibilities for the

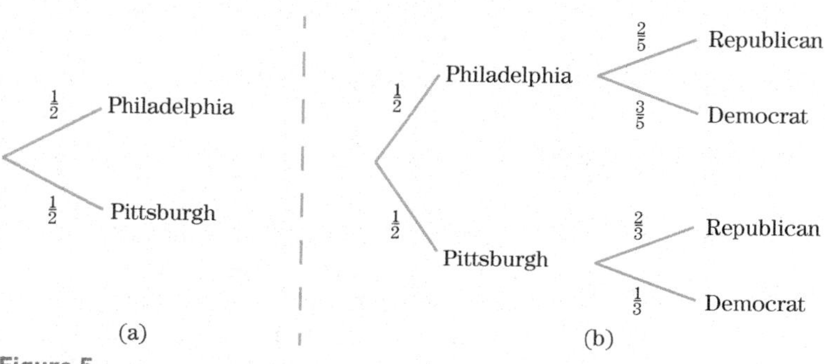

Figure 5

second step: The person selected could favor the Republican or the Democrat. In Fig. 5(b), we have represented these possibilities by drawing branches emanating from each of the outcomes of the first step. The probabilities on the new branches are actually conditional probabilities. For instance,

$$\tfrac{2}{5} = \Pr(\text{Rep} \mid \text{Phila}),$$

the probability that the voter favors the Republican candidate, given that the voter is from Philadelphia.

(b) $\Pr(\text{Phila} \cap \text{Rep}) = \Pr(\text{Phila}) \cdot \Pr(\text{Rep} \mid \text{Phila}) = \tfrac{1}{2} \cdot \tfrac{2}{5} = \tfrac{1}{5}$.

That is, the probability is $\tfrac{1}{5}$ that the combined outcome corresponds to the blue path in Fig. 6(a). We have written the probability $\tfrac{1}{5}$ at the end of the path to which it corresponds.

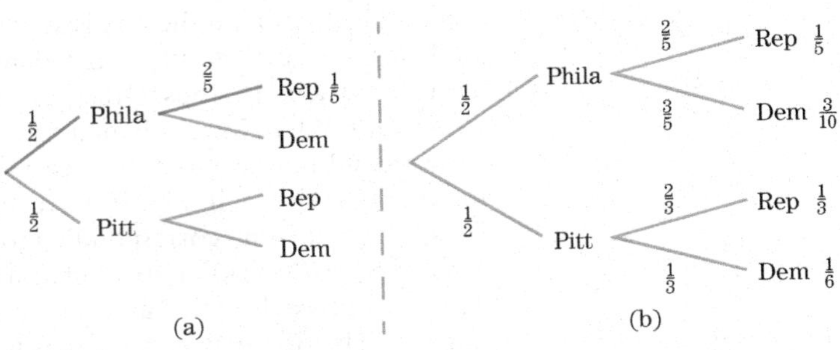

Figure 6

(c) In Fig. 6(b) we have computed the probabilities for each path of the tree as in part (b). Namely, the probability for a given path is the product of the probabilities for each of its segments. We are asked for Pr(Rep). There are two paths through the tree leading to Republican, namely,

$$\text{Philadelphia} \cap \text{Republican} \quad \text{or} \quad \text{Pittsburgh} \cap \text{Republican}.$$

The probabilities of these two paths are $\tfrac{1}{5}$ and $\tfrac{1}{3}$, respectively. So the probability that the Republican is favored equals $\tfrac{1}{5} + \tfrac{1}{3} = \tfrac{8}{15}$.

(d) Here, we are asked for Pr(Phila | Rep). By the definition of conditional probability,

$$\Pr(\text{Phila} \mid \text{Rep}) = \frac{\Pr(\text{Phila} \cap \text{Rep})}{\Pr(\text{Rep})} = \frac{\frac{1}{5}}{\frac{8}{15}} = \frac{3}{8}.$$

» Now Try Exercise 13

Note that, from part (c), we might be led to conclude that the Republican candidate is leading with $\tfrac{8}{15}$ of the vote. However, we must always be careful when interpreting surveys. The results depend heavily on the auto-dialer design. For example, the phone bank drew half of its sample from each of the cities. However, Philadelphia is a much larger city and is leaning toward the Democratic candidate—so much so, in fact, that in terms of popular vote, the Democratic candidate would win, contrary to our expectations drawn from (c).

EXAMPLE 3

Medical Screening Suppose that the reliability of a skin test for active pulmonary tuberculosis (TB) is specified as follows: Of people with TB, 98% have a positive reaction and 2% have a negative reaction; of people free of TB, 99% have a negative reaction and 1% have a positive reaction. From a large population of which 2 per 10,000 persons have TB, a person is selected at random and given a skin test, which turns out to be positive. What is the probability that the person has active pulmonary tuberculosis?

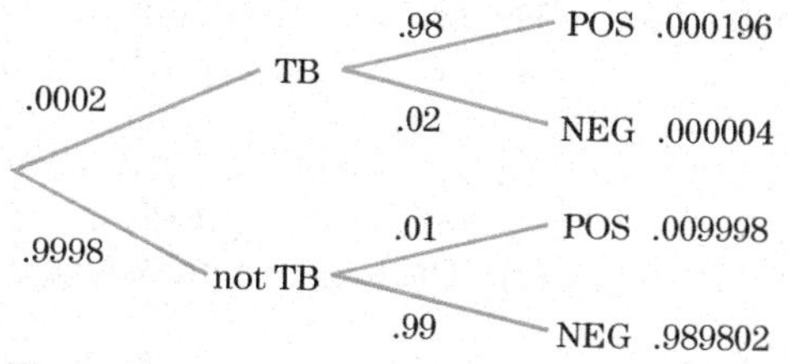

Figure 7

SOLUTION The given data is organized in Fig. 7. The procedure called for is as follows: First select a person at random from the population. There are two possible outcomes: The person has TB,

$$\Pr(\text{TB}) = \frac{2}{10{,}000} = .0002,$$

or the person does not have TB,

$$\Pr(\text{not TB}) = 1 - .0002 = .9998.$$

For each of these two possibilities, the possible test results and conditional probabilities are given. Multiplying the probabilities along each of the paths through the tree gives the probabilities of the different outcomes. The resulting probabilities are written on the right in Fig. 7. The problem asks for the conditional probability that a person has TB, given that the test is positive. By definition,

$$\Pr(\text{TB} \mid \text{POS}) = \frac{\Pr(\text{TB} \cap \text{POS})}{\Pr(\text{POS})} = \frac{.000196}{.000196 + .009998} = \frac{.000196}{.010194} \approx .02.$$

» The numerical data presented in Example 3 is only approximate. Variations in air quality for different localities within the United States cause variations in the incidence of TB and the reliability of skin tests.

Therefore, the probability is .02 that a person with a positive skin test has TB. In other words, although the skin test is quite reliable, only about 2% of those with a positive test turn out to have active TB. This result must be taken into account when large-scale medical diagnostic tests are planned. Because the group of people without TB is so much larger than the group with TB, the small error in the former group is magnified to the point where it dominates the calculation.

» Now Try Exercise 45

DEFINITION The **sensitivity** of a medical test is the probability of a positive test in the presence of the condition. The **specificity** is the probability of a negative test in the absence of the condition. The **positive predictive value** (PPV) is the probability of having the condition, given a positive test result. The **negative predictive value** (NPV) is the probability of not having the condition, given a negative test result.

From Example 3, the sensitivity, specificity, and positive predictive values of the TB skin test are .98, .99, and .02, respectively.

The positive and negative predictive values of a medical test can also be used to determine the probability of a **false positive** result, when a patient does not have the condition but has a positive test result, or a **false negative,** when a patient has the condition but tests negative.

EXAMPLE 4 **Medical Screening** Consider the TB test of Example 3. Find

(a) the probability of a false negative.
(b) the probability of a false positive.
(c) the negative predictive value.

SOLUTION The probabilities can be read directly from Fig. 7.

(a) .02. A false negative occurs when the patient has the condition, but the test result is negative.

(b) .01. A false positive occurs when the patient does not have the condition, but the test result is positive.

(c) The negative predictive value is

$$\Pr(\text{not TB} \mid \text{NEG}) = \frac{\Pr(\text{not TB and NEG})}{\Pr(\text{NEG})} = \frac{.989802}{.000004 + .989802} = \frac{.989802}{.989806} = .999996.$$

>> Now Try Exercise 47

From the preceding definitions and example, we see that

$$\Pr(\text{false positive}) = 1 - \text{sensitivity} \quad \text{and} \quad \Pr(\text{false negative}) = 1 - \text{specificity}.$$ «

Check Your Understanding 2.5

Solutions can be found following the section exercises.

Fifty percent of the students enrolled in a business statistics course had previously taken a finite mathematics course. Thirty percent of these students received an A for the statistics course, whereas 20 percent of the other students received an A for the statistics course.

1. Draw a tree diagram, and label it with the appropriate probabilities.
2. What is the probability that a student selected at random previously took a finite mathematics course and did not receive an A in the statistics course?
3. What is the probability that a student selected at random received an A in the statistics course?
4. What is the conditional probability that a student previously took a finite mathematics course, given that they received an A in the statistics course?

EXERCISES 2.5

In Exercises 1–4, draw trees representing the sequence of experiments.

1. Experiment I is performed. Outcome a occurs with probability .4, and outcome b occurs with probability .6. Then experiment II is performed. Its outcome c occurs with probability .8, and its outcome d occurs with probability .2.
2. Experiment I is performed twice. The three outcomes of experiment I are equally likely.
3. **Personnel Categories** A training program is used by a corporation to direct hirees to appropriate jobs. The program consists of two steps. Step I identifies 30% as management trainees, 60% as nonmanagerial workers, and 10% to be transferred to a different department. In step II, 75% of the management trainees are assigned to managerial positions, 20% are assigned to nonmanagerial positions, and 5% are transferred. In step II, 60% of the nonmanagerial workers are kept in the same category, 10% are assigned to management positions, and 30% are transferred.
4. **Tax Returns** An accounting firm uses a two-step auditing procedure to find problems in erroneous tax returns. Step I identifies the problem in the tax return with probability .7. Step II (which is executed only if step I fails to locate the problem) identifies the problem with probability .6.
5. **Personnel Categories** Refer to Exercise 3. What is the probability that a randomly chosen hiree will be assigned to a management position at the end of the training period?
6. **Tax Returns** Refer to Exercise 4. What is the probability that the procedure will fail to locate the problem?
7. **Personnel Categories** Refer to Exercise 3. What is the probability that a randomly chosen hiree will be transferred by the end of the training period?
8. **Personnel Categories** Refer to Exercise 3. What is the probability that a randomly chosen hiree will be designated a management trainee but *not* be appointed to a management position?
9. **Selecting from Urns** Suppose that there is a white urn containing two white balls and one red ball and there is a red urn containing one white ball and three red balls. An experiment consists of selecting at random a ball from the white urn and then (without replacing the first ball) selecting at random a ball from the urn having the color of the first ball. Find the probability that the second ball is red.
10. **Cards, Coins, Dice** A card is drawn from a 52-card deck. If the card is a face card (jack, queen, or king), we toss a coin. If the card is not a face card, we roll a die. Find the probability that we end the sequence with a "6" on the die. Find the probability that we end the sequence with a "head" on the coin.
11. **Cards** A card is drawn from a 52-card deck. We continue to draw until we have drawn a king or until we have drawn five cards, whichever comes first. Draw a tree diagram that illustrates the experiment. Put the appropriate probabilities on the tree. Find the probability that the drawing ends before the fourth draw.
12. **Balls in an Urn** An urn contains six white balls and two red balls. Balls are selected one at a time (without replacement) until a white ball is selected. Find the probability that the number of balls selected is **(a)** one, **(b)** two, **(c)** three.

13. **Quality Control** Twenty percent of the library books in the fiction section are worn and need replacement. Ten percent of the nonfiction holdings are worn and need replacement. The library's holdings are 40% fiction and 60% nonfiction. Use a tree diagram to find the probability that a book chosen at random from this library is worn and needs replacement.

14. **Water Testing** In a recent environmental study of 440 copper and galvanized steel water lines in Flint, Michigan, 77% of the lines were copper and 23% were galvanized steel. The study demonstrated that water in 6% of the copper lines had elevated levels of lead (above 15 parts per billion), while water in 11% of the galvanized lines had elevated lead levels. Use a tree diagram to find the probability that a water line chosen at random has elevated water lead levels. (*Source:* www.mlive.com)

15. **Color Blindness** Color blindness is a gender-linked inherited condition that is much more common among men than women. Suppose that 8% of all men and .5% of all women are color-blind. A person is chosen at random and found to be color-blind. What is the probability that the person is male? (You may assume that 50% of the population are men and 50% are women.)

16. **Manufacturing** A factory has two machines that produce bolts. Machine I produces 60% of the daily output of bolts, and 3% of its bolts are defective. Machine II produces 40% of the daily output, and 2% of its bolts are defective.
    (a) What is the probability that a bolt selected at random will be defective?
    (b) If a bolt is selected at random and found to be defective, what is the probability that it was produced by machine I?

17. **T-maze** A mouse is put into a T-maze (a maze shaped like a T). In this maze, it has the choice of turning to the left and being rewarded with cheese or going to the right and receiving a mild shock. Before any conditioning takes place (i.e., on trial 1), the mouse is equally likely to go to the left or to the right. After the first trial, its decision is influenced by what happened on the previous trial. If it receives cheese on any trial, the probabilities of going to the left or right become .9 and .1, respectively, on the following trial. If it receives the electric shock on any trial, the probabilities of going to the left or right on the next trial become .7 and .3, respectively. What is the probability that the mouse will turn left on the second trial?

18. **T-maze** Refer to Exercise 17. What is the probability that the mouse will turn left on the third trial?

19. **Heads or Tails** Three ordinary quarters and a fake quarter with two heads are placed in a hat. One quarter is selected at random and tossed twice. If the outcome is "HH," what is the probability that the fake quarter was selected?

20. **Selecting from a Bag** A bag is equally likely to contain either one white ball or one red ball. A white ball is added to the bag, and then a ball is selected at random from the bag. If the selected ball is white, what is the probability that the bag originally contained a white ball? (*Note:* This problem has been attributed to the famous English author Lewis Carroll.)

21. **Tennis** Kim has a strong first serve; whenever it is good (that is, in), she wins the point 75% of the time. Whenever her second serve is good, she wins the point 50% of the time. Sixty percent of her first serves and 75% of her second serves are good.
    (a) What is the probability that Kim wins the point when she serves?
    (b) If Kim wins a service point, what is the probability that her first serve was good?

22. **Tennis** When a tennis player hits his first serve as hard as possible (called a *blast*), he gets the ball *in* (that is, within bounds) 60% of the time. When the blast first serve is *in*, he wins the point 80% of the time. When the first serve is *out*, his gentler second serve wins the point 45% of the time. Draw a tree diagram representing the probabilities of winning the point for the first two serves. Use the tree diagram to determine the probability that the server eventually wins the point when his first serve is a blast.

23. **Accidental Nuclear War** Suppose that, during any year, the probability of an accidental nuclear war is .0001 (provided, of course, that there hasn't been one in a previous year). Draw a tree diagram representing the possibilities for the next three years. What is the probability that there will be an accidental nuclear war during the next three years?

24. **Accidental Nuclear War** Refer to Exercise 23. What is the probability that there will be an accidental nuclear war during the next n years?

25. **Coin Tosses** A coin is to be tossed at most five times. The tosser wins as soon as the number of heads exceeds the number of tails and loses as soon as three tails have been tossed. Use a tree diagram for this game to calculate the probability of winning.

26. **Cards** Suppose that, instead of tossing a coin, the player in Exercise 25 draws up to five cards from a deck consisting only of three red and three black cards. The player wins as soon as the number of red cards exceeds the number of black cards and loses as soon as three black cards have been drawn. Does the tree diagram for the card game have the same shape as the tree diagram for the coin game? Is there any difference in the probability of winning? If so, which game has the greater probability of winning?

27. **Genetics** Traits passed from generation to generation are carried by genes. For a certain type of pea plant, the color of the flower produced by the plant (either red or white) is determined by a pair of genes. Each gene is of one of the types C (dominant gene) or c (recessive gene). Plants for which both genes are of type c (said to have genotype cc) produce white flowers. All other plants—that is, plants of genotypes CC and Cc—produce red flowers. When two plants are crossed, the offspring receives one gene from each parent.

Genotype	Color
cc	white
Cc	red
CC	red

    (a) Suppose that you cross two pea plants of genotype Cc. What is the probability that the offspring produces white flowers? Red flowers?
    (b) Suppose that you have a batch of red-flowering pea plants, of which 60% have genotype Cc and 40% have genotype CC. If you select one of these plants at random and cross it with a white-flowering pea plant, what is the probability that the offspring will produce red flowers?

28. **Genetics** Refer to Exercise 27. Suppose that a batch of 99 pea plants contains 33 plants of each of the three genotypes.
   (a) If you select one of these plants at random and cross it with a white-flowering pea plant, what is the probability that the offspring will produce white flowers?
   (b) If you select one of the 99 pea plants at random and cross it with a white-flowering pea plant, and the offspring produces red flowers, what is the probability that the selected plant had genotype *Cc*?

29. **College Faculty** At a local college, five sections of economics are taught during the day and two sections are taught at night. Sixty percent of the day sections are taught by full-time faculty. Forty percent of the evening sections are taught by full-time faculty. If Jane has a part-time teacher for her economics course, what is the probability that she is taking a night class?

30. **Quality Control** A lightbulb manufacturer knows that .05% of all bulbs manufactured are defective. A testing machine is 99% effective; that is, 99% of good bulbs will be declared fine and 99% of flawed bulbs will be declared defective. If a randomly selected lightbulb is tested and found to be defective, what is the probability that it actually is defective?

31. **Balls in an Urn** Urn I contains 5 red balls and 5 white balls. Urn II contains 12 white balls. A ball is selected at random from urn I and placed in urn II. Then a ball is selected at random from urn II. What is the probability that the second ball is white?

32. **Balls in an Urn** An urn contains five red balls and three green balls. One ball is selected at random and then replaced by a ball of the other color. Then a second ball is selected at random. What is the probability that the second ball is green?

33. **Coin Tosses** Two people toss two coins each. What is the probability that they get the same number of heads?

34. **Selecting from Urns** An urn contains four red marbles and three green marbles. One marble is removed, its color noted, and the marble is not replaced. A second marble is removed and its color noted.
   (a) What is the probability that both marbles are red? Green?
   (b) What is the probability that exactly one marble is red?

35. **Industrial Production** A factory that produces three-dimensional models has two 3D printers. Printer A is very reliable and produces 200 models every week. Printer B is a little less reliable and produces 201 models on 99% of the weeks, but breaks down and produces 0 models the rest of the weeks.
   (a) In a random week, what is the probability that Printer B produces more models that Printer A?
   (b) After 200 weeks have elapsed, what it the probability that Printer B has produced more total models than Printer A? *Hint:* Printer A will have produced 40,000 models. If Printer B breaks down at least once, it will have produced fewer models.

36. **Golf** Bud is a very consistent golfer. On par-three holes, he always scores a 4. Lou, on the other hand, is quite erratic. On par-three holes, Lou scores a 3 seventy percent of the time and scores a 6 thirty percent of the time.
   (a) If Bud and Lou play a single par-three hole together, who is more likely to win—that is, to have the lowest score?
   (b) If Bud and Lou play two consecutive par-three holes, who is more likely to have the lowest total score?

37. **Nontransitive Dice** Consider three dice: one red, one blue, and one green. The sides of the red die contain the numbers 3 3 3 3 3 6, the sides of the blue die contain the numbers 2 2 2 5 5 5, and the sides of the green die contain the numbers 1 4 4 4 4 4.
   (a) Determine the probability that the red die will show a higher number than the blue die when both are tossed.
   (b) Determine the probability that the blue die will show a higher number than the green die when both are tossed.
   (c) Determine the probability that the green die will show a higher number than the red die when both are tossed.
   (d) What is surprising about the results in parts (a)–(c)?

38. **U.S. Car Production** Car production in North America in January 2016 was distributed among car manufacturers as follows.

North American Car Production	Type	Percentage of Type by Brand	
60%	Domestic	Chrysler	33%
		Ford	39%
		General Motors	28%
40%	Foreign	Honda	34%
		Toyota	33%
		Other	33%

Source: www.wardsauto.com

This means that 60% of the cars produced in North America were manufactured by domestic companies; of them, 33% were Chryslers, 39% were Fords, and 28% were General Motors products.
   (a) A January 2016 automobile is chosen at random. What is the probability that it is a General Motors car?
   (b) What is the probability that a randomly selected January 2016 automobile is a Ford or a Toyota?

Exercises 39–44 apply to medical diagnostic tests.

39. (True or False) *Sensitivity* also can be called the *true positive rate.*

40. (True or False) *Specificity* also can be called the *true negative rate.*

41. (True or False) Specificity = 1 − false negative rate.

42. (True or False) Sensitivity = 1 − false positive rate.

43. (True or False) Sensitivity is related to a test's ability to rule *in* a condition.

44. (True or False) Specificity is related to a test's ability to rule *out* a condition.

45. **Medical Screening** Suppose that a test for hepatitis has a sensitivity of 95% and a specificity of 90%. A person is selected at random from a large population, of which .05% of the people have hepatitis, and given the test. What is the positive predictive value of the test?

46. **Medical Screening** The probability .0002 (or .02%) in Fig. 7 on page 78 is called the *prevalence* of the disease. It states that in the population being considered, 2 people per 10,000 have TB. Find the positive predictive value for a population in which 2 people per 100 have TB.

47. **Medical Screening** The results of a trial used to determine the capabilities of a new diagnostic test are shown in Table 1. Use the empirical probabilities obtained from the table to calculate the positive predictive value for the diagnostic test.

Table 1

	Has Condition	Does Not Have Condition	Total
Test positive	9	10	19
Test negative	1	980	981
Total	10	990	1000

48. **Medical Screening** The results of a trial used to determine the capabilities of a new diagnostic test are shown in Table 2. Use the empirical probabilities obtained from the table to calculate the positive predictive value for the diagnostic test.

Table 2

	Has Condition	Does Not Have Condition	Total
Test positive	13	7	20
Test negative	3	77	80
Total	16	84	100

49. **Drug Testing** Suppose that 500 athletes are tested for a drug, 1 in 20 has used the drug, and the test has a 99% specificity and a 100% sensitivity. If an athlete in the group tests positive, what is the probability that they have used the drug?

50. **Polygraph Test** Recent studies have indicated that polygraph tests have a sensitivity of .88 and a specificity of .86. (Currently, polygraph tests are admissible as evidence in court in 19 U.S. states.) Suppose that a robbery is committed and polygraph tests are given to 10 suspects, 1 of whom committed the crime. If the polygraph test for a person indicates that they are guilty, what is the probability they are actually guilty?

Solutions to Check Your Understanding 2.5

1.

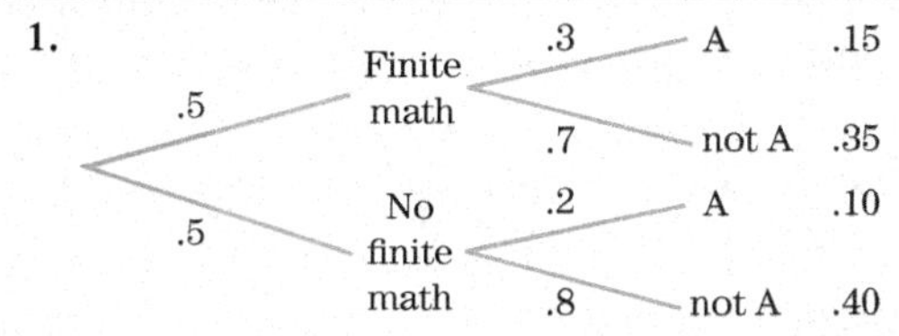

2. The event "finite math and not A" corresponds to the second path of the tree diagram, which has probability .35.

3. This event is satisfied by the first or third paths and therefore has probability .15 + .10 = .25.

4. $\Pr(\text{finite math} \mid \text{A}) = \dfrac{\Pr(\text{finite math and A})}{\Pr(\text{A})} = \dfrac{.15}{.25} = .6.$

2.6 Bayes' Theorem

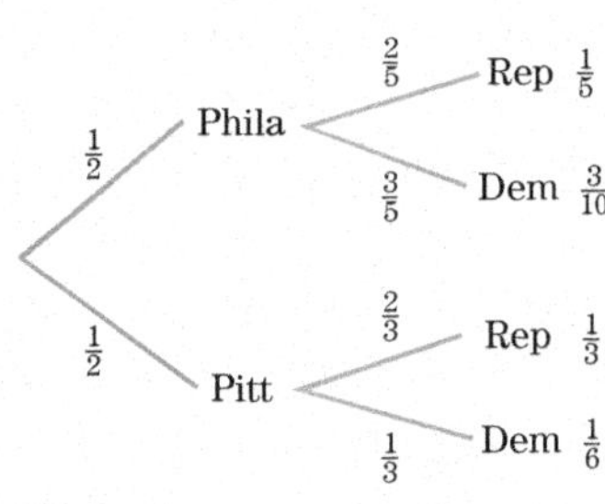

Figure 1

In the preceding section, we explored how to calculate conditional probabilities using tree diagrams. *Bayes' theorem*, named after English statistician Thomas Bayes, gives us a second method for computing these probabilities. The advantages of Bayes' theorem over the use of tree diagrams are that (1) we do not need to draw the tree diagram to calculate the desired probability, and (2) we need not compute extraneous probabilities. These advantages become significant in dealing with experiments having many outcomes.

Let us reconsider the phone survey in Example 2(d) of Section 2.5. (See Fig. 1.) Given that the person chosen at random favors the Republican candidate, what is the probability that the respondent is from Philadelphia? We found this probability by calculating

$$\Pr(\text{Phila} \mid \text{Rep}) = \frac{\Pr(\text{Phila} \cap \text{Rep})}{\Pr(\text{Rep})}.$$

Let us analyze the components of this calculation. First, recall that

$$\Pr(\text{Phila} \cap \text{Rep}) = \Pr(\text{Phila}) \cdot \Pr(\text{Rep} \mid \text{Phila}).$$

Second,

$$\begin{aligned}\Pr(\text{Rep}) &= \Pr(\text{Phila} \cap \text{Rep}) + \Pr(\text{Pitt} \cap \text{Rep})\\ &= \Pr(\text{Phila}) \cdot \Pr(\text{Rep} \mid \text{Phila}) + \Pr(\text{Pitt}) \cdot \Pr(\text{Rep} \mid \text{Pitt}),\end{aligned}$$

by using the tree diagram. Denote the events "Phila," "Pitt," "Rep," and "Dem" by the letters P_1, P_2, R, and D, respectively. Then

$$\begin{aligned}\Pr(\text{Phila}\,|\,\text{Rep}) &= \Pr(P_1\,|\,R)\\ &= \frac{\Pr(P_1 \cap R)}{\Pr(R)}\\ &= \frac{\Pr(P_1)\cdot\Pr(R\,|\,P_1)}{\Pr(P_1)\cdot\Pr(R\,|\,P_1) + \Pr(P_2)\cdot\Pr(R\,|\,P_2)}.\end{aligned}$$

This is a special case of Bayes' theorem.

We summarize a simple form of Bayes' theorem.

> **Bayes' Theorem (n = 2)** If B_1 and B_2 are mutually exclusive events, and $B_1 \cup B_2 = S$ (that is, $B_2 = B_1'$), then
>
> $$\Pr(B_1\,|\,A) = \frac{\Pr(B_1)\cdot\Pr(A\,|\,B_1)}{\Pr(B_1)\cdot\Pr(A\,|\,B_1) + \Pr(B_2)\cdot\Pr(A\,|\,B_2)}$$
>
> for any event A in S with $\Pr(A) \neq 0$.

We have the same type of result for the situation in which we have three mutually exclusive sets B_1, B_2, and B_3, whose union is all of S. We state Bayes' theorem for that case and leave the general case for n mutually exclusive sets for the end of the section.

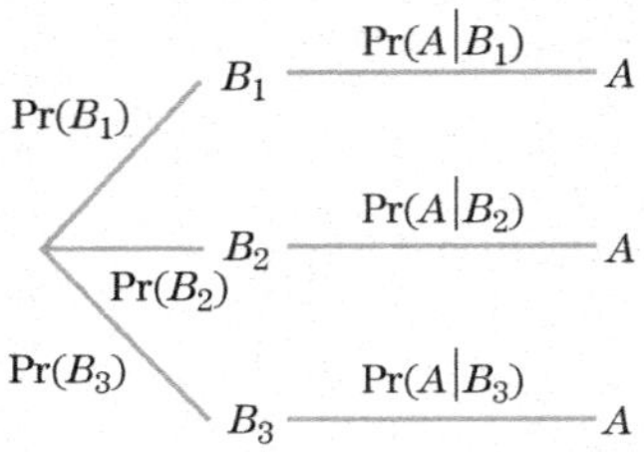

> **Bayes' Theorem (n = 3)** If B_1, B_2, and B_3 are mutually exclusive events, and $B_1 \cup B_2 \cup B_3 = S$, then for any event A in S with $\Pr(A) \neq 0$,
>
> $$\Pr(B_1\,|\,A) = \frac{\Pr(B_1)\cdot\Pr(A\,|\,B_1)}{\Pr(B_1)\cdot\Pr(A\,|\,B_1) + \Pr(B_2)\cdot\Pr(A\,|\,B_2) + \Pr(B_3)\cdot\Pr(A\,|\,B_3)}.$$
>
> See Fig. 2.

Figure 2

EXAMPLE 1 **Medical Screening** Solve the tuberculosis skin test problem of Example 3 of Section 2.5 by using Bayes' theorem.

SOLUTION The observed event A is "positive skin test result." There are two possible events leading to A—namely,

$$B_1 = \text{"person has tuberculosis"}$$
$$B_2 = \text{"person does not have tuberculosis."}$$

We wish to calculate $\Pr(B_1\,|\,A)$. From the data given, we have

$$\begin{aligned}\Pr(B_1) &= \frac{2}{10{,}000} = .0002\\ \Pr(B_2) &= .9998\\ \Pr(A\,|\,B_1) &= \Pr(\text{POS}\,|\,\text{TB}) = .98\\ \Pr(A\,|\,B_2) &= \Pr(\text{POS}\,|\,\text{not TB}) = .01.\end{aligned}$$

Therefore, by Bayes' theorem,

$$\begin{aligned}\Pr(B_1\,|\,A) &= \frac{\Pr(B_1)\Pr(A\,|\,B_1)}{\Pr(B_1)\Pr(A\,|\,B_1) + \Pr(B_2)\Pr(A\,|\,B_2)}\\ &= \frac{(.0002)(.98)}{(.0002)(.98) + (.9998)(.01)} \approx .02,\end{aligned}$$

in agreement with our calculation of Example 3 in Section 2.5. **>> Now Try Exercise 11**

EXAMPLE 2 **Quality Control** A printer has five book-binding machines. For each machine, Table 1 gives the proportion of the total book production that it binds and the probability that the machine produces a defective binding. For instance, machine 1 binds 10% of the books and produces a defective binding with probability .03. Suppose that a book is selected at random and found to have a defective binding. What is the probability that it was bound by machine 1?

Table 1

Machine	Proportion of Books Bound	Probability of Defective Binding
1	.10	.03
2	.10	.02
3	.40	.02
4	.15	.03
5	.25	.01

SOLUTION In this example, we have five mutually exclusive events whose union is the entire sample space (the book was bound by one, and only one, of the five machines). Bayes' theorem can be extended to any finite number of mutually exclusive events.

Let B_i $(i = 1, 2, 3, 4, 5)$ be the event that the book was bound by machine i, and let A be the event that the book has a defective binding. Then, for example,

$$\Pr(B_1) = .10 \quad \text{and} \quad \Pr(A \mid B_1) = .03.$$

The problem asks for the reversed conditional probability, $\Pr(B_1 \mid A)$. By Bayes' theorem,

$$\begin{aligned}
\Pr(B_1 \mid A) &= \frac{\Pr(B_1)\Pr(A \mid B_1)}{\Pr(B_1)\Pr(A \mid B_1) + \Pr(B_2)\Pr(A \mid B_2) + \cdots + \Pr(B_5)\Pr(A \mid B_5)} \\
&= \frac{(.10)(.03)}{(.10)(.03) + (.10)(.02) + (.40)(.02) + (.15)(.03) + (.25)(.01)} \\
&= \frac{.003}{.02} = .15.
\end{aligned}$$

» Now Try Exercise 1

Natural Frequencies

In Example 3 of the previous section, we used a tree diagram to solve the TB medical screening problem. In Example 1 of this section, we solved the same problem with Bayes' theorem. The method of natural frequencies uses simple counts of occurrences of events and provides a third way to obtain the probability. Although the method of natural frequencies is not as rigorous as Bayes' theorem, many people find it easier to use and understand. We will illustrate the method by using it to solve the TB medical screening problem.

EXAMPLE 3 **Medical Screening** Use the method of natural frequencies to solve the TB medical screening problem.

SOLUTION Let us begin with a group of 1 million people. Out of this group, $.0002 \cdot 1{,}000{,}000 = 200$ can be expected to have TB and $.9998 \cdot 1{,}000{,}000 = 999{,}800$ to not have TB. Of the 200 people with TB, $.98 \cdot 200 = 196$ should test positive and $.02 \cdot 200 = 4$ should test negative. Of the 999,800 without TB, $.01 \cdot 999{,}800 = 9998$ should test positive and $.99 \cdot 999{,}800 = 989{,}802$ should test negative. These numbers are displayed in Fig. 3.

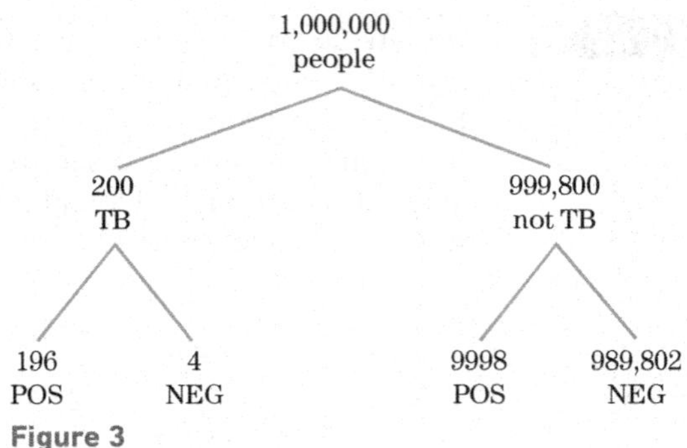

Figure 3

The tree diagram shows that $196 + 9998 = 10{,}194$ of the people tested positive and that 196 of those people actually had TB. Therefore, the probability that a person who tested positive actually has TB is $\frac{196}{10{,}194} = .019227 \approx .02$. » Now Try Exercise 25

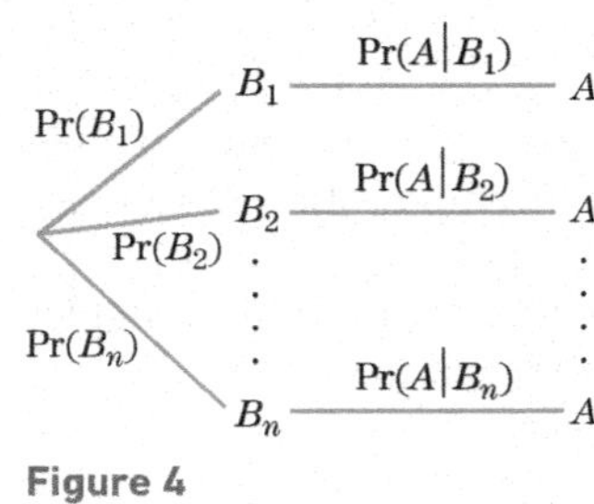

Figure 4

Derivation of Bayes' Theorem To derive Bayes' theorem in general, we consider a two-stage tree. Suppose that, at the first stage, there are the events $B_1, B_2, \ldots, B_n$, which are mutually exclusive and exhaust all possibilities. Let us examine only the paths of the tree leading to event A at the second stage of the experiment. (See Fig. 4.) Suppose we are given that the event A occurs. What is $\Pr(B_1 \mid A)$? First, consider $\Pr(B_1 \cap A)$. This can be seen from Fig. 4 to be $\Pr(B_1) \cdot \Pr(A \mid B_1)$. Next, we calculate $\Pr(A)$. Recall that A occurs at stage 2, preceded at stage 1 by either event $B_1, B_2, \ldots,$ or B_n. Since $B_1, B_2, \ldots, B_n$ are mutually exclusive,

$$\Pr(A) = \Pr(B_1 \cap A) + \Pr(B_2 \cap A) + \cdots + \Pr(B_n \cap A).$$

Each of the elements in the sum can be calculated by the product rule, or directly from Fig. 4:

$$\begin{aligned}
\Pr(B_1 \cap A) &= \Pr(B_1) \cdot \Pr(A \mid B_1) \\
\Pr(B_2 \cap A) &= \Pr(B_2) \cdot \Pr(A \mid B_2) \\
&\vdots \\
\Pr(B_n \cap A) &= \Pr(B_n) \cdot \Pr(A \mid B_n).
\end{aligned}$$

The result is the following:

Bayes' Theorem If $B_1, B_2, \ldots, B_n$ are mutually exclusive events, and if $B_1 \cup B_2 \cup \cdots \cup B_n = S$, then for any event A in S with $\Pr(A) \neq 0$,

$$\Pr(B_1 \mid A) = \frac{\Pr(B_1) \cdot \Pr(A \mid B_1)}{\Pr(B_1) \cdot \Pr(A \mid B_1) + \Pr(B_2) \cdot \Pr(A \mid B_2) + \cdots + \Pr(B_n) \cdot \Pr(A \mid B_n)}$$

$$\Pr(B_2 \mid A) = \frac{\Pr(B_2) \cdot \Pr(A \mid B_2)}{\Pr(B_1) \cdot \Pr(A \mid B_1) + \Pr(B_2) \cdot \Pr(A \mid B_2) + \cdots + \Pr(B_n) \cdot \Pr(A \mid B_n)},$$

and so forth.

Check Your Understanding 2.6

Solutions can be found following the section exercises.

1. **Quality Control** Refer to Example 2. Suppose that a book is selected at random and found to have a defective binding. What is the probability that the book was bound by machine 2?

2. **Political Polling** Use the method of natural frequencies with a group of 30 people to solve the political polling problem presented in Example 2 of the previous section and discussed at the beginning of this section.

EXERCISES 2.6

In Exercises 1–22, use Bayes' theorem to calculate the probabilities.

1. **Accident Rates** An automobile insurance company has determined the accident rate (probability of having at least one accident during a year) for various age groups. (See Table 2.) Suppose that a policyholder calls in to report an accident. What is the probability that they are over 60?

Table 2

Age Group	Proportion of Total Insured	Accident Rate
Under 21	.05	.06
21–30	.10	.04
31–40	.25	.02
41–50	.20	.015
51–60	.30	.025
Over 60	.10	.04

2. **Quality Control** A scoreboard has six different types of LEDs. For each type of LED, Table 3 gives the proportion of the total number of LEDs of that type and the failure rate (probability of failing within one year). If an LED fails, what is the probability that it is type 1?

Table 3

Type	Proportion of Total	Failure Rate
1	.30	.0002
2	.25	.0004
3	.20	.0005
4	.10	.0010
5	.05	.0020
6	.10	.0040

3. **Student Performance** The enrollment in a certain course is 10% first-year students, 30% sophomores, 40% juniors, and 20% seniors. Experience has shown that the likelihood of receiving an A in the course is .2 for first-year students, .4 for sophomores, .3 for juniors, and .1 for seniors. Find the probability that a student who receives an A is a sophomore.

4. **Larceny Rates** A metropolitan police department maintains statistics of larcenies reported in the various precincts of the city. It records the proportion of the city population in each precinct and the precinct larceny rate (= the proportion of the precinct population reporting a larceny within the past year). These statistics are summarized in Table 4. A larceny victim is randomly chosen from the city population. What is the probability that they come from Precinct 3?

Table 4

Precinct	Proportion of Population	Larceny Rate
1	.20	.01
2	.10	.02
3	.40	.05
4	.30	.04

5. **Cars and Income** Table 5 gives the distribution of incomes and shows the proportion of two-car families by income level for a certain suburban county. Suppose that a randomly chosen family has two or more cars. What is the probability that its income is at least $75,000 per year?

Table 5

Annual Family Income	Proportion of People	Proportion Having Two or More Cars
$< \$30,000$	.10	.20
$30,000–$44,999	.20	.50
$45,000–$59,999	.35	.60
$60,000–$74,999	.30	.75
$\geq \$75,000$	.05	.90

6. **Voter Turnout** Table 6 gives the distribution of voter registration and voter turnouts for a certain city. A randomly chosen person is questioned at the polls. What is the probability that the person is an Independent?

Table 6

	Proportion Registered	Proportion of Turnout
Democrat	.50	.4
Republican	.20	.5
Independent	.30	.7

7. **Mathematics Exam** In a calculus course, the instructor gave an algebra exam on the first day of class to help students determine whether or not they had enrolled in the appropriate course. Eighty percent of the students in the class passed the exam. Forty percent of those who passed the exam on the first day of class earned an A in the course, whereas only twenty percent of those who failed the exam earned an A in the course. What is the probability that a student selected at random passed the exam on the first day of class, given that they earned an A in the course?

8. **Demographics** Table 7 shows the percentages of various portions of the U.S. population in 2012, based on age and gender. Suppose that a person is chosen at random from the entire population.

Table 7

	U.S. Population	
Age Group	% of Population	% Male
Under 5 yrs	7	51
5–19 yrs	20	51
20–44 yrs	33	50
45–64 yrs	27	48
Over 64 yrs	13	44

Source: www.census.gov

(a) What is the probability that the person chosen is male?
(b) Given that the person chosen is male, find the probability that he is between 5 and 19 years old.

9. **Bilingual Employees** A multinational company has five divisions: A, B, C, D, and E. The percentage of employees from each division who speak at least two languages fluently is shown in Table 8.

Table 8

Division	Number of Employees	Percentage of Employees Who Are Bilingual
A	20,000	20
B	15,000	15
C	25,000	12
D	30,000	10
E	10,000	10
Total	100,000	

(a) Find the probability that an employee selected at random is bilingual.
(b) Find the probability that a bilingual employee selected at random works for division C.

10. **Customized Dice** A specially made pair of dice has only one- and two-spots on the faces. One of the dice has three faces with a one-spot and three faces with a two-spot. The other die has two faces with a one-spot and four faces with a two-spot. One of the dice is selected at random and then rolled six times. If a two-spot shows up only once, what is the probability that it is the die with four two-spots?

Exercises 11–15 refer to diagnostic tests. A *false negative* in a diagnostic test is a test result that is negative even though the patient has the condition. A *false positive*, on the other hand, is a test result that is positive although the patient does not have the condition.

11. **Mammogram Accuracy** The *New York Times* of January 24, 1997, discussed the recommendation of a special panel concerning mammograms for women in their 40s. About 2% of women aged 40 to 49 years old develop breast cancer in their 40s. But the mammogram used for women in that age group has a high rate of false positives and false negatives; the false positive rate is .30, and the false negative rate is .25. If a woman in her 40s has a positive mammogram, what is the probability that she actually has breast cancer?

12. **Drug Screening** A drug-testing laboratory produces false negative results 2% of the time and false positive results 5% of the time. Suppose that the laboratory has been hired by a company in which 10% of the employees use drugs.
(a) If an employee tests positive for drug use, what is the probability that they actually use drugs?
(b) What is the probability that a nondrug user will test positive for drug use twice in a row?
(c) What is the probability that someone who tests positive twice in a row is not a drug user?

13. **Pregnancy Test** An over-the-counter pregnancy test claims to be 99% accurate. Actually, what the insert says is that if the test is performed properly, it is 99% sure to detect a pregnancy.
(a) What is the probability of a false negative?
(b) Let us assume that the probability is 98% that the test result is negative for a woman who is not pregnant. If the woman estimates that her chances of being pregnant are about 40% and the test result is positive, what is the probability that she is actually pregnant?

14. **Medical Screening** A test for a condition has a high probability of false positives, 20%. Its rate of false negatives is 10%. The condition is estimated to exist in 65% of all patients sent for screening. If the test is positive, what is the chance the patient has the condition? Suppose that the condition is much more rare in the population—say, $\Pr(\text{condition}) = .30$. Given the same testing situation, what is $\Pr(\text{condition} \mid \text{pos})$?

15. **Steroid Testing** It is estimated that 10% of Olympic athletes use steroids. The test currently being used to detect steroids is said to be 93% effective in correctly detecting steroids in users. It yields false positives in only 2% of the tests. A country's best weightlifter tests positive. What is the probability that he actually takes steroids?

16. **Medical Screening** The results of a trial used to determine the capabilities of a new diagnostic test are shown in Table 9. Use the empirical probabilities obtained from the table to calculate the probability that a person who tests positive actually has the condition.

Table 9

	Has Condition	Does Not Have Condition	Total
Test positive	9	11	20
Test negative	1	179	180
Total	10	190	200

17. **Exit Polling** According to exit polling from the 2016 Virginia Democratic primary, 43% of primary voters were men and 57% were women. Fifty-seven percent of Democratic men voting in the primary supported Hillary Clinton, while 70% of Democratic women supported Hillary Clinton. If a Hillary Clinton supporter from the Virginia primary exit poll is chosen at random, what is the probability that they are male?

18. **Exit Polling** According to exit polling from the 2014 U.S. midterm elections, 36% of voters had a household income less than \$50,000, while 64% had a household income of at least \$50,000. Forty-three percent of voters from households making less than \$50,000 voted for the Republican party in the election, while 55% percent of voters from households making at least \$50,000 voted Republican. What is the probability that a randomly selected Republican voter from the exit poll is from a household that makes at least \$50,000?

19. **Cards** Thirteen cards are dealt from a deck of 52 cards.
(a) What is the probability that the ace of spades is one of the 13 cards?
(b) Suppose that one of the 13 cards is chosen at random and found *not* to be the ace of spades. What is the probability that *none* of the 13 cards is the ace of spades?
(c) Suppose that the experiment in part (b) is repeated a total of 10 times (replacing the card looked at each time) and the ace of spades is not seen. What is the probability that the ace of spades actually *is* one of the 13 cards?

20. **College Majors** There are three sections of English 101. In Section I, there are 25 students, of whom 5 are mathematics majors. In Section II, there are 20 students, of whom 6 are mathematics majors. In Section III, there are 35 students, of whom 5 are mathematics majors. A student in English 101 is chosen at random. Find the probability that the student is from Section I, given that they are a mathematics major.

21. **Scholarship Winners** Twenty percent of the contestants in a scholarship competition come from Pylesville High School, 40% come from Millerville High School, and the remainder come from Lakeside High School. Two percent of the Pylesville students are among the scholarship winners; 3% of the Millerville contestants and 5% of the Lakeside contestants win.
    (a) If a winner is chosen at random, what is the probability that they are from Lakeside?
    (b) What percentage of the winners are from Pylesville?

22. **Manufacturing Reliability** Ten percent of the pens made by Apex are defective. Only 5% of the pens made by its competitor, B-ink, are defective. Since Apex pens are cheaper than B-ink pens, an office orders 70% of its stock from Apex and 30% from B-ink. A pen is chosen at random and found to be defective. What is the probability that it was produced by Apex?

In Exercises 23–30, use the method of natural frequencies to calculate the probabilities.

23. Rework Exercise 3, starting with a class size of 50 people.
24. Rework Exercise 6, starting with 100 people.
25. Rework Exercise 7, starting with a class size of 25 people.
26. Rework Exercise 12(a), starting with 1000 people.
27. Rework Exercise 15, starting with 1000 people.
28. Rework Exercise 14, starting with 100 people.
29. Rework Exercise 21(a), starting with 250 students.
30. Rework Exercise 22, starting with 200 pens.

Solutions to Check Your Understanding 2.6

1. The problem asks for $\Pr(B_2 \mid A)$. Bayes' theorem gives this probability as a quotient with numerator $\Pr(B_2)\Pr(A \mid B_2)$ and the same denominator as in the solution to Example 2. Therefore,

$$\Pr(B_2 \mid A) = \frac{\Pr(B_2)\Pr(A \mid B_2)}{.02} = \frac{(.10)(.02)}{.02} = .10.$$

2. Beginning with a group of 30 people, $\frac{1}{2} \cdot 30 = 15$ people will be from Philadelphia, and $\frac{1}{2} \cdot 30 = 15$ people will be from Pittsburgh. Of the 15 people from Philadelphia, $\frac{2}{5} \cdot 15 = 6$ will favor the Republican candidate. The remainder, $15 - 6 = 9$, will favor the Democratic candidate. (*Note:* We could have obtained the number 9 by performing the multiplication $\frac{3}{5} \cdot 15$, but subtracting is easier than multiplying.) Of the 15 people from Pittsburgh, $\frac{2}{3} \cdot 15 = 10$ will favor the Republican candidate, and the rest, $15 - 10 = 5$, will favor the Democratic candidate. These numbers are displayed in Fig. 5.

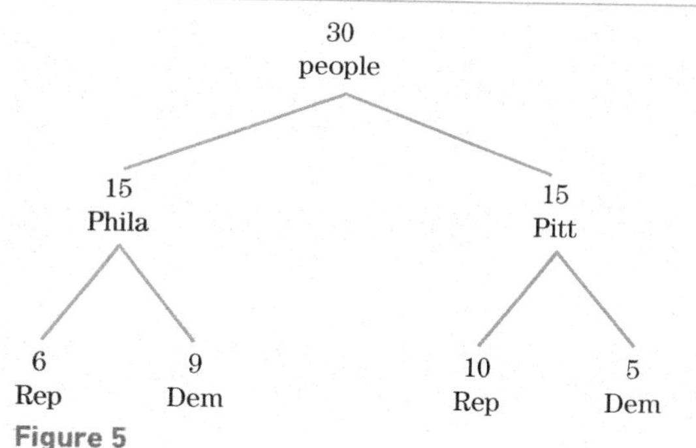

Figure 5

The tree diagram shows that $6 + 10 = 16$ people favor the Republican candidate and that 6 of those people are from Philadelphia. Therefore, the probability that a person who favors the Republican candidate is from Philadelphia is $\frac{6}{16} = \frac{3}{8}$.

3 Random Variables

3.1 Random Variable, Probability Distribution, and Expected Value

- Random Variable and Probability Distribution
- Expected Value of a Random Variable
- Decision Making and Expected Value

Random Variable and Probability Distribution

When performing a random experiment, a sample space S is selected in such a way that all probability problems of interest relative to the experiment can be solved. In many situations we may not be interested in each simple event in the sample space S but in some numerical value associated with the event. For example, if 3 coins are tossed, we may be interested in the number of heads that turn up rather than in the particular pattern that turns up. Or, in selecting a random sample of students, we may be interested in the proportion that are women rather than which particular students are women. In the same way, a "craps" player is usually interested in the sum of the dots on the showing faces of the dice rather than the pattern of dots on each face.

In each of these examples, there is a rule that assigns to each simple event in S a single real number. Mathematically speaking, we are dealing with a function. Historically, this particular type of function has been called a "random variable."

DEFINITION Random Variable

A **random variable** is a function that assigns a numerical value to each simple event in a sample space S.

The term *random variable* is an unfortunate choice, since it is neither random nor a variable—it is a function with a numerical value, and it is defined on a sample space. But the terminology has stuck and is now standard. Capital letters, such as X, are used to represent random variables.

Let us return to the experiment of tossing 3 coins. A sample space S of equally likely simple events is indicated in Table 1. Suppose that we are interested in the number of heads $(0, 1, 2, \text{or } 3)$ appearing on each toss of the 3 coins and the probability of each of these events. We introduce a random variable X (a function) that indicates the number of heads for each simple event in S (see the second column in Table 1). For example, $X(e_1) = 0$, $X(e_2) = 1$, and so on. The random variable X assigns a numerical value to each simple event in the sample space S.

Table 1 Number of Heads in the Toss of 3 Coins

Sample Space S	Number of Heads $X(e_i)$
e_1: TTT	0
e_2: TTH	1
e_3: THT	1
e_4: HTT	1
e_5: THH	2
e_6: HTH	2
e_7: HHT	2
e_8: HHH	3

We are interested in the probability of the occurrence of each image or range value of X, that is, in the probability of the occurrence of 0 heads, 1 head, 2 heads, or 3 heads in the single toss of 3 coins. We indicate this probability by

$$p(x) \qquad \text{where} \quad x \in \{0, 1, 2, 3\}$$

The function p is called the **probability distribution* of the random variable X.**

What is $p(2)$, the probability of getting exactly 2 heads on the single toss of 3 coins? "Exactly 2 heads occur" is the event

$$E = \{\text{THH, HTH, HHT}\}$$

*The probability distribution p of the random variable X is defined by $p(x) = P(\{e_i \in S | X(e_i) = x\})$, which, because of its cumbersome nature, is usually simplified to $p(x) = P(X = x)$ or simply $p(x)$. We will use the simplified notation.

Thus,

$$p(2) = \frac{n(E)}{n(S)} = \frac{3}{8}$$

Table 2 Probability Distribution

Number of Heads x	0	1	2	3
Probability $p(x)$	$\frac{1}{8}$	$\frac{3}{8}$	$\frac{3}{8}$	$\frac{1}{8}$

Proceeding similarly for $p(0)$, $p(1)$, and $p(3)$, we obtain the probability distribution of the random variable X presented in Table 2. Probability distributions are also represented graphically, as shown in Figure 1. The graph of a probability distribution is often called a **histogram**.

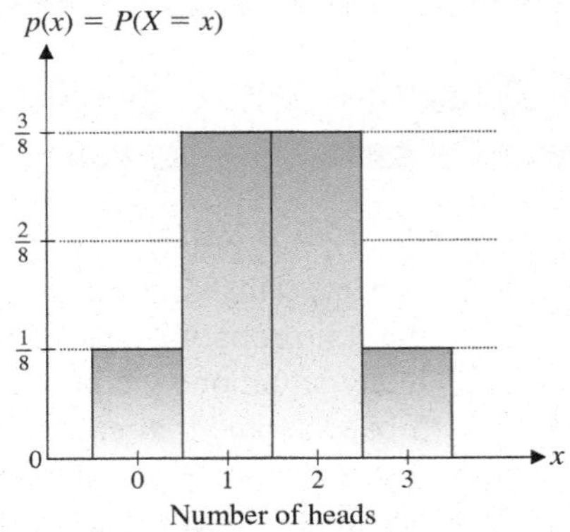

Figure 1 Histogram for a probability distribution

Note from Table 2 or Figure 1 that

1. $0 \le p(x) \le 1, \quad x \in \{0, 1, 2, 3\}$
2. $p(0) + p(1) + p(2) + p(3) = \frac{1}{8} + \frac{3}{8} + \frac{3}{8} + \frac{1}{8} = 1$

These are general properties that any probability distribution of a random variable X associated with a finite sample space must have.

THEOREM 1 Probability Distribution of a Random Variable *X*

The **probability distribution of a random variable** X, denoted by $P(X = x) = p(x)$, satisfies

1. $0 \le p(x) \le 1, \quad x \in \{x_1, x_2, \ldots, x_n\}$
2. $p(x_1) + p(x_2) + \cdots + p(x_n) = 1$

where $\{x_1, x_2, \ldots, x_n\}$ are the (range) values of X (see Fig. 2).

Figure 2 illustrates the process of forming a probability distribution of a random variable.

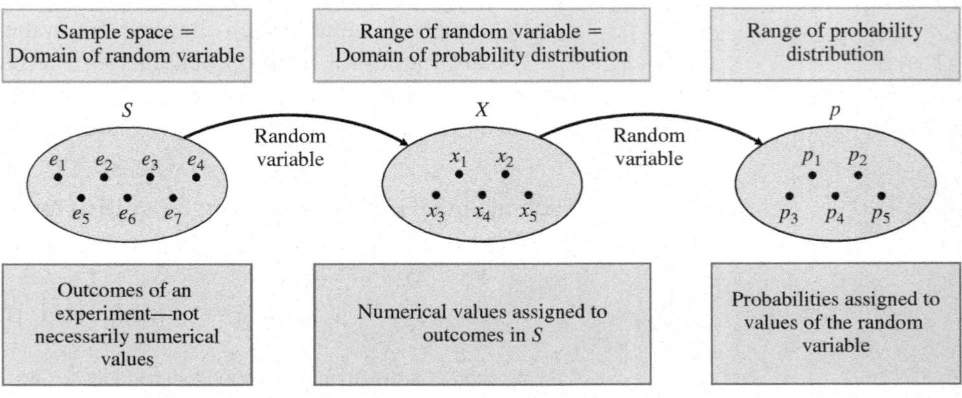

Figure 2 Probability distribution of a random variable for a finite sample space

Expected Value of a Random Variable

Suppose that the experiment of tossing 3 coins was repeated many times. What would be the average number of heads per toss (the total number of heads in all tosses divided by the total number of tosses)? Consulting the probability distribution in Table 2 or Figure 1, we would expect to toss 0 heads $\frac{1}{8}$ of the time, 1 head $\frac{3}{8}$ of the time, 2 heads $\frac{3}{8}$ of the time, and 3 heads $\frac{1}{8}$ of the time. In the long run, we would expect the average number of heads per toss of the 3 coins, or the *expected value* $E(X)$, to be given by

$$E(X) = 0\left(\frac{1}{8}\right) + 1\left(\frac{3}{8}\right) + 2\left(\frac{3}{8}\right) + 3\left(\frac{1}{8}\right) = \frac{12}{8} = 1.5$$

It is important to note that the expected value is not a value that will necessarily occur in a single experiment (1.5 heads cannot occur in the toss of 3 coins), but it is an average of what occurs over a large number of experiments. Sometimes we will toss more than 1.5 heads and sometimes less, but if the experiment is repeated many times, the average number of heads per experiment should be close to 1.5.

We now make the preceding discussion more precise through the following definition of expected value:

DEFINITION Expected Value of a Random Variable *X*

Given the probability distribution for the random variable X,

x_i	x_1	x_2	...	x_n
p_i	p_1	p_2	...	p_n

where $p_i = p(x_i)$, we define the **expected value of X**, denoted **$E(X)$**, by the formula

$$E(X) = x_1p_1 + x_2p_2 + \cdots + x_np_n$$

We again emphasize that the expected value is not the outcome of a single experiment, but a long-run average of outcomes of repeated experiments. The expected value is the weighted average of the possible outcomes, each weighted by its probability.

PROCEDURE Steps for Computing the Expected Value of a Random Variable *X*

Step 1 Form the probability distribution of the random variable X.

Step 2 Multiply each image value of X, x_i, by its corresponding probability of occurrence p_i; then add the results.

EXAMPLE 1 **Expected Value** What is the expected value (long-run average) of the number of dots facing up for the roll of a single die?

SOLUTION If we choose

$$S = \{1, 2, 3, 4, 5, 6\}$$

as our sample space, then each simple event is a numerical outcome reflecting our interest, and each is equally likely. The random variable X in this case is just the identity function (each number is associated with itself). The probability distribution for X is

x_i	1	2	3	4	5	6
p_i	$\frac{1}{6}$	$\frac{1}{6}$	$\frac{1}{6}$	$\frac{1}{6}$	$\frac{1}{6}$	$\frac{1}{6}$

Therefore,

$$E(X) = 1\left(\frac{1}{6}\right) + 2\left(\frac{1}{6}\right) + 3\left(\frac{1}{6}\right) + 4\left(\frac{1}{6}\right) + 5\left(\frac{1}{6}\right) + 6\left(\frac{1}{6}\right)$$

$$= \frac{21}{6} = 3.5$$

Matched Problem 1 Suppose that the die in Example 1 is not fair and we obtain (empirically) the following probability distribution for X:

x_i	1	2	3	4	5	6
p_i	.14	.13	.18	.20	.11	.24

[Note: Sum = 1.]

What is the expected value of X?

Explore and Discuss 1

From Example 1 we can conclude that the probability is 0 that a single roll of a fair die will equal the expected value for a roll of a die (the number of dots facing up is never 3.5). What is the probability that the sum for a single roll of a pair of dice will equal the expected value of the sum for a roll of a pair of dice?

EXAMPLE 2 **Expected Value** A carton of 20 laptop batteries contains 2 defective ones. A random sample of 3 is selected from the 20 and tested. Let X be the random variable associated with the number of defective batteries found in a sample.

(A) Find the probability distribution of X.

(B) Find the expected number of defective batteries in a sample.

SOLUTION

(A) The number of ways of selecting a sample of 3 from 20 (order is not important) is ${}_{20}C_3$. This is the number of simple events in the experiment, each as likely as the other. A sample will have either 0, 1, or 2 defective batteries. These are the values of the random variable in which we are interested. The probability distribution is computed as follows:

$$p(0) = \frac{{}_{18}C_3}{{}_{20}C_3} \approx .716 \quad p(1) = \frac{{}_{2}C_1 \cdot {}_{18}C_2}{{}_{20}C_3} \approx .268 \quad p(2) = \frac{{}_{2}C_2 \cdot {}_{18}C_1}{{}_{20}C_3} \approx .016$$

We summarize these results in a table:

x_i	0	1	2
p_i	.716	.268	.016

[Note: .716 + .268 + .016 = 1.]

(B) The expected number of defective batteries in a sample is readily computed as follows:

$$E(X) = (0)(.716) + (1)(.268) + (2)(.016) = .3$$

The expected value is not one of the random variable values; rather, it is a number that the average number of defective batteries in a sample would approach as the experiment is repeated without end.

Matched Problem 2 Repeat Example 2 using a random sample of 4.

EXAMPLE 3 **Expected Value of a Game** A spinner device is numbered from 0 to 5, and each of the 6 numbers is as likely to come up as any other. A player who bets $1 on any given number wins $4 (and gets the $1 bet back) if the pointer comes to rest on the chosen number; otherwise, the $1 bet is lost. What is the expected value of the game (long-run average gain or loss per game)?

SOLUTION The sample space of equally likely events is

$$S = \{0, 1, 2, 3, 4, 5\}$$

Each sample point occurs with a probability of $\frac{1}{6}$. The random variable X assigns \$4 to the winning number and $-\$1$ to each of the remaining numbers. So the probability of winning \$4 is $\frac{1}{6}$ and of losing \$1 is $\frac{5}{6}$. We form the probability distribution for X, called a **payoff table**, and compute the expected value of the game:

Payoff Table (Probability Distribution for X)

x_i	\$4	$-\$1$
p_i	$\frac{1}{6}$	$\frac{5}{6}$

$$E(X) = \$4\left(\frac{1}{6}\right) + (-\$1)\left(\frac{5}{6}\right) = -\$\frac{1}{6} \approx -\$0.1667 \approx -17¢ \text{ per game}$$

In the long run, the player will lose an average of about 17¢ per game.

Matched Problem 3 Repeat Example 3 with the player winning $5 instead of $4 if the chosen number turns up. The loss is still $1 if any other number turns up. Is this a fair game?

The game in Example 3 is *not* fair: The player tends to lose money in the long run. A game is **fair** if the expected value $E(X)$ is equal to 0; that is, the player neither wins nor loses money in the long run. The fair games discussed in Section 8.2 are fair according to this definition, because their payoff tables have the following form:

Payoff Table

x_i	$\$b$	$-\$a$
p_i	$\frac{a}{a+b}$	$\frac{b}{a+b}$

$$\text{So } E(X) = b\left(\frac{a}{a+b}\right) + (-a)\frac{b}{a+b} = 0$$

EXAMPLE 4 **Expected Value and Insurance** Suppose you are interested in insuring a car video system for $2,000 against theft. An insurance company charges a premium of $225 for coverage for 1 year, claiming an empirically determined probability of .1 that the system will be stolen sometime during the year. What is your expected return from the insurance company if you take out this insurance?

SOLUTION This is actually a game of chance in which your stake is $225. You have a .1 chance of receiving $1,775 from the insurance company ($2,000 minus your stake of $225) and a .9 chance of losing your stake of $225. What is the expected value of this "game"? We form a payoff table (the probability distribution for X) and compute the expected value:

Payoff Table

x_i	\$1,775	−\$225
p_i	.1	.9

$$E(X) = (\$1{,}775)(.1) + (-\$225)(.9) = -\$25$$

This means that if you insure with this company over many years and circumstances remain the same, you would have an average net loss to the insurance company of \$25 per year.

Matched Problem 4 Find the expected value in Example 4 from the insurance company's point of view.

CONCEPTUAL INSIGHT

Suppose that in a class of 10 students, the scores on the first exam are 85, 73, 82, 65, 95, 85, 73, 75, 85, and 75. To compute the class average (mean), we add the scores and divide by the number of scores:

$$\frac{85 + 73 + 82 + 65 + 95 + 85 + 73 + 75 + 85 + 75}{10} = \frac{793}{10} = 79.3$$

Because 1 student scored 95, 3 scored 85, 1 scored 82, 2 scored 75, 2 scored 73, and 1 scored 65, the probability distribution of an exam score, for a student chosen at random from the class, is as follows:

x_i	65	73	75	82	85	95
p_i	.1	.2	.2	.1	.3	.1

The expected value of the probability distribution is

$$65\left(\frac{1}{10}\right) + 73\left(\frac{2}{10}\right) + 75\left(\frac{2}{10}\right) + 82\left(\frac{1}{10}\right) + 85\left(\frac{3}{10}\right) + 95\left(\frac{1}{10}\right) = \frac{793}{10} = 79.3$$

By comparing the two computations, we see that the mean of a data set is just the expected value of the corresponding probability distribution.

Decision Making and Expected Value

We conclude this section with an example in decision making.

EXAMPLE 5 **Decision Analysis** An outdoor concert featuring a popular musical group is scheduled for a Sunday afternoon in a large open stadium. The promoter, worrying about being rained out, contacts a long-range weather forecaster who predicts the chance of rain on that Sunday to be .24. If it does not rain, the promoter is certain to net \$100,000; if it does rain, the promoter estimates that the net will be only \$10,000. An insurance company agrees to insure the concert for \$100,000 against rain at a premium of \$20,000. Should the promoter buy the insurance?

SOLUTION The promoter has a choice between two courses of action; A_1: Insure and A_2: Do not insure. As an aid in making a decision, the expected value is computed for each course of action. Probability distributions are indicated in the payoff table (read vertically):

Payoff Table

	A_1: Insure	A_2: Do Not Insure
p_i	x_i	x_i
.24 (rain)	\$90,000	\$10,000
.76 (no rain)	\$80,000	\$100,000

Note that the \$90,000 entry comes from the insurance company's payoff (\$100,000) minus the premium (\$20,000) plus gate receipts (\$10,000). The reasons for the other entries should be obvious. The expected value for each course of action is computed as follows:

A_1: Insure	A_2: Do Not Insure
$E(X) = x_1 p_1 + x_2 p_2$ $= (\$90{,}000)(.24) + (\$80{,}000)(.76)$ $= \$82{,}400$	$E(X) = (\$10{,}000)(.24) + (\$100{,}000)(.76)$ $= \$78{,}400$

It appears that the promoter's best course of action is to buy the insurance at \$20,000. The promoter is using a long-run average to make a decision about a single event—a common practice in making decisions in areas of uncertainty.

Matched Problem 5 In Example 5, what is the insurance company's expected value if it writes the policy?

Exercises 3.1

Skills Warm-up Exercises

In Problems 1–8, if necessary, review Section B.1.

1. Find the average (mean) of the exam scores 73, 89, 45, 82, and 66.

2. Find the average (mean) of the exam scores 78, 64, 97, 60, 86, and 83.

3. Find the average (mean) of the exam scores in Problem 1, if 4 points are added to each score.

4. Find the average (mean) of the exam scores in Problem 2, if 3 points are subtracted from each score.

5. Find the average (mean) of the exam scores in Problem 1, if each score is multiplied by 2.

6. Find the average (mean) of the exam scores in Problem 2, if each score is divided by 2.

A

7. If the probability distribution for the random variable X is given in the table, what is the expected value of X?

x_i	−3	0	4
p_i	.3	.5	.2

8. If the probability distribution for the random variable X is given in the table, what is the expected value of X?

x_i	−2	−1	0	1	2
p_i	.1	.2	.4	.2	.1

9. You draw and keep a single bill from a hat that contains a \$5, \$20, \$50, and \$100 bill. What is the expected value of the game to you?

10. You draw and keep a single bill from a hat that contains a \$1, \$10, \$20, \$50, and \$100 bill. What is the expected value of the game to you?

11. You draw and keep a single coin from a bowl that contains 15 pennies, 10 dimes, and 25 quarters. What is the expected value of the game to you?

12. You draw and keep a single coin from a bowl that contains 120 nickels and 80 quarters. What is the expected value of the game to you?

13. You draw a single card from a standard 52-card deck. If it is red, you win \$50. Otherwise you get nothing. What is the expected value of the game to you?

14. You draw a single card from a standard 52-card deck. If it is an ace, you win \$104. Otherwise you get nothing. What is the expected value of the game to you?

15. In tossing 2 fair coins, what is the expected number of heads?

16. In a family with 2 children, excluding multiple births and assuming that a boy is as likely as a girl at each birth, what is the expected number of boys?

17. A fair coin is flipped. If a head turns up, you win \$1. If a tail turns up, you lose \$1. What is the expected value of the game? Is the game fair?

18. Repeat Problem 17, assuming an unfair coin with the probability of a head being .55 and a tail being .45.

B

19. After paying \$4 to play, a single fair die is rolled, and you are paid back the number of dollars corresponding to the number of dots facing up. For example, if a 5 turns up, $5 is returned to you for a net gain, or payoff, of $1; if a 1 turns up, $1 is returned for a net gain of −$3; and so on. What is the expected value of the game? Is the game fair?

20. Repeat Problem 19 with the same game costing $3.50 for each play.

21. Two coins are flipped. You win $2 if either 2 heads or 2 tails turn up; you lose $3 if a head and a tail turn up. What is the expected value of the game?

22. In Problem 21, for the game to be fair, how much *should* you lose if a head and a tail turn up?

23. A friend offers the following game: She wins $1 from you if, on four rolls of a single die, a 6 turns up at least once; otherwise, you win $1 from her. What is the expected value of the game to you? To her?

24. On three rolls of a single die, you will lose $10 if a 5 turns up at least once, and you will win $7 otherwise. What is the expected value of the game?

25. A single die is rolled once. You win $5 if a 1 or 2 turns up and $10 if a 3, 4, or 5 turns up. How much should you lose if a 6 turns up in order for the game to be fair? Describe the steps you took to arrive at your answer.

26. A single die is rolled once. You lose $12 if a number divisible by 3 turns up. How much should you win if a number not divisible by 3 turns up in order for the game to be fair? Describe the process and reasoning used to arrive at your answer.

27. A pair of dice is rolled once. Suppose you lose $10 if a 7 turns up and win $11 if an 11 or 12 turns up. How much should you win or lose if any other number turns up in order for the game to be fair?

28. A coin is tossed three times. Suppose you lose $3 if 3 heads appear, lose $2 if 2 heads appear, and win $3 if 0 heads appear. How much should you win or lose if 1 head appears in order for the game to be fair?

29. A card is drawn from a standard 52-card deck. If the card is a king, you win $10; otherwise, you lose $1. What is the expected value of the game?

30. A card is drawn from a standard 52-card deck. If the card is a diamond, you win $10; otherwise, you lose $4. What is the expected value of the game?

31. A 5-card hand is dealt from a standard 52-card deck. If the hand contains at least one king, you win $10; otherwise, you lose $1. What is the expected value of the game?

32. A 5-card hand is dealt from a standard 52-card deck. If the hand contains at least one diamond, you win $10; otherwise, you lose $4. What is the expected value of the game?

33. The payoff table for two courses of action, A_1 or A_2, is given below. Which of the two actions will produce the largest expected value? What is it?

	A_1	A_2
p_i	x_i	x_i
.1	−$200	−$100
.2	$100	$200
.4	$400	$300
.3	$100	$200

34. The payoff table for three possible courses of action is given below. Which of the three actions will produce the largest expected value? What is it?

	A_1	A_2	A_3
P_i	x_i	x_i	x_i
.2	$ 500	$ 400	$ 300
.4	$1,200	$1,100	$1,000
.3	$1,200	$1,800	$1,700
.1	$1,200	$1,800	$2,400

35. Roulette wheels in Nevada generally have 38 equally spaced slots numbered 00, 0, 1, 2, . . . , 36. A player who bets $1 on any given number wins $35 (and gets the bet back) if the ball comes to rest on the chosen number; otherwise, the $1 bet is lost. What is the expected value of this game?

36. In roulette (see Problem 35), the numbers from 1 to 36 are evenly divided between red and black. A player who bets $1 on black wins $1 (and gets the $1 bet back) if the ball comes to rest on black; otherwise (if the ball lands on red, 0, or 00), the $1 bet is lost. What is the expected value of the game?

37. A game has an expected value to you of $100. It costs $100 to play, but if you win, you receive $100,000 (including your $100 bet) for a net gain of $99,900. What is the probability of winning? Would you play this game? Discuss the factors that would influence your decision.

38. A game has an expected value to you of −$0.50. It costs $2 to play, but if you win, you receive $20 (including your $2 bet) for a net gain of $18. What is the probability of winning? Would you play this game? Discuss the factors that would influence your decision.

C **39.** Five thousand tickets are sold at $1 each for a charity raffle. Tickets will be drawn at random and monetary prizes awarded as follows: 1 prize of $500; 3 prizes of $100, 5 prizes of $20, and 20 prizes of $5. What is the expected value of this raffle if you buy 1 ticket?

40. Ten thousand raffle tickets are sold at $2 each for a local library benefit. Prizes are awarded as follows: 2 prizes of $1,000, 4 prizes of $500, and 10 prizes of $100. What is the expected value of this raffle if you purchase 1 ticket?

41. A box of 10 flashbulbs contains 3 defective bulbs. A random sample of 2 is selected and tested. Let X be the random variable associated with the number of defective bulbs in the sample.

(A) Find the probability distribution of X.

(B) Find the expected number of defective bulbs in a sample.

42. A box of 8 flashbulbs contains 3 defective bulbs. A random sample of 2 is selected and tested. Let X be the random variable associated with the number of defective bulbs in a sample.

(A) Find the probability distribution of X.

(B) Find the expected number of defective bulbs in a sample.

43. One thousand raffle tickets are sold at $1 each. Three tickets will be drawn at random (without replacement), and each will pay $200. Suppose you buy 5 tickets.

(A) Create a payoff table for 0, 1, 2, and 3 winning tickets among the 5 tickets you purchased. (If you do not have any winning tickets, you lose $5; if you have 1 winning ticket, you net $195 since your initial $5 will not be returned to you; and so on.)

(B) What is the expected value of the raffle to you?

44. Repeat Problem 43 with the purchase of 10 tickets.

45. A 3-card hand is dealt from a standard deck. You win $20 for each diamond in the hand. If the game is fair, how much should you lose if the hand contains no diamonds?

46. A 3-card hand is dealt from a standard deck. You win $100 for each king in the hand. If the game is fair, how much should you lose if the hand contains no kings?

Applications

47. Insurance. The annual premium for a $5,000 insurance policy against the theft of a painting is $150. If the (empirical) probability that the painting will be stolen during the year is .01, what is your expected return from the insurance company if you take out this insurance?

48. Insurance. An insurance company charges an annual premium of $75 for a $200,000 insurance policy against a house burning down. If the (empirical) probability that a house burns down in a given year is .0003, what is the expected value of the policy to the insurance company?

49. Decision analysis. After careful testing and analysis, an oil company is considering drilling in two different sites. It is estimated that site A will net $30 million if successful (probability .2) and lose $3 million if not (probability .8); site B will net $70 million if successful (probability .1) and lose $4 million if not (probability .9). Which site should the company choose according to the expected return for each site?

50. Decision analysis. Repeat Problem 51, assuming that additional analysis caused the estimated probability of success in field B to be changed from .1 to .11.

51. Genetics. Suppose that at each birth, having a girl is not as likely as having a boy. The probability assignments for the number of boys in a 3-child family are approximated empirically from past records and are given in the table. What is the expected number of boys in a 3-child family?

Number of Boys

x_i	p_i
0	.12
1	.36
2	.38
3	.14

52. Genetics. A pink-flowering plant is of genotype RW. If two such plants are crossed, we obtain a red plant (RR) with probability .25, a pink plant (RW or WR) with probability .50, and a white plant (WW) with probability .25, as shown in the table. What is the expected number of W genes present in a crossing of this type?

Number of W Genes Present

x_i	p_i
0	.25
1	.50
2	.25

53. Lottery. A $2 Powerball lottery ticket has a 1/27.05 probability of winning $4, a 1/317.39 probability of winning $7, a 1/10,376.47 probability of winning $100, a 1/913,129.18 probability of winning $50,000, a 1/11,688,053.52 probability of winning $1,000,000, and a 1/292,201,338 probability of winning the Grand Prize. If the Grand Prize is currently $100,000,000, what is the expected value of a single Powerball lottery ticket?

54. Lottery. Repeat Problem 55, assuming that the Grand Prize is currently $400,000,000.

Answers to Matched Problems

1. $E(X) = 3.73$

2. (A)

x_i	0	1	2
p_i	.632	.337	.032*

*Note: Due to roundoff error, sum = 1.001 ≈ 1.

(B) .4

3. $E(X) = \$0$; the game is fair

4. $E(X) = (-\$1{,}775)(.1) + (\$225)(.9) = \$25$ (This amount, of course, is necessary to cover expenses and profit.)

5. $E(X) = (-\$80{,}000)(.24) + (\$20{,}000)(.76) = -\$4{,}000$ (This means that the insurance company had other information regarding the weather than the promoter had; otherwise, the company would not have written this policy.)

3.2 Binomial Random Variables

In this section, we fix our attention on the simplest experiments: those with just two outcomes. These experiments, called **binomial trials** (or *Bernoulli trials*), occur in many applications. Here are some examples of binomial trials:

1. Toss a coin, and observe the outcome, heads or tails.
2. Administer a drug to a sick individual, and classify the reaction as "effective" or "ineffective."
3. Manufacture a lightbulb, and classify it as "nondefective" or "defective."

The outcomes of a binomial trial are usually called *success* and *failure*. Of course, the labels *success* and *failure* need have no connection with the usual meanings of these words. For example, in experiment 2, we might label the outcome "ineffective" as *success* and "effective" as *failure*.

We will always denote the probability of success by p and probability of failure by q. Since a binomial trial has only two outcomes, we have $p + q = 1$, or

$$q = 1 - p.$$

Consider a particular binomial trial and the following experiment: Repeat the binomial trial n times, and observe the number of successes that occur. Assume that the n successive trials are independent of one another. The fundamental problem of the theory of binomial trials is to calculate the probabilities of the outcomes of this experiment.

Let X be a random variable associated with the experiment. X is the number of successes in the n trials of the experiment. For example, if we toss a coin 20 times and assume that heads is a success, then $X = 3$ means that the experiment resulted in 3 heads and 17 tails. In an experiment of n trials, the number of successes can be any one of the numbers $0, 1, 2, \ldots, n$. These are the possible values of X.

We write $\Pr(X = k)$ to denote the probability that $X = k$, namely, the probability that k of the n trials result in success. We can find the probability distribution of X by using the methods of counting and basic probability principles developed earlier in the book.

Binomial Probability Formula If X is the number of successes in n independent trials, where in each trial the probability of a success is p, then (with $q = 1 - p$)

$$\Pr(X = k) = \binom{n}{k} p^k q^{n-k} \tag{1}$$

for $k = 0, 1, 2, \ldots, n$. *Note:* $\binom{n}{k}$ is the same as $C(n, k)$; that is,

$$\binom{n}{k} = \frac{n!}{k!(n-k)!}$$

Note that the right side of (1) is one of the terms in the binomial expansion of $(p + q)^n$. We say that X is a **binomial random variable** with parameters n and p. The derivation of (1) is given at the end of this section.

If X is a binomial random variable with parameters n and p, $E(X) = np$.

Let X be the number of heads in five tosses of a fair coin. Then X is a binomial random variable with parameters $p = \frac{1}{2}$ and $n = 5$. The probability distribution is

k	$\Pr(X = k)$
0	$\frac{1}{32}$
1	$\frac{5}{32}$
2	$\frac{10}{32}$
3	$\frac{10}{32}$
4	$\frac{5}{32}$
5	$\frac{1}{32}$

By (1),

$$\Pr(X = k) = \binom{5}{k}\left(\frac{1}{2}\right)^k\left(\frac{1}{2}\right)^{5-k}.$$

Substitution of the values of k (0, 1, 2, 3, 4, 5) gives the probabilities in the table.

The expected number of heads that will occur when the coin is tossed 5 times, i.e. $E(X)$, can quickly be calculated to be $np = 5(\frac{1}{2}) = 2.5$. You can verify this using the general formula for $E(X)$ given in Section 3.1, but using $E(X) = np$ will save a lot of calculation when X is known to be a binomial random variable.

EXAMPLE 1

Quality Control A plumbing-supplies manufacturer produces faucet washers, which are packaged in boxes of 300. Quality control studies have shown that 2% of the washers are defective. What is the probability that a box of washers contains exactly 9 defective washers?

SOLUTION Deciding whether a single washer is or is not defective is a binomial trial. Since we wish to consider the number of defective washers in a box, let "success" be the outcome "defective." Then

$$p = .02 \qquad q = 1 - .02 = .98 \qquad n = 300.$$

The probability that 9 out of 300 washers are defective equals

$$\Pr(X = 9) = \binom{300}{9}(.02)^9(.98)^{291} \approx .07.$$

>> Now Try Exercise 17

EXAMPLE 2

Veterinary Medicine The recovery rate for a certain cattle disease is 25%. If 40 cattle are afflicted with the disease, what is the probability that exactly 10 will recover?

SOLUTION In this example, the binomial trial consists of observing a single cow, with recovery as "success." Then

$$p = .25 \qquad q = 1 - .25 = .75 \qquad n = 40.$$

The probability of 10 successes is

$$\Pr(X = 10) = \binom{40}{10}(.25)^{10}(.75)^{30} \approx .14.$$

>> Now Try Exercise 5

NOTE Binomial probabilities can be difficult to calculate by hand. Instead, it is recommended that you use technology to compute probabilities like those in Examples 1 and 2. The Incorporating Technology discussion at the end of this section presents ways to do this. «

EXAMPLE 3 **Baseball** Each time that a baseball player is at bat, the probability that he gets a hit is .300. He comes up to bat four times in a game. Assume that his times at bat are independent trials. Find the probability that he gets

(a) exactly two hits. **(b)** at least two hits.

SOLUTION Each at-bat is considered an independent binomial trial. A "success" is a hit. So $p = .300$, $q = 1 - p = .700$, and $n = 4$. Therefore, X is the number of hits in four at-bats or the number of successes in four trials.

(a) We need to determine $\Pr(X = 2)$.

$$\Pr(X=2) = \binom{4}{2}(.300)^2(.700)^{4-2} \quad \text{Formula (1) with } k = 2$$
$$= 6(.09)(.49) = .2646.$$

(b) "At least two hits" means $X \geq 2$.

$$\Pr(X \geq 2) = \Pr(X=2) + \Pr(X=3) + \Pr(X=4)$$
$$= \binom{4}{2}(.300)^2(.700)^2 + \binom{4}{3}(.300)^3(.700)^1 + \binom{4}{4}(.300)^4(.700)^0$$
$$= 6(.09)(.49) + 4(.027)(.700) + 1(.0081)(1)$$
$$= .2646 + .0756 + .0081 = .3483.$$

So the batter can be expected to get at least two hits out of four at-bats in about 35% of the games.

***»* Now Try Exercise 51**

EXAMPLE 4 **College Acceptance** According to the study *The American Freshman: National Norms 2015* conducted by the Higher Education Research Institute, 76% of college freshmen in 2015 had been accepted by their first-choice college. If five freshmen are selected at random, what is the probability that at least two were accepted by their first-choice college? Assume that each selection is an independent binomial trial.

SOLUTION Let "success" be "accepted by first-choice college." Then

$$p = .76, q = 1 - p = .24, \text{ and } n = 5.$$

Let X be the number of freshmen (out of the five selected) who were accepted by their first-choice college. Then

$$\Pr(X \geq 2) = 1 - \Pr(X=0) - \Pr(X=1) \quad \text{Complement Rule}$$
$$= 1 - \binom{5}{0}(.76)^0(.24)^5 - \binom{5}{1}(.76)^1(.24)^4 \quad \text{Formula (1) with } k = 0, 1$$
$$\approx 1 - .0008 - .0126 = .9866.$$

Thus, in a group of five randomly selected freshmen, there is a 98.66% chance that at least two of them were accepted by their first-choice college.

***»* Now Try Exercise 25**

EXAMPLE 5 **Coin Tosses** How many times must a person toss a coin so that the probability of obtaining at least one head is greater than 90%?

SOLUTION Note that the event "at least one toss is a head" is the complement of the event "every toss is a tail." Therefore, let "success" be the event "a tail is tossed." Then

$$p = \frac{1}{2} \quad q = \frac{1}{2}$$

Table 1 Probability of At Least One Head in n Tosses

n	$1 - (\frac{1}{2})^n$
1	$\frac{1}{2} = .5$
2	$\frac{3}{4} = .75$
3	$\frac{7}{8} = .875$
4	$\frac{15}{16} = .9375$

and, if the coin is tossed n times, the probability of obtaining at least one head is

$$1 - \Pr(X = n) = 1 - \binom{n}{n}\left(\frac{1}{2}\right)^n\left(\frac{1}{2}\right)^0$$
$$= 1 - \left(\frac{1}{2}\right)^n.$$

We wish to determine the smallest value of n for which $1 - (\frac{1}{2})^n$ is at least .90. Table 1 shows the probabilities for increasing values of n.

A minimum of $n = 4$ tosses is needed to guarantee a probability greater than 90%.

» Now Try Exercise 57

Summing Binomial Probabilities

Suppose that, in Example 2, we wanted to find the probability that 16 or more cattle recover. Using formula (1) to compute the probabilities that 16, 17, . . . , 40 cattle recover, the desired probability is

$$\Pr(X = 16) + \Pr(X = 17) + \cdots + \Pr(X = 40)$$
$$= \binom{40}{16}(.25)^{16}(.75)^{24} + \binom{40}{17}(.25)^{17}(.75)^{23} + \cdots + \binom{40}{40}(.25)^{40}(.75)^0. \quad (2)$$

This sum is difficult to compute. We will discuss the traditional method of approximating this sum by using a table of areas. The table which is obtained with technology, is incomplete, and the approximation obtained is not very accurate. The more current method is to go directly to technology to obtain the sum. For instance, using the table gives an approximation of 2.74%, but the more accurate value obtained with a graphing calculator, Excel, or Wolfram|Alpha is 2.62%. See the Incorporating Technology discussion at the end of this section for details.

Verification of Formula (1) Each outcome of n independent trials that contains k successes can be thought of as a sequence of k S's and $(n - k)$ F's. Each such sequence is obtained by selecting k of the n positions for the S's. (The remaining positions will be filled with F's.) Therefore, the number of such sequences is $C(n, k)$—that is, $\binom{n}{k}$. The probability of such a sequence is the product of k p's and $(n - k)$ q's—that is, $p^k q^{n-k}$. Hence, $\Pr(X = k) = \binom{n}{k}p^k q^{n-k}$. «

Check Your Understanding 3.2

Solutions can be found following the section exercises.

1. A number is selected at random from the numbers 0 through 9999. What is the probability that the number is a multiple of 5?
2. If the experiment in Problem 1 is repeated 20 times, with replacement, what is the probability of getting four numbers that are multiples of 5?
3. Consider equation (2) following Example 5. How would you calculate the sum with a graphing calculator, Excel, and Wolfram|Alpha?

EXERCISES 3.2

In Exercises 1–4, calculate $\binom{n}{k}p^k q^{n-k}$ for the given values of n, k, and p.

1. $n = 5, k = 3, p = .3$
2. $n = 6, k = 1, p = .4$
3. $n = 4, k = 3, p = \frac{1}{3}$
4. $n = 3, k = 2, p = \frac{1}{6}$

Coin Tosses A coin is tossed 10 times. In Exercises 5–10, find the probabilities that the number of heads is as stated.

5. Exactly three
6. None
7. Seven or eight
8. Two or three
9. At least one
10. At most seven

Rolling a Die A single die is rolled four times. In Exercises 11–16, find the probabilities that the number of 6s that appear is as stated.

11. Four
12. Exactly two
13. Two or three
14. One or two
15. At most two
16. At least two

Twenty-Somethings Fourteen percent of U.S. residents are in their twenties. Consider a group of eight U.S. residents selected at random. In Exercises 17–22, find the probabilities that the number of people in the group who are in their twenties is as stated.

17. Exactly two
18. None
19. Four or five
20. One or two
21. At least three
22. At most six

Career Training According to the study *The American Freshman: National Norms 2015*, 76.1% of college freshmen said that "to get training for a specific career" was a very important reason for their going to college. Consider a group of seven freshman selected at random. In Exercises 23–26, find the probabilities that the number of people in the group who felt that the reason was very important is as stated.

23. All seven
24. Exactly three of the seven
25. At least six of the seven
26. No more than two of the seven
27. **Children** A family chosen at random has four children.
    (a) What is the probability that there are two boys and two girls?
    (b) What is the probability that there are three children of one gender and one of the other?
    (c) What is the probability that all four children are of the same gender?
28. **New Employees** A manager at a call center notices that 60% of new hires quit within their first year. In a group of 20 new hires, find the probability that
    (a) exactly 15 quit within their first year.
    (b) fewer than 19 quit within their first year.

College Acceptances Exercises 29 and 30 refer to Fig. 4, the histogram for Example 4.

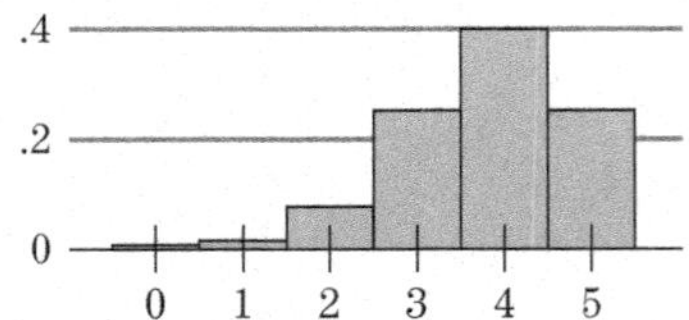

Figure 4 College Acceptances

29. The histogram in Fig. 4 shows that the values of $\Pr(X = 3)$ and $\Pr(X = 5)$ are nearly the same. Calculate the two probabilities to determine which is larger.
30. Use the histogram in Fig. 4 to determine the larger of $\binom{5}{3}(.76)^3(.24)^2$ and $\binom{5}{4}(.76)^4(.24)^1$. Interpret your result in words.

Veterinary Medicine Exercises 31 and 32 refer to Fig. 5, the histogram for Example 2.

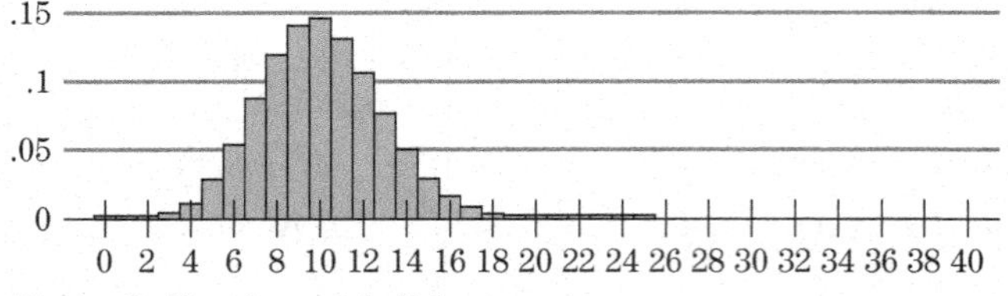

Figure 5 Veterinary Medicine

31. Use the histogram in Fig. 5 to determine the larger of $\binom{40}{10}(.25)^{10}(.75)^{30}$ and $\binom{40}{9}(.25)^9(.75)^{31}$. Interpret your result in words.
32. The histogram in Fig. 5 shows that the values of $\Pr(X = 5)$ and $\Pr(X = 15)$ are nearly the same. Calculate the two probabilities to determine which is larger.
33. **Car Sales** An automotive salesman determines that he has a 30% chance of selling a car to a random customer at his dealership. A group of five customers is chosen at random. State in words the event with probability
$$\binom{5}{3}(.3)^3(.7)^2 + \binom{5}{4}(.3)^4(.7)^1.$$
34. **Insurance Claims** A homeowner's insurance company determines that 10% of their customers will file a claim within the next year. A group of 10 policyholders is chosen at random. State in words the event with probability
$$1 - \binom{10}{0}(.1)^0(.9)^{10}.$$
35. **Coin Tosses** When a coin is tossed 100 times, the probability of obtaining at most 49 heads is .4602 and the probability of obtaining 50 heads is .0796.
    (a) What is the probability of obtaining more than 50 heads?
    (b) What is the probability of obtaining at most 50 heads?
36. **Rolling Dice** When a die is rolled 10 times, the probability of obtaining at most four 6s is .9845 and the probability of obtaining five 6s is .01302.
    (a) What is the probability of obtaining more than five 6s?
    (b) What is the probability of obtaining at most five 6s?
37. Figure 6 shows the histogram for a binomial random variable with $n = 10, p = .5$. Explain why the figure is symmetric with respect to the rectangle at $k = 5$.

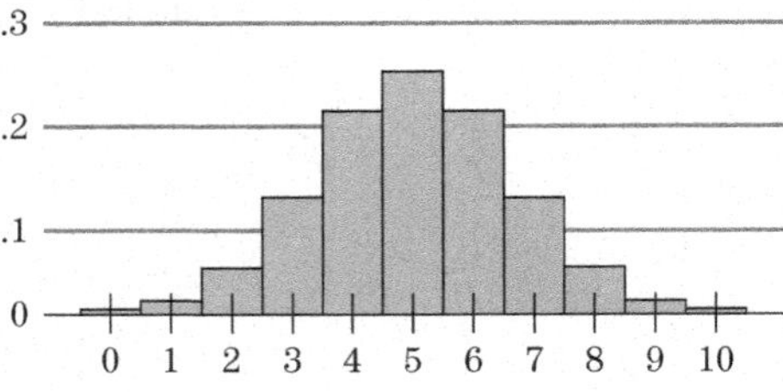

Figure 6

38. Figure 7 shows the histogram for a binomial random variable with $n = 11$, $p = .5$. Without doing any computations, determine $\Pr(X \leq 5)$.

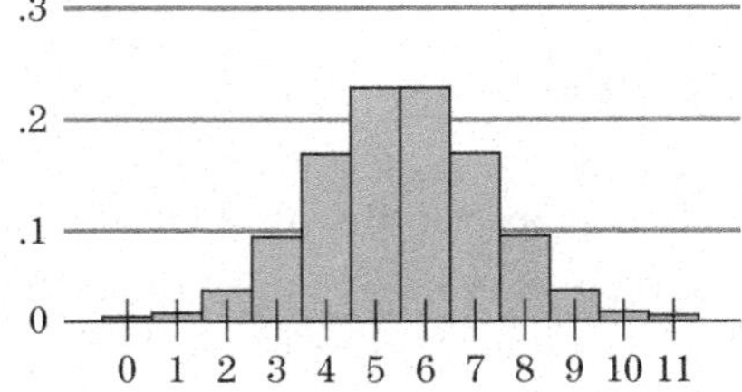

Figure 7

39. Evaluate $\binom{25}{0}(.4)^0(.6)^{25} + \binom{25}{1}(.4)^1(.6)^{24} + \binom{25}{2}(.4)^2(.6)^{23} + \cdots + \binom{25}{24}(.4)^{24}(.6)^1 + \binom{25}{25}(.4)^{25}(.6)^0$.
40. Evaluate $\binom{50}{0}(.7)^0(.3)^{50} + \binom{50}{1}(.7)^1(.3)^{49} + \binom{50}{2}(.7)^2(.3)^{48} + \cdots + \binom{50}{49}(.7)^{49}(.3)^1 + \binom{50}{50}(.7)^{50}(.3)^0$.
41. **Centenarians** The probability that a 20-year-old woman will live to be 100 is 7.5%. What is the probability that at least two out of a group of seventy-seven 20-year-old women will live to be 100?

42. **Left-handedness** Ten percent of the population is left-handed. What is the probability that, in a group of 10 people, at least two will be left-handed?

43. **Drug Reaction** Suppose that the probability of a person's having an adverse reaction to a certain drug is 2%. If the drug is administered to 56 people, what is the probability that three or more people will have an adverse reaction?

44. **Consumer Preferences** Nine customers at a supermarket are asked independently if they use brand X laundry soap. In general, 30% of the population use this brand. What is the probability that, among the nine, more than two people use brand X?

45. **Voter Polling** Suppose that 60% of the voters in a state intend to vote for a certain candidate. What is the probability that a survey polling five people reveals that two or fewer intend to vote for that candidate?

46. **Jury Verdict** A jury has 12 jurors. A vote of at least 10 of 12 for "guilty" is necessary for a defendant to be convicted of a crime. Assume that each juror acts independently of the others and that the probability that any one juror makes the correct decision regarding a defendant is .70. If the defendant is guilty, what is the probability that the jury makes the correct decision?

47. **Quality Control** Three percent of the circuit boards produced by a certain machine are defective. What is the probability that a box of 20 circuit boards contains two or more defective boards?

48. **Quality Control** Refer to Example 1. What is the probability that a box of washers contains at most two defective washers?

49. **Genetics** Every offspring inherits a gene for hair color from each parent. We denote the dominant gene by A and the recessive gene by a. If a person has AA or Aa, then the person exhibits the dominant characteristic. We call a person with the genes Aa a hybrid. A person with aa exhibits the recessive characteristic. Two hybrid parents have three children. Find the probability that at least one child exhibits the recessive characteristic.

50. **Theft of Gold** A small country owns 10,000 gold ingots that are stored in 100 guarded bins, each holding 100 ingots. One of the guards has stolen an ingot from each bin and replaced it with a bar of pyrite (fool's gold). The captain of the guards is suspicious that thievery has taken place and is considering two methods for detecting the theft. The first method is to select and examine one ingot from each bin. The second method is to select 25 bins and then select four ingots from each bin. Which method has the best chance of detecting the theft?

51. **Baseball** A .300 hitter comes to bat four times in a game. What is the probability of his getting no hits? Three hits?

52. **Basketball** A basketball player makes free throws with probability .9. What is the probability of making exactly two out of five free throws?

53. **Basketball** A basketball player makes 82% of her free throws. What is the most likely number of free throws for her to make in her next 10 tries? *Note:* First make a guess in order to test your intuition. Then calculate the probabilities of 8 free throws and 9 free throws.

54. **Darts** The probability is .64 that a dartist scores a bull's-eye on a single toss of a dart. What is the most probable number of bull's-eyes for them to score in their next 10 tosses? *Note:* First make a guess in order to test your intuition. Then calculate the probabilities of 6 successes and 7 successes.

55. **Tennis** A single match at the men's U.S. Open consists of a sequence of at most five sets that terminates when one person wins his third set. Suppose that the stronger person (the *favorite*) has probability p (where $p > \frac{1}{2}$) of winning any particular set. Then the probability of the weaker person (the *underdog*) winning any particular set is $1 - p$.
    - **(a)** Explain why the probability that the underdog wins the match in five sets is $\binom{4}{2}p^2(1-p)^3$.
    - **(b)** Determine the probability that the underdog wins the match in three sets. In four sets.
    - **(c)** Show that, if $p = .7$, then the probability that the underdog wins the match is .16308.
    - **(d)** Explain why the probability in part (c) is the same as $\binom{5}{0}p^0(1-p)^5 + \binom{5}{1}p^1(1-p)^4 + \binom{5}{2}p^2(1-p)^3$.

56. **Baseball** The World Series consists of a sequence of at most seven games that terminates when one team wins its fourth game. Suppose that the stronger team (the *favorite*) has probability p (where $p > \frac{1}{2}$) of winning any particular game. Then the probability of the weaker team (the *underdog*) winning any particular game is $1 - p$.
    - **(a)** Explain why the probability that the underdog wins the series in five games is $\binom{4}{3}(1-p)^4 p$.
    - **(b)** Determine the probability that the underdog wins the World Series in four games. Six games. Seven games.
    - **(c)** Show that, if $p = .6$, then the probability that the underdog wins the World Series is .289792.
    - **(d)** Explain why the probability in part (c) is the same as $\binom{7}{0}p^0(1-p)^7 + \binom{7}{1}p^1(1-p)^6 + \binom{7}{2}p^2(1-p)^5 + \binom{7}{3}p^3(1-p)^4$.

Solutions to Check Your Understanding 3.2

1. The number of multiples of 5 that occur in the numbers from 0 to 9999 is 2000. Since each of the 10,000 choices is as likely as any other, the probability is $2000/10{,}000 = .2$.

2. Let "success" be "the selected number is a multiple of 5." Then the selection of a number at random is a binomial trial with $p = .2$ and $n = 20$.

$$\Pr(X = 4) = \binom{20}{4}(.2)^4(.8)^{16} \approx .2182$$

3. Graphing calculator: `1-binomcdf(40, .25, 15)`
Excel: **= 1 − BINOM.DIST(15, 40, .25, 1)**
Wolfram|Alpha: **P(16 <= X <= 40) for X binomial(40, .25)**

CHAPTER 4

Matrices

We begin this chapter by developing a method for solving systems of linear equations in any number of variables. Our discussion of this method will lead naturally into the study of mathematical objects called *matrices*. The arithmetic and applications of matrices are the main topics of the chapter. We discuss in detail the application of matrix arithmetic to input–output analysis, which can be (and is) used to make production decisions for large businesses and entire economies.

4.1 Systems of Linear Equations with Unique Solutions

Systems of linear equations that involve only two variables can be quickly solved using the method of substitution. When a system of equations involves more that two variables, as often happens in applications, other methods are needed to find solutions.

EXAMPLE 1 **Manufacturing** The Upside Down Company specializes in making down jackets, ski vests, and comforters. The requirements for down and labor and the profits earned are given in the following chart:

	Down (pounds)	Time (labor-hours)	Profit ($)
Jacket	3	2	6
Vest	2	1	6
Comforter	4	1	2

Each week, the company has available 600 pounds of down and 275 labor-hours. It wants to earn a weekly profit of $1150. How many of each item should the company make each week?

SOLUTION The requirements and earnings can be expressed by a system of equations. Let x be the number of jackets, y the number of vests, and z the number of comforters. If 600 pounds of down are used, then

$$\begin{aligned}[\text{down in jackets}] + [\text{down in vests}] + [\text{down in comforters}] &= 600\\ 3\,[\text{no. jackets}] \quad + \quad 2\,[\text{no. vests}] \quad + \quad 4\,[\text{no. comforters}] &= 600.\end{aligned}$$

That is,

$$3x + 2y + 4z = 600.$$

Similarly, the equation for labor is

$$2x + y + z = 275,$$

and the equation for the profit is

$$6x + 6y + 2z = 1150.$$

The numbers x, y, and z must simultaneously satisfy a system of three linear equations in three variables.

$$\begin{cases} 3x + 2y + 4z = 600 \\ 2x + y + z = 275 \\ 6x + 6y + 2z = 1150. \end{cases} \tag{1}$$

Later, we present a method for determining the solution to this system. This method yields the solution $x = 50$, $y = 125$, and $z = 50$. It is easy to confirm that these values of x, y, and z satisfy all three equations:

$$\begin{aligned} 3(50) + 2(125) + 4(50) &= 600\\ 2(50) + (125) + (50) &= 275\\ 6(50) + 6(125) + 2(50) &= 1150. \end{aligned}$$

Thus, the Upside Down Company can make a profit of $1150 by producing 50 jackets, 125 vests, and 50 comforters. «

In this section, we develop a step-by-step procedure for solving systems of linear equations such as (1). The procedure, called the **Gauss–Jordan elimination method**, consists of repeatedly simplifying the system, using so-called elementary row operations, until the solution stares us in the face!

In the system of linear equations (1), the equations have been written in such a way that the x-terms, the y-terms, and the z-terms lie in different columns. We shall always be careful to display systems of equations with separate columns for each variable. One of the key ideas of the Gauss–Jordan elimination method is to think of the solution as a system of linear equations in its own right. For example, we can write the solution of system (1) as

$$\begin{cases} 1x + 0y + 0z = 50 \\ 0x + 1y + 0z = 125 \\ 0x + 0y + 1z = 50 \end{cases} \quad \text{or} \quad \begin{cases} x \qquad\quad = 50 \\ \quad y \quad = 125 \\ \qquad z = 50. \end{cases} \tag{2}$$

This is just a system of linear equations in which the coefficients of most terms are zero! Since the only terms with nonzero coefficients are arranged on a diagonal, such a system is said to be in **diagonal form**.

Our method for solving a system of linear equations consists of repeatedly using three operations that alter the system but do not change the solutions. The operations are used to transform the system into a system in diagonal form. Since the operations involve only elementary arithmetic and are applied to entire equations (i.e., rows of the system), they are called **elementary row operations**. Let us begin our study of the Gauss–Jordan elimination method by introducing these operations.

Elementary Row Operation 1 Interchange any two equations.

This operation is harmless enough. It certainly does not change the solutions of the system.

Elementary Row Operation 2 Multiply an equation by a nonzero number.

For example, if we are given the system of linear equations

$$\begin{cases} 2x - 3y + 4z = 11 \\ 4x - 19y + z = 31 \\ 5x + 7y - z = 12, \end{cases}$$

then we may replace it by a new system obtained by leaving the last two equations unchanged and multiplying the first equation by 3. To accomplish this, multiply each term of the first equation by 3. The transformed system is

$$\begin{cases} 6x - 9y + 12z = 33 \\ 4x - 19y + z = 31 \\ 5x + 7y - z = 12. \end{cases}$$

The operation of multiplying an equation by a nonzero number does not change the solution of the system. For if a particular set of values of the variables satisfies the original equation, it satisfies the resulting equation, and vice versa.

Elementary row operation 2 may be used to make the coefficient of a particular variable 1.

EXAMPLE 2 **Demonstrating Elementary Row Operation 2** Replace the system

$$\begin{cases} -5x + 10y + 20z = 4 \\ x \qquad\quad - 12z = 1 \\ x + y + z = 0 \end{cases}$$

by an equivalent system in which the coefficient of x in the first equation is 1.

SOLUTION The coefficient of x in the first equation is -5, so we use elementary row operation 2 to multiply the first equation by $-\frac{1}{5}$. Multiplying each term of the first equation by $-\frac{1}{5}$ gives

$$\begin{cases} x - 2y - 4z = -\frac{4}{5} \\ x \qquad\quad - 12z = 1 \\ x + y + z = 0. \end{cases}$$

» Now Try Exercise 1

Another operation that can be performed on a system without changing its solutions is to replace one equation by its sum with some other equation. For example, consider this system of equations:

$$\text{A:}\quad \begin{cases} x + y - 2z = 3 \\ x + 2y - 5z = 4 \\ 5x + 8y - 18z = 14. \end{cases}$$

We can replace the second equation by the sum of the first and the second. Since

$$\begin{array}{rr} & x + y - 2z = 3 \\ + & x + 2y - 5z = 4 \\ \hline & 2x + 3y - 7z = 7, \end{array}$$

the resulting system is

$$\text{B:}\quad \begin{cases} x + y - 2z = 3 \\ 2x + 3y - 7z = 7 \\ 5x + 8y - 18z = 14. \end{cases}$$

If a particular choice of x, y, and z satisfies system A, it also satisfies system B. This is because system B results from adding equations. Similarly, system A can be derived from system B by subtracting equations. So any particular solution of system A is a solution of system B, and vice versa.

The operation of adding equations is usually used in conjunction with elementary row operation 2. That is, an equation is changed by adding to it a nonzero multiple of another equation. For example, consider the system

$$\begin{cases} x + y - 2z = 3 \\ x + 2y - 5z = 4 \\ 5x + 8y - 18z = 14. \end{cases}$$

Let us change the second equation by adding to it twice the first. Since

$$\begin{array}{rr} \text{2(first)} & 2x + 2y - 4z = 6 \\ +\text{(second)} & x + 2y - 5z = 4 \\ \hline & 3x + 4y - 9z = 10, \end{array}$$

the new second equation is

$$3x + 4y - 9z = 10$$

and the transformed system is

$$\begin{cases} x + y - 2z = 3 \\ 3x + 4y - 9z = 10 \\ 5x + 8y - 18z = 14. \end{cases}$$

Since addition of equations and elementary row operation 2 are often used together, let us define a third elementary row operation.

Elementary Row Operation 3 Change an equation by adding to it a multiple of another equation.

For reference, let us summarize the elementary row operations that we have just defined.

Elementary Row Operations

1. Interchange any two equations.
2. Multiply an equation by a nonzero number.
3. Change an equation by adding to it a multiple of another equation.

The idea of the Gauss–Jordan elimination method is to transform an arbitrary system of linear equations into diagonal form by repeated applications of the three elementary row operations. To see how the method works, consider the following example:

EXAMPLE 3 **Solving a System of Equations by Gauss–Jordan Elimination** Solve the following system by the Gauss–Jordan elimination method:

$$\begin{cases} x - 3y = 7 \\ -3x + 4y = -1. \end{cases}$$

SOLUTION Let us transform this system into diagonal form by examining one column at a time, starting from the left. Examine the first column:

$$\begin{matrix} x \\ -3x \end{matrix}$$

The coefficient of the top x is 1, which is exactly what it should be for the system to be in diagonal form. So we do nothing to this term. Now, examine the next term in the column, $-3x$. In diagonal form, this term must be absent. In order to accomplish this, we add a multiple of the first equation to the second. Since the coefficient of x in the second is -3, we add three times the first equation to the second equation in order to cancel the x-term. (Abbreviation: $R_2 + 3R_1$. The R_2 refers to the second equation—that is, the equation in the second row of the system of equations. The expression $R_2 + 3R_1$ means that we are replacing the second equation by the original equation plus 3 times the first equation.)

$$\begin{cases} x - 3y = 7 \\ -3x + 4y = -1 \end{cases} \xrightarrow{R_2 + 3R_1} \begin{cases} x - 3y = 7 \\ \quad - 5y = 20. \end{cases}$$

The first column now has the proper form, so we proceed to the second column. In diagonal form, that column will have one nonzero term—namely, the second—and the coefficient of y in that term must be 1. To bring this about, multiply the second equation by $-\frac{1}{5}$ [abbreviation $\left(-\frac{1}{5}\right)R_2$]:

$$\begin{cases} x - 3y = 7 \\ \quad - 5y = 20 \end{cases} \xrightarrow{(-\frac{1}{5})R_2} \begin{cases} x - 3y = 7 \\ \quad\quad y = -4. \end{cases}$$

The second column still does not have the correct form. We must get rid of the $-3y$-term in the first equation. We do this by adding a multiple of the second equation to the first. Since the coefficient of the term to be canceled is -3, we add three times the second equation to the first:

$$\begin{cases} x - 3y = 7 \\ \quad\quad y = -4 \end{cases} \xrightarrow{R_1 + 3R_2} \begin{cases} x \quad\quad = -5 \\ \quad\quad y = -4. \end{cases}$$

The system is now in diagonal form, and the solution can be read off: $x = -5$, $y = -4$.

» *Now Try Exercise 47*

NOTE The abbreviation for interchanging the first and second equation is $R_1 \leftrightarrow R_2$. «

EXAMPLE 4 **Solving a System of Equations by Gauss–Jordan Elimination** Use the Gauss–Jordan elimination method to solve the system

$$\begin{cases} 2x - 6y = -8 \\ -5x + 13y = 1. \end{cases}$$

SOLUTION We can perform the calculations in a mechanical way, proceeding column by column from the left:

$$\begin{cases} 2x - 6y = -8 \\ -5x + 13y = 1 \end{cases} \xrightarrow{\frac{1}{2}R_1} \begin{cases} x - 3y = -4 \\ -5x + 13y = 1 \end{cases}$$

$$\xrightarrow{R_2 + 5R_1} \begin{cases} x - 3y = -4 \\ -2y = -19 \end{cases}$$

$$\xrightarrow{(-\frac{1}{2})R_2} \begin{cases} x - 3y = -4 \\ y = \frac{19}{2} \end{cases}$$

$$\xrightarrow{R_1 + 3R_2} \begin{cases} x = \frac{49}{2} \\ y = \frac{19}{2}. \end{cases}$$

So the solution of the system is $x = \frac{49}{2}$, $y = \frac{19}{2}$. ***>> Now Try Exercise 55***

The calculation becomes easier to follow if we omit writing down the variables at each stage and work only with the coefficients. At each stage of the computation, the system is represented by a rectangular array of numbers. For instance, the original system is written as

$$\left[\begin{array}{rr|r} 2 & -6 & -8 \\ -5 & 13 & 1 \end{array}\right].$$

The vertical line between the second and third columns is a placemarker that separates the data obtained from the left- and right-hand sides of the equations. Each row of the array corresponds to an equation, and each column to the left of the vertical line corresponds to a variable.

The elementary row operations are performed on the rows of this rectangular array just as if the variables were there. So, for example, the first step in the preceding solution is to multiply the first equation by $\frac{1}{2}$. This corresponds to multiplying the first row of the array by $\frac{1}{2}$ to get

$$\left[\begin{array}{rr|r} 1 & -3 & -4 \\ -5 & 13 & 1 \end{array}\right].$$

The diagonal form corresponds to the array

$$\left[\begin{array}{rr|r} 1 & 0 & \frac{49}{2} \\ 0 & 1 & \frac{19}{2} \end{array}\right].$$

Note that this array has ones down the diagonal and zeros everywhere else on the left. The solution of the system appears on the right.

A rectangular array of numbers is called a **matrix** (plural *matrices*). Matrices (such as the one above) that are derived from systems of linear equations are called **augmented matrices**. In the next example, we use augmented matrices to carry out the Gauss–Jordan elimination method.

EXAMPLE 5 **Solving a System of Equations by Gauss—Jordan Elimination** Use the Gauss—Jordan elimination method to solve the system

$$\begin{cases} 3x - 6y + 9z = 0 \\ 4x - 6y + 8z = -4 \\ -2x - y + z = 7. \end{cases}$$

SOLUTION The initial array corresponding to the system is

$$\left[\begin{array}{rrr|r} 3 & -6 & 9 & 0 \\ 4 & -6 & 8 & -4 \\ -2 & -1 & 1 & 7 \end{array}\right].$$

We must use elementary row operations to transform this array into diagonal form—that is, with ones down the diagonal, and zeros everywhere else to the left of the vertical line:

$$\left[\begin{array}{rrr|r} 1 & 0 & 0 & * \\ 0 & 1 & 0 & * \\ 0 & 0 & 1 & * \end{array}\right].$$

We proceed one column at a time.

$$\left[\begin{array}{rrr|r} 3 & -6 & 9 & 0 \\ 4 & -6 & 8 & -4 \\ -2 & -1 & 1 & 7 \end{array}\right] \xrightarrow{\frac{1}{3}R_1} \left[\begin{array}{rrr|r} 1 & -2 & 3 & 0 \\ 4 & -6 & 8 & -4 \\ -2 & -1 & 1 & 7 \end{array}\right] \xrightarrow{R_2 + (-4)R_1}$$

$$\left[\begin{array}{rrr|r} 1 & -2 & 3 & 0 \\ 0 & 2 & -4 & -4 \\ -2 & -1 & 1 & 7 \end{array}\right] \xrightarrow{R_3 + 2R_1} \left[\begin{array}{rrr|r} 1 & -2 & 3 & 0 \\ 0 & 2 & -4 & -4 \\ 0 & -5 & 7 & 7 \end{array}\right] \xrightarrow{\frac{1}{2}R_2}$$

$$\left[\begin{array}{rrr|r} 1 & -2 & 3 & 0 \\ 0 & 1 & -2 & -2 \\ 0 & -5 & 7 & 7 \end{array}\right] \xrightarrow{R_1 + 2R_2} \left[\begin{array}{rrr|r} 1 & 0 & -1 & -4 \\ 0 & 1 & -2 & -2 \\ 0 & -5 & 7 & 7 \end{array}\right] \xrightarrow{R_3 + 5R_2}$$

$$\left[\begin{array}{rrr|r} 1 & 0 & -1 & -4 \\ 0 & 1 & -2 & -2 \\ 0 & 0 & -3 & -3 \end{array}\right] \xrightarrow{(-\frac{1}{3})R_3} \left[\begin{array}{rrr|r} 1 & 0 & -1 & -4 \\ 0 & 1 & -2 & -2 \\ 0 & 0 & 1 & 1 \end{array}\right] \xrightarrow{R_1 + 1R_3}$$

$$\left[\begin{array}{rrr|r} 1 & 0 & 0 & -3 \\ 0 & 1 & -2 & -2 \\ 0 & 0 & 1 & 1 \end{array}\right] \xrightarrow{R_2 + 2R_3} \left[\begin{array}{rrr|r} 1 & 0 & 0 & -3 \\ 0 & 1 & 0 & 0 \\ 0 & 0 & 1 & 1 \end{array}\right]$$

The last array is in diagonal form, so we just put back the variables and read off the solution:

$$x = -3, \qquad y = 0, \qquad z = 1.$$

Because so much arithmetic has been performed, it is a good idea to check the solution by substituting the values for x, y, and z into each of the equations of the original system. This will uncover any arithmetic errors that may have occurred.

$$\begin{cases} 3x - 6y + 9z = 0 \\ 4x - 6y + 8z = -4 \\ -2x - y + z = 7 \end{cases} \qquad \begin{cases} 3(-3) - 6(0) + 9(1) = 0 \\ 4(-3) - 6(0) + 8(1) = -4 \\ -2(-3) - (0) + (1) = 7 \end{cases}$$

$$\begin{cases} -9 - 0 + 9 = 0 \\ -12 - 0 + 8 = -4 \\ 6 - 0 + 1 = 7 \end{cases}$$

$$\begin{cases} 0 = 0 \\ -4 = -4 \\ 7 = 7 \end{cases}$$

So we have indeed found a solution of the system. **»** ***Now Try Exercise 53***

NOTE Note that so far we have not had to use elementary row operation 1, which allows interchange of equations. But in some examples, it is definitely needed.

Consider this system:

$$\begin{cases} \quad\; y + z = 0 \\ 3x - y + z = 6 \\ 6x \quad\;\; - z = 3. \end{cases}$$

The first step of the Gauss–Jordan elimination method consists of making the x-coefficient 1 in the first equation. But we cannot do this, since the first equation does not involve x. To remedy this difficulty, just interchange the first two equations to guarantee that the first equation involves x. Now, proceed as before. Of course, in terms of the matrix of coefficients, interchanging equations corresponds to interchanging rows of the matrix. «

Check Your Understanding 4.1

Solutions can be found following the section exercises.

1. Determine whether the following systems of linear equations are in diagonal form:

(a) $\begin{cases} x \quad + z = 3 \\ \quad y \quad = 2 \\ \quad\quad z = 7 \end{cases}$ (b) $\begin{cases} x \quad\quad = -1 \\ \quad y \quad = 0 \\ \quad 3z = 4 \end{cases}$

2. Give the meaning of each of the following abbreviations for row operations on a matrix.
(a) $R_i \leftrightarrow R_j$ (b) $cR_i, c \neq 0$ (c) $R_i + cR_j$

3. Perform the indicated elementary row operation.

(a) $\begin{cases} x - 3y = 2 \\ 2x + 3y = 5 \end{cases} \xrightarrow{R_2 + (-2)R_1}$

(b) $\begin{cases} x + y = 3 \\ -x + 2y = 5 \end{cases} \xrightarrow{R_2 + 1R_1}$

4. State the next elementary row operation that should be performed when applying the Gauss–Jordan elimination method.

(a) $\left[\begin{array}{ccc|c} 0 & 2 & 4 & 1 \\ 0 & 3 & -7 & 0 \\ 3 & 6 & -3 & 3 \end{array}\right]$ (b) $\left[\begin{array}{ccc|c} 1 & -3 & 4 & 5 \\ 0 & 2 & 3 & 4 \\ -6 & 5 & -7 & 0 \end{array}\right]$

EXERCISES 4.1

In Exercises 1–8, perform the indicated elementary row operation and give its abbreviation.

1. Operation 2: Multiply the first equation by 2.

$$\begin{cases} \frac{1}{2}x - 3y = 2 \\ 5x + 4y = 1 \end{cases}$$

2. Operation 2: Multiply the second equation by -1.

$$\begin{cases} x + 4y = 6 \\ \quad -y = 2 \end{cases}$$

3. Operation 3: Change the second equation by adding to it 5 times the first equation.

$$\begin{cases} x + 2y = 3 \\ -5x + 4y = 1 \end{cases}$$

4. Operation 3: Change the second equation by adding to it $(-\frac{1}{2})$ times the first equation.

$$\begin{cases} x - 6y = 4 \\ \frac{1}{2}x + 2y = 1 \end{cases}$$

5. Operation 3: Change the third equation by adding to it (-4) times the first equation.

$$\begin{cases} x - 2y + z = 0 \\ \quad y - 2z = 4 \\ 4x + y + 3z = 5 \end{cases}$$

6. Operation 3: Change the third equation by adding to it 3 times the second equation.

$$\begin{cases} x + 6y - 4z = 1 \\ \quad y + 3z = 1 \\ -3y + 7z = 2 \end{cases}$$

7. Operation 3: Change the first row by adding to it $\frac{1}{2}$ times the second row.

$$\left[\begin{array}{cc|c} 1 & -\frac{1}{2} & 3 \\ 0 & 1 & 4 \end{array}\right]$$

8. Operation 3: Change the third row by adding to it (-4) times the second row.

$$\left[\begin{array}{ccc|c} 1 & 0 & 7 & 9 \\ 0 & 1 & -2 & 3 \\ 0 & 4 & 8 & 5 \end{array}\right]$$

In Exercises 9–12, write the augmented matrix corresponding to the system of linear equations.

9. $\begin{cases} -3x + 4y = -2 \\ x - 7y = 8 \end{cases}$

10. $\begin{cases} \frac{2}{3}x - 3y = 4 \\ \quad y = -5 \end{cases}$

11. $\begin{cases} x + 13y - 2z = 0 \\ 2x \quad\quad - z = 3 \\ \quad y \quad\quad = 5 \end{cases}$

12. $\begin{cases} \quad y - z = 22 \\ 2x \quad\quad = 17 \\ x - 3y \quad = 12 \end{cases}$

In Exercises 13–16, write the system of linear equations corresponding to the matrix.

13. $\left[\begin{array}{cc|c} 0 & -2 & 3 \\ 1 & 7 & -4 \end{array}\right]$

14. $\left[\begin{array}{cc|c} -5 & \frac{2}{3} & 3 \\ 1 & 7 & -\frac{5}{8} \end{array}\right]$

15. $\left[\begin{array}{ccc|c} 3 & 2 & 0 & -3 \\ 0 & 1 & -6 & 4 \\ -5 & -1 & 7 & 0 \end{array}\right]$

16. $\left[\begin{array}{ccc|c} \frac{6}{5} & -1 & 12 & -\frac{2}{3} \\ -1 & 0 & 0 & 5 \\ 0 & 2 & -1 & 6 \end{array}\right]$

In Exercises 17–22, describe in your own words the meaning of the notation with respect to a matrix.

17. $\frac{1}{3}R_2$
18. $R_2 + (-4)R_1$
19. $R_1 + 3R_2$
20. $(-1)R_1$
21. $R_2 \leftrightarrow R_3$
22. $R_1 \leftrightarrow R_2$

In Exercises 23–28, carry out the indicated elementary row operation.

23. $\left[\begin{array}{cc|c} 1 & 2 & 0 \\ -3 & 4 & 5 \end{array}\right] \xrightarrow{R_2 + 3R_1} \left[\quad\right]$

24. $\left[\begin{array}{cc|c} -\frac{1}{2} & 2 & \frac{3}{4} \\ -3 & 4 & 9 \end{array}\right] \xrightarrow{(-2)R_1} \left[\quad\right]$

25. $\left[\begin{array}{cc|c} \frac{1}{7} & \frac{2}{7} & \frac{3}{7} \\ 3 & -2 & 0 \end{array}\right] \xrightarrow{7R_1} \left[\quad\right]$

26. $\left[\begin{array}{cc|c} 1 & 3 & -2 \\ 4 & 4 & 5 \end{array}\right] \xrightarrow{R_2 + (-4)R_1} \left[\quad\right]$

27. $\left[\begin{array}{cc|c} 0 & 1 & 7 \\ 1 & 3 & -5 \end{array}\right] \xrightarrow{R_1 \leftrightarrow R_2} \left[\quad\right]$

28. $\left[\begin{array}{cc|c} 4 & 5 & 6 \\ -3 & 2 & 0 \end{array}\right] \xrightarrow{R_1 + 1R_2} \left[\quad\right]$

In Exercises 29–36, state the next elementary row operation that should be performed in order to put the matrix into diagonal form. Do not perform the operation.

29. $\left[\begin{array}{cc|c} 1 & -5 & 1 \\ -2 & 4 & 6 \end{array}\right]$

30. $\left[\begin{array}{cc|c} 1 & 3 & 4 \\ 0 & 2 & 6 \end{array}\right]$

31. $\left[\begin{array}{cc|c} 1 & 2 & 3 \\ 0 & 1 & 4 \end{array}\right]$

32. $\left[\begin{array}{ccc|c} 1 & -2 & 5 & 7 \\ 0 & -3 & 0 & 9 \\ 4 & 5 & -6 & 7 \end{array}\right]$

33. $\left[\begin{array}{ccc|c} 0 & 5 & -3 & 6 \\ 2 & -3 & 4 & 5 \\ 4 & 1 & -7 & 8 \end{array}\right]$

34. $\left[\begin{array}{ccc|c} 1 & 4 & -2 & 5 \\ 0 & -3 & 6 & 9 \\ 0 & 4 & 3 & 1 \end{array}\right]$

35. $\left[\begin{array}{ccc|c} 1 & 0 & 3 & 4 \\ 0 & 1 & 2 & 5 \\ 0 & 0 & 1 & 6 \end{array}\right]$

36. $\left[\begin{array}{ccc|c} 1 & 2 & 4 & 5 \\ 0 & 0 & 3 & 6 \\ 0 & 1 & 1 & 7 \end{array}\right]$

In Exercises 37 and 38, two steps of the Gauss–Jordan elimination method are shown. Fill in the missing numbers.

37. $\left[\begin{array}{ccc|c} 1 & 1 & -1 & 6 \\ -3 & 7 & 5 & 0 \\ 2 & -4 & 3 & -1 \end{array}\right] \rightarrow \left[\begin{array}{ccc|c} 1 & 1 & -1 & 6 \\ 0 & 10 & \square & \square \\ 0 & -6 & \square & \square \end{array}\right]$

38. $\left[\begin{array}{ccc|c} 1 & 2 & 7 & -3 \\ 1 & -5 & -4 & 2 \\ -4 & 6 & 9 & 3 \end{array}\right] \rightarrow \left[\begin{array}{ccc|c} 1 & 2 & 7 & -3 \\ 0 & -7 & \square & \square \\ 0 & 14 & \square & \square \end{array}\right]$

In Exercises 39–52, solve the linear system by the Gauss–Jordan elimination method.

39. $\begin{cases} x + 9y = 8 \\ 2x + 8y = 6 \end{cases}$

40. $\begin{cases} \frac{1}{3}x + 2y = 1 \\ -2x - 4y = 6 \end{cases}$

41. $\begin{cases} x - 3y + 4z = 1 \\ 4x - 10y + 10z = 4 \\ -3x + 9y - 5z = -6 \end{cases}$

42. $\begin{cases} \frac{1}{2}x + y = 4 \\ -4x - 7y + 3z = -31 \\ 6x + 14y + 7z = 50 \end{cases}$

43. $\begin{cases} 2x - 2y + 4 = 0 \\ 3x + 4y - 1 = 0 \end{cases}$

44. $\begin{cases} 2x + 3y = 4 \\ -x + 2y = -2 \end{cases}$

45. $\begin{cases} 4x - 4y + 4z = -8 \\ x - 2y - 2z = -1 \\ 2x + y + 3z = 1 \end{cases}$

46. $\begin{cases} x + 2y + 2z - 11 = 0 \\ x - y - z + 4 = 0 \\ 2x + 5y + 9z - 39 = 0 \end{cases}$

47. $\begin{cases} .2x + .3y = 4 \\ .6x + 1.1y = 15 \end{cases}$

48. $\begin{cases} \frac{3}{2}x + 6y = 9 \\ \frac{1}{2}x - \frac{2}{3}y = 11 \end{cases}$

49. $\begin{cases} x + y + 4z = 3 \\ 4x + y - 2z = -6 \\ -3x + 2z = 1 \end{cases}$

50. $\begin{cases} -2x - 3y + 2z = -2 \\ x + y = 3 \\ -x - 3y + 5z = 8 \end{cases}$

51. $\begin{cases} -x + y = -1 \\ x + z = 4 \\ 6x - 3y + 2z = 10 \end{cases}$

52. $\begin{cases} x + 2z = 9 \\ y + z = 1 \\ 3x - 2y = 9 \end{cases}$

53. A baked potato smothered with cheddar cheese weighs 180 grams and contains 10.5 grams of protein. If cheddar cheese contains 25% protein and a baked potato contains 2% protein, how many grams of cheddar cheese are there?

54. A high school math department purchased brand A calculators for \$80 each and brand B calculators for \$95 each. It purchased a total of 20 calculators at a total cost of \$1780. How many brand A calculators did the department purchase?

Exercises 55 and 56 are multiple choice exercises with five possible choices. Each exercise consists of a question and two statements that may or may not provide sufficient information to answer the question. Select the response (a)–(e) that best describes the situation.

(a) Statement I alone is sufficient to answer the question, but statement II is not sufficient.

(b) Statement II alone is sufficient to answer the question, but statement I is not sufficient.

(c) Both statements together are sufficient to answer the question, but neither alone is sufficient.

(d) Each statement alone is sufficient to answer the question.

(e) Both statements together are not sufficient to answer the question.

55. A box of golf balls and a golf glove cost a total of \$20. How much does the box of balls cost?

Statement I: The golf glove costs three times as much as the box of golf balls.

Statement II: The golf glove costs \$15.

56. I have four nickels and three pennies in my pocket. What is the total weight of these coins?

Statement I: A nickel weighs twice as much as a penny.

Statement II: The total weight of a nickel and two pennies is 10 grams.

57. **Sales** A street vendor has a total of 350 short- and long-sleeve T-shirts. If they sell the short-sleeve shirts for \$10 each and the long-sleeve shirts for \$14 each, how many of each did they sell if they sold all of their stock for \$4300?

58. **Sales** A grocery store carries two brands of bleach. A 30-ounce bottle of the national brand sells for \$2.59, while the same-size bottle of the store brand sells for \$2.09. How many bottles of each brand were sold if a total of 82 bottles were sold for \$194.88?

59. **Movie Tickets** A 275-seat movie theater charges \$11.25 admission for adults and \$8.50 for children. If the theater is full and \$2860 is collected, how many adults and how many children are in the audience?

60. **Batting Average** A baseball player's batting average is determined by dividing the number of hits by the number of times at bat and multiplying by 1000. (Batting averages are usually, but not necessarily, rounded to the nearest whole number.) For instance, if a player gets 2 hits in 5 times at bat, his batting average is 400: $\left(\frac{2}{5} \times 1000 = 400\right)$. Partway through the season, a player thinks to himself, "If I get a hit in my next time at bat, my average will go up to 250; if I don't get a hit, it will drop to 187.5." How many times has this player batted, how many hits has he had, and what is his current batting average?

61. **Areas of Countries** The United States and Canada are the largest of the 23 countries that make up North America. The bar graph in Fig. 5 shows their areas and that of the remaining North American countries in millions of square miles. The total area of North America is 9.5 million square miles. Canada is 200,000 sq. mi. larger than the United States. The area of the United States is one-half the area of Canada plus 1.75 million sq. mi. Let x, y, and z represent the three areas shown in the figure. Use the methods of this section to determine the values of x, y, and z.

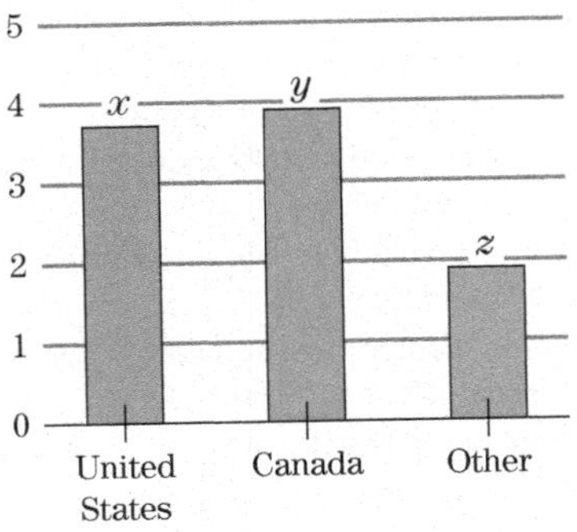

Figure 5 Areas in North America

62. **College Majors** The bar graph in Fig. 6 gives the intended majors of a group of 100 randomly selected college freshmen. (The biology category includes the biological and life sciences.) Six more students intend to major in biology than intend to major in business. The number of students intending to major in fields other than business or biology is 4 more than twice the number of students majoring in business or biology. Let x, y, and z represent the three numbers shown in the figure. Use the methods of this section to determine the values of x, y, and z.

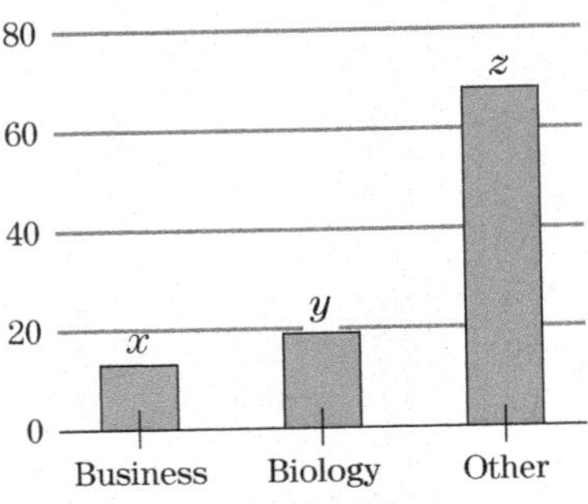

Figure 6 Intended Majors

63. **Coffee Blends** A one-pound blend of coffee uses Brazilian (60 ¢ per ounce), Columbian (50 ¢ per ounce), and Peruvian (70 ¢ per ounce) coffee beans and costs \$9.70. The blend contains twice the weight of Brazilian beans as Columbian beans. How many ounces of each type of bean does the blend contain?

64. **Nut Mixture** A one-pound mixture of nuts contains cashews (70 ¢ per ounce), almonds (60 ¢ per ounce), and walnuts (80 ¢ per ounce) and costs \$11.10. The mixture contains the same weight of cashews as walnuts. How many ounces of each type of nut does the mixture contain?

65. **Investment Planning** A bank wishes to invest a \$100,000 trust fund in three sources: a bond fund paying 8%; a health sciences fund paying 7%; and a real estate fund paying 10%. The bank wishes to realize an \$8000 annual income from the investment. A condition of the trust is that the total amount invested in the bond fund and the health sciences fund must be triple the amount invested in the real estate fund. How much should the bank invest in each possible category?

66. **Nutrition Planning** A dietitian wishes to plan a meal around three foods. Each ounce of food I contains 10% of the daily requirements for carbohydrates, 10% for protein, and 15% for vitamin C. Each ounce of food II contains 10% of the daily requirements for carbohydrates, 5% for protein, and 0% for vitamin C. Each ounce of food III contains 10% of the daily requirements for carbohydrates, 25% for protein, and 10% for vitamin C. How many ounces of each food should be served in order to supply exactly the daily requirement for each nutrient?

67. **Candy Assortments** A small candy store makes three types of party mixes. The first type contains 40% nonpareils and 60% peanut clusters, while the second type contains 30% peanut clusters and 70% chocolate-covered raisins. The third type consists of 40% nonpareils, 30% peanut clusters, and 30% chocolate-covered raisins. If the store has 90 pounds of nonpareils, 100 pounds of peanut clusters, and 120 pounds of chocolate-covered raisins available, how many pounds of each type of party mix should be made?

68. **Investment Planning** New parents Jim and Lucy want to start saving for their son's college education. They have \$5000 to invest in three different types of plans. A traditional savings account pays 1% annual interest, a certificate of deposit pays 3.6% annual interest, and a prepaid college plan pays 5.5% annual interest. If they want to invest the same amount in the prepaid college fund as in the other two plans together, how much should they invest in each plan to realize an interest income of \$195 for the first year?

Solutions to Check Your Understanding 4.1

1. (a) Not in diagonal form, since the first equation contains both x and z.

   (b) Not in diagonal form, since the coefficient of z is not 1.

2. (a) Interchange the ith and j^{th} rows of the matrix.

   (b) Multiply the ith row of the matrix by the number c.

   (c) Add c times the jth row of the matrix to the ith row of the matrix in order to change the ith row.

3. (a) Change the system into another system in which the second equation is altered by having (-2) (first equation) added to it. The new system is

$$\begin{cases} x - 3y = 2 \\ \quad\;\; 9y = 1. \end{cases}$$

   The equation $9y = 1$ was obtained as follows:

$$\begin{array}{lrl} (-2)(\text{first equation}) & -2x + 6y = & -4 \\ +\,(\text{second equation}) & 2x + 3y = & \;\;5 \\ \hline & 9y = & \;\;1. \end{array}$$

   (b) Change the second equation by adding to it 1 times the first equation. The result is

$$\begin{cases} x + \;\; y = 3 \\ \quad\;\; 3y = 8. \end{cases}$$

   In general, notation of the form $R_i + kR_j$ specifies that the first row mentioned, R_i, be changed by adding to it a multiple, k, of the second row mentioned, R_j. The row R_j is not changed by the operation.

4. (a) The first row should contain a nonzero number as its first entry. This can be accomplished by interchanging the first and third rows. The notation for this operation is

$$R_1 \leftrightarrow R_3.$$

   (b) The first column can be put into proper form by eliminating the -6. To accomplish this, multiply the first row by 6 and add this product to the third row. The notation for this operation is

$$R_3 + 6R_1.$$

4.2 General Systems of Linear Equations

In this section, we introduce the operation of pivoting and consider systems of linear equations that do not have exactly one solution.

Roughly speaking, the Gauss–Jordan elimination method applied to a matrix proceeds as follows: Consider the columns one at a time, from left to right. For each column, use the elementary row operations to transform the appropriate entry to a one and the remaining entries in the column to zeros. (The "appropriate" entry is the first entry in the first column, the second entry in the second column, and so forth.) This sequence of elementary row operations performed for each column is called **pivoting**. More precisely,

> **Method** To pivot a matrix about a given nonzero entry,
>
> 1. Transform the given entry into a one.
> 2. Transform all other entries in the same column into zeros.

Pivoting is used in solving problems other than systems of linear equations. It is the basis for the simplex method of solving linear programming problems.

EXAMPLE 1 **Pivoting** Pivot the matrix about the circled element.

$$\left[\begin{array}{cc|c} 18 & \textcircled{-6} & 15 \\ 5 & -2 & 4 \end{array}\right]$$

SOLUTION The first step is to transform the -6 to a 1. We do this by multiplying the first row by $-\frac{1}{6}$.

$$\left[\begin{array}{cc|c} 18 & -6 & 15 \\ 5 & -2 & 4 \end{array}\right] \xrightarrow{(-\frac{1}{6})R_1} \left[\begin{array}{cc|c} -3 & 1 & -\frac{5}{2} \\ 5 & -2 & 4 \end{array}\right].$$

Next, we transform the −2 (the only remaining entry in column 2) into a 0:

$$\left[\begin{array}{rr|r} -3 & 1 & -\frac{5}{2} \\ 5 & -2 & 4 \end{array}\right] \xrightarrow{R_2 + 2R_1} \left[\begin{array}{rr|r} -3 & 1 & -\frac{5}{2} \\ -1 & 0 & -1 \end{array}\right].$$

The last matrix is the result of pivoting the original matrix about the circled entry.

>> ***Now Try Exercise 1***

In terms of pivoting, we can give the following summary of the Gauss–Jordan elimination method:

Gauss–Jordan Elimination Method to Transform a System of Linear Equations into Diagonal Form

1. Write down the matrix corresponding to the linear system.
2. Make sure that the first entry in the first column is nonzero. Do this by interchanging the first row with one of the rows below it, if necessary.
3. Pivot the matrix about the first entry in the first column.
4. Make sure that the second entry in the second column is nonzero. Do this by interchanging the second row with one of the rows below it, if necessary.
5. Pivot the matrix about the second entry in the second column.
6. Continue in this manner until the left side of the matrix is in diagonal form.
7. Write the system of linear equations corresponding to the matrix.

All of the systems considered in the preceding section had only a single solution. In this case, we say that the solution is **unique**. Let us now use the Gauss–Jordan elimination method to study the various possibilities other than a unique solution.

EXAMPLE 2 **A System of Equations That Has No Solution** Find all solutions of the system

$$\begin{cases} x - y + z = 3 \\ x + y - z = 5 \\ -2x + 4y - 4z = 1. \end{cases}$$

SOLUTION We apply the Gauss–Jordan elimination method to the matrix of the system. (The elements pivoted about are circled.)

$$\left[\begin{array}{rrr|r} \textcircled{1} & -1 & 1 & 3 \\ 1 & 1 & -1 & 5 \\ -2 & 4 & -4 & 1 \end{array}\right] \xrightarrow[R_3 + 2R_1]{R_2 + (-1)R_1} \left[\begin{array}{rrr|r} 1 & -1 & 1 & 3 \\ 0 & \textcircled{2} & -2 & 2 \\ 0 & 2 & -2 & 7 \end{array}\right]$$

$$\xrightarrow[R_3 + (-2)R_2]{\frac{1}{2}R_2 \quad R_1 + 1R_2} \left[\begin{array}{rrr|r} 1 & 0 & 0 & 4 \\ 0 & 1 & -1 & 1 \\ 0 & 0 & 0 & 5 \end{array}\right]$$

We cannot pivot about the last zero in the third column, so we have carried the method as far as we can. Let us write out the equations corresponding to the last matrix:

$$\begin{cases} x \qquad\quad = 4 \\ \quad y - z = 1 \\ \qquad\quad 0 = 5. \end{cases}$$

Note that the last equation is a built-in contradiction. The last equation can never be satisfied, no matter what the values of x, y, and z are. Thus, the original system has no solution. Systems with no solution can always be detected by the presence of a matrix row of the form $[0 \quad 0 \quad \cdots \quad 0 \mid a]$, where a is a nonzero number.

>> ***Now Try Exercise 25***

EXAMPLE 3 **Solving a System of Equations That Has Infinitely Many Solutions** Determine all solutions of the system

$$\begin{cases} 2x + 2y + 4z = 8 \\ x - \ \ y + 2z = 2 \\ -x + 5y - 2z = 2. \end{cases}$$

SOLUTION We set up the matrix corresponding to the system and perform the appropriate pivoting operations.

$$\left[\begin{array}{rrr|r} \textcircled{2} & 2 & 4 & 8 \\ 1 & -1 & 2 & 2 \\ -1 & 5 & -2 & 2 \end{array}\right] \xrightarrow[\substack{R_2 + (-1)R_1 \\ R_3 + 1R_2}]{\frac{1}{2}R_1} \left[\begin{array}{rrr|r} 1 & 1 & 2 & 4 \\ 0 & \textcircled{-2} & 0 & -2 \\ 0 & 6 & 0 & 6 \end{array}\right]$$

$$\xrightarrow[\substack{R_1 + (-1)R_2 \\ R_3 + (-6)R_2}]{(-\frac{1}{2})R_2} \left[\begin{array}{rrr|r} 1 & 0 & 2 & 3 \\ 0 & 1 & 0 & 1 \\ 0 & 0 & 0 & 0 \end{array}\right]$$

Note that our method must terminate here, since there is no way to transform the third entry in the third column into a 1 without disturbing the columns already in appropriate form. The equations corresponding to the last matrix read

$$\begin{cases} x \quad + 2z = 3 \\ \quad y \quad\ \ = 1 \\ \qquad\ \ 0 = 0. \end{cases}$$

The last equation does not involve any of the variables and so may be omitted. This leaves the two equations

$$\begin{cases} x \quad + 2z = 3 \\ \quad y \quad\ \ = 1. \end{cases}$$

Now, taking the $2z$-term in the first equation to the right side, we can write the equations

$$\begin{cases} x = 3 - 2z \\ y = 1. \end{cases}$$

The value of y is given: $y = 1$. The value of x is given in terms of z. To find a solution to this system, assign any value to z. Then, the first equation gives a value for x and thereby a specific solution to the system. For example, if we take $z = 1$, then the corresponding specific solution is

$$z = 1$$
$$x = 3 - 2(1) = 1$$
$$y = 1.$$

If we take $z = -3$, the corresponding specific solution is

$$z = -3$$
$$x = 3 - 2(-3) = 9$$
$$y = 1.$$

Thus, we see that the original system has infinitely many specific solutions, corresponding to the infinitely many possible different choices for z.

We say that the **general solution** of the system is

$$z = \text{any value}$$
$$x = 3 - 2z$$
$$y = 1.$$

»» *Now Try Exercise 27*

Gauss–Jordan Elimination Method for the Matrix of a Linear System That Cannot Be Transformed into Diagonal Form

1. Apply the Gauss–Jordan elimination method to put as many columns as possible into proper form. (A column is in proper form if one entry is 1 and the other entries are 0.) Proceed from left to right, but do not disturb columns that have already been put into proper form. As much as possible, each row should have a 1 in its leftmost nonzero entry. (Such a 1 is called a *leading 1*.) The column for each leading 1 should be to the right of the columns for the leading 1s in the rows above it.
2. If at any time one or more of the rows is of the form $[0\ 0\ \cdots\ 0\,|\,a]$, where a is a nonzero number, then the linear system has no solution.
3. Otherwise, there are infinitely many solutions. Variables corresponding to columns not in proper form can assume any value. The other variables can then be expressed in terms of these variables.

EXAMPLE 4 **Solving a System of Equations That Has Infinitely Many Solutions** Find all solutions of the linear system

$$\begin{cases} x + 2y - z + 3w = 5 \\ \quad\;\; y + 2z + w = 7. \end{cases}$$

SOLUTION The Gauss–Jordan elimination method proceeds as follows:

$$\left[\begin{array}{cccc|c} 1 & 2 & -1 & 3 & 5 \\ 0 & \textcircled{1} & 2 & 1 & 7 \end{array}\right] \quad \text{(The first column is already in proper form.)}$$

$$\xrightarrow{R_1 + (-2)R_1} \left[\begin{array}{cccc|c} 1 & 0 & -5 & 1 & -9 \\ 0 & 1 & 2 & 1 & 7 \end{array}\right].$$

We cannot do anything further with the third and fourth columns (without disturbing the first two columns), so the corresponding variables, z and w, can assume any values. Writing down the equations corresponding to the last matrix yields

$$\begin{cases} x \quad\; - 5z + w = -9 \\ \quad y + 2z + w = \;\;\, 7 \end{cases}$$

or

$$\begin{aligned} z &= \text{any value} \\ w &= \text{any value} \\ x &= -9 + 5z - w \\ y &= \;\;\, 7 - 2z - w. \end{aligned}$$

To determine a specific solution, let, for example, $z = 1$ and $w = 2$. Then, a specific solution of the original system is

$$\begin{aligned} z &= 1 \\ w &= 2 \\ x &= -9 + 5(1) - (2) = -6 \\ y &= \;\;\, 7 - 2(1) - (2) = \;\;\, 3. \end{aligned}$$

» Now Try Exercise 33

EXAMPLE 5 **Solving a System of Equations That Has Infinitely Many Solutions** Find all solutions of the system of equations

$$\begin{cases} \;\; x - \;\, 7y + \;\, z = 3 \\ 2x - 14y + 3z = 4. \end{cases}$$

SOLUTION The first pivot operation is routine:

$$\left[\begin{array}{ccc|c} \textcircled{1} & -7 & 1 & 3 \\ 2 & -14 & 3 & 4 \end{array}\right] \xrightarrow{R_2 + (-2)R_1} \left[\begin{array}{ccc|c} 1 & -7 & 1 & 3 \\ 0 & 0 & 1 & -2 \end{array}\right].$$

However, it is impossible to pivot about the zero in the second column. So skip the second column and pivot about the second entry in the third column to get

$$\xrightarrow{R_1 + (-1)R_2} \left[\begin{array}{ccc|c} 1 & -7 & 0 & 5 \\ 0 & 0 & 1 & -2 \end{array}\right].$$

This is as far as we can go. The variable corresponding to the second column—namely, y—can assume any value, and the general solution of the system is obtained from the equations

$$\begin{cases} x - 7y \quad = 5 \\ \qquad\quad z = -2. \end{cases}$$

Therefore, the general solution of the system is

$$y = \text{any value}$$
$$x = 5 + 7y$$
$$z = -2.$$

» Now Try Exercise 37

EXAMPLE 6 **Finding Specific Solutions** A high school music department purchased a total of 20 new clarinets, trumpets, and violins in anticipation of increased interest in these instruments. Each clarinet cost \$1400, each trumpet cost \$1200, and each violin cost \$900. If the music department spent a total of \$24,900, give two different combinations for the number of each type of instrument purchased.

SOLUTION Let x be the number of clarinets purchased, y be the number of trumpets purchased, and z be the number of violins purchased. Since a total of 20 instruments are purchased, $x + y + z = 20$. Since the cost of each instrument is given, the total cost is given by $1400x + 1200y + 900z = 24900$.

So we need to solve the system

$$\begin{cases} x + y + z = 20 \\ 1400x + 1200y + 900z = 24900 \end{cases}$$

Applying the Gauss-Jordan elimination method to this system we get

$$\left[\begin{array}{ccc|c} 1 & 1 & 1 & 20 \\ 1400 & 1200 & 900 & 24900 \end{array}\right] \xrightarrow{R_2 + (-1400)R_1} \left[\begin{array}{ccc|c} 1 & 1 & 1 & 20 \\ 0 & -200 & -500 & -3100 \end{array}\right]$$

$$\xrightarrow{-\frac{1}{200}R_2} \left[\begin{array}{ccc|c} 1 & 1 & 1 & 20 \\ 0 & 1 & \frac{5}{2} & \frac{31}{2} \end{array}\right] \xrightarrow{R_1 + (-1)R_2} \left[\begin{array}{ccc|c} 1 & 0 & -\frac{3}{2} & \frac{9}{2} \\ 0 & 1 & \frac{5}{2} & \frac{31}{2} \end{array}\right].$$

So the general solution to this system of equations is

$$x = \tfrac{9}{2} + \tfrac{3}{2}z,\ y = \tfrac{31}{2} - \tfrac{5}{2}z,\ z = \text{any value}.$$

However this problem is about instruments so z can't really be ANY value. Notice that if $z = 0$, then $x = \frac{9}{2} = 4.5$ which doesn't make sense since x is the number of clarinets. So we need to be careful in selecting values for z. If $z = 1$, then $x = 6$ and $y = 13$ which are all sensible values for a number of instruments. Similarly, if we let $z = 3$, then $x = 9$ and $y = 8$ are also sensible values. Therefore, the music department could have purchased 6 clarinets, 13 trumpets, and 1 violin, or 9 clarinets, 8 trumpets, and 3 violins.

» Now Try Exercise 45

At first, it might seem strange that some systems have no solution, some have one, and yet others have infinitely many. The reason for the difference can be explained geometrically. For simplicity, consider the case of systems of two equations in two variables. Each equation in this case has a graph in the xy-plane, and the graph is a straight line. As we have seen, solving the system corresponds to finding the points lying on both lines. There are three possibilities. First, the two lines may intersect. In this case, the solution is unique. Second, the two lines may be parallel. Then, the two lines do not intersect and the system has no solution. Finally, the two equations may represent the same line, as for example, the equations $2x + 3y = 1$ and $4x + 6y = 2$ do. In this case, every point on the line is a solution of the system; that is, there are infinitely many solutions (Fig. 1).

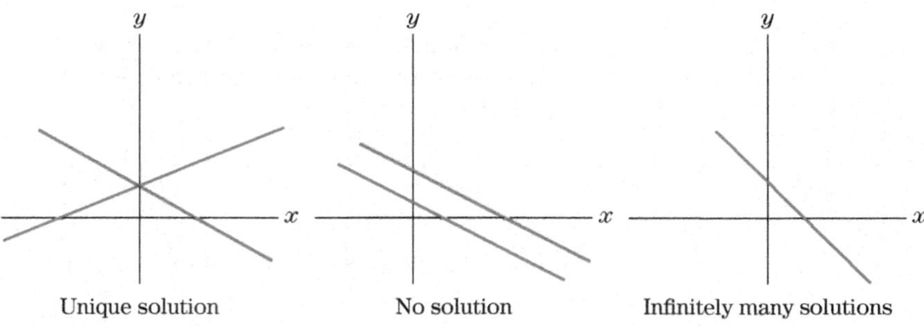

Figure 1

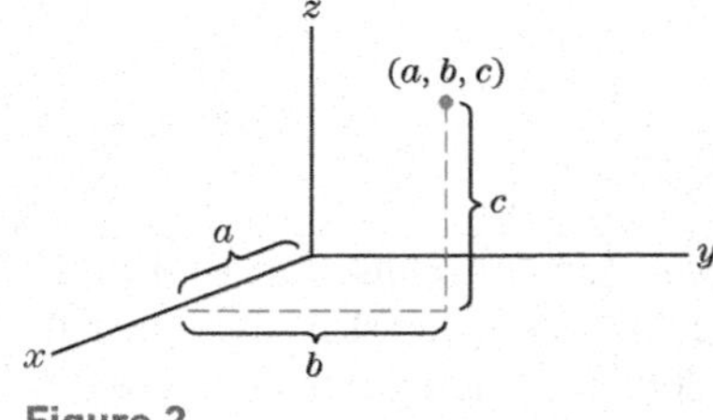

Figure 2

Systems of three equations in three variables can be examined in an analogous way by using a 3-dimensional coordinate system. The point having coordinates (a, b, c) is obtained by starting at the origin and moving a units in the x-direction, b units in the y-direction, and then c units in the z-direction (up if c is positive, down if c is negative). See Fig. 2. The collection of points that satisfy a specific linear equation in three variables forms a plane. Therefore, the solution of a system of linear equations in three variables consists of all points that are simultaneously on the planes corresponding to each equation. Figure 3 shows some possible configurations for these planes.

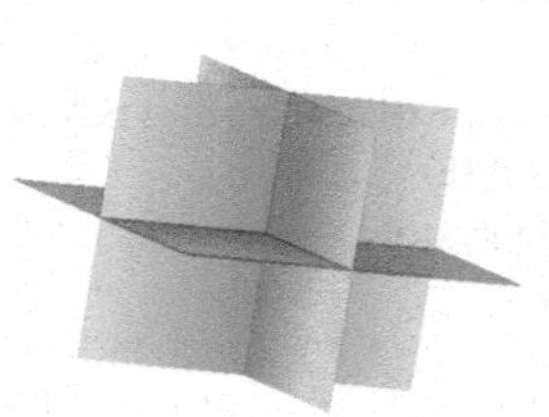

Unique solution

No solution

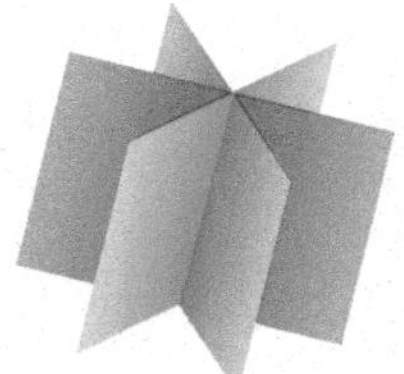

Infinitely many solutions

Figure 3

Check Your Understanding 4.2

Solutions can be found following the section exercises.

1. Find a specific solution to a system of linear equations whose general solution is

$$\begin{aligned} w &= \text{any value} \\ y &= \text{any value} \\ z &= 7 + 6w \\ x &= 26 - 2y + 14w. \end{aligned}$$

2. Find all solutions of this system of linear equations.

$$\begin{cases} 2x + 4y - 4z - 4w = 24 \\ -3x - 6y + 10z - 18w = -8 \\ -x - 2y + 4z - 10w = 2 \end{cases}$$

EXERCISES 4.2

In Exercises 1–8, pivot the matrix about the circled element.

1. $\begin{bmatrix} \textcircled{2} & -4 & 6 \\ 3 & 7 & 1 \end{bmatrix}$

2. $\begin{bmatrix} 1 & 2 & 3 \\ 4 & \textcircled{8} & -12 \end{bmatrix}$

3. $\begin{bmatrix} 7 & 1 & 4 & 5 \\ -1 & 1 & \textcircled{2} & 6 \\ 4 & 0 & 2 & 3 \end{bmatrix}$

4. $\begin{bmatrix} 5 & 10 & -10 & 12 \\ 4 & 3 & 6 & 12 \\ 4 & \textcircled{-4} & 4 & -16 \end{bmatrix}$

5. $\begin{bmatrix} \textcircled{2} & 3 \\ 6 & 0 \\ 1 & 5 \end{bmatrix}$

6. $\begin{bmatrix} 2 & 1 \\ \textcircled{-1} & 0 \end{bmatrix}$

7. $\begin{bmatrix} 4 & 3 & 0 \\ \frac{2}{3} & 0 & -2 \\ 1 & 3 & \textcircled{6} \end{bmatrix}$

8. $\begin{bmatrix} 1 & 0 & 2 \\ -1 & 1 & \textcircled{-2} \\ 1 & 2 & 6 \end{bmatrix}$

In Exercises 9–28, use the Gauss–Jordan elimination method to find all solutions of the system of linear equations.

9. $\begin{cases} 2x - 4y = 6 \\ -x + 2y = -3 \end{cases}$

10. $\begin{cases} -\frac{1}{2}x + y = \frac{3}{2} \\ -3x + 6y = 10 \end{cases}$

11. $\begin{cases} -x + 3y = 11 \\ 3x - 9y = -30 \end{cases}$

12. $\begin{cases} .25x - .75y = 1 \\ -2x + 6y = -8 \end{cases}$

13. $\begin{cases} x + 2y = 5 \\ 3x - y = 1 \\ -x + 3y = 5 \end{cases}$

14. $\begin{cases} x - 6y = 12 \\ -\frac{1}{2}x + 3y = -6 \\ \frac{1}{3}x - 2y = 4 \end{cases}$

15. $\begin{cases} 4x + 5y = 3 \\ 3x + 6y = 1 \\ 2x - 3y = 7 \end{cases}$

16. $\begin{cases} 2x + 3y = 12 \\ 2x - 3y = 0 \\ 5x - y = 13 \end{cases}$

17. $\begin{cases} x - y + 3z = 3 \\ -2x + 3y - 11z = -4 \\ x - 2y + 8z = 6 \end{cases}$

18. $\begin{cases} x - 3y + z = 5 \\ -2x + 7y - 6z = -9 \\ x - 2y - 3z = 6 \end{cases}$

19. $\begin{cases} x + y + z = -1 \\ 2x + 3y + 2z = 3 \\ 2x + y + 2z = -7 \end{cases}$

20. $\begin{cases} x - 3y + 2z = 10 \\ -x + 3y - z = -6 \\ -x + 3y + 2z = 6 \end{cases}$

21. $\begin{cases} 6x - 2y + 2z = 4 \\ 3x - y + 2z = 2 \\ -12x + 4y - 8z = 8 \end{cases}$

22. $\begin{cases} x + 2y + 3z = 4 \\ 5x + 6y + 7z = 8 \\ x + 2y + 3z = 5 \end{cases}$

23. $\begin{cases} x + 2y + 8z = 1 \\ 3x - y + 4z = 10 \\ -x + 5y + 10z = -8 \\ x + y + z = 3 \end{cases}$

24. $\begin{cases} 2x + 6y + 6z = 0 \\ -3x - 10y + z = 1 \\ -x - 4y + 3z = 1 \\ 5x + 6y + 8z = 9 \end{cases}$

25. $\begin{cases} x + y - 2z + 2w = 5 \\ 2x + y - 4z + w = 5 \\ 3x + 4y - 6z + 9w = 20 \\ 4x + 4y - 8z + 8w = 20 \end{cases}$

26. $\begin{cases} 2y + z - w = 1 \\ x - y + z + w = 14 \\ -x - 9y - z + 4w = 11 \\ x + y + z = 9 \end{cases}$

27. $\begin{cases} x - y + z + w = 1 \\ y + 3z + 2w = -7 \\ y - z - 3w = 1 \\ x + 4z + 3w = 0 \end{cases}$

28. $\begin{cases} x + y + 2w = 4 \\ x + 2y + 2z = 7 \\ 2x + y - z + 6w = 5 \\ -x + y + 2z - 6w = 2 \end{cases}$

In Exercises 29–32, find three solutions to the system of equations.

29. $\begin{cases} x + 2y + z = 5 \\ y + 3z = 9 \end{cases}$

30. $\begin{cases} x + 5y + 3z = 9 \\ 2x + 9y + 7z = 5 \end{cases}$

31. $\begin{cases} x + 7y - 3z = 8 \\ z = 5 \end{cases}$

32. $\begin{cases} x = 4 \\ y - 3z = 7 \end{cases}$

33. **Nutrition Planning** In a laboratory experiment, a researcher wants to provide a rabbit with exactly 1000 units of vitamin A, exactly 1600 units of vitamin C, and exactly 2400 units of vitamin E. The rabbit is fed a mixture of three foods whose nutritional content is given by the accompanying table. How many grams of each food should the rabbit be fed?

	Food 1	Food 2	Food 3
Vitamin A (units per gram)	2	4	6
Vitamin C (units per gram)	3	7	10
Vitamin E (units per gram)	5	9	14

34. **Nutrition Planning** Rework Exercise 41 with the requirement for vitamin E changed to 2000 units.

35. **Nutrition Planning** The nutritional content of three foods is given by the accompanying table. Use the methods of this section to show that no combination of these three foods can contain 72 units of B-12, 68 calories, and 60 units of iron.

	Food A	Food B	Food C
B-12 (units per gram)	3	10	15
Calories (per gram)	4	12	8
Iron (units per gram)	5	14	1

36. **Nutrition Planning** Refer to Exercise 43. Show that when the required units of iron are increased to 64 units, there are several combinations of the three foods that meet the requirement. Give two such combinations.

37. **Furniture Manufacturing** A furniture manufacturer makes sofas, chairs, and ottomans. The accompanying table gives the number of hours of labor required for the carpentry and upholstery that goes into each item. Suppose that, each day, 380 labor-hours are available for carpentry and 450 labor-hours are available for upholstery. Give three different combinations for the numbers of each type of furniture that can be manufactured each day.

	Ottoman	Sofa	Chair
Carpentry	1 hour	3 hours	6 hours
Upholstery	3 hours	6 hours	3 hours

38. **Computer Equipment** An office manager placed an order for computers, printers, and scanners. Each computer cost \$1000, each printer cost \$100, and each scanner cost \$400. She ordered 15 items for \$10,200. Give two different combinations for the numbers of each type of item that she could have purchased.

39. **Quilting** Granny's Custom Quilts receives an order for a patchwork quilt made from square patches of three types: solid green, solid blue, and floral. The quilt is to be 8 squares by 12 squares, and there must be 15 times as many solid squares as floral squares. If Granny's charges \$3 per solid square and \$5 per floral square, and if the customer wishes to spend exactly \$300, how many of each type of square may be used in the quilt?

40. **Purchasing Options** Amanda is decorating her new home and wants to buy some house plants. She is interested in three types of plants costing \$7, \$10, and \$13. If she has budgeted exactly \$150 for the plants and wants to buy exactly 15 of them, what are her options?

41. For what values(s) of k will the following system of linear equations have no solution? Infinitely many solutions?

$$\begin{cases} 2x - 3y = 4 \\ -6x + 9y = k \end{cases}$$

42. For what value of k will the following system of linear equations have a solution?

$$\begin{cases} 2x + 6y = 4 \\ x + 7y = 10 \\ kx + 8y = 4 \end{cases}$$

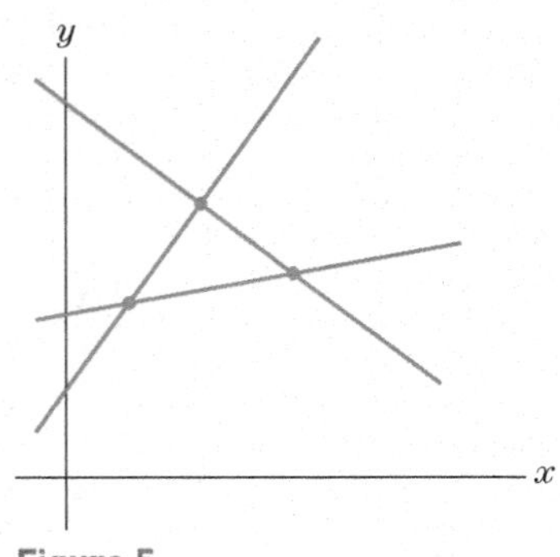

Figure 5

43. Figure 5 shows the graphs of the equations from a system of three linear equations in two variables. How many solutions does the system have?

44. Suppose that after the Gauss–Jordan elimination method has been applied to a matrix corresponding to a system of linear equations, the matrix has a row of all zeros. Must the system have infinitely many solutions?

Solutions to Check Your Understanding 4.2

1. Since w and y can each assume any value, select any numbers—say, $w = 1$ and $y = 2$. Then, $z = 7 + 6(1) = 13$ and $x = 26 - 2(2) + 14(1) = 36$. So $x = 36$, $y = 2$, $z = 13$, $w = 1$ is a specific solution. There are infinitely many different specific solutions, since there are infinitely many different choices for w and y.

2. Apply the Gauss–Jordan elimination method to the matrix of the system.

$$\left[\begin{array}{rrrr|r} \textcircled{2} & 4 & -4 & -4 & 24 \\ -3 & -6 & 10 & -18 & -8 \\ -1 & -2 & 4 & -10 & 2 \end{array}\right]$$

$$\xrightarrow[\substack{R_2 + 3R_1 \\ R_3 + 1R_1}]{\frac{1}{2}R_1} \left[\begin{array}{rrrr|r} 1 & 2 & -2 & -2 & 12 \\ 0 & 0 & \textcircled{4} & -24 & 28 \\ 0 & 0 & 2 & -12 & 14 \end{array}\right]$$

$$\xrightarrow[\substack{R_1 + 2R_2 \\ R_3 + (-2)R_2}]{\frac{1}{4}R_2} \left[\begin{array}{rrrr|r} 1 & 2 & 0 & -14 & 26 \\ 0 & 0 & 1 & -6 & 7 \\ 0 & 0 & 0 & 0 & 0 \end{array}\right]$$

The corresponding system of equations is

$$\begin{cases} x + 2y \qquad - 14w = 26 \\ \qquad\qquad z - \ 6w = 7. \end{cases}$$

The general solution is

$$w = \text{any value}$$
$$y = \text{any value}$$
$$z = 7 + 6w$$
$$x = 26 - 2y + 14w.$$

4.3 Arithmetic Operations on Matrices

We introduced matrices in Sections 4.1 and 4.2 to display the coefficients of a system of linear equations. For example, the linear system

$$\begin{cases} 5x - 3y = \frac{1}{2} \\ 4x + 3y = -1 \end{cases}$$

is represented by the matrix

$$\left[\begin{array}{rr|r} 5 & -3 & \frac{1}{2} \\ 4 & 2 & -1 \end{array}\right].$$

After we have become accustomed to using such matrices in solving linear systems, we may omit the vertical line that separates the left and right sides of the equations. We need only remember that the right side of the equations is recorded in the right column. So, for example, we would write the preceding matrix in the form

$$\begin{bmatrix} 5 & -3 & \frac{1}{2} \\ 4 & 2 & -1 \end{bmatrix}.$$

A matrix is *any* rectangular array of numbers and may be of any size. Here are some examples of matrices of various sizes.

$$\begin{bmatrix} 3 & 7 \\ 0 & -1 \end{bmatrix}, \quad \begin{bmatrix} 1 \\ 2 \end{bmatrix}, \quad [2 \quad 1], \quad [6], \quad \begin{bmatrix} 5 & 7 & -1 \\ 0 & 3 & 5 \\ 6 & 0 & 5 \end{bmatrix}.$$

Matrices can be added, subtracted, and multiplied. This section discusses these arithmetic operations and how they are used in applications. Before we can do so, however, we need some vocabulary with which to describe matrices.

A matrix is described by its **size**—that is, the number of rows and columns that it contains. For example, the matrix

$$\begin{bmatrix} 7 & 5 \\ \frac{1}{2} & -2 \\ 2 & -11 \end{bmatrix}$$

has three rows and two columns and is referred to as a *3 × 2* (read: "three-by-two") *matrix*. The matrix $[4 \quad 5 \quad 0]$ has one row and three columns and is a *1 × 3 matrix*. A matrix with only one row is called a **row matrix**. A matrix, such as

$$\begin{bmatrix} 2 \\ 7 \end{bmatrix},$$

that has only one column is called a **column matrix**. If a matrix has the same number of rows and columns, it is called a **square matrix**. Here are some square matrices of various sizes:

$$[5], \quad \begin{bmatrix} 1 & 2 \\ 3 & 4 \end{bmatrix}, \quad \begin{bmatrix} 2 & -1 & 0 \\ 3 & 5 & 4 \\ 0 & 3 & -7 \end{bmatrix}.$$

The rows of a matrix are numbered from the top down, and the columns are numbered from left to right. For example, the first row of the matrix

$$A = \begin{bmatrix} 1 & -1 & 0 \\ 2 & 1 & 7 \\ -3 & 2 & 4 \end{bmatrix}$$

is $[1 \quad -1 \quad 0]$, and its third column is

$$\begin{bmatrix} 0 \\ 7 \\ 4 \end{bmatrix}.$$

The numbers in a matrix, called **entries**, may be identified in terms of the row and column containing the entry in question. For example, the entry in the first row, third column, of matrix A is 0:

$$\begin{bmatrix} 1 & -1 & 0 \\ 2 & 1 & 7 \\ -3 & 2 & 4 \end{bmatrix};$$

the entry in the second row, first column, is 2:

$$\begin{bmatrix} 1 & -1 & 0 \\ 2 & 1 & 7 \\ -3 & 2 & 4 \end{bmatrix};$$

and the entry in the third row, third column, is 4:

$$\begin{bmatrix} 1 & -1 & 0 \\ 2 & 1 & 7 \\ -3 & 2 & 4 \end{bmatrix}.$$

We use double-subscripted lowercase letters to indicate the locations of the entries of a matrix. We denote the entry in the ith row, jth column, of the matrix A by a_{ij}. For instance, we have $a_{13} = 0$, $a_{21} = 2$, and $a_{33} = 4$.

We say that two matrices A and B are **equal**, denoted $A = B$, provided that they have the same size and that all of their corresponding entries are equal.

Addition and Subtraction of Matrices

We define the sum $A + B$ of two matrices A and B only if A and B are two matrices of the same size—that is, if A and B have the same number of rows and the same number of columns. In this case, $A + B$ is the matrix formed by adding the corresponding entries of A and B. For example,

$$\begin{bmatrix} 2 & 0 \\ 1 & 1 \\ 5 & 3 \end{bmatrix} + \begin{bmatrix} 5 & 4 \\ 0 & 2 \\ 2 & 6 \end{bmatrix} = \begin{bmatrix} 2+5 & 0+4 \\ 1+0 & 1+2 \\ 5+2 & 3+6 \end{bmatrix} = \begin{bmatrix} 7 & 4 \\ 1 & 3 \\ 7 & 9 \end{bmatrix}.$$

We subtract matrices of the same size by subtracting corresponding entries. Thus, we have

$$\begin{bmatrix} 7 \\ 1 \end{bmatrix} - \begin{bmatrix} 3 \\ 2 \end{bmatrix} = \begin{bmatrix} 7-3 \\ 1-2 \end{bmatrix} = \begin{bmatrix} 4 \\ -1 \end{bmatrix}.$$

Multiplication of Matrices

It might seem that, to define the product of two matrices, one would start with two matrices of like size and multiply the corresponding entries. But this definition is not useful, since the calculations that arise in applications require a somewhat more complex multiplication. In the interests of simplicity, we start by defining the product of a row matrix times a column matrix.

If A is a row matrix and B is a column matrix, then we can form the product $A \cdot B$ provided that the two matrices have the same length. The product $A \cdot B$ is the 1×1 matrix obtained by multiplying corresponding entries of A and B and then forming the sum.

We may put this definition into algebraic terms as follows. Suppose that A is the row matrix

$$A = [a_1 \quad a_2 \quad \cdots \quad a_n],$$

and B is the column matrix

$$B = \begin{bmatrix} b_1 \\ b_2 \\ \vdots \\ b_n \end{bmatrix}.$$

Note that A and B are both of the same length—namely, n. Then,

$$A \cdot B = [a_1 \quad a_2 \quad \cdots \quad a_n] \cdot \begin{bmatrix} b_1 \\ b_2 \\ \vdots \\ b_n \end{bmatrix}$$

is calculated by multiplying corresponding entries of A and B and forming the sum; that is,

$$A \cdot B = [a_1b_1 + a_2b_2 + \cdots + a_nb_n].$$

Notice that the product is a 1×1 matrix—namely, a single number in brackets.

Here are some examples of the product of a row matrix times a column matrix:

$$\begin{bmatrix} 3 & \frac{1}{2} \end{bmatrix} \cdot \begin{bmatrix} 1 \\ 4 \end{bmatrix} = \begin{bmatrix} 3 \cdot 1 + \frac{1}{2} \cdot 4 \end{bmatrix} = [5];$$

$$[2 \quad 0 \quad -1] \cdot \begin{bmatrix} 6 \\ 5 \\ 3 \end{bmatrix} = [2 \cdot 6 + 0 \cdot 5 + (-1) \cdot 3] = [9].$$

In multiplying a row matrix times a column matrix, it helps to use both of your hands. Use your left index finger to point to the first element of the row matrix and your right to point to the first element of the column matrix. Multiply the elements that you are pointing to, and keep a running total of the products in your head. After each multiplication, move your fingers to the next elements of each matrix. With a little practice, you should be able to multiply a row times a column quickly and accurately.

The preceding definition of *multiplication* may seem strange. But products of this sort occur in many down-to-earth problems. Consider, for instance, the next example.

EXAMPLE 1 **Total Revenue as a Matrix Product** A dairy farm produces three items—milk, eggs, and cheese. The wholesale prices of the three items are \$1.70 per gallon, \$.80 per dozen, and \$3.30 per pound, respectively. In a certain week, the dairy farm sells 30,000 gallons of milk, 2000 dozen eggs, and 5000 pounds of cheese. Represent its total revenue as a matrix product.

SOLUTION The total revenue equals

$$(1.70)(30{,}000) + (.80)(2000) + (3.30)(5000).$$

This suggests that we define two matrices. The first displays the prices of the various items:

$$[1.70 \quad .80 \quad 3.30].$$

The second represents the production:

$$\begin{bmatrix} 30{,}000 \\ 2000 \\ 5000 \end{bmatrix}.$$

Then, the revenue for the week, when placed in a 1×1 matrix, equals

$$[1.70 \quad .80 \quad 3.30] \begin{bmatrix} 30{,}000 \\ 2000 \\ 5000 \end{bmatrix} = [69{,}100].$$

» Now Try Exercise 89

The principle behind Example 1 is this: Any sum of products of the form $a_1b_1 + a_2b_2 + \cdots + a_nb_n$, when placed in a 1×1 matrix, can be written as the matrix product

$$[a_1b_1 + a_2b_2 + \cdots + a_nb_n] = [a_1 \quad a_2 \quad \cdots \quad a_n] \cdot \begin{bmatrix} b_1 \\ b_2 \\ \vdots \\ b_n \end{bmatrix}.$$

Let us illustrate the procedure for multiplying more general matrices by working out a typical product:

$$\begin{bmatrix} 2 & 1 \\ 0 & 1 \\ 1 & 0 \end{bmatrix} \cdot \begin{bmatrix} 1 & 1 \\ 4 & 2 \end{bmatrix}.$$

To obtain the entries of the product, we multiply the rows of the left matrix by the columns of the right matrix, taking care to arrange the products in a specific way to yield a matrix, as follows. Start with the first row on the left, $[2 \quad 1]$, and the first column on the right, $\begin{bmatrix} 1 \\ 4 \end{bmatrix}$. Their product is [6], so we enter 6 as the element in the first row, first column, of the product:

$$\begin{bmatrix} 2 & 1 \\ 0 & 1 \\ 1 & 0 \end{bmatrix} \cdot \begin{bmatrix} 1 & 1 \\ 4 & 2 \end{bmatrix} = \begin{bmatrix} 6 & \\ & \\ & \end{bmatrix}.$$

The product of the first row of the left matrix and the second column of the right matrix is [4], so we put a 4 in the first row, second column, of the product:

$$\begin{bmatrix} 2 & 1 \\ 0 & 1 \\ 1 & 0 \end{bmatrix} \cdot \begin{bmatrix} 1 & 1 \\ 4 & 2 \end{bmatrix} = \begin{bmatrix} 6 & 4 \\ & \\ & \end{bmatrix}.$$

There are no more columns that can be multiplied by the first row, so let us move to the second row and shift back to the first column. Correspondingly, we move down one row in the product.

$$\begin{bmatrix} 2 & 1 \\ 0 & 1 \\ 1 & 0 \end{bmatrix} \cdot \begin{bmatrix} 1 & 1 \\ 4 & 2 \end{bmatrix} = \begin{bmatrix} 6 & 4 \\ 4 & \\ & \end{bmatrix};$$

$$\begin{bmatrix} 2 & 1 \\ 0 & 1 \\ 1 & 0 \end{bmatrix} \cdot \begin{bmatrix} 1 & 1 \\ 4 & 2 \end{bmatrix} = \begin{bmatrix} 6 & 4 \\ 4 & 2 \\ & \end{bmatrix}.$$

We have now exhausted the second row of the left matrix, so we shift to the third row and, correspondingly, move down one row in the product:

$$\begin{bmatrix} 2 & 1 \\ 0 & 1 \\ 1 & 0 \end{bmatrix} \cdot \begin{bmatrix} 1 & 1 \\ 4 & 2 \end{bmatrix} = \begin{bmatrix} 6 & 4 \\ 4 & 2 \\ 1 & \end{bmatrix};$$

$$\begin{bmatrix} 2 & 1 \\ 0 & 1 \\ 1 & 0 \end{bmatrix} \cdot \begin{bmatrix} 1 & 1 \\ 4 & 2 \end{bmatrix} = \begin{bmatrix} 6 & 4 \\ 4 & 2 \\ 1 & 1 \end{bmatrix}.$$

Note that we have now multiplied every row of the left matrix by every column of the right matrix. This completes the computation of the product:

$$\begin{bmatrix} 2 & 1 \\ 0 & 1 \\ 1 & 0 \end{bmatrix} \cdot \begin{bmatrix} 1 & 1 \\ 4 & 2 \end{bmatrix} = \begin{bmatrix} 6 & 4 \\ 4 & 2 \\ 1 & 1 \end{bmatrix}.$$

EXAMPLE 2 **Matrix Multiplication** Calculate the following product:

$$\begin{bmatrix} 1 & 5 \\ 3 & 2 \end{bmatrix} \cdot \begin{bmatrix} 1 & 2 \\ 1 & 0 \end{bmatrix}.$$

SOLUTION

$$\begin{bmatrix} 1 & 5 \\ 3 & 2 \end{bmatrix} \cdot \begin{bmatrix} 1 & 2 \\ 1 & 0 \end{bmatrix} = \begin{bmatrix} 6 & \\ & \end{bmatrix}$$

$$\begin{bmatrix} 1 & 5 \\ 3 & 2 \end{bmatrix} \cdot \begin{bmatrix} 1 & 2 \\ 1 & 0 \end{bmatrix} = \begin{bmatrix} 6 & 2 \\ & \end{bmatrix}$$

$$\begin{bmatrix} 1 & 5 \\ 3 & 2 \end{bmatrix} \cdot \begin{bmatrix} 1 & 2 \\ 1 & 0 \end{bmatrix} = \begin{bmatrix} 6 & 2 \\ 5 & \end{bmatrix}$$

$$\begin{bmatrix} 1 & 5 \\ 3 & 2 \end{bmatrix} \cdot \begin{bmatrix} 1 & 2 \\ 1 & 0 \end{bmatrix} = \begin{bmatrix} 6 & 2 \\ 5 & 6 \end{bmatrix}$$

Thus,

$$\begin{bmatrix} 1 & 5 \\ 3 & 2 \end{bmatrix} \cdot \begin{bmatrix} 1 & 2 \\ 1 & 0 \end{bmatrix} = \begin{bmatrix} 6 & 2 \\ 5 & 6 \end{bmatrix}.$$

» Now Try Exercise 33

Notice that we cannot use the preceding method to compute the product $A \cdot B$ of *any* matrices A and B. For the procedure to work, it is crucial that the number of entries of each row of A be the same as the number of entries of each column of B. (Or, to put it another way, the number of columns of the left matrix must equal the number of rows of the right matrix.) Therefore, in order for us to form the product $A \cdot B$, the sizes of A and B must match up in a special way. If A is $m \times n$ and B is $p \times q$, then the product $A \cdot B$ is defined only in case the "inner" dimensions n and p are equal. In that case, the size of the product is determined by the "outer" dimensions m and q. It is an $m \times q$ matrix:

$$\underset{m \times n}{A} \cdot \underset{p \times q}{B} = \underset{m \times q}{C}.$$

equal

So, for example,

$$\underset{3 \times 4}{\begin{bmatrix} & & & \\ & & & \\ & & & \end{bmatrix}} \underset{4 \times 2}{\begin{bmatrix} & \\ & \\ & \\ & \end{bmatrix}} = \underset{3 \times 2}{\begin{bmatrix} & \\ & \\ & \end{bmatrix}}$$

$$\underset{2 \times 2}{\begin{bmatrix} & \\ & \end{bmatrix}} \underset{2 \times 1}{\begin{bmatrix} \\ \end{bmatrix}} = \underset{2 \times 1}{\begin{bmatrix} \\ \end{bmatrix}}.$$

If the sizes of A and B do not match up in the way just described, the product $A \cdot B$ is not defined.

EXAMPLE 3 **Matrix Multiplication** Calculate the following products, if defined:

(a) $\begin{bmatrix} 3 & -1 \\ 2 & 0 \\ 1 & 5 \end{bmatrix} \begin{bmatrix} 1 & 0 \\ 5 & -4 \\ 2 & -1 \end{bmatrix}$ **(b)** $\begin{bmatrix} 3 & -1 \\ 2 & 0 \\ 1 & 5 \end{bmatrix} \begin{bmatrix} 5 & 4 \\ -2 & 3 \end{bmatrix}$

SOLUTION

(a) The matrices to be multiplied are 3×2 and 3×2. The inner dimensions do not match, so the product is undefined.

(b) We are asked to multiply a 3×2 matrix times a 2×2 matrix. The inner dimensions match, so the product is defined and has size determined by the outer dimensions—that is, 3×2.

$$\begin{bmatrix} 3 & -1 \\ 2 & 0 \\ 1 & 5 \end{bmatrix} \begin{bmatrix} 5 & 4 \\ -2 & 3 \end{bmatrix} = \begin{bmatrix} 3 \cdot 5 + (-1) \cdot (-2) & 3 \cdot 4 + (-1) \cdot 3 \\ 2 \cdot 5 + 0 \cdot (-2) & 2 \cdot 4 + 0 \cdot 3 \\ 1 \cdot 5 + 5 \cdot (-2) & 1 \cdot 4 + 5 \cdot 3 \end{bmatrix}$$

$$= \begin{bmatrix} 17 & 9 \\ 10 & 8 \\ -5 & 19 \end{bmatrix}.$$

» ***Now Try Exercise 35***

Multiplication of matrices has many properties in common with multiplication of ordinary numbers. However, there is at least one important difference. With matrix multiplication, the order of the factors is usually important. For example, the product of a 2×3 matrix times a 3×2 matrix is defined: The product is a 2×2 matrix. If the order is reversed to a 3×2 matrix times a 2×3 matrix, the product is a 3×3 matrix. So reversing the order may change the size of the product. Even when it does not, reversing the order may still change the entries in the product, as the following two products demonstrate:

$$\begin{bmatrix} 1 & 5 \\ 3 & 2 \end{bmatrix} \begin{bmatrix} 1 & 2 \\ 1 & 0 \end{bmatrix} = \begin{bmatrix} 6 & 2 \\ 5 & 6 \end{bmatrix}; \quad \begin{bmatrix} 1 & 2 \\ 1 & 0 \end{bmatrix} \begin{bmatrix} 1 & 5 \\ 3 & 2 \end{bmatrix} = \begin{bmatrix} 7 & 9 \\ 1 & 5 \end{bmatrix}.$$

EXAMPLE 4 **Investment Earnings** An investment trust has investments in three states. Its deposits in each state are divided among bond funds, real estate funds, and capital funds. On January 1, the amount (in millions of dollars) invested in each category by state is given by the matrix

$$\begin{array}{l} \\ \\ \text{State A} \\ \text{State B} \\ \text{State C} \end{array} \begin{array}{c} \text{Bond} \\ \text{funds} \\ \left[\begin{array}{ccc} 10 & 5 & 20 \\ 30 & 12 & 10 \\ 15 & 6 & 25 \end{array}\right] \end{array} .$$

	Bond funds	Real estate funds	Capital funds
State A	10	5	20
State B	30	12	10
State C	15	6	25

The current average yields are 5% for bond funds, 10% for real estate funds, and 7% for capital funds. Determine the earnings of the trust from its investments in each state.

SOLUTION Define the matrix of investment yields by

$$\begin{array}{c}\text{Yield}\\ \begin{bmatrix} .05 \\ .10 \\ .07 \end{bmatrix}\end{array} \begin{array}{l} \\ \text{Bond funds} \\ \text{Real estate funds} \\ \text{Capital funds.} \end{array}$$

The amount earned in state A, for instance, is

$$\begin{aligned} &\begin{bmatrix}\text{amount of}\\ \text{bond funds}\end{bmatrix}\cdot\begin{bmatrix}\text{yield of}\\ \text{bond funds}\end{bmatrix} + \begin{bmatrix}\text{amount of}\\ \text{real estate}\\ \text{funds}\end{bmatrix}\cdot\begin{bmatrix}\text{yield of}\\ \text{real estate}\\ \text{funds}\end{bmatrix} \\ &\qquad + \begin{bmatrix}\text{amount of}\\ \text{capital funds}\end{bmatrix}\cdot\begin{bmatrix}\text{yield of}\\ \text{capital funds}\end{bmatrix} \\ &\qquad = (10)\cdot(.05) + (5)\cdot(.10) + (20)\cdot(.07) \end{aligned}$$

And this is just the first entry of the product:

$$\begin{bmatrix} 10 & 5 & 20 \\ 30 & 12 & 10 \\ 15 & 6 & 25 \end{bmatrix}\begin{bmatrix} .05 \\ .10 \\ .07 \end{bmatrix}.$$

Similarly, the earnings for the other states are the second and third entries of the product. Carrying out the arithmetic, we find that

$$\begin{bmatrix} 10 & 5 & 20 \\ 30 & 12 & 10 \\ 15 & 6 & 25 \end{bmatrix}\begin{bmatrix} .05 \\ .10 \\ .07 \end{bmatrix} = \begin{bmatrix} 2.40 \\ 3.40 \\ 3.10 \end{bmatrix}.$$

Therefore, the trust earns $2.40 million in state A, $3.40 million in state B, and $3.10 million in state C.

>> Now Try Exercise 69(b)

EXAMPLE 5 **Manufacturing Revenue** A clothing manufacturer has factories in Los Angeles, San Antonio, and Newark. Sales (in thousands of items) during the first quarter of last year are summarized in the production matrix

	Los Angeles	San Antonio	Newark
Coats	12	13	38
Shirts	25	5	26
Sweaters	11	8	8
Ties	5	0	12

During this period, the selling price of a coat was \$100, a shirt \$20, a sweater \$35, and a tie \$25.

(a) Use a matrix calculation to determine the total revenue produced by each of the factories.

(b) Suppose that the prices had been \$120, \$15, \$50, and \$20, respectively. How would this have affected the revenue of each factory?

SOLUTION

(a) For each factory, we wish to multiply the price of each item by the number produced to arrive at revenue. Since the production figures for the various items of clothing are arranged down the columns, we arrange the prices in a row matrix, ready for multiplication. The price matrix is

$$\begin{array}{r} \\ \text{Price} \end{array}\begin{array}{cccc} \text{Coat} & \text{Shirt} & \text{Sweater} & \text{Tie} \\ [\ 100 & 20 & 35 & 25\ ]. \end{array}$$

The revenues of the various factories are then the entries of the product

$$[100 \quad 20 \quad 35 \quad 25]\begin{bmatrix} 12 & 13 & 38 \\ 25 & 5 & 26 \\ 11 & 8 & 8 \\ 5 & 0 & 12 \end{bmatrix} = \begin{array}{ccc} \text{Los Angeles} & \text{San Antonio} & \text{Newark} \\ [\ 2210 & 1680 & 4900\ ]. \end{array}$$

Since the production figures are in thousands, the revenue figures are in thousands of dollars. That is, the Los Angeles factory has revenues of \$2,210,000, the San Antonio factory \$1,680,000, and the Newark factory \$4,900,000.

(b) In a similar way, we determine the revenue of each factory if the price matrix had been $[120 \quad 15 \quad 50 \quad 20]$.

$$[120 \quad 15 \quad 50 \quad 20]\begin{bmatrix} 12 & 13 & 38 \\ 25 & 5 & 26 \\ 11 & 8 & 8 \\ 5 & 0 & 12 \end{bmatrix} = \begin{array}{ccc} \text{Los Angeles} & \text{San Antonio} & \text{Newark} \\ [\ 2465 & 2035 & 5590\ ]. \end{array}$$

The change in revenue at each factory can be read from the difference of the revenue matrices:

$$[2465 \quad 2035 \quad 5590] - [2210 \quad 1680 \quad 4900] = [255 \quad 355 \quad 690].$$

If prices had been as given in (b), revenues of the Los Angeles factory would have increased by \$255,000, revenues at San Antonio would have increased by \$355,000, and revenues at Newark would have increased by \$690,000.

>> ***Now Try Exercise 73***

Identity Matrix

There are special matrices analogous to the number 1. Such matrices are called *identity matrices*.

> **DEFINITION** The **identity matrix** I_n is the $n \times n$ square matrix with all zeros except for ones down the upper-left-to-lower-right diagonal.

Here are the identity matrices of sizes 2, 3, and 4:

$$I_2 = \begin{bmatrix} 1 & 0 \\ 0 & 1 \end{bmatrix}; \quad I_3 = \begin{bmatrix} 1 & 0 & 0 \\ 0 & 1 & 0 \\ 0 & 0 & 1 \end{bmatrix}; \quad I_4 = \begin{bmatrix} 1 & 0 & 0 & 0 \\ 0 & 1 & 0 & 0 \\ 0 & 0 & 1 & 0 \\ 0 & 0 & 0 & 1 \end{bmatrix}.$$

The characteristic property of an identity matrix is that it plays the role of the number 1; that is,

$$I_n \cdot A = A \cdot I_n = A$$

for all $n \times n$ matrices A.

Scalar Multiplication

The **scalar product** of the number c and the matrix A, denoted cA, is the matrix obtained by multiplying each element of A by c. For instance, if A is the matrix $\begin{bmatrix} 3 & 0 \\ 4 & -1 \end{bmatrix}$, then $2A$ is the matrix $\begin{bmatrix} 2 \cdot 3 & 2 \cdot 0 \\ 2 \cdot 4 & 2 \cdot (-1) \end{bmatrix}$. That is,

$$2A = \begin{bmatrix} 6 & 0 \\ 8 & -2 \end{bmatrix}.$$

EXAMPLE 6 **Scalar Multiplication** Consider the price matrix $[100 \quad 20 \quad 35 \quad 25]$, and call it P, from the solution of part (a) of Example 5. Calculate the new price matrix that results from increasing each price by 5%.

SOLUTION Since 5% is .05, each price p will be increased to $p + .05p$.

$$\begin{aligned} p + .05p &= 1 \cdot p + .05p \\ &= (1 + .05)p \\ &= 1.05p. \end{aligned}$$

Since each entry of matrix P should be multiplied by 1.05, the new matrix is

$$1.05P = [105 \quad 21 \quad 36.75 \quad 26.25].$$

» Now Try Exercise 65(c)

One of the principal uses of matrices is in dealing with systems of linear equations. Matrices provide a compact way to write and solve linear systems.

EXAMPLE 7 **Representing a System of Equations as a Matrix Equation** Write the system of linear equations

$$\begin{cases} -2x + 4y = 2 \\ -3x + 7y = 7 \end{cases}$$

as a matrix equation.

SOLUTION The system of equations can be written in the form

$$\begin{bmatrix} -2x + 4y \\ -3x + 7y \end{bmatrix} = \begin{bmatrix} 2 \\ 7 \end{bmatrix}.$$

So consider the matrices

$$A = \begin{bmatrix} -2 & 4 \\ -3 & 7 \end{bmatrix}, \quad X = \begin{bmatrix} x \\ y \end{bmatrix}, \quad B = \begin{bmatrix} 2 \\ 7 \end{bmatrix}.$$

Notice that

$$AX = \begin{bmatrix} -2 & 4 \\ -3 & 7 \end{bmatrix} \begin{bmatrix} x \\ y \end{bmatrix} = \begin{bmatrix} -2x + 4y \\ -3x + 7y \end{bmatrix}.$$

Thus, AX is a 2×1 column matrix whose entries correspond to the left side of the given system of linear equations. Since the entries of B correspond to the right side of the system of equations, we can rewrite the given system in the form

$$AX = B$$

—that is,

$$\begin{bmatrix} -2 & 4 \\ -3 & 7 \end{bmatrix} \begin{bmatrix} x \\ y \end{bmatrix} = \begin{bmatrix} 2 \\ 7 \end{bmatrix}.$$

» Now Try Exercise 57

The matrix A of the preceding example displays the coefficients of the variables x and y, and so it is called the **coefficient matrix** of the system.

Check Your Understanding 4.3

Solutions can be found following the section exercises.

1. Compute

$$\begin{bmatrix} 3 & 1 & 2 \\ -1 & 0 & \frac{1}{2} \\ 0 & 4 & 1 \end{bmatrix}\begin{bmatrix} 7 & -1 & 0 \\ 5 & 4 & 2 \\ -6 & 0 & 4 \end{bmatrix}.$$

2. Give the system of linear equations that is equivalent to the matrix equation

$$\begin{bmatrix} 3 & -6 \\ 2 & 1 \end{bmatrix}\begin{bmatrix} x \\ y \end{bmatrix} = \begin{bmatrix} 5 \\ 0 \end{bmatrix}.$$

3. Give a matrix equation equivalent to this system of equations:

$$\begin{cases} 8x + 3y = 7 \\ 9x - 2y = -5. \end{cases}$$

EXERCISES 4.3

In Exercises 1–6, give the size and special characteristics of the given matrix (such as square, column, row, identity).

1. $\begin{bmatrix} 3 & 2 & 4 \\ \frac{1}{2} & 0 & 6 \end{bmatrix}$
2. $\begin{bmatrix} 3 \\ -1 \end{bmatrix}$
3. $[2 \quad \frac{1}{3} \quad 0]$
4. $\begin{bmatrix} 1 & 0 \\ 0 & 1 \end{bmatrix}$
5. $\begin{bmatrix} 1 & 0 \\ 0 & 0 \end{bmatrix}$
6. $[5]$

Exercises 7–10 refer to the 2×3 matrix $A = \begin{bmatrix} 2 & -4 & 6 \\ 0 & 3 & -1 \end{bmatrix}$.

7. Find a_{12} and a_{21}.
8. Find a_{23} and a_{11}.
9. For what values of i and j does $a_{ij} = 6$?
10. For what values of i and j does $a_{ij} = 3$?

In Exercises 11–26, perform the indicated matrix calculation.

11. $\begin{bmatrix} 4 & -2 \\ 3 & 0 \end{bmatrix} + \begin{bmatrix} 5 & 5 \\ 4 & -1 \end{bmatrix}$
12. $\begin{bmatrix} 8 \\ -3 \end{bmatrix} + \begin{bmatrix} 5 \\ 6 \end{bmatrix}$
13. $\begin{bmatrix} 1.3 & 5 & 2.3 \\ -6 & 0 & .7 \end{bmatrix} + \begin{bmatrix} .7 & -1 & .2 \\ .5 & 1 & .5 \end{bmatrix}$
14. $[\frac{5}{6} \quad 10 \quad \frac{1}{2}] + [\frac{2}{3} \quad -7 \quad \frac{3}{2}]$
15. $\begin{bmatrix} 2 & 8 \\ \frac{4}{3} & 4 \\ 1 & -2 \end{bmatrix} - \begin{bmatrix} 1 & 5 \\ \frac{1}{3} & 2 \\ -3 & 0 \end{bmatrix}$
16. $\begin{bmatrix} 1 & 0 \\ 0 & 1 \end{bmatrix} - \begin{bmatrix} .8 & .5 \\ .2 & .5 \end{bmatrix}$
17. $\begin{bmatrix} -5 \\ \frac{1}{2} \end{bmatrix} - \begin{bmatrix} 2 \\ \frac{1}{3} \end{bmatrix}$
18. $\begin{bmatrix} 1.4 & 0 & 3 \\ .5 & -1.2 & 2.5 \end{bmatrix} - \begin{bmatrix} .6 & -1 & 3 \\ .1 & .4 & 1 \end{bmatrix}$
19. $[5 \quad 3]\begin{bmatrix} 1 \\ 2 \end{bmatrix}$
20. $[1 \quad 0 \quad 0]\begin{bmatrix} \frac{1}{2} \\ 6 \\ 2 \end{bmatrix}$
21. $[6 \quad 1 \quad 5]\begin{bmatrix} \frac{1}{2} \\ -3 \\ 2 \end{bmatrix}$
22. $[0 \quad 0]\begin{bmatrix} 5 \\ -3 \end{bmatrix}$
23. $\frac{2}{3}\begin{bmatrix} 6 & 0 & -1 \\ -9 & \frac{3}{4} & \frac{1}{2} \end{bmatrix}$
24. $1.5\begin{bmatrix} 4 & .5 \\ 0 & 1.2 \end{bmatrix}$
25. $2\begin{bmatrix} \frac{1}{2} & -1 \\ 4 & 0 \end{bmatrix} + 3\begin{bmatrix} \frac{2}{3} & 7 \\ 5 & 1 \end{bmatrix}$
26. $\frac{3}{5}[10 \quad 25] - [6 \quad -3]$

In Exercises 27–32, the sizes of two matrices are given. Tell whether or not the product AB is defined. If so, give its size.

27. A, 3×4; B, 4×5
28. A, 3×3; B, 3×4
29. A, 3×2; B, 3×2
30. A, 1×1; B, 1×1
31. A, 3×3; B, 3×1
32. A, 4×2; B, 3×4

In Exercises 33–52, perform the multiplication.

33. $\begin{bmatrix} 3 & 1 \\ 0 & 2 \end{bmatrix}\begin{bmatrix} 1 & 4 \\ 3 & 5 \end{bmatrix}$
34. $\begin{bmatrix} 4 & -1 \\ 2 & \frac{1}{2} \end{bmatrix}\begin{bmatrix} 3 \\ 2 \end{bmatrix}$
35. $\begin{bmatrix} 4 & 1 & 0 \\ -2 & 0 & 3 \\ 1 & 5 & -1 \end{bmatrix}\begin{bmatrix} 5 \\ 1 \\ 2 \end{bmatrix}$
36. $\begin{bmatrix} 0 & 0 \\ 0 & 0 \\ 0 & 0 \end{bmatrix}\begin{bmatrix} 1 & 2 \\ 3 & 4 \end{bmatrix}$
37. $\begin{bmatrix} 1 & 0 \\ 0 & 1 \end{bmatrix}\begin{bmatrix} 5 & 6 \\ 7 & 8 \end{bmatrix}$
38. $\begin{bmatrix} 1 & 2 \\ 1 & 3 \end{bmatrix}\begin{bmatrix} 3 & -2 \\ -1 & 1 \end{bmatrix}$
39. $\begin{bmatrix} .6 & .3 \\ .4 & .7 \end{bmatrix}\begin{bmatrix} .6 & .3 \\ .4 & .7 \end{bmatrix}$
40. $\begin{bmatrix} 0 & 1 & 2 \\ -1 & 4 & \frac{1}{2} \\ 1 & 3 & 0 \end{bmatrix}\begin{bmatrix} 3 & -1 & 5 \\ 0 & 2 & 2 \\ 4 & -6 & 0 \end{bmatrix}$
41. $\begin{bmatrix} 2 & -1 & 4 \\ 0 & 1 & 0 \\ \frac{1}{2} & 3 & -2 \end{bmatrix}\begin{bmatrix} 4 & 8 & 0 \\ 3 & -1 & 2 \\ 5 & 0 & 1 \end{bmatrix}$
42. $\begin{bmatrix} 1 & 0 & 0 \\ 0 & 1 & 0 \\ 0 & 0 & 1 \end{bmatrix}\begin{bmatrix} 1 \\ 2 \\ 3 \end{bmatrix}$
43. $\begin{bmatrix} \frac{1}{3} & \frac{2}{3} \\ \frac{1}{3} & \frac{2}{3} \end{bmatrix}\begin{bmatrix} \frac{1}{3} & \frac{2}{3} \\ \frac{1}{3} & \frac{2}{3} \end{bmatrix}$
44. $\begin{bmatrix} .4 & .4 & .4 \\ .4 & .4 & .4 \\ .2 & .2 & .2 \end{bmatrix}\begin{bmatrix} .4 & .4 & .4 \\ .4 & .4 & .4 \\ .2 & .2 & .2 \end{bmatrix}$
45. $[2 \quad 5]\begin{bmatrix} 0 & 3 \\ 6 & 7 \end{bmatrix}$
46. $[4 \quad 0 \quad 1]\begin{bmatrix} 2 & 3 \\ 4 & 5 \\ 0 & 6 \end{bmatrix}$
47. $\begin{bmatrix} 2 & 0 \\ 0 & 3 \end{bmatrix}\begin{bmatrix} 5 & 0 \\ 0 & 5 \end{bmatrix}$
48. $\begin{bmatrix} \frac{1}{3} & 0 \\ 0 & \frac{1}{4} \end{bmatrix}\begin{bmatrix} 6 & 0 \\ 0 & 8 \end{bmatrix}$
49. $\begin{bmatrix} 0 & 0 \\ 0 & 0 \end{bmatrix}\begin{bmatrix} 2.34 & 5.6 \\ -3.7 & .08 \end{bmatrix}$
50. $\begin{bmatrix} -78 & 56 \\ 312 & 23 \end{bmatrix}\begin{bmatrix} 0 & 0 \\ 0 & 0 \end{bmatrix}$
51. $\begin{bmatrix} 23 & 24 \\ 25 & 26 \end{bmatrix}\begin{bmatrix} 1 & 0 \\ 0 & 1 \end{bmatrix}$
52. $\begin{bmatrix} 1 & 0 \\ 0 & 1 \end{bmatrix}\begin{bmatrix} 2.4 & 5.6 \\ 7.8 & 9.9 \end{bmatrix}$

In Exercises 53–56, give the system of linear equations that is equivalent to the matrix equation. Do not solve.

53. $\begin{bmatrix} 2 & 3 \\ 4 & 5 \end{bmatrix}\begin{bmatrix} x \\ y \end{bmatrix} = \begin{bmatrix} 6 \\ 7 \end{bmatrix}$
54. $\begin{bmatrix} -3 & 4 \\ 0 & 1 \end{bmatrix}\begin{bmatrix} x \\ y \end{bmatrix} = \begin{bmatrix} 1 \\ 1 \end{bmatrix}$

55. $\begin{bmatrix} 1 & 2 & 3 \\ 4 & 5 & 6 \\ 7 & 8 & 9 \end{bmatrix}\begin{bmatrix} x \\ y \\ z \end{bmatrix} = \begin{bmatrix} 10 \\ 11 \\ 12 \end{bmatrix}$ 56. $\begin{bmatrix} 1 & 0 & 0 \\ 0 & 1 & 0 \\ 0 & 0 & 1 \end{bmatrix}\begin{bmatrix} x \\ y \\ z \end{bmatrix} = \begin{bmatrix} 1 \\ 2 \\ 3 \end{bmatrix}$

In Exercises 57–60, write the given system of linear equations as a matrix equation.

57. $\begin{cases} 3x + 2y = -1 \\ 7x - y = 2 \end{cases}$ 58. $\begin{cases} 5x - 2y = 6 \\ -2x + 4y = 0 \end{cases}$

59. $\begin{cases} x - 2y + 3z = 5 \\ y + z = 6 \\ z = 2 \end{cases}$ 60. $\begin{cases} -2x + 4y - z = 5 \\ x + 6y + 3z = -1 \\ 7x + 4z = 8 \end{cases}$

The *distributive law* says that $(A + B)C = AC + BC$. That is, adding A and B and then multiplying on the right by C gives the same result as first multiplying each of A and B on the right by C and then adding. In Exercises 61 and 62, verify the distributive law for the given matrices.

61. $A = \begin{bmatrix} 1 & 2 \\ 0 & 3 \end{bmatrix}, B = \begin{bmatrix} 3 & -2 \\ 4 & 5 \end{bmatrix}, C = \begin{bmatrix} 1 & 6 \\ 2 & 0 \end{bmatrix}$

62. $A = \begin{bmatrix} 1 & 0 & 0 \\ 0 & 1 & 0 \\ 0 & 0 & 1 \end{bmatrix}, B = \begin{bmatrix} 2 & 1 & 3 \\ 0 & 5 & -1 \\ 3 & 6 & 0 \end{bmatrix}, C = \begin{bmatrix} 0 \\ 3 \\ -4 \end{bmatrix}$

Two $n \times n$ matrices A and B are called *inverses* (of one another) if both products AB and BA equal I_n. Check that the pairs of matrices in Exercises 63 and 64 are inverses.

63. $\begin{bmatrix} 3 & -1 \\ -1 & \frac{1}{2} \end{bmatrix}, \begin{bmatrix} 1 & 2 \\ 2 & 6 \end{bmatrix}$

64. $\begin{bmatrix} 2 & 8 & -11 \\ -1 & -5 & 7 \\ 1 & 2 & -3 \end{bmatrix}, \begin{bmatrix} 1 & 2 & 1 \\ 4 & 5 & -3 \\ 3 & 4 & -2 \end{bmatrix}$

65. **Wardrobe Costs** The quantities of pants, shirts, and jackets owned by Mike and Don are given by the matrix A, and the costs of these items are given by matrix B.

$$\begin{array}{c} \\ \text{Mike} \\ \text{Don} \end{array} \begin{array}{c} \text{Pants} \quad \text{Shirts} \quad \text{Jackets} \\ \begin{bmatrix} 6 & 8 & 2 \\ 2 & 5 & 3 \end{bmatrix} \end{array} = A$$

$$\begin{array}{c} \\ \text{Pants} \\ \text{Shirts} \\ \text{Jackets} \end{array} \begin{array}{c} \text{Cost} \\ \begin{bmatrix} 20 \\ 15 \\ 50 \end{bmatrix} \end{array} = B$$

(a) Calculate the matrix AB.
(b) Interpret the entries of the matrix AB.
(c) Calculate the matrix $1.25B$.
(d) Interpret the entries of the matrix $1.25B$.

66. **Retail Sales** Two stores sell the exact same brand and style of a dresser, a nightstand, and a bookcase. Matrix A gives the retail prices (in dollars) for the items. Matrix B gives the number of each item sold at each store in one month.

$$A = \begin{array}{c} \text{Dresser} \quad \text{Nightstand} \quad \text{Bookcase} \\ \begin{bmatrix} 250 & 80 & 60 \end{bmatrix} \end{array}$$

$$B = \begin{array}{c} \text{Store 1} \quad \text{Store 2} \\ \begin{bmatrix} 40 & 35 \\ 30 & 35 \\ 50 & 75 \end{bmatrix} \end{array} \begin{array}{l} \\ \text{Dresser} \\ \text{Nightstand} \\ \text{Bookcase} \end{array}$$

(a) Calculate AB.
(b) Interpret the entries of AB.
(c) Calculate the matrix $1.1A$.
(d) Interpret the entries of the matrix $1.1A$.

67. **Retail Sales** A candy shop sells various items for the price per pound (in dollars) indicated in matrix A. Matrix B gives the number of pounds of coated peanuts, raisins, and espresso beans prepared in a week. Matrix C gives the total number of pounds of white chocolate-covered, milk chocolate-covered, and dark chocolate-covered items sold each week.

$$A = \begin{array}{c} \text{White} \quad \text{Milk} \quad \text{Dark} \\ \begin{bmatrix} 3 & 3 & 5.8 \\ 2.5 & 3.5 & 6 \\ 9 & 8 & 9.5 \end{bmatrix} \end{array} \begin{array}{l} \\ \text{Peanuts} \\ \text{Raisins} \\ \text{Espresso beans} \end{array}$$

$$B = \begin{array}{c} \text{Peanuts} \quad \text{Raisins} \quad \text{Espresso beans} \\ \begin{bmatrix} 210 & 175 & 135 \end{bmatrix} \end{array}$$

$$C = \begin{bmatrix} 105 \\ 390 \\ 285 \end{bmatrix} \begin{array}{l} \text{White} \\ \text{Milk} \\ \text{Dark} \end{array}$$

Determine and interpret the following matrices.
(a) BA (b) AC (c) $.9C$

68. **Wholesale and Retail Sales** A company has three appliance stores that sell washers, dryers, and ranges. Matrices W and R give the wholesale and retail prices of these items, respectively. Matrices N and D give the quantities of these items sold by the three stores in November and December, respectively.

$$W = \begin{array}{c} \text{Washers} \quad \text{Dryers} \quad \text{Ranges} \\ \begin{bmatrix} 300 & 250 & 450 \end{bmatrix} \end{array}$$

$$R = \begin{array}{c} \text{Washers} \quad \text{Dryers} \quad \text{Ranges} \\ \begin{bmatrix} 500 & 450 & 750 \end{bmatrix} \end{array}$$

$$N = \begin{array}{c} \text{Store 1} \quad \text{Store 2} \quad \text{Store 3} \\ \begin{bmatrix} 30 & 40 & 20 \\ 20 & 30 & 10 \\ 10 & 5 & 35 \end{bmatrix} \end{array} \begin{array}{l} \\ \text{Washers} \\ \text{Dryers} \\ \text{Ranges} \end{array}$$

$$D = \begin{array}{c} \text{Store 1} \quad \text{Store 2} \quad \text{Store 3} \\ \begin{bmatrix} 20 & 50 & 30 \\ 30 & 10 & 20 \\ 10 & 20 & 30 \end{bmatrix} \end{array} \begin{array}{l} \\ \text{Washers} \\ \text{Dryers} \\ \text{Ranges} \end{array}$$

Determine and interpret the following matrices:
(a) WN (b) WD
(c) RN (d) RD
(e) $R - W$ (f) $(R - W)N$
(g) $(R - W)D$ (h) $N + D$
(i) $(R - W)(N + D)$ (j) $.95R$

69. **Course Grades** Three professors teaching the same course have entirely different grading policies. The percentage of students given each grade by the professors is summarized in the following matrix:

$$\begin{array}{l} \\ \text{Prof. I} \\ \text{Prof. II} \\ \text{Prof. III} \end{array} \begin{array}{c} \text{Grade} \\ \text{A} \quad \text{B} \quad \text{C} \quad \text{D} \quad \text{F} \\ \begin{bmatrix} 25 & 35 & 30 & 10 & 0 \\ 10 & 20 & 40 & 20 & 10 \\ 5 & 10 & 20 & 40 & 25 \end{bmatrix} \end{array}.$$

(a) The point values of the grades are A = 4, B = 3, C = 2, D = 1, and F = 0. Use matrix multiplication to determine the average grade given by each professor.

(b) Professor I has 240 students, professor II has 120 students, and professor III has 40 students. Use matrix multiplication to determine the numbers of As, Bs, Cs, Ds, and Fs given.

70. **Semester Grades** A professor bases semester grades on four 100-point items: homework, quizzes, a midterm exam, and a final exam. Students may choose one of three schemes summarized in the accompanying matrix for weighting the points from the four items. Use matrix multiplication to determine the most advantageous weighting scheme for a student who earned 97 points on homework, 72 points on the quizzes, 83 points on the midterm exam, and 75 points on the final exam.

	Items			
	HW	Qu	ME	FE
Scheme I	.10	.10	.30	.50
Scheme II	.10	.20	.30	.40
Scheme III	.15	.15	.35	.35

71. **Voter Analysis** In a certain town, the proportions of voters voting Democratic and Republican by various age groups is summarized by this matrix:

	Dem.	Rep.
Under 30	.65	.35
30–50	.55	.45
Over 50	.45	.55

$= A$.

The population of voters in the town by age group is given by the matrix

$$B = [\underbrace{6000}_{\text{Under } 30} \quad \underbrace{8000}_{30\text{–}50} \quad \underbrace{4000}_{\text{Over } 50}].$$

Interpret the entries of the matrix product BA.

72. **Voter Analysis** Refer to Exercise 71.
(a) According to the data, which party would win and what would be the percentage of the winning vote?
(b) Suppose that the population of the town shifted toward older residents, as reflected in the population matrix $B = [2000 \quad 4000 \quad 12{,}000]$. What would be the result of the election now?

73. **Labor Costs** Suppose that a contractor employs carpenters, bricklayers, and plumbers, working three shifts per day. The number of labor-hours employed in each of the shifts is summarized in the following matrix:

	Shift		
	1	2	3
Carpenters	50	20	10
Bricklayers	30	30	15
Plumbers	20	20	5

Labor in shift 1 costs \$20 per hour, in shift 2 \$30 per hour, and in shift 3 \$40 per hour. Use matrix multiplication to compute the dollar amount spent on each type of labor.

74. **Epidemiology** A flu epidemic hits a large city. Each resident of the city is either sick, well, or a carrier. The proportion of people in each of the categories is expressed by the following matrix:

	Age		
	0–10	10–30	Over 30
Well	.70	.70	.60
Sick	.10	.20	.30
Carrier	.20	.10	.10

$= A$.

The population of the city is distributed by age and sex as follows:

Age	Male	Female
0–10	60,000	65,000
10–30	100,000	110,000
Over 30	200,000	230,000

$= B$.

(a) Compute AB.
(b) How many sick males are there?
(c) How many female carriers are there?

75. **Nutrition Analysis** Mikey's diet consists of food X and food Y. The matrix N represents the number of units of nutrients 1, 2, and 3 per ounce for each of the foods.

$$N = \begin{bmatrix} 60 & 50 & 38 \\ 42 & 50 & 67 \end{bmatrix} \begin{matrix} X \\ Y \end{matrix} \quad (\text{columns } 1, 2, 3)$$

The matrices B, L, and D represent the number of ounces of each food that Mikey eats each day for breakfast, lunch, and dinner, respectively.

$$B = [2 \quad 1] \quad L = [1 \quad 3] \quad D = [2 \quad 4] \quad (\text{columns } X, Y)$$

Calculate and interpret the following:
(a) BN (b) LN (c) DN
(d) $B + L + D$ (e) $(B + L + D)N$

76. **Bakery Sales** A bakery makes three types of cookies, I, II, and III. Each type of cookie is made from the four ingredients A, B, C, and D. The number of units of each ingredient used in each type of cookie is given by the matrix M. The cost per unit of each of the four ingredients (in cents) is given by the matrix N. The selling price for each of the cookies (in cents) is given by the matrix S. The baker receives an order for 10 type I cookies, 20 type II cookies, and 15 type III cookies, as represented by the matrix R.

$$M = \begin{bmatrix} 1 & 0 & 2 & 4 \\ 3 & 2 & 1 & 1 \\ 2 & 5 & 3 & 1 \end{bmatrix} \begin{matrix} \text{I} \\ \text{II} \\ \text{III} \end{matrix} \quad (\text{columns } A, B, C, D) \qquad N = \begin{bmatrix} 10 \\ 20 \\ 15 \\ 17 \end{bmatrix} \begin{matrix} A \\ B \\ C \\ D \end{matrix} \quad (\text{Cost})$$

$$S = \begin{bmatrix} 175 \\ 150 \\ 225 \end{bmatrix} \begin{matrix} \text{I} \\ \text{II} \\ \text{III} \end{matrix} \quad (\text{Selling price}) \qquad R = [10 \quad 20 \quad 15] \ \text{Order} \quad (\text{columns I, II, III})$$

Calculate and interpret the following:
(a) RM (b) MN (c) RMN
(d) $S - MN$ (e) $R(S - MN)$ (f) RS

77. **Revenue** A community fitness center has a pool and a weight room. The admission prices (in dollars) for residents and nonresidents are given by the matrix

$$P = \begin{bmatrix} 4.50 \\ 5.00 \end{bmatrix} \begin{matrix} \text{Residents} \\ \text{Nonresidents.} \end{matrix} \quad (\text{Price})$$

The average daily numbers of customers for the fitness center are given by the matrix

$$\begin{matrix} & \text{Residents} & \text{Nonresidents} & \\ A = & \begin{bmatrix} 90 & 63 \\ 78 & 59 \end{bmatrix} & \begin{matrix} \text{Pool} \\ \text{Weight room.} \end{matrix} \end{matrix}$$

(a) Compute AP.
(b) What is the average amount of money taken in by the pool each day?

78. **Production Planning** A company makes DVD players and TV sets. Each DVD player requires 3 hours of assembly and $\frac{1}{2}$ hour of packaging, while each TV set requires 5 hours of assembly and 1 hour of packaging.
(a) Write a matrix T representing the required time for assembly and packaging of DVD players and TV sets.
(b) The company receives an order from a retail outlet for 30 DVD players and 20 TV sets. Find a matrix S so that either ST or TS gives the total assembly time and the total packaging time required to fill the order. What is the total assembly time? What is the total packaging time?

79. **Production Planning** A bakery sells Boston cream pies and carrot cakes. Each Boston cream pie requires 30 minutes preparation time, 30 minutes baking time, and 15 minutes for finishing. Each carrot cake requires 45 minutes preparation time, 50 minutes baking time, and 10 minutes for finishing.
(a) Write a matrix T representing the required time for preparation, baking, and finishing for the Boston cream pies and the carrot cakes.
(b) The bakery receives an order for 20 Boston cream pies and 8 carrot cakes for a large party. Find a matrix S so that either ST or TS gives the total preparation, baking, and finishing times required to fill this order.
(c) What is the total baking time? What is the total finishing time?

80. **Time Requirements** A beauty salon offers manicures and pedicures. A manicure requires 20 minutes for preparation, 5 minutes for lacquering, and 15 minutes for drying. A pedicure requires 30 minutes for preparation, 5 minutes for lacquering, and 20 minutes for drying.
(a) Construct a matrix T representing the time required for preparation, lacquering, and drying for manicures and pedicures.
(b) Suppose that the salon will be giving manicures and pedicures to a large wedding party. If 15 members of the wedding party want manicures and 9 want pedicures, find a matrix S so that either ST or TS gives the total amount of time required for each of the three steps.
(c) What is the total time required for drying?

81. **Production and Revenue** The J.E. Carrying Company makes two types of backpacks. The larger Huge One backpack requires 2 hours for cutting, 3 hours for sewing, and 2 hours for finishing, and sells for \$32. The smaller Regular Joe backpack requires 1.5 hours for cutting, 2 hours for sewing, and 1 hour for finishing, and sells for \$24.
(a) Construct a matrix T representing the time required for each of the three steps in making the backpacks.
(b) Construct a matrix S representing the sales prices for the two types of backpacks.
(c) Suppose that the J.E. Carrying Company receives an order for 27 Huge One backpacks and 56 Regular Joe backpacks. Construct a matrix A so that either AT or TA gives the total time required to construct the backpacks in this order, and either AS or SA gives the total revenue generated by this order.
(d) How much total time is needed for sewing to fill this order?
(e) What is the total revenue for this order?

82. **MP3 Sales** A store sells three types of MP3 players. Matrix A contains information about size (in gigabytes), battery life (in hours), and weight (in ounces) of the three MP3 players. Matrix B contains the sales prices (in dollars) of the MP3 players, while matrix C contains the number of each type of player sold in one week.

$$\begin{matrix} & \text{Type I} & \text{Type II} & \text{Type III} & \\ A = & \begin{bmatrix} 4 & 8 & 16 \\ 25 & 30 & 30 \\ 1 & 1.9 & 1.1 \end{bmatrix} & & & \begin{matrix} \text{Size} \\ \text{Battery Life} \\ \text{Weight} \end{matrix} \end{matrix}$$

$$\begin{matrix} & \text{Type I} & \text{Type II} & \text{Type III} \\ B = [& 40 & 75 & 150 \;] \end{matrix}$$

$$C = \begin{bmatrix} 25 \\ 16 \\ 32 \end{bmatrix} \begin{matrix} \text{Type I} \\ \text{Type II} \\ \text{Type III} \end{matrix}$$

Calculate and interpret the following:
(a) BC (b) AC
(c) the row 2, column 1 entry of AC

83. Make up an application whose answer is that the total cost is given by

$$\begin{bmatrix} 20 & 30 \end{bmatrix} \begin{bmatrix} 600 \\ 700 \end{bmatrix}.$$

84. Find the values of a and b for which $A \cdot B = I_3$, where

$$A = \begin{bmatrix} 3 & 2 & 0 \\ 1 & 1 & 0 \\ 0 & 0 & 1 \end{bmatrix} \quad \text{and} \quad B = \begin{bmatrix} a & b & 0 \\ -1 & 3 & 0 \\ 0 & 0 & 1 \end{bmatrix}.$$

85. If A is a 3×4 matrix and $A(BB)$ is defined, what is the size of matrix B?

86. If B is a 3×5 matrix and $(AA)B$ is defined, what is the size of matrix A?

87. **School Enrollments** Table 1 gives the number of public school teachers (elementary and secondary) and the average number of pupils per teacher for three mid-Atlantic states in a recent year. Set up a product of two matrices that

gives the total number of pupils in the three states. (Source: National Center for Education Statistics, *Digest of Education Statistics.*)

Table 1 Teachers and Pupils

	Delaware	Maryland	Virginia
Teachers	9257	57,718	89,389
Pupils per Teacher	13.9	14.9	14.2

88. **Population** Table 2 gives the area and 2015 population density for three West Coast states. Set up a product of two matrices that gives total population of the three states.

Table 2 State Areas and Densities

	California	Oregon	Washington
Land Area (sq. mi.)	155,959	95,997	66,544
Pop. Density (per sq. mile)	250.0	42.0	107.8

Solutions to Check Your Understanding 4.3

1. Answer:

$$\begin{bmatrix} 3 & 1 & 2 \\ -1 & 0 & \frac{1}{2} \\ 0 & 4 & 1 \end{bmatrix}\begin{bmatrix} 7 & -1 & 0 \\ 5 & 4 & 2 \\ -6 & 0 & 4 \end{bmatrix} = \begin{bmatrix} 14 & 1 & 10 \\ -10 & 1 & 2 \\ 14 & 16 & 12 \end{bmatrix}.$$

The systematic steps to be taken are as follows:

(a) Determine the size of the product matrix. Since we have a

$$\underbrace{(3) \times 3 \quad \text{times a} \quad 3 \times (3)}_{\text{outer dimensions}},$$

the size of the product is given by the outer dimensions, or 3×3. Begin by drawing a 3×3 rectangular array.

(b) Find the entries one at a time. To find the entry in the first row, first column of the product, look at the first row of the left matrix and the first column of the right matrix, and form their product. In this case,

$$\begin{bmatrix} 3 & 1 & 2 \\ -1 & 0 & \frac{1}{2} \\ 0 & 4 & 1 \end{bmatrix}\begin{bmatrix} 7 & -1 & 0 \\ 5 & 4 & 2 \\ -6 & 0 & 4 \end{bmatrix} = \begin{bmatrix} 14 & & \\ & & \\ & & \end{bmatrix},$$

since $3 \cdot 7 + 1 \cdot 5 + 2(-6) = 14$. In general, to find the entry in the ith row, jth column of the product, put one finger on the ith row of the left matrix and another finger on the jth column of the right matrix. Then, multiply the row matrix times the column matrix to get the desired entry.

2. Denote the three matrices by A, X, and B, respectively. Since b_{11} (the entry of the first row, first column of B) is 5, this means that

$$[\text{first row of } A]\begin{bmatrix} \text{first} \\ \text{column} \\ \text{of } X \end{bmatrix} = [b_{11}].$$

That is,

$$\begin{bmatrix} 3 & -6 \end{bmatrix}\begin{bmatrix} x \\ y \end{bmatrix} = [5] \quad \text{or} \quad 3x - 6y = 5.$$

Similarly, $b_{21} = 0$ says that $2x + y = 0$. Therefore, the corresponding system of linear equations is

$$\begin{cases} 3x - 6y = 5 \\ 2x + y = 0. \end{cases}$$

3. The coefficient matrix is

$$\begin{bmatrix} 8 & 3 \\ 9 & -2 \end{bmatrix}.$$

So the system is equivalent to the matrix equation

$$\begin{bmatrix} 8 & 3 \\ 9 & -2 \end{bmatrix}\begin{bmatrix} x \\ y \end{bmatrix} = \begin{bmatrix} 7 \\ -5 \end{bmatrix}.$$

4.4 The Inverse of a Square Matrix

In Section 4.3, we introduced the operations of addition, subtraction, and multiplication of matrices. In this section, let us pursue the algebra of matrices a bit further and consider equations involving matrices. Specifically, we consider equations of the form

$$AX = B, \tag{1}$$

where A and B are given matrices and X is an unknown matrix whose entries are to be determined. Such equations among matrices are intimately bound up with the theory of systems of linear equations. Indeed, we described the connection in a special case in Example 7 of Section 4.3. In that example, we wrote the system of linear equations

$$\begin{cases} -2x + 4y = 2 \\ -3x + 7y = 7 \end{cases}$$

as a matrix equation of the form (1), where

$$A = \begin{bmatrix} -2 & 4 \\ -3 & 7 \end{bmatrix}, \quad B = \begin{bmatrix} 2 \\ 7 \end{bmatrix}, \quad X = \begin{bmatrix} x \\ y \end{bmatrix}.$$

Note that, by determining the entries (x and y) of the unknown matrix X, we solve the system of linear equations. We will return to this example after we have made a complete study of the matrix equation (1).

As motivation for our solution of equation (1), let us consider the analogous equation among numbers:

$$ax = b,$$

where a and b are given numbers and x is to be determined. We may as well assume that $a \neq 0$. Otherwise, x does not occur. Let us examine its solution in great detail. Multiply both sides by $1/a$. (Note that $1/a$ makes sense, since $a \neq 0$.)

$$\begin{aligned}\left(\frac{1}{a}\right)\cdot(ax) &= \frac{1}{a}\cdot b\\ \left(\frac{1}{a}\cdot a\right)\cdot x &= \frac{1}{a}\cdot b\\ 1\cdot x &= \frac{1}{a}\cdot b\\ x &= \frac{1}{a}\cdot b\end{aligned}$$

Let us model our solution of equation (1) on the preceding calculation. To do so, we need to multiply both sides of the equation by a matrix that plays the same role in matrix arithmetic as $1/a$ plays in ordinary arithmetic. Our first task, then, will be to introduce this matrix and study its properties.

The number $1/a$ has the following relationship to the number a:

$$\frac{1}{a}\cdot a = a\cdot\frac{1}{a} = 1. \tag{2}$$

The matrix analog of the number 1 is an identity matrix I. This prompts us to generalize equation (2) to matrices as follows.

DEFINITION Let A be an $n \times n$ matrix. The **inverse of A**, denoted A^{-1}, is the $n \times n$ matrix with the properties

$$A^{-1}A = I_n \quad\text{and}\quad AA^{-1} = I_n.$$

The matrix A^{-1} is the matrix analog of the number $1/a$. It can be shown that a matrix A has, at most, one inverse. However, A may not have an inverse at all.

If we are given a matrix A, then it is easy to determine whether or not a given matrix is its inverse. Merely check the two equations in the definition with the given matrix substituted for A^{-1}. For example, if

$$A = \begin{bmatrix}-2 & 4\\ -3 & 7\end{bmatrix}, \quad\text{then}\quad A^{-1} = \begin{bmatrix}-\frac{7}{2} & 2\\ -\frac{3}{2} & 1\end{bmatrix}.$$

Indeed, we have

$$\underset{A^{-1}}{\begin{bmatrix}-\frac{7}{2} & 2\\ -\frac{3}{2} & 1\end{bmatrix}}\underset{A}{\begin{bmatrix}-2 & 4\\ -3 & 7\end{bmatrix}} = \begin{bmatrix}7-6 & -14+14\\ 3-3 & -6+7\end{bmatrix} = \underset{I_2}{\begin{bmatrix}1 & 0\\ 0 & 1\end{bmatrix}}$$

and

$$\underset{A}{\begin{bmatrix}-2 & 4\\ -3 & 7\end{bmatrix}}\underset{A^{-1}}{\begin{bmatrix}-\frac{7}{2} & 2\\ -\frac{3}{2} & 1\end{bmatrix}} = \begin{bmatrix}7-6 & -4+4\\ \frac{21}{2}-\frac{21}{2} & -6+7\end{bmatrix} = \underset{I_2}{\begin{bmatrix}1 & 0\\ 0 & 1\end{bmatrix}}.$$

NOTE The definition of the inverse of a square matrix requires the verification of two equations. However, if one of the equations is confirmed, then the other equation will also be satisfied. Therefore, it is sufficient to confirm only one of the two equations. «

We provide a rather efficient computational method for calculating A^{-1} in the next section. For now, however, let us be content with the following general formula for A^{-1} in the case where A is a 2×2 matrix.

Inverse of a 2 × 2 Matrix To determine the inverse of a 2×2 matrix, let

$$A = \begin{bmatrix} a & b \\ c & d \end{bmatrix}.$$

Let $D = ad - bc$, and assume that $D \neq 0$. Then, A^{-1} is given by the formula

$$A^{-1} = \frac{1}{D}\begin{bmatrix} d & -b \\ -c & a \end{bmatrix}. \tag{3}$$

We will omit the derivation of this formula. Notice that formula (3) involves division by D. Since division by 0 is not permissible, it is necessary that $D \neq 0$ for formula (3) to be applied.

Obtaining equation (3) can be reduced to a simple step-by-step procedure.

Inverse of a 2 × 2 Matrix Method

To determine the inverse of $\begin{bmatrix} a & b \\ c & d \end{bmatrix}$ if $D = ad - bc \neq 0$,

1. Interchange a and d to get $\begin{bmatrix} d & b \\ c & a \end{bmatrix}$.
2. Change the signs of b and c to get $\begin{bmatrix} d & -b \\ -c & a \end{bmatrix}$.
3. Divide all entries by D to get $\begin{bmatrix} \frac{d}{D} & -\frac{b}{D} \\ -\frac{c}{D} & \frac{a}{D} \end{bmatrix}$.

EXAMPLE 1 **Using the Formula for the Inverse of a 2 × 2 Matrix** Calculate the inverse of

$$\begin{bmatrix} -2 & 4 \\ -3 & 7 \end{bmatrix}.$$

SOLUTION $D = (-2) \cdot 7 - 4 \cdot (-3) = -2$; so $D \neq 0$, and we may use the preceding computation.

1. Interchange a and d:

$$\begin{bmatrix} 7 & 4 \\ -3 & -2 \end{bmatrix}.$$

2. Change the signs of b and c:

$$\begin{bmatrix} 7 & -4 \\ 3 & -2 \end{bmatrix}.$$

3. Divide all entries by $D = -2$:

$$\begin{bmatrix} -\frac{7}{2} & 2 \\ -\frac{3}{2} & 1 \end{bmatrix}.$$

Thus,

$$\begin{bmatrix} -2 & 4 \\ -3 & 7 \end{bmatrix}^{-1} = \begin{bmatrix} -\frac{7}{2} & 2 \\ -\frac{3}{2} & 1 \end{bmatrix}.$$

» Now Try Exercise 5

NOTE Not every square matrix has an inverse. This phenomenon can even occur in the case of 2×2 matrices. One can show that *if* $D = 0$, *then the matrix does not have an inverse.* «

We were led to introduce the inverse of a matrix from a discussion of the matrix equation $AX = B$. Let us now return to that discussion. Suppose that A and B are given matrices and that we wish to solve the matrix equation

$$AX = B$$

for the unknown matrix X. Suppose further that A has an inverse A^{-1}. Multiply both sides of the equation on the left by A^{-1} to obtain

$$A^{-1} \cdot AX = A^{-1}B.$$

Because $A^{-1} \cdot A = I$, we have

$$IX = A^{-1}B$$
$$X = A^{-1}B.$$

Thus, the matrix X is found by simply multiplying B on the left by A^{-1}, and we can summarize our findings as follows:

Solving a Matrix Equation If the matrix A has an inverse, then the solution of the matrix equation

$$AX = B \quad \text{is given by} \quad X = A^{-1}B.$$

Solving Systems of Linear Equations with Inverses

Matrix equations can be used to solve systems of linear equations, as illustrated in the next example.

EXAMPLE 2 **Using a Matrix Inverse to Solve a System of Equations** Use a matrix equation to solve the system of linear equations

$$\begin{cases} -2x + 4y = 2 \\ -3x + 7y = 7. \end{cases}$$

SOLUTION In Example 7 of Section 4.3, we saw that the system could be written as a matrix equation:

$$\underset{A}{\begin{bmatrix} -2 & 4 \\ -3 & 7 \end{bmatrix}} \underset{X}{\begin{bmatrix} x \\ y \end{bmatrix}} = \underset{B}{\begin{bmatrix} 2 \\ 7 \end{bmatrix}}.$$

We happen to know A^{-1} from Example 1—namely,

$$A^{-1} = \begin{bmatrix} -\frac{7}{2} & 2 \\ -\frac{3}{2} & 1 \end{bmatrix}.$$

So we may compute the matrix $X = A^{-1}B$:

$$X = \begin{bmatrix} x \\ y \end{bmatrix} = \begin{bmatrix} -\frac{7}{2} & 2 \\ -\frac{3}{2} & 1 \end{bmatrix} \begin{bmatrix} 2 \\ 7 \end{bmatrix} = \begin{bmatrix} 7 \\ 4 \end{bmatrix}.$$

Thus, the solution of the system is $x = 7$, $y = 4$.

» Now Try Exercise 11

EXAMPLE 3 **Analyzing Marriage Trends** Let x and y denote the number of married and single adults in a certain town as of January 1. Let m and s denote the corresponding numbers for the following year. A statistical survey shows that x, y, m, and s are related by the equations

$$\begin{aligned} .9x + .2y &= m \\ .1x + .8y &= s. \end{aligned}$$

In a given year, there were found to be 490,000 married adults and 147,000 single adults.
(a) How many married adults were there in the preceding year?
(b) How many married adults were there two years ago?

SOLUTION **(a)** The given equations can be written in the matrix form

$$AX = B,$$

where

$$A = \begin{bmatrix} .9 & .2 \\ .1 & .8 \end{bmatrix}, \quad X = \begin{bmatrix} x \\ y \end{bmatrix}, \quad B = \begin{bmatrix} m \\ s \end{bmatrix}.$$

Let's calculate A^{-1}. First, $D = (.9)(.8) - (.2)(.1) = .7 \neq 0$. Therefore,

$$A^{-1} = \frac{1}{.7}\begin{bmatrix} .8 & -.2 \\ -.1 & .9 \end{bmatrix} = \begin{bmatrix} \frac{8}{7} & -\frac{2}{7} \\ -\frac{1}{7} & \frac{9}{7} \end{bmatrix}.$$

We are given that $B = \begin{bmatrix} 490{,}000 \\ 147{,}000 \end{bmatrix}$. So, since $X = A^{-1}B$, we have

$$X = \begin{bmatrix} \frac{8}{7} & -\frac{2}{7} \\ -\frac{1}{7} & \frac{9}{7} \end{bmatrix}\begin{bmatrix} 490{,}000 \\ 147{,}000 \end{bmatrix} = \begin{bmatrix} 518{,}000 \\ 119{,}000 \end{bmatrix}.$$

Thus, last year there were 518,000 married adults and 119,000 single adults.

(b) We deduce x and y for two years ago from the values of m and s for last year—namely, $m = 518{,}000$, $s = 119{,}000$.

$$X = A^{-1}B = \begin{bmatrix} \frac{8}{7} & -\frac{2}{7} \\ -\frac{1}{7} & \frac{9}{7} \end{bmatrix}\begin{bmatrix} 518{,}000 \\ 119{,}000 \end{bmatrix} = \begin{bmatrix} 558{,}000 \\ 79{,}000 \end{bmatrix}.$$

That is, two years ago there were 558,000 married adults and 79,000 single adults.

» Now Try Exercise 17

Using the method of matrix equations to solve a system of linear equations is especially efficient if one wishes to solve a number of systems all having the same left-hand sides, but different right-hand sides. For then, A^{-1} must be computed only once for all of the systems under consideration. (This point is useful in Exercises 19–26.)

EXAMPLE 4 **Using a Matrix Inverse to Solve Systems of Equations** In Section 4.5, we will show that if

$$A = \begin{bmatrix} 4 & -2 & 3 \\ 8 & -3 & 5 \\ 7 & -2 & 4 \end{bmatrix}, \quad \text{then} \quad A^{-1} = \begin{bmatrix} -2 & 2 & -1 \\ 3 & -5 & 4 \\ 5 & -6 & 4 \end{bmatrix}.$$

(a) Use this fact to solve the system of linear equations

$$\begin{cases} 4x - 2y + 3z = 1 \\ 8x - 3y + 5z = 4 \\ 7x - 2y + 4z = 5. \end{cases}$$

(b) Solve the system of equations

$$\begin{cases} 4x - 2y + 3z = 4 \\ 8x - 3y + 5z = 7 \\ 7x - 2y + 4z = 6. \end{cases}$$

SOLUTION **(a)** The system can be written in the matrix form

$$\underset{A}{\begin{bmatrix} 4 & -2 & 3 \\ 8 & -3 & 5 \\ 7 & -2 & 4 \end{bmatrix}} \underset{X}{\begin{bmatrix} x \\ y \\ z \end{bmatrix}} = \underset{B}{\begin{bmatrix} 1 \\ 4 \\ 5 \end{bmatrix}}.$$

The solution of this matrix equation is $X = A^{-1}B$, or

$$\begin{bmatrix} x \\ y \\ z \end{bmatrix} = \begin{bmatrix} -2 & 2 & -1 \\ 3 & -5 & 4 \\ 5 & -6 & 4 \end{bmatrix} \begin{bmatrix} 1 \\ 4 \\ 5 \end{bmatrix} = \begin{bmatrix} 1 \\ 3 \\ 1 \end{bmatrix}.$$

Thus, the solution of the system is $x = 1$, $y = 3$, $z = 1$.

(b) This system has the same left-hand side as the preceding system, so its solution is

$$\begin{bmatrix} x \\ y \\ z \end{bmatrix} = \begin{bmatrix} -2 & 2 & -1 \\ 3 & -5 & 4 \\ 5 & -6 & 4 \end{bmatrix} \begin{bmatrix} 4 \\ 7 \\ 6 \end{bmatrix} = \begin{bmatrix} 0 \\ 1 \\ 2 \end{bmatrix}.$$

That is, the solution of the system is $x = 0$, $y = 1$, $z = 2$. **>> Now Try Exercise 19**

Check Your Understanding 4.4

Solutions can be found following the section exercises.

1. Show that the inverse of

$$\begin{bmatrix} -4 & 1 & 2 \\ 7 & -1 & -4 \\ -\frac{1}{2} & 0 & \frac{1}{2} \end{bmatrix} \text{ is } \begin{bmatrix} 1 & 1 & 4 \\ 3 & 2 & 4 \\ 1 & 1 & 6 \end{bmatrix}.$$

2. Use the method of this section to solve the system of linear equations

$$\begin{cases} .8x + .6y = 5 \\ .2x + .4y = 2. \end{cases}$$

EXERCISES 4.4

In Exercises 1 and 2, use the fact that

$$\begin{bmatrix} 2 & 2 \\ \frac{1}{2} & 1 \end{bmatrix}^{-1} = \begin{bmatrix} 1 & -2 \\ -\frac{1}{2} & 2 \end{bmatrix}.$$

1. Solve $\begin{cases} 2x + 2y = 4 \\ \frac{1}{2}x + y = 1. \end{cases}$

2. Solve $\begin{cases} 2x + 2y = 14 \\ \frac{1}{2}x + y = 4. \end{cases}$

In Exercises 3–10, find the inverse of the given matrix.

3. $\begin{bmatrix} 7 & 2 \\ 3 & 1 \end{bmatrix}$

4. $\begin{bmatrix} 2 & 3 \\ 5 & 7 \end{bmatrix}$

5. $\begin{bmatrix} 6 & 2 \\ 5 & 2 \end{bmatrix}$

6. $\begin{bmatrix} 1 & .5 \\ 0 & .5 \end{bmatrix}$

7. $\begin{bmatrix} .7 & .2 \\ .3 & .8 \end{bmatrix}$

8. $\begin{bmatrix} 0 & 1 \\ 1 & 0 \end{bmatrix}$

9. $[3]$

10. $[.2]$

In Exercises 11–14, use a matrix equation to solve the system of linear equations.

11. $\begin{cases} x + 2y = 3 \\ 2x + 6y = 5 \end{cases}$

12. $\begin{cases} 5x + 3y = 1 \\ 7x + 4y = 2 \end{cases}$

13. $\begin{cases} \frac{1}{2}x + 2y = 4 \\ 3x + 16y = 0 \end{cases}$

14. $\begin{cases} .8x + .6y = 2 \\ .2x + .4y = 1 \end{cases}$

15. Marriage Trends It is found that the number of married and single adults in a certain town are subject to the statistics that follow. Suppose that x and y denote the number of married and single adults, respectively, in a given year (say, as of January 1) and let m and s denote the corresponding numbers for the following year. Then,

$$\begin{aligned} .8x + .3y &= m \\ .2x + .7y &= s. \end{aligned}$$

(a) Write this system of equations in matrix form.

(b) Solve the resulting matrix equation for $X = \begin{bmatrix} x \\ y \end{bmatrix}$.

(c) Suppose that, in a given year, there were found to be 100,000 married adults and 50,000 single adults. How many married and single adults were there the preceding year?

(d) How many married and single adults were there two years ago?

16. Epidemiology A flu epidemic is spreading through a town of 48,000 people. It is found that, if x and y denote the numbers of people sick and well in a given week, respectively, and if s and w denote the corresponding numbers for the following week, then

$$\begin{aligned}\tfrac{1}{3}x + \tfrac{1}{4}y &= s\\ \tfrac{2}{3}x + \tfrac{3}{4}y &= w.\end{aligned}$$

(a) Write this system of equations in matrix form.

(b) Solve the resulting matrix equation for $X = \begin{bmatrix} x \\ y \end{bmatrix}$.

(c) Suppose that 13,000 people are sick in a given week. How many were sick the preceding week?

(d) Same question as part (c), except assume that 14,000 are sick.

17. **Housing Trends** Statistics show that, at a certain university, 70% of the students who live on campus during a given semester will remain on campus the following semester, and 90% of students living off campus during a given semester will remain off campus the following semester. Let x and y denote the number of students who live on and off campus this semester, and let u and v be the corresponding numbers for the next semester. Then,

$$\begin{aligned}.7x + .1y &= u\\ .3x + .9y &= v.\end{aligned}$$

(a) Write this system of equations in matrix form.

(b) Solve the resulting matrix equation for $X = \begin{bmatrix} x \\ y \end{bmatrix}$.

(c) Suppose that, out of a group of 9000 students, 6000 currently live on campus and 3000 live off campus. How many lived on campus last semester? How many will live off campus next semester?

18. **Performance on Tests** A teacher estimates that, of the students who pass a test, 80% will pass the next test, while of the students who fail a test, 50% will pass the next test. Let x and y denote the number of students who pass and fail a given test, and let u and v be the corresponding numbers for the following test.

(a) Write a matrix equation relating $\begin{bmatrix} x \\ y \end{bmatrix}$ to $\begin{bmatrix} u \\ v \end{bmatrix}$.

(b) Suppose that 25 of the teacher's students pass the third test and 8 fail the third test. How many students will pass the fourth test? Approximately how many passed the second test?

In Exercises 19–22, use the fact that the following two matrices are inverses of each other to solve the system of linear equations.

$$\begin{bmatrix} 1 & 2 & 2 \\ 1 & 3 & 2 \\ 1 & 2 & 3 \end{bmatrix} \quad \text{and} \quad \begin{bmatrix} 5 & -2 & -2 \\ -1 & 1 & 0 \\ -1 & 0 & 1 \end{bmatrix}$$

19. $\begin{cases} x + 2y + 2z = 1 \\ x + 3y + 2z = -1 \\ x + 2y + 3z = -1 \end{cases}$

20. $\begin{cases} x + 2y + 2z = 1 \\ x + 3y + 2z = 0 \\ x + 2y + 3z = 0 \end{cases}$

21. $\begin{cases} 5x - 2y - 2z = 3 \\ -x + y = 4 \\ -x + z = 5 \end{cases}$

22. $\begin{cases} 5x - 2y - 2z = 0 \\ -x + y = 1 \\ -x + z = 2 \end{cases}$

In Exercises 23–26, use the fact that the following two matrices are inverses of each other to solve the system of linear equations.

$$\begin{bmatrix} 9 & 0 & 2 & 0 \\ -20 & -9 & -5 & 5 \\ 4 & 0 & 1 & 0 \\ -4 & -2 & -1 & 1 \end{bmatrix} \quad \text{and} \quad \begin{bmatrix} 1 & 0 & -2 & 0 \\ 0 & 1 & 0 & -5 \\ -4 & 0 & 9 & 0 \\ 0 & 2 & 1 & -9 \end{bmatrix}$$

23. $\begin{cases} 9x + 2z = 1 \\ -20x - 9y - 5z + 5w = 0 \\ 4x + z = 0 \\ -4x - 2y - z + w = -1 \end{cases}$

24. $\begin{cases} 9x + 2z = 2 \\ -20x - 9y - 5z + 5w = 1 \\ 4x + z = 3 \\ -4x - 2y - z + w = 0 \end{cases}$

25. $\begin{cases} x - 2z = 0 \\ y - 5w = 1 \\ -4x + 9z = 2 \\ 2y + z - 9w = 0 \end{cases}$

26. $\begin{cases} x - 2z = -1 \\ y - 5w = 0 \\ -4x + 9z = 0 \\ 2y + z - 9w = 1 \end{cases}$

27. Show that if $a \neq 0$ and $b \neq 0$, then the inverse of $\begin{bmatrix} a & 0 \\ 0 & b \end{bmatrix}$ is $\begin{bmatrix} \frac{1}{a} & 0 \\ 0 & \frac{1}{b} \end{bmatrix}$.

28. (True or False) If B is the inverse of A, then A is the inverse of B.

29. **Age Distribution** There are two age groups for a particular species of organism. Group I consists of all organisms aged under 1 year, while group II consists of all organisms aged from 1 to 2 years. No organism survives more than 2 years. The average number of offspring per year born to each member of group I is 1, while the average number of offspring per year born to each member of group II is 2. Nine-tenths of group I survive to enter group II each year.

(a) Let x and y represent the initial number of organisms in groups I and II, respectively. Let a and b represent the number of organisms in groups I and II, respectively, after one year. Write a matrix equation relating $\begin{bmatrix} x \\ y \end{bmatrix}$ to $\begin{bmatrix} a \\ b \end{bmatrix}$.

(b) If there are initially 450,000 organisms in group I and 360,000 organisms in group II, calculate the number of organisms in each of the groups after 1 year and after 2 years.

(c) Suppose that, at a certain time, there were 810,000 organisms in group I and 630,000 organisms in group II. Determine the population of each group 1 year earlier.

30. If $A^2 = \begin{bmatrix} -2 & -1 \\ 2 & -1 \end{bmatrix}$ and $A^3 = \begin{bmatrix} -2 & 1 \\ -2 & -3 \end{bmatrix}$, what is A?

31. Show that, if AB is a matrix of all zeros and A has an inverse, then B is a matrix of all zeros.

32. Consider the matrices $A = \begin{bmatrix} 3 & 1 \\ 5 & 2 \end{bmatrix}$ and $B = \begin{bmatrix} 6 & 2 \\ 5 & 2 \end{bmatrix}$. Show that $(AB)^{-1} = B^{-1}A^{-1}$.

33. Find a 2×2 matrix A and a 2×1 column matrix B for which $AX = B$ has no solution.

34. Find a 2×2 matrix A and a 2×1 column matrix B for which $AX = B$ has infinitely many solutions.

Solutions to Check Your Understanding 4.4

1. To see whether this matrix is indeed the inverse, multiply it by the original matrix and find out if the product is an identity matrix.

$$\begin{bmatrix} 1 & 1 & 4 \\ 3 & 2 & 4 \\ 1 & 1 & 6 \end{bmatrix}\begin{bmatrix} -4 & 1 & 2 \\ 7 & -1 & -4 \\ -\frac{1}{2} & 0 & \frac{1}{2} \end{bmatrix} = \begin{bmatrix} 1 & 0 & 0 \\ 0 & 1 & 0 \\ 0 & 0 & 1 \end{bmatrix}.$$

2. The matrix form of this system is

$$\begin{bmatrix} .8 & .6 \\ .2 & .4 \end{bmatrix}\begin{bmatrix} x \\ y \end{bmatrix} = \begin{bmatrix} 5 \\ 2 \end{bmatrix}.$$

Therefore, the solution is

$$\begin{bmatrix} x \\ y \end{bmatrix} = \begin{bmatrix} .8 & .6 \\ .2 & .4 \end{bmatrix}^{-1}\begin{bmatrix} 5 \\ 2 \end{bmatrix}.$$

To compute the inverse of the 2×2 matrix, first compute D.

$$D = ad - bc = (.8)(.4) - (.6)(.2) = .32 - .12 = .2$$

Thus,

$$\begin{bmatrix} .8 & .6 \\ .2 & .4 \end{bmatrix}^{-1} = \begin{bmatrix} .4/.2 & -.6/.2 \\ -.2/.2 & .8/.2 \end{bmatrix} = \begin{bmatrix} 2 & -3 \\ -1 & 4 \end{bmatrix}.$$

Therefore,

$$\begin{bmatrix} x \\ y \end{bmatrix} = \begin{bmatrix} 2 & -3 \\ -1 & 4 \end{bmatrix}\begin{bmatrix} 5 \\ 2 \end{bmatrix} = \begin{bmatrix} 4 \\ 3 \end{bmatrix},$$

so the solution is $x = 4$, $y = 3$.

4.5 The Gauss–Jordan Method for Calculating Inverses

Of the several popular methods for finding the inverse of a matrix, the **Gauss–Jordan method** is probably the easiest to describe. It can be used on square matrices of any size. Also, the mechanical nature of the computations allows this method to be programmed for a computer, with relative ease. We shall illustrate the procedure with a 2×2 matrix, whose inverse can also be calculated by using the method of the previous section. Let

$$A = \begin{bmatrix} \frac{1}{2} & 1 \\ 1 & 3 \end{bmatrix}.$$

It is simple to check that

$$A^{-1} = \begin{bmatrix} 6 & -2 \\ -2 & 1 \end{bmatrix}.$$

Let us now derive this result, using the Gauss–Jordan method.

Step 1 Write down the matrix A, and on its right append an identity matrix of the same size.

This is most conveniently done by placing I_2 beside A in a single matrix.

$$\left[\underbrace{\begin{matrix} \frac{1}{2} & 1 \\ 1 & 3 \end{matrix}}_{A} \;\middle|\; \underbrace{\begin{matrix} 1 & 0 \\ 0 & 1 \end{matrix}}_{I_2}\right]$$

Step 2 Perform elementary row operations on the left-hand matrix so as to transform it into an identity matrix. Each operation performed on the left-hand matrix is also performed on the right-hand matrix.

This step proceeds exactly like the Gauss–Jordan elimination method and may be most conveniently expressed in terms of pivoting. Thus, we have

$$\left[\begin{matrix} \textcircled{\tfrac{1}{2}} & 1 \\ 1 & 3 \end{matrix}\;\middle|\;\begin{matrix} 1 & 0 \\ 0 & 1 \end{matrix}\right] \xrightarrow[R_2 + (-1)R_1]{2R_1} \left[\begin{matrix} 1 & 2 \\ 0 & \textcircled{1} \end{matrix}\;\middle|\;\begin{matrix} 2 & 0 \\ -2 & 1 \end{matrix}\right] \xrightarrow{R_1 + (-2)R_2} \left[\begin{matrix} 1 & 0 \\ 0 & 1 \end{matrix}\;\middle|\;\begin{matrix} 6 & -2 \\ -2 & 1 \end{matrix}\right].$$

Step 3 When the matrix on the left becomes an identity matrix, the matrix on the right will be the desired inverse.

So, from the last matrix of our preceding calculation, we have

$$A^{-1} = \begin{bmatrix} 6 & -2 \\ -2 & 1 \end{bmatrix}.$$

This is the same result mentioned earlier.

EXAMPLE 1 **Finding the Inverse of a Matrix by the Gauss–Jordan Method** Find the inverse of the matrix

$$A = \begin{bmatrix} 4 & -2 & 3 \\ 8 & -3 & 5 \\ 7 & -2 & 4 \end{bmatrix}.$$

SOLUTION

$$\left[\begin{array}{ccc|ccc} \textcircled{4} & -2 & 3 & 1 & 0 & 0 \\ 8 & -3 & 5 & 0 & 1 & 0 \\ 7 & -2 & 4 & 0 & 0 & 1 \end{array}\right]$$

$$\left[\begin{array}{ccc|ccc} 1 & -\frac{1}{2} & \frac{3}{4} & \frac{1}{4} & 0 & 0 \\ 0 & \textcircled{1} & -1 & -2 & 1 & 0 \\ 0 & \frac{3}{2} & -\frac{5}{4} & -\frac{7}{4} & 0 & 1 \end{array}\right]$$

$$\left[\begin{array}{ccc|ccc} 1 & 0 & \frac{1}{4} & -\frac{3}{4} & \frac{1}{2} & 0 \\ 0 & 1 & -1 & -2 & 1 & 0 \\ 0 & 0 & \textcircled{\frac{1}{4}} & \frac{5}{4} & -\frac{3}{2} & 1 \end{array}\right]$$

$$\left[\begin{array}{ccc|ccc} 1 & 0 & 0 & -2 & 2 & -1 \\ 0 & 1 & 0 & 3 & -5 & 4 \\ 0 & 0 & 1 & 5 & -6 & 4 \end{array}\right]$$

Therefore,

$$A^{-1} = \begin{bmatrix} -2 & 2 & -1 \\ 3 & -5 & 4 \\ 5 & -6 & 4 \end{bmatrix}.$$

***»* Now Try Exercise 7**

Not all square matrices have inverses. If a matrix does not have an inverse, this will become apparent when applying the Gauss–Jordan method. At some point, there will be no way to continue transforming the left-hand matrix into an identity matrix. This is illustrated in the next example.

EXAMPLE 2 **Demonstrating That a Matrix Does Not Have an Inverse** Find the inverse of the matrix

$$A = \begin{bmatrix} 1 & 3 & 2 \\ 0 & 1 & 4 \\ 1 & 5 & 10 \end{bmatrix}.$$

SOLUTION

$$\left[\begin{array}{ccc|ccc} \textcircled{1} & 3 & 2 & 1 & 0 & 0 \\ 0 & 1 & 4 & 0 & 1 & 0 \\ 1 & 5 & 10 & 0 & 0 & 1 \end{array}\right]$$

$$\left[\begin{array}{ccc|ccc} 1 & 3 & 2 & 1 & 0 & 0 \\ 0 & \textcircled{1} & 4 & 0 & 1 & 0 \\ 0 & 2 & 8 & -1 & 0 & 1 \end{array}\right]$$

$$\left[\begin{array}{ccc|ccc} 1 & 0 & -10 & 1 & -3 & 0 \\ 0 & 1 & 4 & 0 & 1 & 0 \\ 0 & 0 & 0 & -1 & -2 & 1 \end{array}\right]$$

Since the third row of the left-hand matrix has only zero entries, it is impossible to complete the Gauss–Jordan method. Therefore, the matrix A has no inverse matrix.

***»* Now Try Exercise 9**

Check Your Understanding 4.5

Solutions can be found following the section exercises.

1. Use the Gauss–Jordan method to calculate the inverse of the matrix

$$\begin{bmatrix} 1 & 0 & 2 \\ 0 & 1 & -4 \\ 0 & 0 & 2 \end{bmatrix}.$$

2. Solve the system of linear equations

$$\begin{cases} x \quad\;\; + 2z = 4 \\ \quad y - 4z = 6 \\ \qquad\;\; 2z = 9. \end{cases}$$

EXERCISES 4.5

In Exercises 1–12, use the Gauss–Jordan method to compute the inverse, if it exists, of the matrix.

1. $\begin{bmatrix} 7 & 3 \\ 5 & 2 \end{bmatrix}$

2. $\begin{bmatrix} 5 & -2 \\ 6 & 2 \end{bmatrix}$

3. $\begin{bmatrix} 2 & 3 \\ -4 & -7 \end{bmatrix}$

4. $\begin{bmatrix} 1 & -3 \\ 0 & 1 \end{bmatrix}$

5. $\begin{bmatrix} 2 & -4 \\ -1 & 2 \end{bmatrix}$

6. $\begin{bmatrix} 1 & 3 & 1 \\ -1 & 2 & 0 \\ 2 & 11 & 3 \end{bmatrix}$

7. $\begin{bmatrix} 1 & 2 & -2 \\ 1 & 1 & 1 \\ 0 & 0 & 1 \end{bmatrix}$

8. $\begin{bmatrix} 2 & 2 & 0 \\ 0 & -2 & 0 \\ 3 & 0 & 1 \end{bmatrix}$

9. $\begin{bmatrix} -2 & 5 & 2 \\ 1 & -3 & -1 \\ -1 & 2 & 1 \end{bmatrix}$

10. $\begin{bmatrix} 1 & 0 & 0 \\ 2 & 1 & -2 \\ -1 & 2 & 1 \end{bmatrix}$

11. $\begin{bmatrix} 1 & 6 & 0 & 0 \\ 1 & 5 & 0 & 0 \\ 0 & 0 & 4 & 2 \\ 0 & 0 & 50 & 2 \end{bmatrix}$

12. $\begin{bmatrix} 6 & 0 & 2 & 0 \\ -6 & 1 & 0 & 1 \\ 1 & 0 & 1 & 0 \\ -9 & 0 & -1 & 1 \end{bmatrix}$

In Exercises 13–18, use an inverse matrix to solve the system of linear equations.

13. $\begin{cases} x + y + 2z = 3 \\ 3x + 2y + 2z = 4 \\ x + y + 3z = 5 \end{cases}$

14. $\begin{cases} x + 2y + 3z = 4 \\ 3x + 5y + 5z = 3 \\ 2x + 4y + 2z = 4 \end{cases}$

15. $\begin{cases} x + 4y + 3z = 15 \\ x + 3y + 4z = 17 \\ 2x + 3y + 3z = 16 \end{cases}$

16. $\begin{cases} y + 2z = 1 \\ 2x + y + 3z = 2 \\ x + y + 2z = 3 \end{cases}$

17. $\begin{cases} x \qquad - 2z - 2w = 0 \\ \quad y \qquad - 5w = 1 \\ -4x \quad + 9z + 9w = 2 \\ \quad 2y + z - 8w = 3 \end{cases}$

18. $\begin{cases} x + 2y - z + w = 15 \\ 2x - y + z + w = 12 \\ 2x \quad + z + 2w = 18 \\ 3x + 2y \quad - w = 21 \end{cases}$

19. Find a 2×2 matrix A for which

$$A\begin{bmatrix} 2 & 5 \\ 1 & 3 \end{bmatrix} = \begin{bmatrix} -1 & 0 \\ 4 & 2 \end{bmatrix}.$$

20. Find a 2×2 matrix A for which

$$\begin{bmatrix} 2 & 5 \\ 1 & 3 \end{bmatrix}A = \begin{bmatrix} -1 & 0 \\ 4 & 2 \end{bmatrix}.$$

21. **College Degrees** Figure 1 gives the responses of a group of 100 randomly selected college freshmen when asked for the highest academic degree that they intended to obtain. Twice as many students intended to obtain master's degrees as their highest degree than intended to obtain bachelor's degrees as their highest degree. The number of students intending to obtain bachelor's or master's degrees as their highest degree was 26 more than the number who intended to obtain other degrees as their highest degree. Let x, y, and z represent the three numbers shown in Fig. 1. Use the methods of this section to determine the values of x, y, and z.

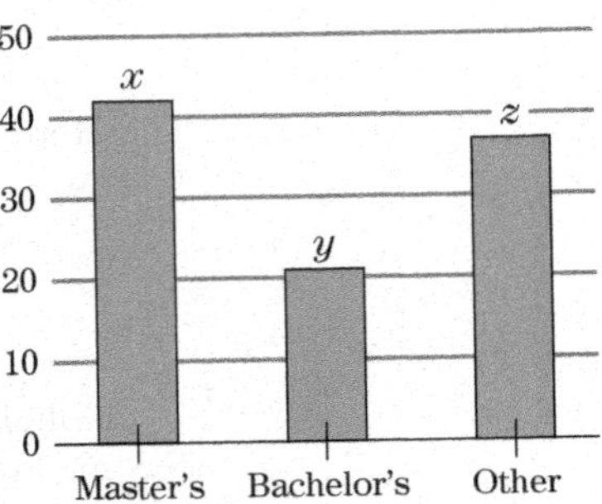

Figure 1 Highest Degree Intended

22. **College Choices** Figure 2 gives the responses of a group of 100 randomly selected college freshmen when asked whether the college they were attending was their first choice or second choice. The number of students who attended their first-choice college was 16 more than the students who did not. The number of students who attended their second-choice college was 46 less than the number of students who did not. Let x, y, and z represent the three numbers shown in Fig. 2. Use the methods of this section to determine the values of x, y, and z.

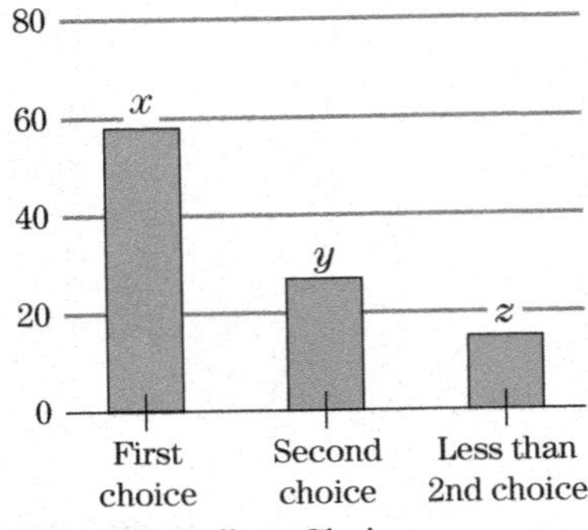

Figure 2 College Choice

23. **High School Attended** Figure 3 gives the responses of a group of 100 randomly selected college freshmen when asked for the type of high school attended. The number of students who attended public schools was 5 times the number who attended private schools minus 3 times the number who were homeschooled. The number of students who were homeschooled was 29 times the number who attended private schools minus 6 times the number who attended public schools. Use the methods of this section to determine the values of x, y, and z in Fig. 3.

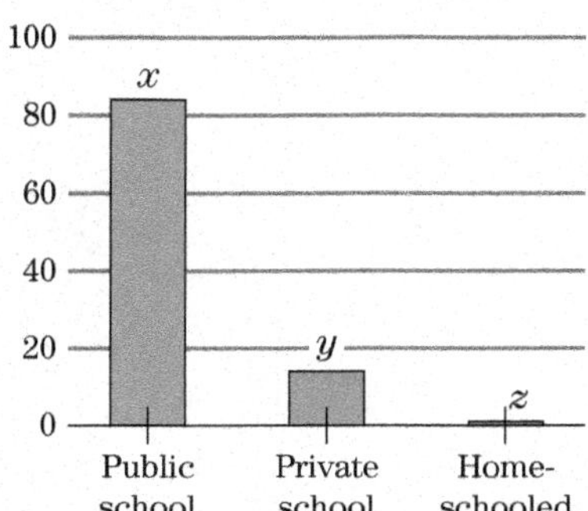

Figure 3 Type of High School Attended

24. **Placement Tests** Figure 4 gives the responses of a group of randomly selected college freshmen when asked for the types of placement tests taken. A total of 82 placement tests were taken. The number of mathematics placement tests taken was 2 more than twice the number of writing placement tests taken. Eight more writing placement tests were taken than reading placement tests. Determine the values of x, y, and z in Fig. 4.

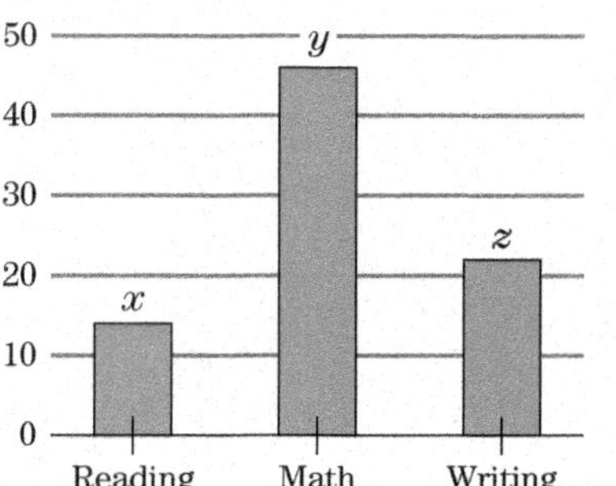

Figure 4 Type of Placement Tests Taken

Solutions to Check Your Understanding 4.5

1. First, write the given matrix beside an identity matrix of the same size

$$\left[\begin{array}{ccc|ccc} 1 & 0 & 2 & 1 & 0 & 0 \\ 0 & 1 & -4 & 0 & 1 & 0 \\ 0 & 0 & 2 & 0 & 0 & 1 \end{array}\right].$$

The object is to use elementary row operations to transform the 3×3 matrix on the left into the identity matrix. The first two columns are already in the correct form.

$$\left[\begin{array}{ccc|ccc} 1 & 0 & 2 & 1 & 0 & 0 \\ 0 & 1 & -4 & 0 & 1 & 0 \\ 0 & 0 & 2 & 0 & 0 & 1 \end{array}\right]$$

$$\xrightarrow{\frac{1}{2}R_3} \left[\begin{array}{ccc|ccc} 1 & 0 & 2 & 1 & 0 & 0 \\ 0 & 1 & -4 & 0 & 1 & 0 \\ 0 & 0 & 1 & 0 & 0 & \frac{1}{2} \end{array}\right]$$

$$\xrightarrow{R_1 + (-2)R_3} \left[\begin{array}{ccc|ccc} 1 & 0 & 0 & 1 & 0 & -1 \\ 0 & 1 & -4 & 0 & 1 & 0 \\ 0 & 0 & 1 & 0 & 0 & \frac{1}{2} \end{array}\right]$$

$$\xrightarrow{R_2 + (4)R_3} \left[\begin{array}{ccc|ccc} 1 & 0 & 0 & 1 & 0 & -1 \\ 0 & 1 & 0 & 0 & 1 & 2 \\ 0 & 0 & 1 & 0 & 0 & \frac{1}{2} \end{array}\right]$$

Thus, the inverse of the given matrix is

$$\begin{bmatrix} 1 & 0 & -1 \\ 0 & 1 & 2 \\ 0 & 0 & \frac{1}{2} \end{bmatrix}.$$

2. The matrix form of this system of equations is $AX = B$, where A is the matrix whose inverse was found in Problem 1, and

$$B = \begin{bmatrix} 4 \\ 6 \\ 9 \end{bmatrix}.$$

Therefore, $X = A^{-1}B$, so that

$$\begin{bmatrix} x \\ y \\ z \end{bmatrix} = \begin{bmatrix} 1 & 0 & -1 \\ 0 & 1 & 2 \\ 0 & 0 & \frac{1}{2} \end{bmatrix} \begin{bmatrix} 4 \\ 6 \\ 9 \end{bmatrix} = \begin{bmatrix} -5 \\ 24 \\ \frac{9}{2} \end{bmatrix}.$$

So the solution of the system is $x = -5$, $y = 24$, $z = \frac{9}{2}$.

5 Linear Programming

Introduction

Real-world problems often involve limitations on materials, time, and money. To express such constraints mathematically, we formulate systems of inequalities. In Chapter 5 we discuss systems of inequalities in two variables and introduce a relatively new mathematical tool called linear programming. Linear programming can be used in the textile industry, for example, to determine how blended yarns should be combined to produce a fabric of maximum strength (see Problems 59 and 60 in Section 5.1).

5.1 Linear Inequalities in Two Variables

- Graphing Linear Inequalities in Two Variables
- Application

Graphing Linear Inequalities in Two Variables

We know how to graph first-degree equations such as

$$y = 2x - 3 \quad \text{and} \quad 2x - 3y = 5$$

but how do we graph first-degree inequalities such as the following?

$$y \le 2x - 3 \quad \text{and} \quad 2x - 3y > 5$$

We will find that graphing these inequalities is similar to graphing the equations, but first we must discuss some important subsets of a plane in a rectangular coordinate system.

A line divides the plane into two regions called **half-planes.** A vertical line divides it into **left** and **right half-planes**; a nonvertical line divides it into **upper** and **lower half-planes.** In either case, the dividing line is called the **boundary line** of each half-plane, as indicated in Figure 1.

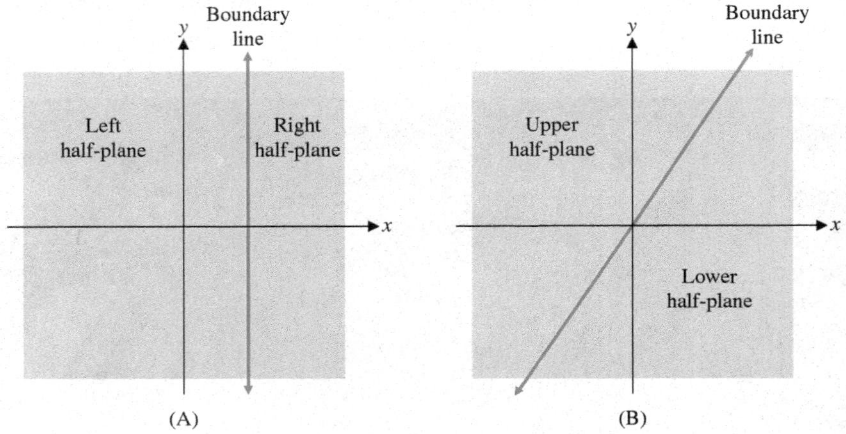

Figure 1

To find the half-planes determined by a linear equation such as $y - x = -2$, we rewrite the equation as $y = x - 2$. For any given value of x, there is exactly one value for y such that (x, y) lies on the line. For example, for $x = 4$, we have $y = 4 - 2 = 2$. For the same x and smaller values of y, the point (x, y) will lie below the line since $y < x - 2$. So the lower half-plane corresponds to the solution of the inequality $y < x - 2$. Similarly, the upper half-plane corresponds to $y > x - 2$, as shown in Figure 2.

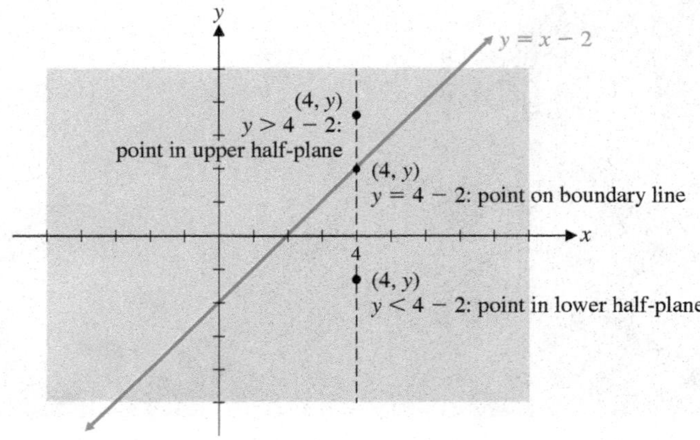

Figure 2

The four inequalities formed from $y = x - 2$, replacing the = sign by $>$, $\geq$, $<$, and $\leq$, respectively, are

$$y > x - 2 \qquad y \geq x - 2 \qquad y < x - 2 \qquad y \leq x - 2$$

The graph of each is a half-plane, excluding the boundary line for $<$ and $>$ and including the boundary line for $\leq$ and $\geq$. In Figure 3, the half-planes are indicated with small arrows on the graph of $y = x - 2$ and then graphed as shaded regions. Excluded boundary lines are shown as dashed lines, and included boundary lines are shown as solid lines.

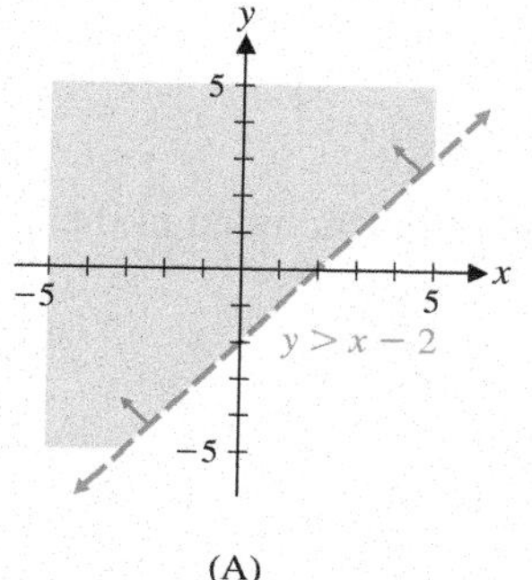

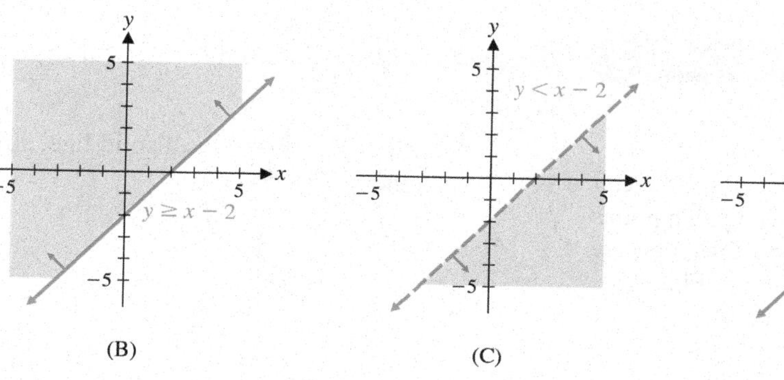

Figure 3

Figure 4 shows the graphs of Figures 3B and 3D on a graphing calculator. Note that it is impossible to show a dotted boundary line when using shading on a calculator.

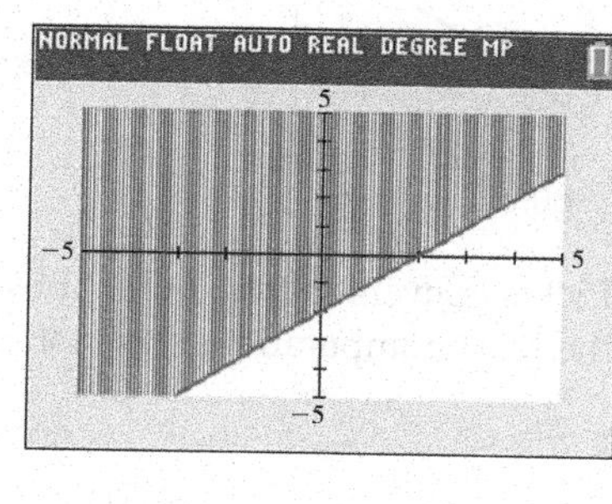

(A)

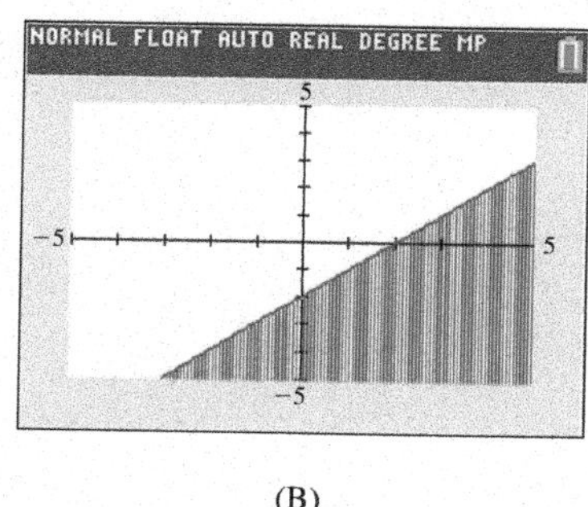

(B)

Figure 4

The preceding discussion suggests the following theorem, which is stated without proof:

THEOREM 1 Graphs of Linear Inequalities

The graph of the linear inequality

$$Ax + By < C \qquad \text{or} \qquad Ax + By > C$$

with $B \neq 0$, is either the upper half-plane or the lower half-plane (but not both) determined by the line $Ax + By = C$.

If $B = 0$ and $A \neq 0$, the graph of

$$Ax < C \qquad \text{or} \qquad Ax > C$$

is either the left half-plane or the right half-plane (but not both) determined by the line $Ax = C$.

As a consequence of this theorem, we state a simple and fast mechanical procedure for graphing linear inequalities.

PROCEDURE Graphing Linear Inequalities

Step 1 First graph $Ax + By = C$ as a dashed line if equality is not included in the original statement, or as a solid line if equality is included.

Step 2 Choose a test point anywhere in the plane not on the line [the origin $(0, 0)$ usually requires the least computation], and substitute the coordinates into the inequality.

Step 3 Does the test point satisfy the original inequality? If so, shade the half-plane that contains the test point. If not, shade the opposite half-plane.

EXAMPLE 1 **Graphing a Linear Inequality** Graph $2x - 3y \le 6$.

SOLUTION

Step 1 Graph $2x - 3y = 6$ as a solid line, since equality is included in the original statement (Fig. 5).

Reminder

Recall that the line $2x - 3y = 6$ can be graphed by finding any two points on the line. The x and y intercepts are usually a good choice (see Fig. 5).

x	y
0	-2
3	0

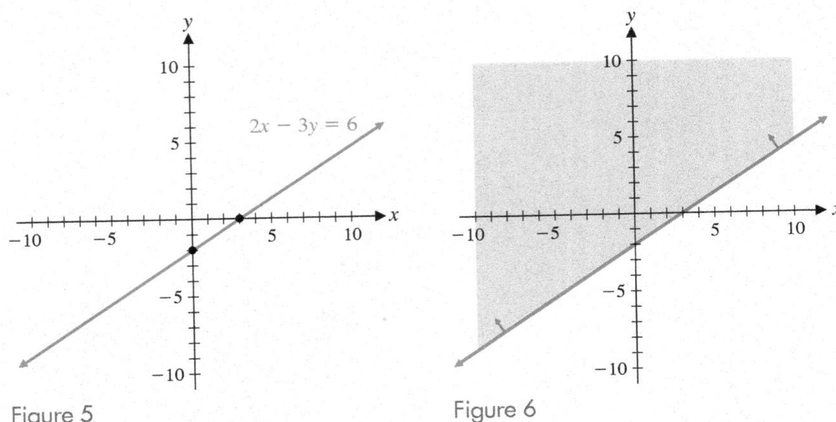

Figure 5 Figure 6

Step 2 Pick a convenient test point above or below the line. The origin $(0, 0)$ requires the least computation, so substituting $(0, 0)$ into the inequality, we get

$$2x - 3y \le 6$$

$$2(0) - 3(0) = 0 \le 6$$

This is a true statement; therefore, the point $(0, 0)$ is in the solution set.

Step 3 The line $2x - 3y = 6$ and the half-plane containing the origin form the graph of $2x - 3y \le 6$, as shown in Figure 6.

Matched Problem 1 Graph $6x - 3y > 18$.

Explore and Discuss 1

In Step 2 of Example 1, $(0, 0)$ was used as a test point in graphing a linear inequality. Describe those linear inequalities for which $(0, 0)$ is not a valid test point. In that case, how would you choose a test point to make calculation easy?

EXAMPLE 2 **Graphing Inequalities** Graph

(A) $y > -3$ (B) $2x \le 5$ (C) $x \le 3y$

SOLUTION

(A) Step 1 Graph the horizontal line $y = -3$ as a dashed line, since equality is not included in the original statement (Fig. 7).

Step 2 Substituting $x = 0$ and $y = 0$ in the inequality produces a true statement, so the point $(0, 0)$ is in the solution set.

Step 3 The graph of the solution set is the upper half-plane, excluding the boundary line (Fig. 8).

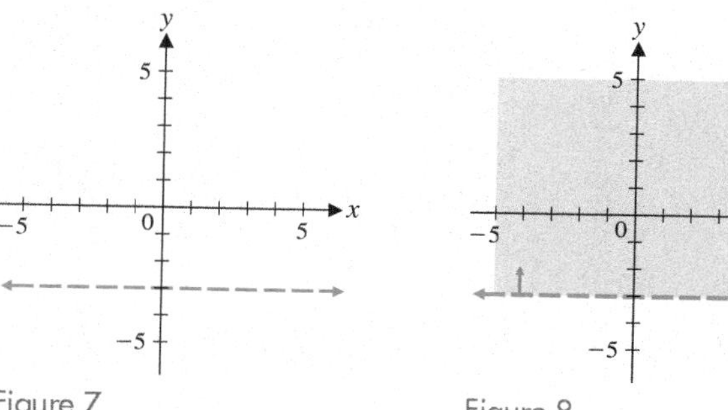

Figure 7 Figure 8

(B) Step 1 Graph the vertical line $2x = 5$ as a solid line, since equality is included in the original statement (Fig. 9).

Step 2 Substituting $x = 0$ and $y = 0$ in the inequality produces a true statement, so the point $(0, 0)$ is in the solution set.

Step 3 The graph of the solution set is the left half-plane, including the boundary line (Fig. 10).

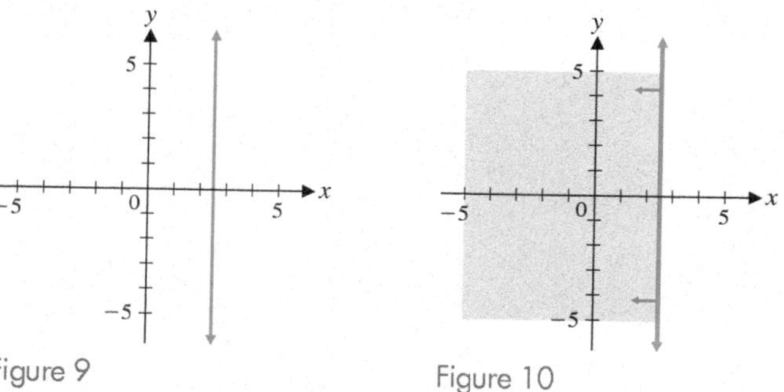

Figure 9 Figure 10

(C) Step 1 Graph the line $x = 3y$ as a solid line, since equality is included in the original statement (Fig. 11).

Step 2 Since the line passes through the origin, we must use a different test point. We choose $(0, 2)$ for a test point and conclude that this point is in the solution set.

Step 3 The graph of the solution set is the upper half-plane, including the boundary line (Fig. 12).

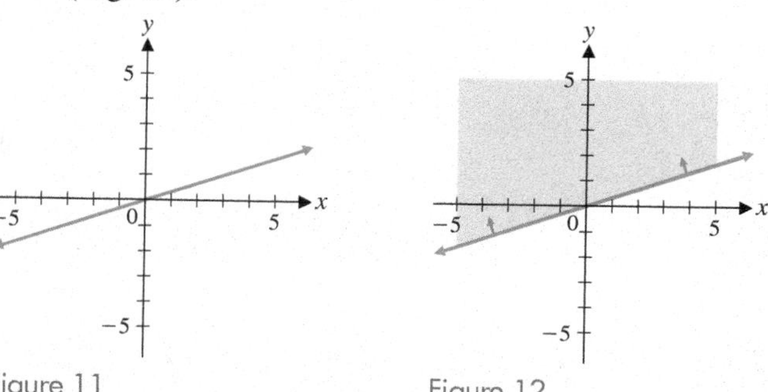

Figure 11 Figure 12

Matched Problem 2 Graph

(A) $y < 4$ (B) $4x \geq -9$ (C) $3x \geq 2y$

EXAMPLE 3 **Interpreting a Graph** Find the linear inequality whose graph is given in Figure 13. Write the boundary line equation in the form $Ax + By = C$, where A, B, and C are integers, before stating the inequality.

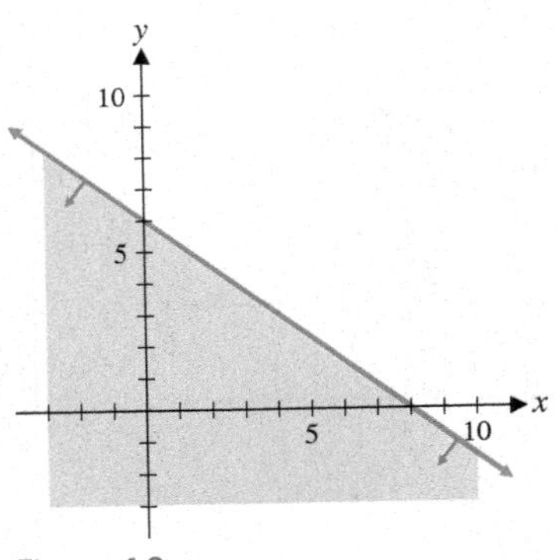
Figure 13

SOLUTION The boundary line (Fig. 13) passes through the points $(0, 6)$ and $(8, 0)$. We use the slope-intercept form to find the equation of this line:

$$\text{Slope: } m = \frac{0-6}{8-0} = -\frac{6}{8} = -\frac{3}{4}$$

$$y \text{ intercept: } b = 6$$

$$\text{Boundary line equation: } y = -\frac{3}{4}x + 6 \qquad \text{Multiply both sides by 4.}$$

$$4y = -3x + 24 \qquad \text{Add } 3x \text{ to both sides.}$$

$$3x + 4y = 24 \qquad \text{Form: } Ax + By = C$$

Since $(0, 0)$ is in the shaded region in Figure 13 and the boundary line is solid, the graph in Figure 13 is the graph of $3x + 4y \le 24$.

Matched Problem 3 Find the linear inequality whose graph is given in Figure 14. Write the boundary line equation in the form $Ax + By = C$, where A, B, and C are integers, before stating the inequality.

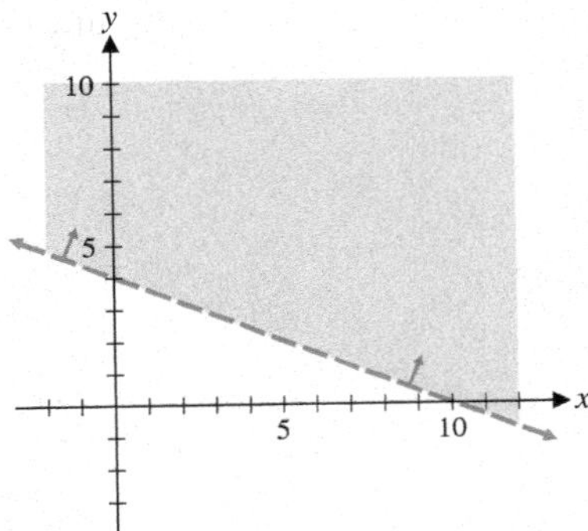
Figure 14

Application

EXAMPLE 4 **Sales** A concert promoter wants to book a rock group for a stadium concert. A ticket for admission to the stadium playing field will cost \$125, and a ticket for a seat in the stands will cost \$175. The group wants to be guaranteed total ticket sales of at least \$700,000. How many tickets of each type must be sold to satisfy the group's guarantee? Express the answer as a linear inequality and draw its graph.

SOLUTION

Let x = Number of tickets sold for the playing field
y = Number of tickets sold for seats in the stands

We use these variables to translate the following statement from the problem into a mathematical statement:

The group wants to be guaranteed total ticket sales of at least \$700,000.

$$\binom{\text{Sales for the}}{\text{playing field}} + \binom{\text{Sales for seats}}{\text{in the stands}} \binom{\text{At}}{\text{least}} \binom{\text{Total sales}}{\text{guaranteed}}$$

$$125x \quad + \quad 175y \quad \ge \quad 700{,}000$$

Dividing both sides of this inequality by 25, x, and y must satisfy

$$5x + 7y \ge 28{,}000$$

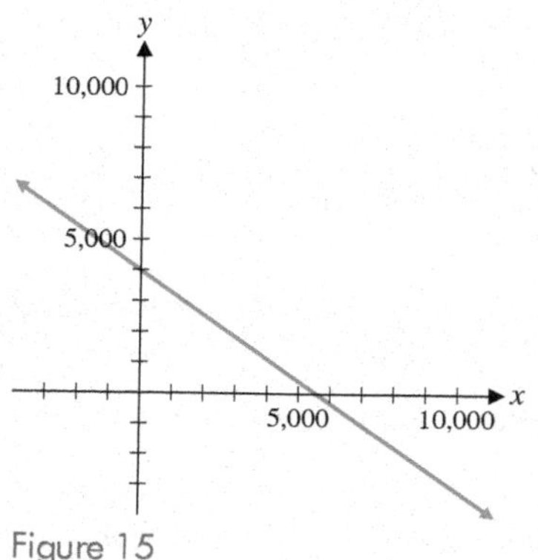

Figure 15

We use the three-step procedure to graph this inequality.

Step 1 Graph $5x + 7y = 28{,}000$ as a solid line (Fig. 15).

Step 2 Substituting $x = 0$ and $y = 0$ in the inequality produces a false statement, so the point $(0, 0)$ is not in the solution set.

Step 3 The graph of the inequality is the upper half-plane including the boundary line (Fig. 16), but does this graph really represent ticket sales?

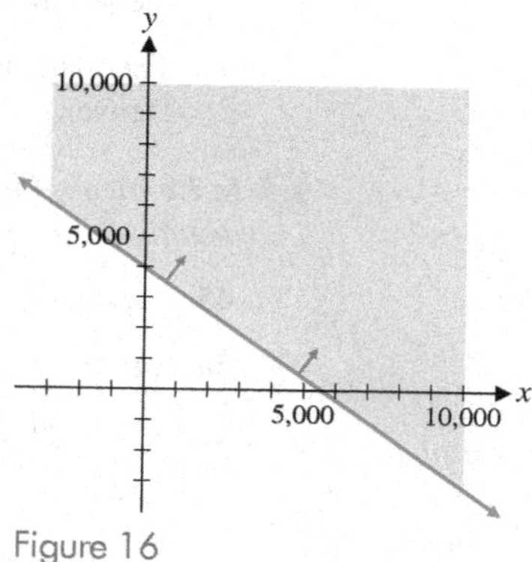

Figure 16

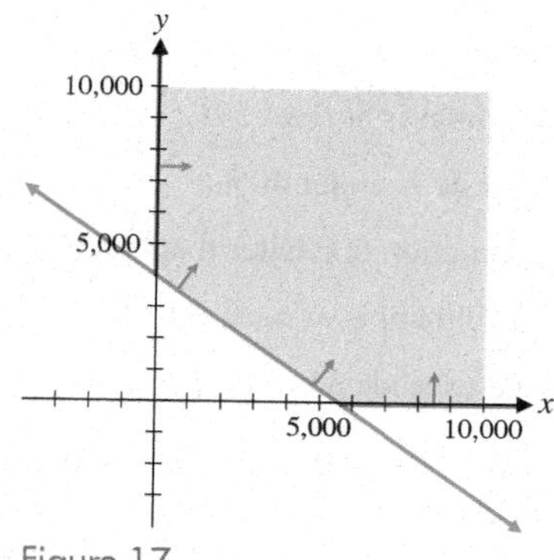

Figure 17

The shaded region in Figure 16 contains points in the second quadrant (where $x < 0$) and the fourth quadrant (where $y < 0$). It is not possible to sell a negative number of tickets, so we must restrict both x and y to the first quadrant. With this restriction, the solution becomes

$$5x + 7y \geq 28{,}000$$
$$x \geq 0, \ y \geq 0$$

and the graph is shown in Figure 17. There is yet another restriction on x and y. It is not possible to sell a fractional number of tickets, so both x and y must be integers. So the solutions of the original problem correspond to those points of the shaded region in Figure 17 that have integer coordinates. This restriction is not indicated in Figure 17, because the points with integer coordinates are too close together (about 9,000 such points per inch) to be visually distinguishable from other points.

Matched Problem 4 A food vendor at a rock concert sells hot dogs for \$4 and hamburgers for \$5. How many of these sandwiches must be sold to produce sales of at least \$1,000? Express the answer as a linear inequality and draw its graph.

Exercises 5.1

Skills Warm-up Exercises

For Problems 1–8, if necessary, review Section 1.2.

1. Is the point $(3, 5)$ on the line $y = 2x + 1$?

2. Is the point $(7, 9)$ on the line $y = 3x - 11$?

3. Is the point $(3, 5)$ in the solution set of $y \leq 2x + 1$?

4. Is the point $(7, 9)$ in the solution set of $y \leq 3x - 11$?

5. Is the point $(10, 12)$ on the line $13x - 11y = 2$?

6. Is the point $(21, 25)$ on the line $30x - 27y = 1$?

7. Is the point $(10, 12)$ in the solution set of $13x - 11y \geq 2$?

8. Is the point $(21, 25)$ in the solution set of $30x - 27y \leq 1$?

A *Graph each inequality in Problems 9–18.*

9. $y \leq x - 1$

10. $y > x + 1$

11. $3x - 2y > 6$

12. $2x - 5y \leq 10$

13. $x \geq -4$

14. $y < 5$

15. $6x + 4y \geq 24$

16. $4x + 8y \geq 32$

17. $5x \leq -2y$

18. $6x \geq 4y$

In Problems 19–22,

(A) *graph the set of points that satisfy the inequality.*

(B) *graph the set of points that do not satisfy the inequality.*

19. $2x + 3y < 18$

20. $3x + 4y > 24$

21. $5x - 2y \geq 20$

22. $3x - 5y \leq 30$

In Problems 23–32, define the variable and translate the sentence into an inequality.

23. There are fewer than 10 applicants.

24. She consumes no more than 900 calories per day.

25. He practices no less than 2.5 hours per day.

26. The average attendance is less than 15,000.

27. The monthly take-home pay is over $3,000.

28. The discount is at least 5%.

29. The tax rate is under 40%.

30. The population is greater than 500,000.

31. The enrollment is at most 30.

32. Mileage exceeds 35 miles per gallon.

B *In Exercises 33–38, state the linear inequality whose graph is given in the figure. Write the boundary-line equation in the form $Ax + By = C$, where A, B, and C are integers, before stating the inequality.*

33.

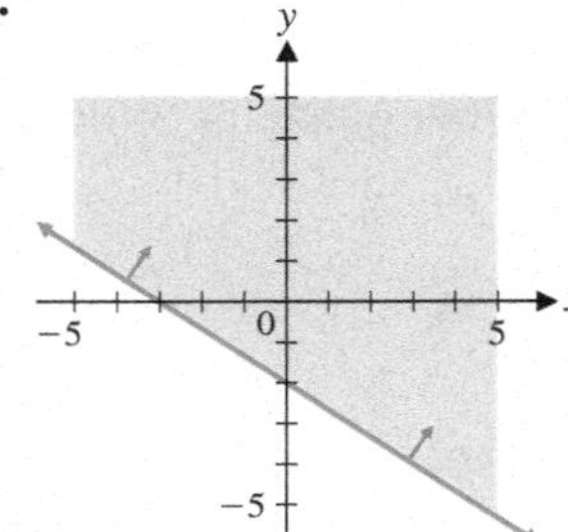

34.

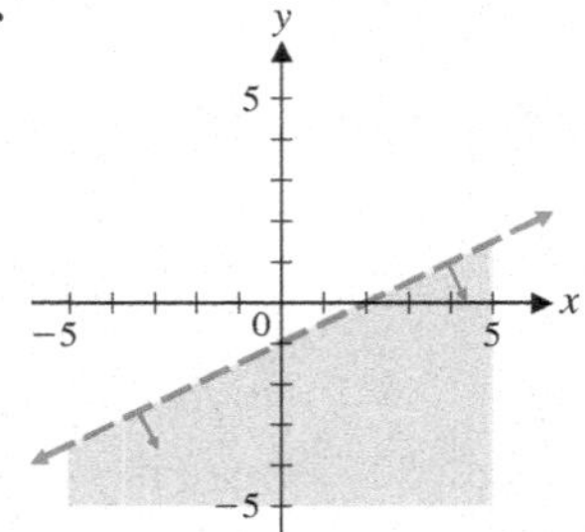

35.

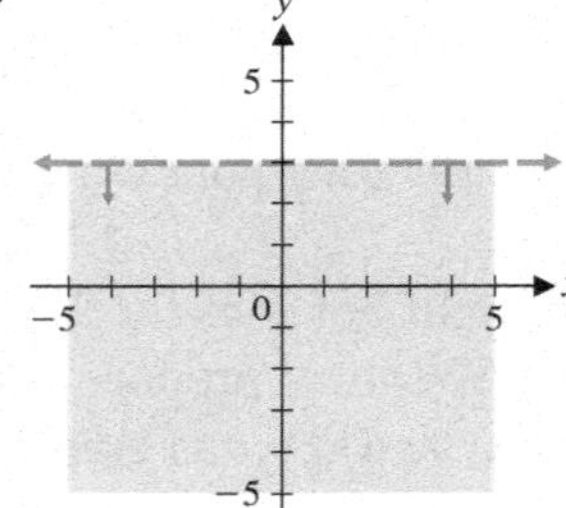

36.

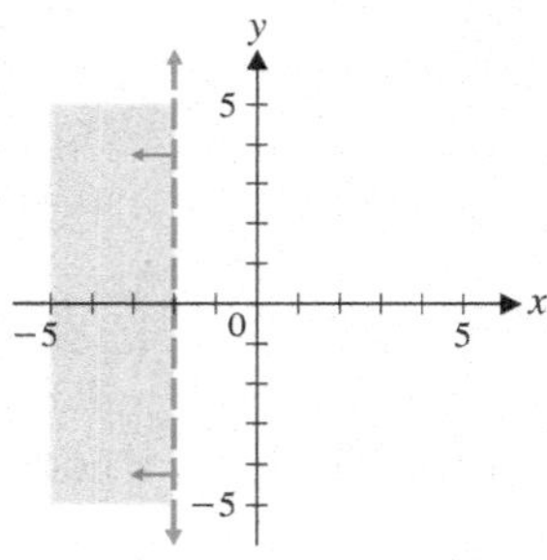

37.

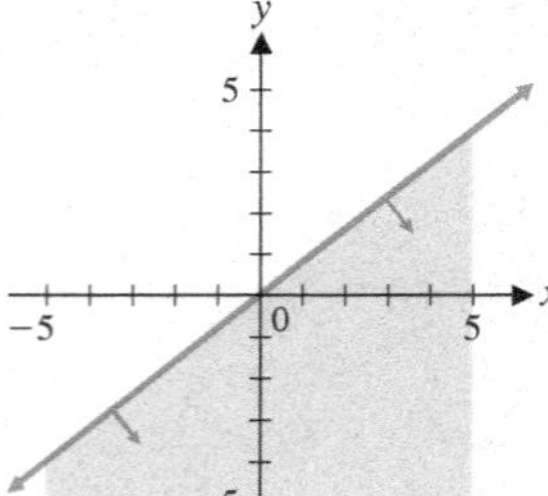

38.

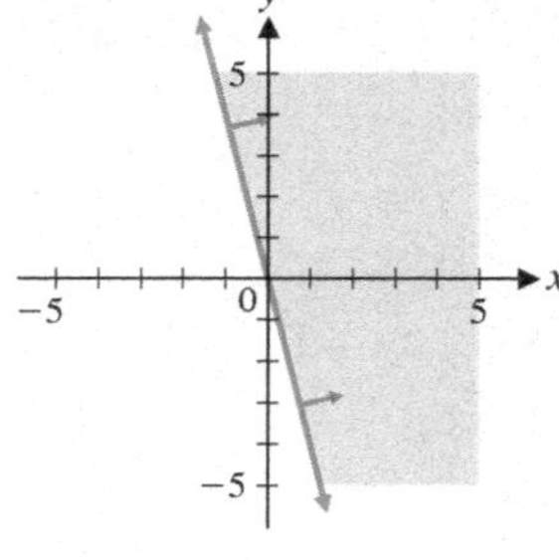

In Problems 39–44, define two variables and translate the sentence into an inequality.

39. Enrollment in finite mathematics plus enrollment in calculus is less than 300.

40. New-car sales and used-car sales combined are at most $500,000.

41. Revenue is at least $20,000 under the cost.

42. The Democratic candidate beat the Republican by at least seven percentage points.

43. The number of grams of saturated fat is more than three times the number of grams of unsaturated fat.

44. The plane is at least 500 miles closer to Chicago than to Denver.

C *In Problems 45–54, graph each inequality subject to the nonnegative restrictions.*

45. $25x + 40y \le 3{,}000,\ x \ge 0,\ y \ge 0$

46. $24x + 30y > 7{,}200,\ x \ge 0,\ y \ge 0$

47. $15x - 50y < 1{,}500,\ x \ge 0,\ y \ge 0$

48. $16x - 12y \ge 4{,}800,\ x \ge 0,\ y \ge 0$

49. $-18x + 30y \ge 2{,}700,\ x \ge 0,\ y \ge 0$

50. $-14x + 22y < 1{,}540,\ x \ge 0,\ y \ge 0$

51. $40x - 55y > 0,\ x \ge 0,\ y \ge 0$

52. $-35x + 75y \le 0,\ x \ge 0,\ y \ge 0$

53. $25x + 75y < -600,\ x \ge 0,\ y \ge 0$

54. $75x + 25y > -600,\ x \ge 0,\ y \ge 0$

Applications

In Problems 55–66, express your answer as a linear inequality with appropriate nonnegative restrictions and draw its graph.

55. Seed costs. Seed costs for a farmer are $90 per acre for corn and $70 per acre for soybeans. How many acres of each crop should the farmer plant if he wants to spend no more than $11,000 on seed?

56. Labor costs. Labor costs for a farmer are $120 per acre for corn and $100 per acre for soybeans. How many acres of each crop should the farmer plant if he wants to spend no more than $15,000 on labor?

57. Fertilizer. A farmer wants to use two brands of fertilizer for his corn crop. Brand *A* contains 26% nitrogen, 3% phosphate, and 3% potash. Brand *B* contains 16% nitrogen, 8% phosphate, and 8% potash.

(*Source:* Spectrum Analytic, Inc.)

(A) How many pounds of each brand of fertilizer should he add to each acre if he wants to add at least 120 pounds of nitrogen to each acre?

(B) How many pounds of each brand of fertilizer should he add to each acre if he wants to add at most 28 pounds of phosphate to each acre?

58. Fertilizer. A farmer wants to use two brands of fertilizer for his soybean crop. Brand *A* contains 18% nitrogen, 24% phosphate, and 12% potash. Brand *B* contains 5% nitrogen, 10% phosphate, and 15% potash.

(*Source:* Spectrum Analytic, Inc.)

(A) How many pounds of each brand of fertilizer should he add to each acre if he wants to add at least 50 pounds of phosphate to each acre?

(B) How many pounds of each brand of fertilizer should he add to each acre if he wants to add at most 60 pounds of potash to each acre?

59. Textiles. A textile mill uses two blended yarns—a standard blend that is 30% acrylic, 30% wool, and 40% nylon and a deluxe blend that is 9% acrylic, 39% wool, and 52% nylon—to produce various fabrics. How many pounds of each yarn should the mill use to produce a fabric that is at least 20% acrylic?

60. Textiles. Refer to Exercise 59. How many pounds of each yarn should the mill use to produce a fabric that is at least 45% nylon?

61. Customized vehicles. A company uses sedans and minivans to produce custom vehicles for transporting hotel guests to and from airports. Plant *A* can produce 10 sedans and 8 minivans per week, and Plant *B* can produce 8 sedans and 6 minivans per week. How many weeks should each plant operate in order to produce at least 400 sedans?

62. Customized vehicles. Refer to Exercise 61. How many weeks should each plant operate in order to produce at least 480 minivans?

63. Political advertising. A candidate has budgeted \$10,000 to spend on radio and television advertising. A radio ad costs \$200 per 30-second spot, and a television ad costs \$800 per 30-second spot. How many radio and television spots can the candidate purchase without exceeding the budget?

64. Political advertising. Refer to Problem 63. The candidate decides to replace the television ads with newspaper ads that cost \$500 per ad. How many radio spots and newspaper ads can the candidate purchase without exceeding the budget?

65. Mattresses. A company produces foam mattresses in two sizes: regular and king. It takes 5 minutes to cut the foam for a regular mattress and 6 minutes for a king mattress. If the cutting department has 50 labor-hours available each day, how many regular and king mattresses can be cut in one day?

66. Mattresses. Refer to Problem 65. It takes 15 minutes to cover a regular mattress and 20 minutes to cover a king mattress. If the covering department has 160 labor-hours available each day, how many regular and king mattresses can be covered in one day?

Answers to Matched Problems

1.

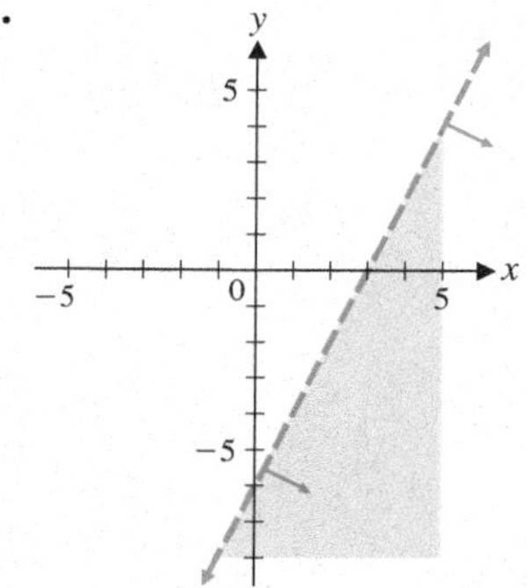

2. (A)

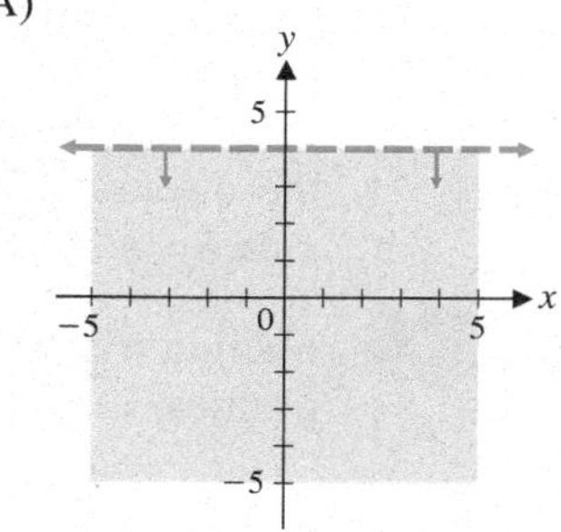

(B)

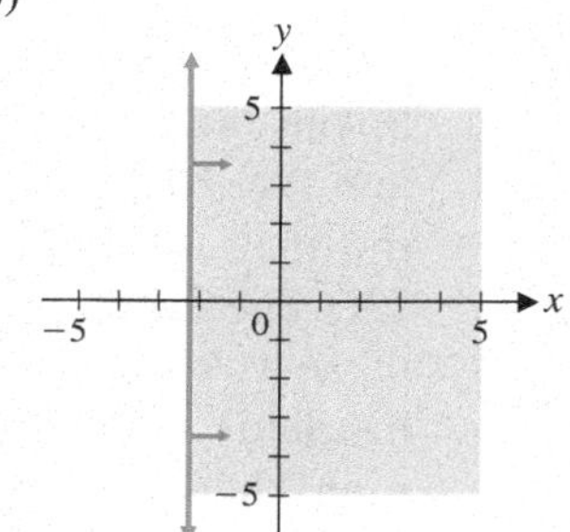

(C)

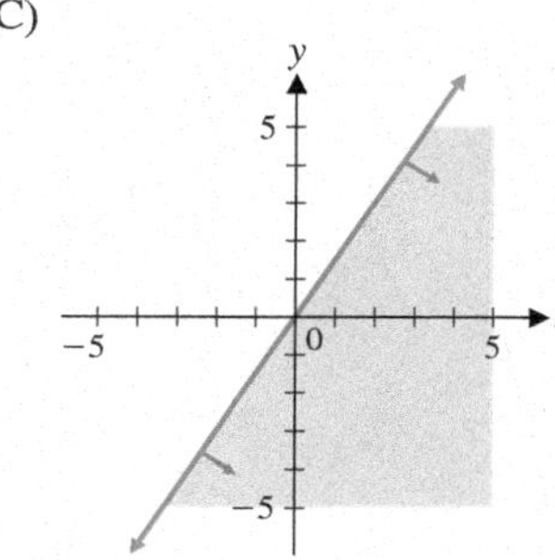

3. $2x + 5y > 20$

4. Let x = Number of hot dogs sold

y = Number of hamburgers sold

$4x + 5y \geq 1{,}000 \qquad x \geq 0, y \geq 0$

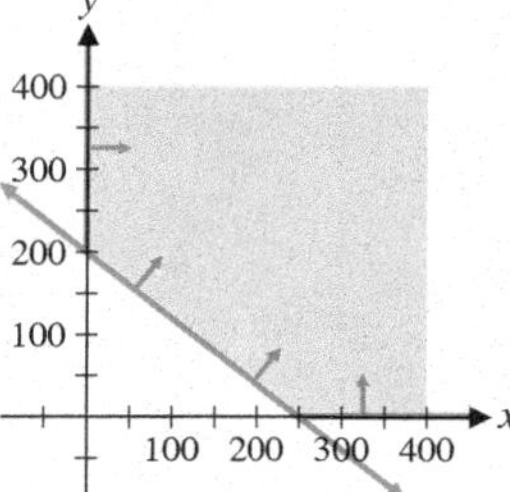

5.2 Systems of Linear Inequalities in Two Variables

- Solving Systems of Linear Inequalities Graphically
- Applications

Solving Systems of Linear Inequalities Graphically

We now consider systems of linear inequalities such as

$$\begin{aligned} x + y &\geq 6 \\ 2x - y &\geq 0 \end{aligned} \qquad \text{and} \qquad \begin{aligned} 2x + y &\leq 22 \\ x + y &\leq 13 \\ 2x + 5y &\leq 50 \\ x &\geq 0 \\ y &\geq 0 \end{aligned}$$

We wish to **solve** such systems **graphically**—that is, to find the graph of all ordered pairs of real numbers (x, y) that simultaneously satisfy all the inequalities in the system. The graph is called the **solution region** for the system (the solution region is also known as the **feasible region**). To find the solution region, we graph each inequality in the system and then take the intersection of all the graphs. To simplify the discussion that follows, *we consider only systems of linear inequalities where equality is included in each statement in the system.*

EXAMPLE 1 **Solving a System of Linear Inequalities Graphically** Solve the following system of linear inequalities graphically:

$$\begin{aligned} x + y &\geq 6 \\ 2x - y &\geq 0 \end{aligned}$$

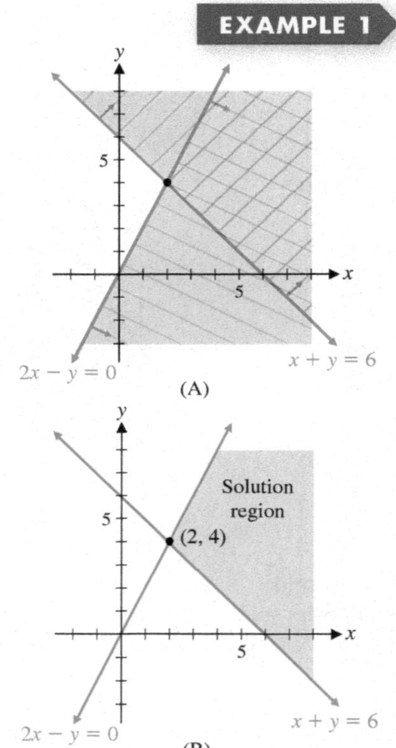

Figure 1

SOLUTION Graph the line $x + y = 6$ and shade the region that satisfies the linear inequality $x + y \geq 6$. This region is shaded with red lines in Figure 1A. Next, graph the line $2x - y = 0$ and shade the region that satisfies the inequality $2x - y \geq 0$. This region is shaded with blue lines in Figure 1A. The solution region for the system of inequalities is the intersection of these two regions. This is the region shaded in both red and blue (cross-hatched) in Figure 1A and redrawn in Figure 1B with only the solution region shaded. The coordinates of any point in the shaded region of Figure 1B specify a solution to the system. For example, the points $(2, 4)$, $(6, 3)$, and $(7.43, 8.56)$ are three of infinitely many solutions, as can be easily checked. The intersection point $(2, 4)$ is obtained by solving the equations $x + y = 6$ and $2x - y = 0$ simultaneously using any of the techniques.

Solve the following system of linear inequalities graphically:

$$\begin{aligned} 3x + y &\leq 21 \\ x - 2y &\leq 0 \end{aligned}$$

CONCEPTUAL INSIGHT

To check that you have shaded a solution region correctly, choose a test point in the region and check that it satisfies each inequality in the system. For example, choosing the point $(5, 4)$ in the shaded region in Figure 1B, we have

$$\begin{aligned} x + y &\geq 6 \\ 5 + 4 &\overset{?}{\geq} 6 \\ 9 &\overset{\checkmark}{\geq} 6 \end{aligned} \qquad \begin{aligned} 2x - y &\geq 0 \\ 10 - 4 &\overset{?}{\geq} 0 \\ 6 &\overset{\checkmark}{\geq} 0 \end{aligned}$$

The points of intersection of the lines that form the boundary of a solution region will play a fundamental role in the solution of linear programming problems, which are discussed in the next section.

DEFINITION Corner Point

A **corner point** of a solution region is a point in the solution region that is the intersection of two boundary lines.

For example, the point $(2, 4)$ is the only corner point of the solution region in Example 1 (Fig. 1B).

EXAMPLE 2 **Solving a System of Linear Inequalities Graphically** Solve the following system of linear inequalities graphically and find the corner points:

$$\begin{aligned} 2x + y &\le 22 \\ x + y &\le 13 \\ 2x + 5y &\le 50 \\ x &\ge 0 \\ y &\ge 0 \end{aligned}$$

SOLUTION The inequalities $x \ge 0$ and $y \ge 0$ indicate that the solution region will lie in the first quadrant. So we can restrict our attention to that portion of the plane. First, we graph the lines

$$\begin{aligned} 2x + y &= 22 \\ x + y &= 13 \\ 2x + 5y &= 50 \end{aligned}$$

Find the x and y intercepts of each line; then sketch the line through these points.

Next, choosing $(0, 0)$ as a test point, we see that the graph of each of the first three inequalities in the system consists of its corresponding line and the half-plane lying below the line, as indicated by the small arrows in Figure 2. The solution region of the system consists of the points in the first quadrant that simultaneously lie on or below all three of these lines (see the shaded region in Fig. 2).

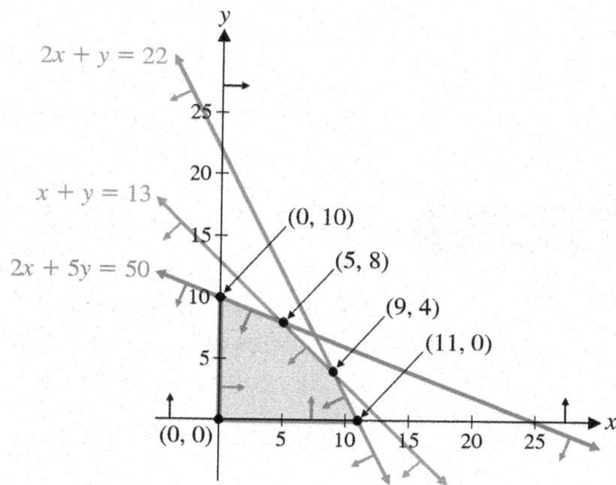

Figure 2

The corner points $(0, 0)$, $(0, 10)$, and $(11, 0)$ can be determined from the graph. The other two corner points are determined as follows:

Solve the system	Solve the system
$2x + 5y = 50$	$2x + y = 22$
$x + y = 13$	$x + y = 13$
to obtain $(5, 8)$.	to obtain $(9, 4)$.

Note that the lines $2x + 5y = 50$ and $2x + y = 22$ also intersect, but the intersection point is not part of the solution region and so is not a corner point.

Matched Problem 2 Solve the following system of linear inequalities graphically and find the corner points:

$$\begin{aligned} 5x + y &\geq 20 \\ x + y &\geq 12 \\ x + 3y &\geq 18 \\ x &\geq 0 \\ y &\geq 0 \end{aligned}$$

If we compare the solution regions of Examples 1 and 2, we see that there is a fundamental difference between these two regions. We can draw a circle around the solution region in Example 2; however, it is impossible to include all the points in the solution region in Example 1 in any circle, no matter how large we draw it. This leads to the following definition:

DEFINITION Bounded and Unbounded Solution Regions

A solution region of a system of linear inequalities is **bounded** if it can be enclosed within a circle. If it cannot be enclosed within a circle, it is **unbounded**.

The solution region for Example 2 is bounded, and the solution region for Example 1 is unbounded. This definition will be important in the next section.

Explore and Discuss 1

Determine whether the solution region of each system of linear inequalities is bounded or unbounded.

(A) $y \leq 1$, $x \geq 0$, $y \geq 0$

(B) $x \leq 100$, $y \leq 200$, $x \geq 0$, $y \geq 0$

(C) $x \leq y$, $y \leq x$, $x \geq 0$, $y \geq 0$

Applications

EXAMPLE 3 **Nutrition** A patient on a brown rice and skim milk diet is required to have at least 800 calories and at least 32 grams of protein per day. Each serving of brown rice contains 200 calories and 5 grams of protein. Each serving of skim milk contains 80 calories and 8 grams of protein. How many servings of each food should be eaten per day to meet the minimum daily requirements?

SOLUTION To answer the question, we need to solve for x and y, where

$$x = \text{number of daily servings of brown rice}$$

$$y = \text{number of daily servings of skim milk}$$

We arrange the information given in the problem in a table, with columns corresponding to x and y.

	Brown Rice	Skim Milk	Minimum Daily Requirement
Calories	200 cal/svg	80 cal/svg	800 cal
Protein	5 g/svg	8 g/svg	32 g

The number of calories in x servings of brown rice is $200x$, and the number of calories in y servings of skim milk is $80y$. So, to meet the minimum daily requirement for calories, $200x + 80y$ must be greater than or equal to 800. This gives the first of the inequalities below. The second inequality expresses the condition that the minimum daily requirement for protein is met. The last two inequalities express the fact that the number of servings of each food cannot be a negative number.

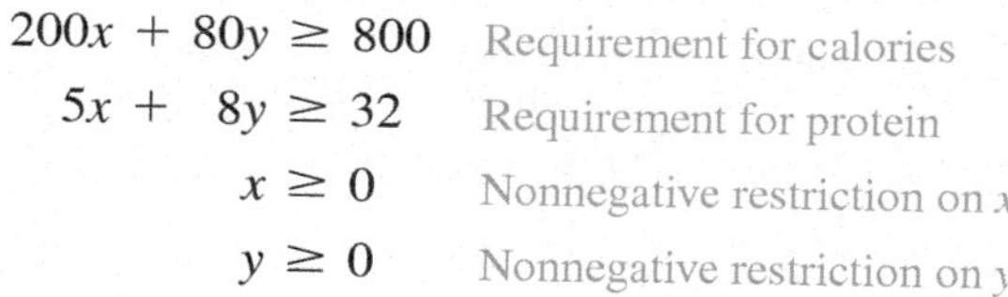

$$200x + 80y \ge 800 \quad \text{Requirement for calories}$$
$$5x + 8y \ge 32 \quad \text{Requirement for protein}$$
$$x \ge 0 \quad \text{Nonnegative restriction on } x$$
$$y \ge 0 \quad \text{Nonnegative restriction on } y$$

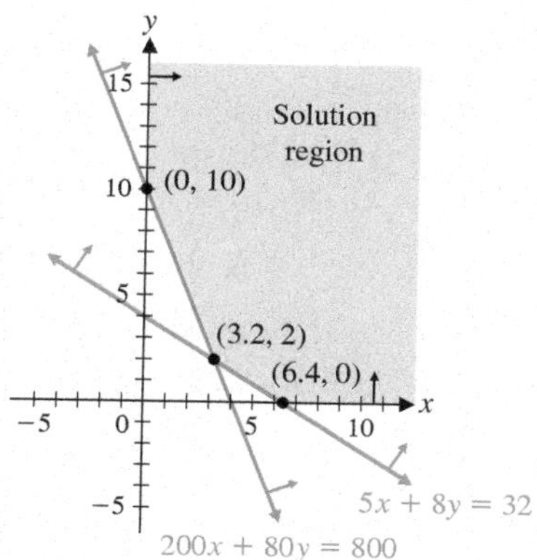

Figure 3

We graph this system of inequalities, and shade the solution region (Figure 3). Each point in the shaded area, including the straight-line boundaries, will meet the minimum daily requirements for calories and protein; any point outside the shaded area will not. For example, 4 servings of brown rice and 2 servings of skim milk will meet the minimum daily requirements, but 3 servings of brown rice and 2 servings of skim milk will not. Note that the solution region is unbounded.

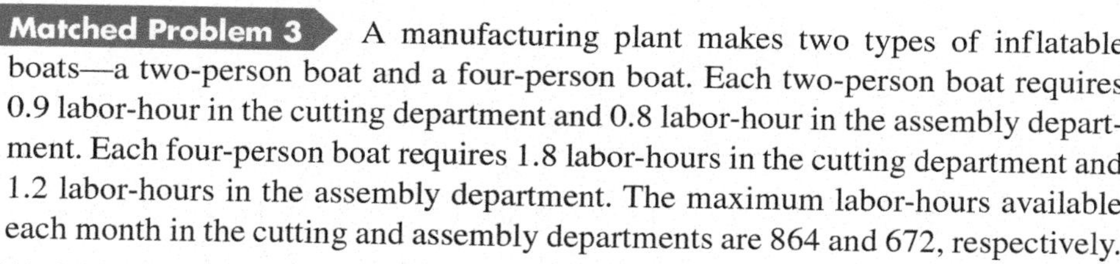

Matched Problem 3 A manufacturing plant makes two types of inflatable boats—a two-person boat and a four-person boat. Each two-person boat requires 0.9 labor-hour in the cutting department and 0.8 labor-hour in the assembly department. Each four-person boat requires 1.8 labor-hours in the cutting department and 1.2 labor-hours in the assembly department. The maximum labor-hours available each month in the cutting and assembly departments are 864 and 672, respectively.

(A) Summarize this information in a table.

(B) If x two-person boats and y four-person boats are manufactured each month, write a system of linear inequalities that reflects the conditions indicated. Graph the feasible region.

Exercises 5.2

Skills Warm-up Exercises

For Problems 1–8, if necessary, review Section 1.2. Problems 1–4 refer to the following system of linear inequalities:

$$4x + y \le 20$$
$$3x + 5y \le 37$$
$$x \ge 0$$
$$y \ge 0$$

1. Is the point $(3, 5)$ in the solution region?

2. Is the point $(4, 5)$ in the solution region?

3. Is the point $(3, 6)$ in the solution region?

4. Is the point $(2, 6)$ in the solution region?

Problems 5–8 refer to the following system of linear inequalities:

$$5x + y \le 32$$
$$7x + 4y \ge 45$$
$$x \ge 0$$
$$y \ge 0$$

5. Is the point $(4, 3)$ in the solution region?

6. Is the point $(5, 3)$ in the solution region?

7. Is the point $(6, 2)$ in the solution region?

8. Is the point $(5, 2)$ in the solution region?

A *In Problems 9–12, match the solution region of each system of linear inequalities with one of the four regions shown in the figure.*

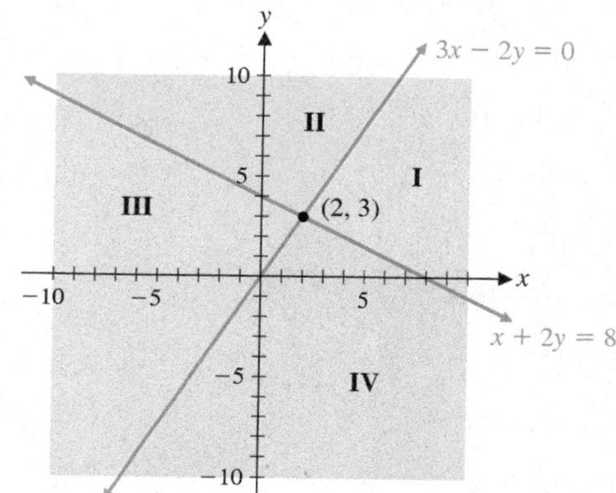

9. $x + 2y \le 8$
$3x - 2y \ge 0$

10. $x + 2y \ge 8$
$3x - 2y \le 0$

11. $x + 2y \ge 8$
$3x - 2y \ge 0$

12. $x + 2y \le 8$
$3x - 2y \le 0$

In Problems 13–16, solve each system of linear inequalities graphically.

13. $3x + y \geq 6$
$x \leq 4$

14. $3x + 4y \leq 12$
$y \geq -3$

15. $x - 2y \leq 12$
$2x + y \geq 4$

16. $2x + 5y \leq 20$
$x - 5y \geq -5$

B *In Problems 17–20, match the solution region of each system of linear inequalities with one of the four regions shown in the figure. Identify the corner points of each solution region.*

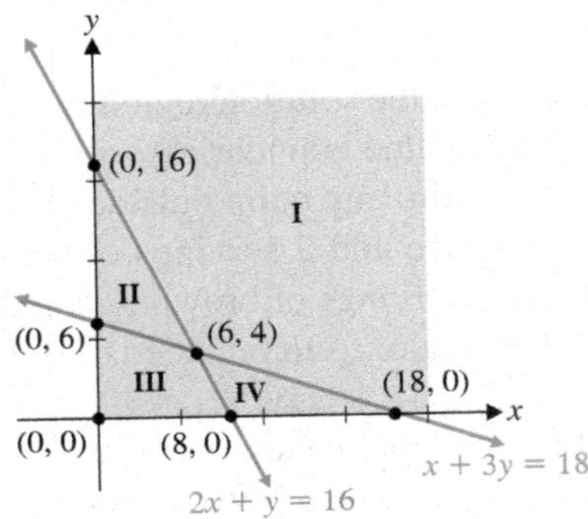

17. $x + 3y \leq 18$
$2x + y \geq 16$
$x \geq 0$
$y \geq 0$

18. $x + 3y \leq 18$
$2x + y \leq 16$
$x \geq 0$
$y \geq 0$

19. $x + 3y \geq 18$
$2x + y \geq 16$
$x \geq 0$
$y \geq 0$

20. $x + 3y \geq 18$
$2x + y \leq 16$
$x \geq 0$
$y \geq 0$

In Problems 21–28, is the solution region bounded or unbounded?

21. $3x + y \leq 6$
$x \geq 0$
$y \geq 0$

22. $x + 2y \geq 4$
$x \geq 0$
$y \geq 0$

23. $5x - 2y \geq 10$
$x \geq 0$
$y \geq 0$

24. $4x - 3y \leq 12$
$x \geq 0$
$y \geq 0$

25. $-x + y \leq 4$
$x \leq 10$
$x \geq 0$
$y \geq 0$

26. $x - y \leq 3$
$x \leq 9$
$x \geq 0$
$y \geq 0$

27. $-x + 2y \geq 2$
$2x - y \leq 2$
$x \geq 0$
$y \geq 0$

28. $-x + 2y \leq 2$
$2x - y \leq 2$
$x \geq 0$
$y \geq 0$

Solve the systems in Problems 29–38 graphically and indicate whether each solution region is bounded or unbounded. Find the coordinates of each corner point.

29. $2x + 3y \leq 12$
$x \geq 0$
$y \geq 0$

30. $3x + 4y \leq 24$
$x \geq 0$
$y \geq 0$

31. $2x + y \leq 10$
$x + 2y \leq 8$
$x \geq 0$
$y \geq 0$

32. $6x + 3y \leq 24$
$3x + 6y \leq 30$
$x \geq 0$
$y \geq 0$

33. $2x + y \geq 10$
$x + 2y \geq 8$
$x \geq 0$
$y \geq 0$

34. $4x + 3y \geq 24$
$3x + 4y \geq 8$
$x \geq 0$
$y \geq 0$

35. $2x + y \leq 10$
$x + y \leq 7$
$x + 2y \leq 12$
$x \geq 0$
$y \geq 0$

36. $3x + y \leq 21$
$x + y \leq 9$
$x + 3y \leq 21$
$x \geq 0$
$y \geq 0$

37. $2x + y \geq 16$
$x + y \geq 12$
$x + 2y \geq 14$
$x \geq 0$
$y \geq 0$

38. $3x + y \geq 24$
$x + y \geq 16$
$x + 3y \geq 30$
$x \geq 0$
$y \geq 0$

C *Solve the systems in Problems 39–48 graphically and indicate whether each solution region is bounded or unbounded. Find the coordinates of each corner point.*

39. $x + 4y \leq 32$
$3x + y \leq 30$
$4x + 5y \geq 51$

40. $x + y \leq 11$
$x + 5y \geq 15$
$2x + y \geq 12$

41. $4x + 3y \leq 48$
$2x + y \geq 24$
$x \leq 9$

42. $2x + 3y \geq 24$
$x + 3y \leq 15$
$y \geq 4$

43. $x - y \leq 0$
$2x - y \leq 4$
$0 \leq x \leq 8$

44. $2x + 3y \geq 12$
$-x + 3y \leq 3$
$0 \leq y \leq 5$

45. $-x + 3y \geq 1$
$5x - y \geq 9$
$x + y \leq 9$
$x \leq 5$

46. $x + y \leq 10$
$5x + 3y \geq 15$
$-2x + 3y \leq 15$
$2x - 5y \leq 6$

47. $16x + 13y \leq 120$
$3x + 4y \geq 25$
$-4x + 3y \leq 11$

48. $2x + 2y \leq 21$
$-10x + 5y \leq 24$
$3x + 5y \geq 37$

Problems 49 and 50 introduce an algebraic process for finding the corner points of a solution region without drawing a graph. We will discuss this process later in the chapter.

49. Consider the following system of inequalities and corresponding boundary lines:

$$\begin{aligned} 3x + 4y &\le 36 \qquad & 3x + 4y &= 36 \\ 3x + 2y &\le 30 \qquad & 3x + 2y &= 30 \\ x &\ge 0 \qquad & x &= 0 \\ y &\ge 0 \qquad & y &= 0 \end{aligned}$$

(A) Use algebraic methods to find the intersection points (if any exist) for each possible pair of boundary lines. (There are six different possible pairs.)

(B) Test each intersection point in all four inequalities to determine which are corner points.

50. Repeat Problem 49 for

$$\begin{aligned} 2x + y &\le 16 \qquad & 2x + y &= 16 \\ 2x + 3y &\le 36 \qquad & 2x + 3y &= 36 \\ x &\ge 0 \qquad & x &= 0 \\ y &\ge 0 \qquad & y &= 0 \end{aligned}$$

Applications

51. Water skis. A manufacturing company makes two types of water skis, a trick ski and a slalom ski. The trick ski requires 6 labor-hours for fabricating and 1 labor-hour for finishing. The slalom ski requires 4 labor-hours for fabricating and 1 labor-hour for finishing. The maximum labor-hours available per day for fabricating and finishing are 108 and 24, respectively. If x is the number of trick skis and y is the number of slalom skis produced per day, write a system of linear inequalities that indicates appropriate restraints on x and y. Find the set of feasible solutions graphically for the number of each type of ski that can be produced.

52. Furniture. A furniture manufacturing company manufactures dining-room tables and chairs. A table requires 8 labor-hours for assembling and 2 labor-hours for finishing. A chair requires 2 labor-hours for assembling and 1 labor-hour for finishing. The maximum labor-hours available per day for assembly and finishing are 400 and 120, respectively. If x is the number of tables and y is the number of chairs produced per day, write a system of linear inequalities that indicates appropriate restraints on x and y. Find the set of feasible solutions graphically for the number of tables and chairs that can be produced.

53. Water skis. Refer to Problem 51. The company makes a profit of \$50 on each trick ski and a profit of \$60 on each slalom ski.

(A) If the company makes 10 trick skis and 10 slalom skis per day, the daily profit will be \$1,100. Are there other production schedules that will result in a daily profit of \$1,100? How are these schedules related to the graph of the line $50x + 60y = 1{,}100$?

(B) Find a production schedule that will produce a daily profit greater than \$1,100 and repeat part (A) for this schedule.

(C) Discuss methods for using lines like those in parts (A) and (B) to find the largest possible daily profit.

54. Furniture. Refer to Problem 52. The company makes a profit of \$50 on each table and a profit of \$15 on each chair.

(A) If the company makes 20 tables and 20 chairs per day, the daily profit will be \$1,300. Are there other production schedules that will result in a daily profit of \$1,300? How are these schedules related to the graph of the line $50x + 15y = 1{,}300$?

(B) Find a production schedule that will produce a daily profit greater than \$1,300 and repeat part (A) for this schedule.

(C) Discuss methods for using lines like those in parts (A) and (B) to find the largest possible daily profit.

55. Plant food. A farmer can buy two types of plant food, mix A and mix B. Each cubic yard of mix A contains 20 pounds of phosphoric acid, 30 pounds of nitrogen, and 5 pounds of potash. Each cubic yard of mix B contains 10 pounds of phosphoric acid, 30 pounds of nitrogen, and 10 pounds of potash. The minimum monthly requirements are 460 pounds of phosphoric acid, 960 pounds of nitrogen, and 220 pounds of potash. If x is the number of cubic yards of mix A used and y is the number of cubic yards of mix B used, write a system of linear inequalities that indicates appropriate restraints on x and y. Find the set of feasible solutions graphically for the amounts of mix A and mix B that can be used.

56. Nutrition. A dietitian in a hospital is to arrange a special diet using two foods. Each ounce of food M contains 30 units of calcium, 10 units of iron, and 10 units of vitamin A. Each ounce of food N contains 10 units of calcium, 10 units of iron, and 30 units of vitamin A. The minimum requirements in the diet are 360 units of calcium, 160 units of iron, and 240 units of vitamin A. If x is the number of ounces of food M used and y is the number of ounces of food N used, write a system of linear inequalities that reflects the conditions indicated. Find the set of feasible solutions graphically for the amount of each kind of food that can be used.

57. Psychology. A psychologist uses two types of boxes when studying mice and rats. Each mouse spends 10 minutes per day in box A and 20 minutes per day in box B. Each rat spends 20 minutes per day in box A and 10 minutes per day in box B. The total maximum time available per day is 800 minutes for box A and 640 minutes for box B. If x is the number of mice used and y the number of rats used, write a system of linear inequalities that indicates appropriate restrictions on x and y. Find the set of feasible solutions graphically.

Answers to Matched Problems

1.

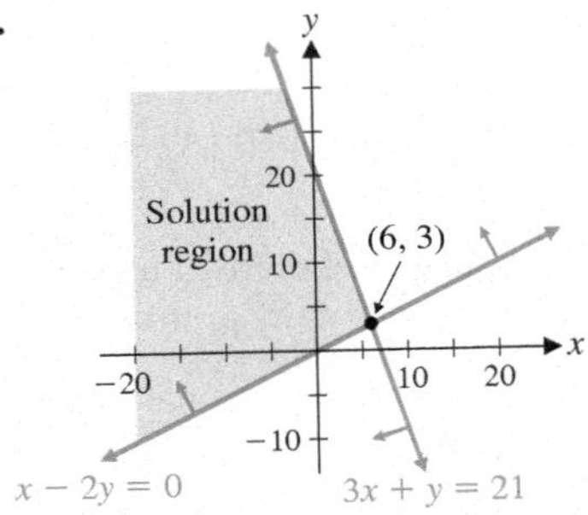

2.

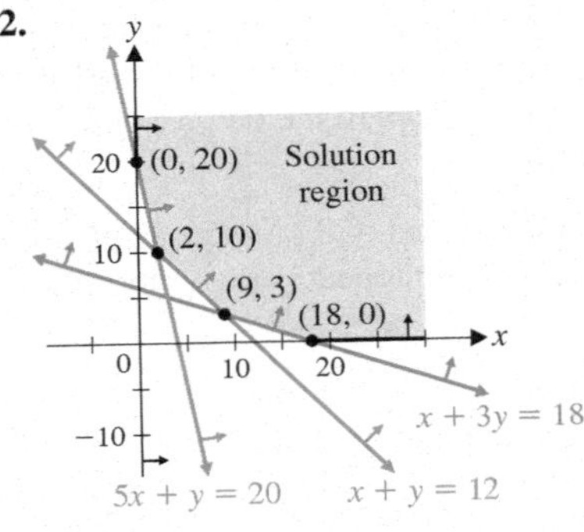

3. (A)

	Labor-Hours Required		Maximum Labor-Hours Available per Month
	Two-Person Boat	Four-Person Boat	
Cutting Department	0.9	1.8	864
Assembly Department	0.8	1.2	672

(B) $0.9x + 1.8y \leq 864$
$0.8x + 1.2y \leq 672$
$x \geq 0$
$y \geq 0$

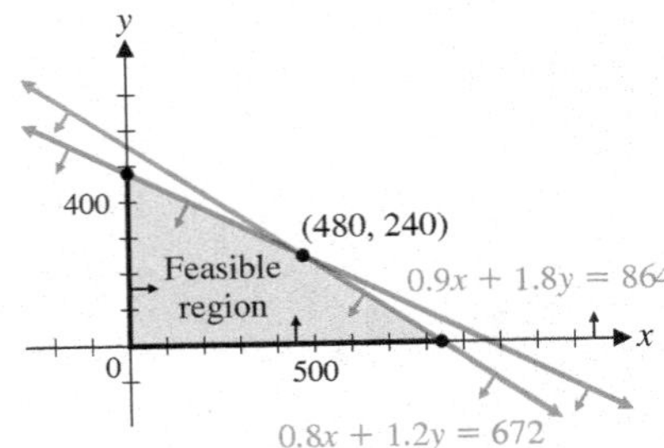

5.3 A Geometric Approach to Linear Programming

- A Linear Programming Problem
- General Description of Linear Programming
- Geometric Method for Solving Linear Programming Problems
- Applications

Several problems discussed in the preceding section are related to a more general type of problem called a *linear programming problem.* **Linear programming** is a mathematical process that has been developed to help management in decision making. We introduce this topic by considering an example in detail, using an intuitive geometric approach. Insight gained from this approach will prove invaluable when later we consider an algebraic approach that is less intuitive but necessary to solve most real-world problems.

A Linear Programming Problem

We begin our discussion with a concrete example. The solution method will suggest two important theorems and a simple general geometric procedure for solving linear programming problems in two variables.

EXAMPLE 1

Production Scheduling A manufacturer of lightweight mountain tents makes a standard model and an expedition model. Each standard tent requires 1 labor-hour from the cutting department and 3 labor-hours from the assembly department. Each expedition tent requires 2 labor-hours from the cutting department and 4 labor-hours from the assembly department. The maximum labor-hours available per day in the cutting and assembly departments are 32 and 84, respectively. If the company makes a profit of \$50 on each standard tent and \$80 on each expedition tent, how many tents of each type should be manufactured each day to maximize the total daily profit (assuming that all tents can be sold)?

SOLUTION This is an example of a linear programming problem. We begin by analyzing the question posed in this example.

According to the question, the *objective* of management is to maximize profit. Since the profits for standard and expedition tents differ, management must decide how many of each type of tent to manufacture. So it is reasonable to introduce the following **decision variables**:

$$\text{Let } x = \text{number of standard tents produced per day}$$

$$y = \text{number of expedition tents produced per day}$$

Now we summarize the manufacturing requirements, objectives, and restrictions in Table 1, with the decision variables related to the columns in the table.

Table 1

	Labor-Hours per Tent		Maximum Labor-Hours Available per Day
	Standard Model	Expedition Model	
Cutting department	1	2	32
Assembly department	3	4	84
Profit per tent	\$50	\$80	

Using the last line of Table 1, we form the **objective function**, in this case the profit P, in terms of the decision variables (we assume that all tents manufactured are sold):

$$P = 50x + 80y \quad \text{Objective function}$$

The **objective** is to find values of the decision variables that produce the **optimal value** (in this case, maximum value) of the objective function.

The form of the objective function indicates that the profit can be made as large as we like, simply by producing enough tents. But any manufacturing company has limits imposed by available resources, plant capacity, demand, and so on. These limits are referred to as **problem constraints**. Using the information in Table 1, we can determine two problem constraints.

$$\begin{pmatrix}\text{daily cutting}\\ \text{time for } x\\ \text{standard tents}\end{pmatrix} + \begin{pmatrix}\text{daily cutting}\\ \text{time for } y\\ \text{expedition tents}\end{pmatrix} \le \begin{pmatrix}\text{maximum labor-}\\ \text{hours available}\\ \text{per day}\end{pmatrix} \quad \begin{matrix}\text{Cutting}\\ \text{department}\\ \text{constraint}\end{matrix}$$

$$1x \quad + \quad 2y \quad \le \quad 32$$

$$\begin{pmatrix}\text{daily assembly}\\ \text{time for } x\\ \text{standard tents}\end{pmatrix} + \begin{pmatrix}\text{daily assembly}\\ \text{time for } y\\ \text{expedition tents}\end{pmatrix} \le \begin{pmatrix}\text{maximum labor-}\\ \text{hours available}\\ \text{per day}\end{pmatrix} \quad \begin{matrix}\text{Assembly}\\ \text{department}\\ \text{constraint}\end{matrix}$$

$$3x \quad + \quad 4y \quad \le \quad 84$$

It is not possible to manufacture a negative number of tents; thus, we have the **nonnegative constraints**

$$x \ge 0 \text{ and } y \ge 0$$

which we usually write in the form

$$x, y \ge 0 \quad \text{Nonnegative constraints}$$

We now have a **mathematical model** for the problem under consideration:

$$\begin{aligned} \text{Maximize} \quad & P = 50x + 80y && \text{Objective function} \\ \text{subject to} \quad & \left.\begin{aligned} x + 2y &\le 32 \\ 3x + 4y &\le 84 \end{aligned}\right\} && \text{Problem constraints} \\ & x, y \ge 0 && \text{Nonnegative constraints} \end{aligned}$$

Solving the set of linear inequality constraints **graphically**, we obtain the feasible region for production schedules (Fig. 1).

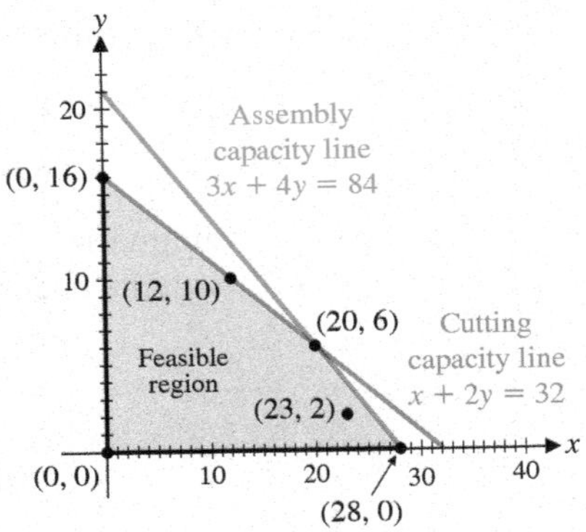

Figure 1

By choosing a production schedule (x, y) from the feasible region, a profit can be determined using the objective function

$$P = 50x + 80y$$

For example, if $x = 12$ and $y = 10$, the profit for the day would be

$$\begin{aligned} P &= 50(12) + 80(10) \\ &= \$1{,}400 \end{aligned}$$

Or if $x = 23$ and $y = 2$, the profit for the day would be

$$\begin{aligned} P &= 50(23) + 80(2) \\ &= \$1{,}310 \end{aligned}$$

Out of all possible production schedules (x, y) from the feasible region, which schedule(s) produces the *maximum* profit? This is a **maximization problem**. Since point-by-point checking is impossible (there are infinitely many points to check), we must find another way.

By assigning P in $P = 50x + 80y$ a particular value and plotting the resulting equation in the coordinate system shown in Figure 1, we obtain a **constant-profit line**. Every point in the feasible region on this line represents a production schedule that will produce the same profit. By doing this for a number of values for P, we obtain a family of constant-profit lines (Fig. 2) that are parallel to each other, since they all have the same slope. To see this, we write $P = 50x + 80y$ in the slope-intercept form

$$y = -\frac{5}{8}x + \frac{P}{80}$$

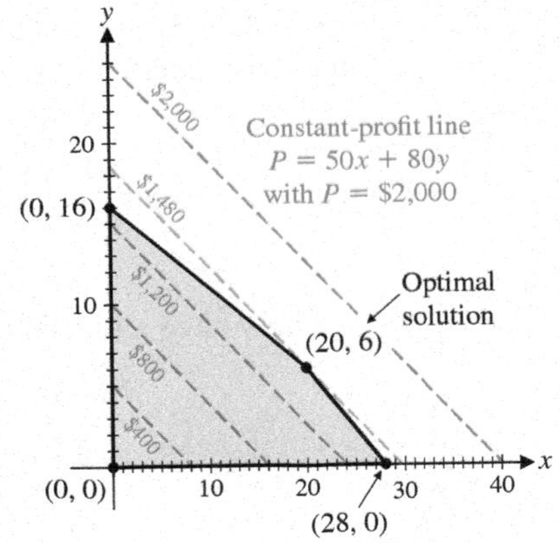

Figure 2 Constant-profit lines

and note that for any profit P, the constant-profit line has slope $-\frac{5}{8}$. We also observe that as the profit P increases, the y intercept ($P/80$) increases, and the line moves away from the origin.

Therefore, the maximum profit occurs at a point where a constant-profit line is the farthest from the origin but still in contact with the feasible region, in this example, at $(20, 6)$ (see Fig. 2). So profit is maximized if the manufacturer makes 20 standard tents and 6 expedition tents per day, and the maximum profit is

$$
\begin{aligned}
P &= 50(20) + 80(6) \\
&= \$1{,}480
\end{aligned}
$$

The point $(20, 6)$ is called an **optimal solution** to the problem because it maximizes the objective (profit) function and is in the feasible region. In general, it appears that a maximum profit occurs at one of the corner points. We also note that the minimum profit $(P = 0)$ occurs at the corner point $(0, 0)$.

Matched Problem 1 A manufacturing plant makes two types of inflatable boats—a two-person boat and a four-person boat. Each two-person boat requires 0.9 labor-hour from the cutting department and 0.8 labor-hour from the assembly department. Each four-person boat requires 1.8 labor-hours from the cutting department and 1.2 labor-hours from the assembly department. The maximum labor-hours available per month in the cutting department and the assembly department are 864 and 672, respectively. The company makes a profit of \$25 on each two-person boat and \$40 on each four-person boat.

(A) Identify the decision variables.

(B) Summarize the relevant material in a table similar to Table 1 in Example 1.

(C) Write the objective function P.

(D) Write the problem constraints and nonnegative constraints.

(E) Graph the feasible region. Include graphs of the objective function for $P = \$5{,}000$, $P = \$10{,}000$, $P = \$15{,}000$, and $P = \$21{,}600$.

(F) From the graph and constant-profit lines, determine how many boats should be manufactured each month to maximize the profit. What is the maximum profit?

Before proceeding further, let's summarize the steps we used to form the model in Example 1.

PROCEDURE Constructing a Model for an Applied Linear Programming Problem

Step 1 Introduce decision variables.

Step 2 Summarize relevant material in table form, relating columns to the decision variables, if possible (see Table 1).

Step 3 Determine the objective and write a linear objective function.

Step 4 Write problem constraints using linear equations and/or inequalities.

Step 5 Write nonnegative constraints.

Explore and Discuss 1

Refer to the feasible region S shown in Figure 3.

(A) Let $P = x + y$. Graph the constant-profit lines through the points $(5, 5)$ and $(10, 10)$. Place a straightedge along the line with the smaller profit and slide it in the direction of increasing profit, without changing its slope. What is the maximum value of P? Where does this maximum value occur?

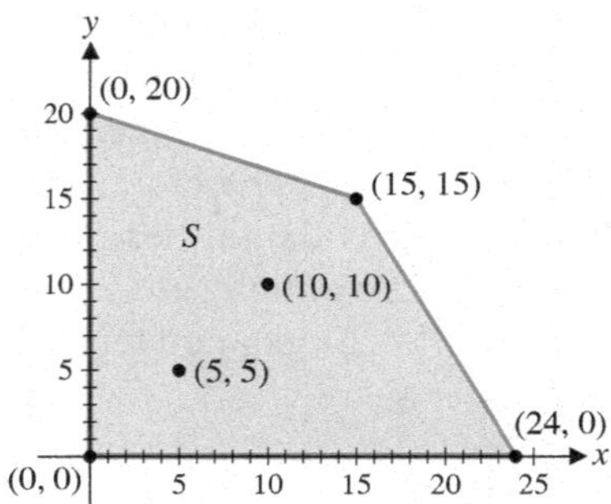

Figure 3

(B) Repeat part (A) for $P = x + 10y$.

(C) Repeat part (A) for $P = 10x + y$.

General Description of Linear Programming

In Example 1 and Matched Problem 1, the optimal solution occurs at a corner point of the feasible region. Is this always the case? The answer is a qualified yes, as we will see in Theorem 1. First, we give a few general definitions.

A **linear programming problem** is one that is concerned with finding the **optimal value** (maximum or minimum value) of a linear **objective function** z of the form

$$z = ax + by, \text{ where } a \text{ and } b \text{ do not both } = 0$$

and the **decision variables** x and y are subject to **problem constraints** in the form of $\leq$ or $\geq$ linear inequalities and equations. In addition, the decision variables must satisfy the **nonnegative constraints** $x \geq 0, y \geq 0$. The set of points satisfying both the problem constraints and the nonnegative constraints is called the **feasible region** for the problem. Any point in the feasible region that produces the optimal value of the objective function over the feasible region is called an **optimal solution**.

THEOREM 1 Fundamental Theorem of Linear Programming

If the optimal value of the objective function in a linear programming problem exists, then that value must occur at one or more of the corner points of the feasible region.

Theorem 1 provides a simple procedure for solving a linear programming problem, *provided that the problem has an optimal solution—not all do*. In order to use Theorem 1, we must know that the problem under consideration has an optimal solution. Theorem 2 provides some conditions that will ensure that a linear programming problem has an optimal solution.

THEOREM 2 Existence of Optimal Solutions

(A) If the feasible region for a linear programming problem is bounded, then both the maximum value and the minimum value of the objective function always exist.

(B) If the feasible region is unbounded and the coefficients of the objective function are positive, then the minimum value of the objective function exists but the maximum value does not.

(C) If the feasible region is empty (that is, there are no points that satisfy all the constraints), then both the maximum value and the minimum value of the objective function do not exist.

Geometric Method for Solving Linear Programming Problems

The preceding discussion leads to the following procedure for the geometric solution of linear programming problems with two decision variables:

PROCEDURE Geometric Method for Solving a Linear Programming Problem with Two Decision Variables

Step 1 Graph the feasible region. Then, if an optimal solution exists according to Theorem 2, find the coordinates of each corner point.

Step 2 Construct a **corner point table** listing the value of the objective function at each corner point.

Step 3 Determine the optimal solution(s) from the table in Step 2.

Step 4 For an applied problem, interpret the optimal solution(s) in terms of the original problem.

Before we consider more applications, let's use this procedure to solve some linear programming problems where the model has already been determined.

EXAMPLE 2 **Solving a Linear Programming Problem**

(A) Minimize and maximize $z = 3x + y$

subject to

$$2x + y \le 20$$
$$10x + y \ge 36$$
$$2x + 5y \ge 36$$
$$x, y \ge 0$$

(B) Minimize and maximize $z = 10x + 20y$

subject to

$$6x + 2y \ge 36$$
$$2x + 4y \ge 32$$
$$y \le 20$$
$$x, y \ge 0$$

SOLUTION

(A) Step 1 Graph the feasible region S (Fig. 4). Then, after checking Theorem 2 to determine whether an optimal solution exists, find the coordinates of each corner point. Since S is bounded, z will have both a maximum and a minimum value on S (Theorem 2A) and these will both occur at corner points (Theorem 1).

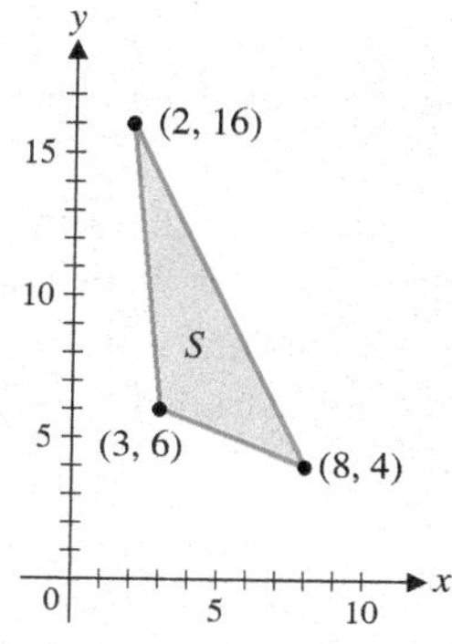

Figure 4

Step 2 Evaluate the objective function at each corner point, as shown in the table.

Corner Point	
(x, y)	$z = 3x + y$
(3, 6)	15
(2, 16)	22
(8, 4)	28

Step 3 Determine the optimal solutions from Step 2. Examining the values in the table, we see that the minimum value of z is 15 at (3, 6) and the maximum value of z is 28 at (8, 4).

(B) Step 1 Graph the feasible region S (Fig. 5). Then, after checking Theorem 2 to determine whether an optimal solution exists, find the coordinates of each corner point. Since S is unbounded and the coefficients of the

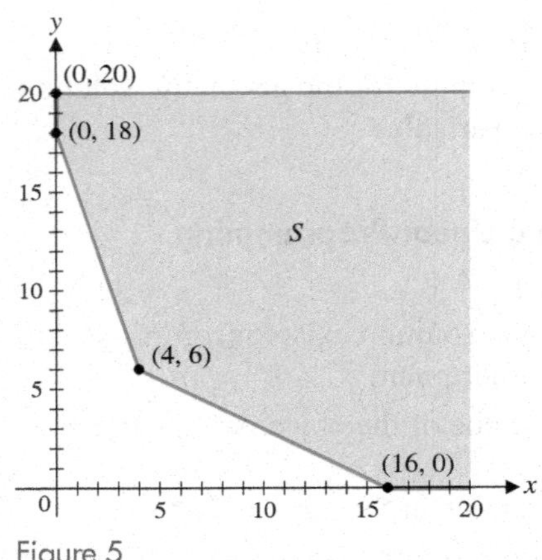

Figure 5

objective function are positive, z has a minimum value on S but no maximum value (Theorem 2B).

Step 2 Evaluate the objective function at each corner point, as shown in the table.

Corner Point	
(x, y)	$z = 10x + 20y$
$(0, 20)$	400
$(0, 18)$	360
$(4, 6)$	160
$(16, 0)$	160

Step 3 Determine the optimal solution from Step 2. The minimum value of z is 160 at $(4, 6)$ and at $(16, 0)$.

The solution to Example 2B is a **multiple optimal solution**. In general, if two corner points are both optimal solutions to a linear programming problem, then any point on the line segment joining them is also an optimal solution. This is the only way that optimal solutions can occur at noncorner points.

Matched Problem 2

(A) Maximize and minimize $z = 4x + 2y$ subject to the constraints given in Example 2A.

(B) Maximize and minimize $z = 20x + 5y$ subject to the constraints given in Example 2B.

CONCEPTUAL INSIGHT

Determining that an optimal solution exists is a critical step in the solution of a linear programming problem. If you skip this step, you may examine a corner point table like the one in the solution of Example 2B and erroneously conclude that the maximum value of the objective function is 400.

Explore and Discuss 2

In Example 2B we saw that there was no optimal solution for the problem of maximizing the objective function z over the feasible region S. We want to add an additional constraint to modify the feasible region so that an optimal solution for the maximization problem does exist. Which of the following constraints will accomplish this objective?

(A) $x \le 20$ (B) $y \ge 4$ (C) $x \le y$ (D) $y \le x$

For an illustration of Theorem 2C, consider the following:

$$\begin{aligned} \text{Maximize} \quad & P = 2x + 3y \\ \text{subject to} \quad & x + y \ge 8 \\ & x + 2y \le 8 \\ & 2x + y \le 10 \\ & x, y \ge 0 \end{aligned}$$

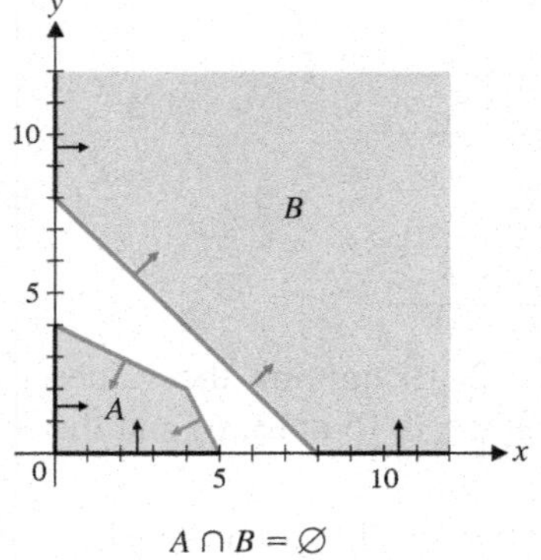

Figure 6

The intersection of the graphs of the constraint inequalities is the empty set (Fig. 6); so the *feasible region is empty*. If this happens, the problem should be reexamined to see if it has been formulated properly. If it has, the management may have to reconsider items such as labor-hours, overtime, budget, and supplies allocated to the project in order to obtain a nonempty feasible region and a solution to the original problem.

Applications

EXAMPLE 3 **Medication** A hospital patient is required to have at least 84 units of drug A and 120 units of drug B each day (assume that an overdose of either drug is harmless). Each gram of substance M contains 10 units of drug A and 8 units of drug B, and each gram of substance N contains 2 units of drug A and 4 units of drug B. Now, suppose that both M and N contain an undesirable drug D: 3 units per gram in M and 1 unit per gram in N. How many grams of each of substances M and N should be mixed to meet the minimum daily requirements and simultaneously minimize the intake of drug D? How many units of the undesirable drug D will be in this mixture?

SOLUTION First we construct the mathematical model.

Step 1 Introduce decision variables. According to the questions asked, we must decide how many grams of substances M and N should be mixed to form the daily dose of medication. These two quantities are the decision variables:

$$x = \text{number of grams of substance } M \text{ used}$$

$$y = \text{number of grams of substance } N \text{ used}$$

Step 2 Summarize relevant material in a table, relating the columns to substances M and N.

	Amount of Drug per Gram		Minimum Daily Requirement
	Substance M	Substance N	
Drug A	10 units/gram	2 units/gram	84 units
Drug B	8 units/gram	4 units/gram	120 units
Drug D	3 units/gram	1 unit/gram	

Step 3 Determine the objective and the objective function. The objective is to minimize the amount of drug D in the daily dose of medication. Using the decision variables and the information in the table, we form the linear objective function

$$C = 3x + y$$

Step 4 Write the problem constraints. The constraints in this problem involve minimum requirements, so the inequalities will take a different form:

$$10x + 2y \geq 84 \quad \text{Drug } A \text{ constraint}$$

$$8x + 4y \geq 120 \quad \text{Drug } B \text{ constraint}$$

Step 5 Add the nonnegative constraints and summarize the model.

$$\begin{aligned} \text{Minimize} \quad & C = 3x + y && \text{Objective function} \\ \text{subject to} \quad & 10x + 2y \geq 84 && \text{Drug } A \text{ constraint} \\ & 8x + 4y \geq 120 && \text{Drug } B \text{ constraint} \\ & x, y \geq 0 && \text{Nonnegative constraints} \end{aligned}$$

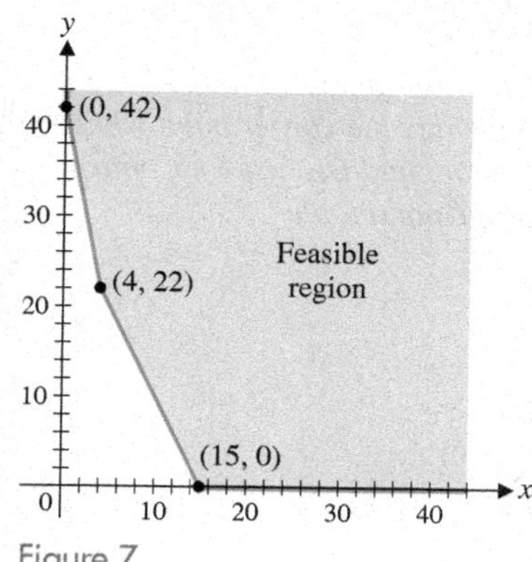

Figure 7

Corner Point	
(x, y)	$C = 3x + y$
$(0, 42)$	42
$(4, 22)$	34
$(15, 0)$	45

Now we use the geometric method to solve the problem.

Step 1 Graph the feasible region (Fig. 7). Then, after checking Theorem 2 to determine whether an optimal solution exists, find the coordinates of each corner point. Since the feasible region is unbounded and the coefficients of the objective function are positive, this minimization problem has a solution.

Step 2 Evaluate the objective function at each corner point, as shown in the table.

Step 3 Determine the optimal solution from Step 2. The optimal solution is $C = 34$ at the corner point $(4, 22)$.

Step 4 Interpret the optimal solution in terms of the original problem. If we use 4 grams of substance M and 22 grams of substance N, we will supply the minimum daily requirements for drugs A and B and minimize the intake of the undesirable drug D at 34 units. (Any other combination of M and N from the feasible region will result in a larger amount of the undesirable drug D.)

Matched Problem 3 A chicken farmer can buy a special food mix A at 20¢ per pound and a special food mix B at 40¢ per pound. Each pound of mix A contains 3,000 units of nutrient N_1 and 1,000 units of nutrient N_2; each pound of mix B contains 4,000 units of nutrient N_1 and 4,000 units of nutrient N_2. If the minimum daily requirements for the chickens collectively are 36,000 units of nutrient N_1 and 20,000 units of nutrient N_2, how many pounds of each food mix should be used each day to minimize daily food costs while meeting (or exceeding) the minimum daily nutrient requirements? What is the minimum daily cost? Construct a mathematical model and solve using the geometric method.

CONCEPTUAL INSIGHT

Refer to Example 3. If we change the minimum requirement for drug B from 120 to 125, the optimal solution changes to 3.6 grams of substance M and 24.1 grams of substance N, correct to one decimal place.

Now refer to Example 1. If we change the maximum labor-hours available per day in the assembly department from 84 to 79, the solution changes to 15 standard tents and 8.5 expedition tents.

We can measure 3.6 grams of substance M and 24.1 grams of substance N, but how can we make 8.5 tents? Should we make 8 tents? Or 9 tents? If the solutions to a problem must be integers and the optimal solution found graphically involves decimals, then rounding the decimal value to the nearest integer does not always produce the *optimal integer solution* (see Problem 44, Exercises 5.3). Finding optimal integer solutions to a linear programming problem is called *integer programming* and requires special techniques that are beyond the scope of this book. As mentioned earlier, if we encounter a solution like 8.5 tents per day, we will interpret this as an *average* value over many days of production.

Exercises 5.3

W **Skills Warm-up Exercises**

In Problems 1–8, if necessary, review Theorem 1. In Problems 1–4, the feasible region is the set of points on and inside the rectangle with vertices $(0, 0)$, $(12, 0)$, $(0, 5)$, *and* $(12, 5)$. *Find the maximum and minimum values of the objective function Q over the feasible region.*

1. $Q = 7x + 14y$

2. $Q = 3x + 15y$

3. $Q = 10x - 12y$

4. $Q = -9x + 20y$

In Problems 5–8, the feasible region is the set of points on and inside the triangle with vertices $(0, 0)$, $(8, 0)$, *and* $(0, 10)$. *Find the maximum and minimum values of the objective function Q over the feasible region.*

5. $Q = -4x - 3y$

6. $Q = 3x + 2y$

7. $Q = -6x + 4y$

8. $Q = 10x - 8y$

A *In Problems 9–12, graph the constant-profit lines through* $(3, 3)$ *and* $(6, 6)$. *Use a straightedge to identify the corner point where the maximum profit occurs (see Explore and Discuss 1). Confirm your answer by constructing a corner-point table.*

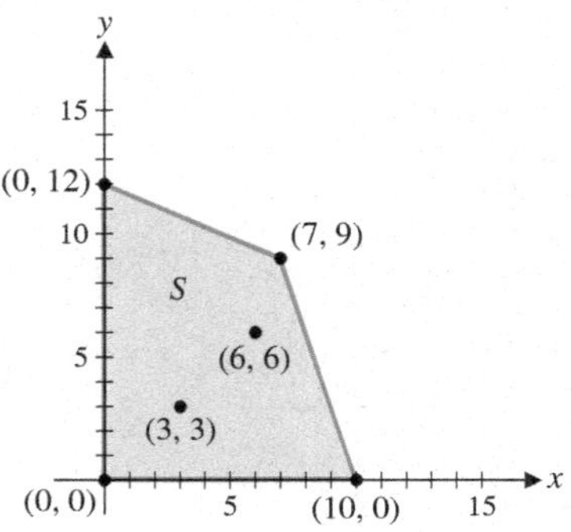

9. $P = x + y$

10. $P = 4x + y$

11. $P = 3x + 7y$

12. $P = 9x + 3y$

In Problems 13–16, graph the constant-cost lines through $(9, 9)$ and $(12, 12)$. Use a straightedge to identify the corner point where the minimum cost occurs. Confirm your answer by constructing a corner-point table.

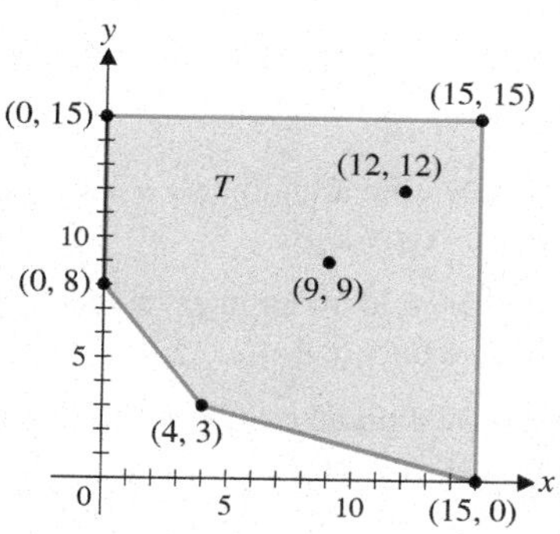

13. $C = 7x + 4y$

14. $C = 7x + 9y$

15. $C = 3x + 8y$

16. $C = 2x + 11y$

B *Solve the linear programming problems stated in Problems 17–38.*

17. Maximize $P = 10x + 75y$
subject to $x + 8y \le 24$
$x, y \ge 0$

18. Maximize $P = 30x + 12y$
subject to $3x + y \le 18$
$x, y \ge 0$

19. Minimize $C = 8x + 9y$
subject to $5x + 6y \ge 60$
$x, y \ge 0$

20. Minimize $C = 15x + 25y$
subject to $4x + 7y \ge 28$
$x, y \ge 0$

21. Maximize $P = 5x + 5y$
subject to $2x + y \le 10$
$x + 2y \le 8$
$x, y \ge 0$

22. Maximize $P = 3x + 2y$
subject to $6x + 3y \le 24$
$3x + 6y \le 30$
$x, y \ge 0$

23. Minimize and maximize
$z = 2x + 3y$
subject to $2x + y \ge 10$
$x + 2y \ge 8$
$x, y \ge 0$

24. Minimize and maximize
$z = 8x + 7y$
subject to $4x + 3y \ge 24$
$3x + 4y \ge 8$
$x, y \ge 0$

25. Maximize $P = 30x + 40y$
subject to $2x + y \le 10$
$x + y \le 7$
$x + 2y \le 12$
$x, y \ge 0$

26. Maximize $P = 20x + 10y$
subject to $3x + y \le 21$
$x + y \le 9$
$x + 3y \le 21$
$x, y \ge 0$

27. Minimize and maximize
$z = 10x + 30y$
subject to $2x + y \ge 16$
$x + y \ge 12$
$x + 2y \ge 14$
$x, y \ge 0$

28. Minimize and maximize
$z = 400x + 100y$
subject to $3x + y \ge 24$
$x + y \ge 16$
$x + 3y \ge 30$
$x, y \ge 0$

29. Minimize and maximize
$P = 30x + 10y$
subject to $2x + 2y \ge 4$
$6x + 4y \le 36$
$2x + y \le 10$
$x, y \ge 0$

30. Minimize and maximize
$P = 2x + y$
subject to $x + y \ge 2$
$6x + 4y \le 36$
$4x + 2y \le 20$
$x, y \ge 0$

31. Minimize and maximize
$P = 3x + 5y$
subject to $x + 2y \le 6$
$x + y \le 4$
$2x + 3y \ge 12$
$x, y \ge 0$

32. Minimize and maximize
$P = -x + 3y$
subject to $2x - y \ge 4$
$-x + 2y \le 4$
$y \le 6$
$x, y \ge 0$

33. Minimize and maximize

$$\begin{aligned} P &= 20x + 10y \\ \text{subject to} \quad 2x + 3y &\ge 30 \\ 2x + y &\le 26 \\ -2x + 5y &\le 34 \\ x, y &\ge 0 \end{aligned}$$

34. Minimize and maximize

$$\begin{aligned} P &= 12x + 14y \\ \text{subject to} \quad -2x + y &\ge 6 \\ x + y &\le 15 \\ 3x - y &\ge 0 \\ x, y &\ge 0 \end{aligned}$$

35. Maximize $P = 20x + 30y$

$$\begin{aligned} \text{subject to} \quad 0.6x + 1.2y &\le 960 \\ 0.03x + 0.04y &\le 36 \\ 0.3x + 0.2y &\le 270 \\ x, y &\ge 0 \end{aligned}$$

36. Minimize $C = 30x + 10y$

$$\begin{aligned} \text{subject to} \quad 1.8x + 0.9y &\ge 270 \\ 0.3x + 0.2y &\ge 54 \\ 0.01x + 0.03y &\ge 3.9 \\ x, y &\ge 0 \end{aligned}$$

37. Maximize $P = 525x + 478y$

$$\begin{aligned} \text{subject to} \quad 275x + 322y &\le 3{,}381 \\ 350x + 340y &\le 3{,}762 \\ 425x + 306y &\le 4{,}114 \\ x, y &\ge 0 \end{aligned}$$

38. Maximize $P = 300x + 460y$

$$\begin{aligned} \text{subject to} \quad 245x + 452y &\le 4{,}181 \\ 290x + 379y &\le 3{,}888 \\ 390x + 299y &\le 4{,}407 \\ x, y &\ge 0 \end{aligned}$$

C *In Problems 39 and 40, explain why Theorem 2 cannot be used to conclude that a maximum or minimum value exists. Graph the feasible regions and use graphs of the objective function $z = x - y$ for various values of z to discuss the existence of a maximum value and a minimum value.*

39. Minimize and maximize

$$\begin{aligned} z &= x - y \\ \text{subject to} \quad x - 2y &\le 0 \\ 2x - y &\le 6 \\ x, y &\ge 0 \end{aligned}$$

40. Minimize and maximize

$$\begin{aligned} z &= x - y \\ \text{subject to} \quad x - 2y &\ge -6 \\ 2x - y &\ge 0 \\ x, y &\ge 0 \end{aligned}$$

Problems 41–48 refer to the bounded feasible region with corner points $O = (0, 0), A = (0, 5), B = (4, 3)$, and $C = (5, 0)$ that is determined by the system of inequalities

$$\begin{aligned} x + 2y &\le 10 \\ 3x + y &\le 15 \\ x, y &\ge 0 \end{aligned}$$

41. If $P = ax + 10y$, find all numbers a such that the maximum value of P occurs only at B.

42. If $P = ax + 10y$, find all numbers a such that the maximum value of P occurs only at A.

43. If $P = ax + 10y$, find all numbers a such that the maximum value of P occurs only at C.

44. If $P = ax + 10y$, find all numbers a such that the maximum value of P occurs at both A and B.

45. If $P = ax + 10y$, find all numbers a such that the maximum value of P occurs at both B and C.

46. If $P = ax + 10y$, find all numbers a such that the minimum value of P occurs only at C.

47. If $P = ax + 10y$, find all numbers a such that the minimum value of P occurs at both O and C.

48. If $P = ax + 10y$, explain why the minimum value of P cannot occur at B.

Applications

In Problems 49–64, construct a mathematical model in the form of a linear programming problem. (The answers in the back of the book for these application problems include the model.) Then solve by the geometric method.

49. Water skis. A manufacturing company makes two types of water skis—a trick ski and a slalom ski. The relevant manufacturing data are given in the table below.

	Labor-Hours per Ski		Maximum Labor-Hours
Department	Trick Ski	Slalom Ski	Available per Day
Fabricating	6	4	108
Finishing	1	1	24

(A) If the profit on a trick ski is \$40 and the profit on a slalom ski is \$30, how many of each type of ski should be manufactured each day to realize a maximum profit? What is the maximum profit?

(B) Discuss the effect on the production schedule and the maximum profit if the profit on a slalom ski decreases to \$25.

(C) Discuss the effect on the production schedule and the maximum profit if the profit on a slalom ski increases to \$45.

50. Furniture. A furniture manufacturing company manufactures dining-room tables and chairs. The relevant manufacturing data are given in the table below.

Department	Labor-Hours per Unit Table	Chair	Maximum Labor-Hours Available per Day
Assembly	8	2	400
Finishing	2	1	120
Profit per unit	$90	$25	

(A) How many tables and chairs should be manufactured each day to realize a maximum profit? What is the maximum profit?

(B) Discuss the effect on the production schedule and the maximum profit if the marketing department of the company decides that the number of chairs produced should be at least four times the number of tables produced.

51. **Production scheduling.** A furniture company has two plants that produce the lumber used in manufacturing tables and chairs. In 1 day of operation, plant *A* can produce the lumber required to manufacture 20 tables and 60 chairs, and plant *B* can produce the lumber required to manufacture 25 tables and 50 chairs. The company needs enough lumber to manufacture at least 200 tables and 500 chairs.

(A) If it costs $1,000 to operate plant *A* for 1 day and $900 to operate plant *B* for 1 day, how many days should each plant be operated to produce a sufficient amount of lumber at a minimum cost? What is the minimum cost?

(B) Discuss the effect on the operating schedule and the minimum cost if the daily cost of operating plant *A* is reduced to $600 and all other data in part (A) remain the same.

(C) Discuss the effect on the operating schedule and the minimum cost if the daily cost of operating plant *B* is reduced to $800 and all other data in part (A) remain the same.

52. **Computers.** An electronics firm manufactures two types of personal computers—a standard model and a portable model. The production of a standard computer requires a capital expenditure of $400 and 40 hours of labor. The production of a portable computer requires a capital expenditure of $250 and 30 hours of labor. The firm has $20,000 capital and 2,160 labor-hours available for production of standard and portable computers.

(A) What is the maximum number of computers the company is capable of producing?

(B) If each standard computer contributes a profit of $320 and each portable model contributes a profit of $220, how much profit will the company make by producing the maximum number of computers determined in part (A)? Is this the maximum profit? If not, what is the maximum profit?

53. **Transportation.** The officers of a high school senior class are planning to rent buses and vans for a class trip. Each bus can transport 40 students, requires 3 chaperones, and costs $1,200 to rent. Each van can transport 8 students, requires 1 chaperone, and costs $100 to rent. Since there are 400 students in the senior class that may be eligible to go on the trip, the officers must plan to accommodate at least 400 students. Since only 36 parents have volunteered to serve as chaperones, the officers must plan to use at most 36 chaperones. How many vehicles of each type should the officers rent in order to minimize the transportation costs? What are the minimal transportation costs?

54. **Transportation.** Refer to Problem 53. If each van can transport 7 people and there are 35 available chaperones, show that the optimal solution found graphically involves decimals. Find all feasible solutions with integer coordinates and identify the one that minimizes the transportation costs. Can this optimal integer solution be obtained by rounding the optimal decimal solution? Explain.

55. **Investment.** An investor has $60,000 to invest in a CD and a mutual fund. The CD yields 5% and the mutual fund yields an average of 9%. The mutual fund requires a minimum investment of $10,000, and the investor requires that at least twice as much should be invested in CDs as in the mutual fund. How much should be invested in CDs and how much in the mutual fund to maximize the return? What is the maximum return?

56. **Investment.** An investor has $24,000 to invest in bonds of AAA and B qualities. The AAA bonds yield an average of 6%, and the B bonds yield 10%. The investor requires that at least three times as much money should be invested in AAA bonds as in B bonds. How much should be invested in each type of bond to maximize the return? What is the maximum return?

57. **Pollution control.** Because of new federal regulations on pollution, a chemical plant introduced a new, more expensive process to supplement or replace an older process used in the production of a particular chemical. The older process emitted 20 grams of sulfur dioxide and 40 grams of particulate matter into the atmosphere for each gallon of chemical produced. The new process emits 5 grams of sulfur dioxide and 20 grams of particulate matter for each gallon produced. The company makes a profit of 60¢ per gallon and 20¢ per gallon on the old and new processes, respectively.

(A) If the government allows the plant to emit no more than 16,000 grams of sulfur dioxide and 30,000 grams of particulate matter daily, how many gallons of the chemical should be produced by each process to maximize daily profit? What is the maximum daily profit?

(B) Discuss the effect on the production schedule and the maximum profit if the government decides to restrict emissions of sulfur dioxide to 11,500 grams daily and all other data remain unchanged.

(C) Discuss the effect on the production schedule and the maximum profit if the government decides to restrict emissions of sulfur dioxide to 7,200 grams daily and all other data remain unchanged.

58. **Capital expansion.** A fast-food chain plans to expand by opening several new restaurants. The chain operates two types of restaurants, drive-through and full-service. A drive-through restaurant costs $100,000 to construct, requires 5 employees, and has an expected annual revenue of $200,000. A full-service restaurant costs $150,000 to construct, requires 15 employees, and has an expected annual revenue of $500,000. The chain has $2,400,000 in capital available for expansion. Labor contracts require that they hire no more than 210 employees, and licensing restrictions require that they open no more than 20 new restaurants. How many

restaurants of each type should the chain open in order to maximize the expected revenue? What is the maximum expected revenue? How much of their capital will they use and how many employees will they hire?

59. Fertilizer. A fruit grower can use two types of fertilizer in his orange grove, brand A and brand B. The amounts (in pounds) of nitrogen, phosphoric acid, and chloride in a bag of each brand are given in the table. Tests indicate that the grove needs at least 1,000 pounds of phosphoric acid and at most 400 pounds of chloride.

	Pounds per Bag	
	Brand *A*	**Brand *B***
Nitrogen	8	3
Phosphoric acid	4	4
Chloride	2	1

(A) If the grower wants to maximize the amount of nitrogen added to the grove, how many bags of each mix should be used? How much nitrogen will be added?

(B) If the grower wants to minimize the amount of nitrogen added to the grove, how many bags of each mix should be used? How much nitrogen will be added?

60. Nutrition. A dietitian is to arrange a special diet composed of two foods, M and N. Each ounce of food M contains 30 units of calcium, 10 units of iron, 10 units of vitamin A, and 8 units of cholesterol. Each ounce of food N contains 10 units of calcium, 10 units of iron, 30 units of vitamin A, and 4 units of cholesterol. If the minimum daily requirements are 360 units of calcium, 160 units of iron, and 240 units of vitamin A, how many ounces of each food should be used to meet the minimum requirements and at the same time minimize the cholesterol intake? What is the minimum cholesterol intake?

61. Plant food. A farmer can buy two types of plant food, mix A and mix B. Each cubic yard of mix A contains 20 pounds of phosphoric acid, 30 pounds of nitrogen, and 5 pounds of potash. Each cubic yard of mix B contains 10 pounds of phosphoric acid, 30 pounds of nitrogen, and 10 pounds of potash. The minimum monthly requirements are 460 pounds of phosphoric acid, 960 pounds of nitrogen, and 220 pounds of potash. If mix A costs \$30 per cubic yard and mix B costs \$35 per cubic yard, how many cubic yards of each mix should the farmer blend to meet the minimum monthly requirements at a minimal cost? What is this cost?

62. Animal food. A laboratory technician in a medical research center is asked to formulate a diet from two commercially packaged foods, food A and food B, for a group of animals. Each ounce of food A contains 8 units of fat, 16 units of carbohydrate, and 2 units of protein. Each ounce of food B contains 4 units of fat, 32 units of carbohydrate, and 8 units of protein. The minimum daily requirements are 176 units of fat, 1,024 units of carbohydrate, and 384 units of protein. If food A costs 5¢ per ounce and food B costs 5¢ per ounce, how many ounces of each food should be used to meet the minimum daily requirements at the least cost? What is the cost for this amount of food?

63. Psychology. A psychologist uses two types of boxes with mice and rats. The amount of time (in minutes) that each mouse and each rat spends in each box per day is given in the table. What is the maximum number of mice and rats that can be used in this experiment? How many mice and how many rats produce this maximum?

	Time		Maximum Time Available per Day
	Mice	**Rats**	
Box *A*	10 min	20 min	800 min
Box *B*	20 min	10 min	640 min

64. Sociology. A city council voted to conduct a study on inner-city community problems using sociologists and research assistants from a nearby university. Allocation of time and costs per week are given in the table. How many sociologists and how many research assistants should be hired to minimize the cost and meet the weekly labor-hour requirements? What is the minimum weekly cost?

	Labor-Hours		Minimum Labor-Hours Needed per Week
	Sociologist	**Research Assistant**	
Fieldwork	10	30	180
Research center	30	10	140
Costs per week	\$500	\$300	

Answers to Matched Problems

1. (A) $x =$ number of two-person boats produced each month
$y =$ number of four-person boats produced each month

(B)

	Labor-Hours Required		Maximum Labor-Hours Available per Month
	Two-Person Boat	**Four-Person Boat**	
Cutting department	0.9	1.8	864
Assembly department	0.8	1.2	672
Profit per boat	\$25	\$40	

(C) $P = 25x + 40y$

(D) $0.9x + 1.8y \le 864$
$0.8x + 1.2y \le 672$
$x, y \ge 0$

(E)

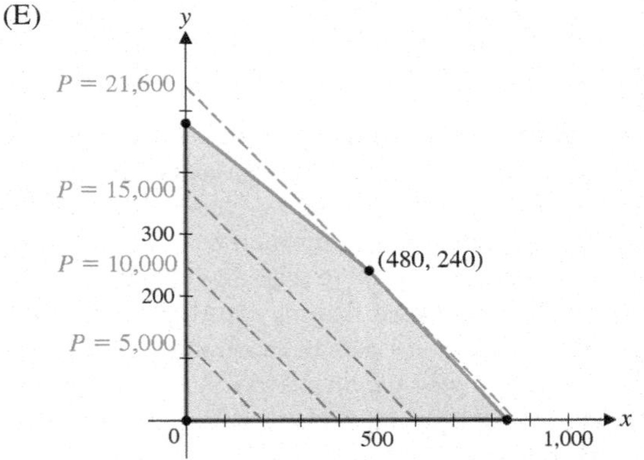

(F) 480 two-person boats, 240 four-person boats; Max $P = \$21{,}600$ per month

2. (A) Min $z = 24$ at $(3, 6)$; Max $z = 40$ at $(2, 16)$ and $(8, 4)$ (multiple optimal solution)

(B) Min $z = 90$ at $(0, 18)$; no maximum value

3. Min $C = 0.2x + 0.4y$

subject to $3{,}000x + 4{,}000y \geq 36{,}000$

$1{,}000x + 4{,}000y \geq 20{,}000$

$x, y \geq 0$

8 lb of mix A, 3 lb of mix B; Min $C = \$2.80$ per day

Chapter 5 Summary and Review

Important Terms, Symbols, and Concepts

EXAMPLES

5.1 Linear Inequalities in Two Variables

- A line divides the plane into two regions called **half-planes**. A vertical line divides the plane into **left** and **right half-planes**; a nonvertical line divides it into **upper** and **lower half-planes**. In either case, the dividing line is called the **boundary line** of each half-plane.
- The **graph of a linear inequality** is the half-plane obtained by following the procedure on page 152. — Ex. 1, p. 152; Ex. 2, p. 152
- The variables in an applied problem are often required to be nonnegative. — Ex. 3, p. 154; Ex. 4, p. 154

5.2 System of Linear Inequalities in Two Variables

- The **solution region** (also called the **feasible region**) of a system of linear inequalities is the graph of all ordered pairs that simultaneously satisfy all the inequalities in the system. — Ex. 1, p. 158
- A **corner point** of a solution region is a point in the region that is the intersection of two boundary lines. — Ex. 2, p. 159
- A solution region is **bounded** if it can be enclosed in a circle and **unbounded** if it cannot. — Ex. 3, p. 160

5.3 Linear Programming in Two Dimensions: A Geometric Approach

- The problem of finding the optimal (maximum or minimum) value of a linear objective function on a feasible region is called a **linear programming problem**. — Ex. 1, p. 164
- The optimal value (if it exists) of the objective function in a linear programming problem must occur at one (or more) of the corner points of the feasible region (Theorem 1, page 168). Existence criteria are described in Theorem 2, page 168, and a solution procedure is listed on page 169. — Ex. 2, p. 169; Ex. 3, p. 171

Review Exercises

Work through all the problems in this chapter review and check answers in the back of the book. Answers to all review problems are there, and following each answer is a number in italics indicating the section in which that type of problem is discussed. Where weaknesses show up, review appropriate sections in the text.

A *Graph each inequality.*

1. $x > 2y - 3$

2. $3y - 5x \leq 30$

Graph the systems in Problems 3–6 and indicate whether each solution region is bounded or unbounded. Find the coordinates of each corner point.

3. $5x + 9y \leq 90$
$x, y \geq 0$

4. $15x + 16y \geq 1{,}200$
$x, y \geq 0$

5. $2x + y \leq 8$
$3x + 9y \leq 27$
$x, y \geq 0$

6. $3x + y \geq 9$
$2x + 4y \geq 16$
$x, y \geq 0$

B *In Exercises 7 and 8, state the linear inequality whose graph is given in the figure. Write the boundary line equation in the form $Ax + By = C$, with A, B, and C integers, before stating the inequality.*

7.

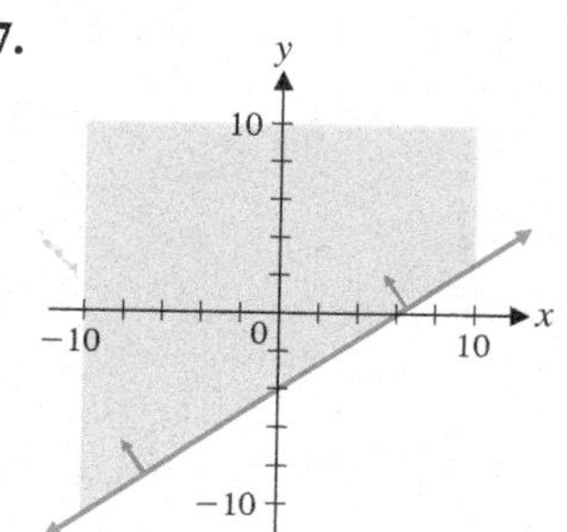

8.

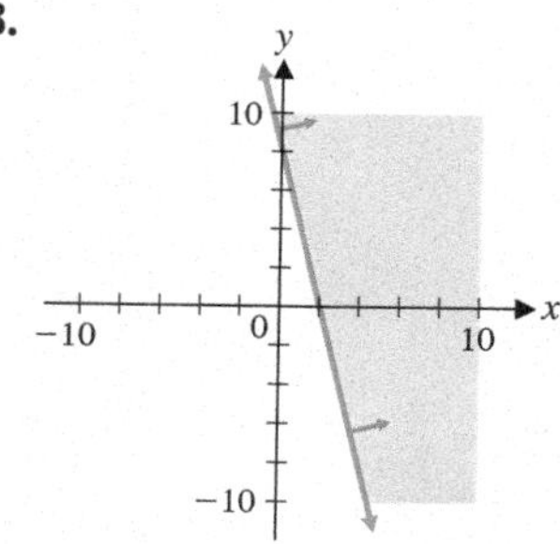

Solve the linear programming problems in Problems 9–13.

9. Maximize $P = 2x + 6y$

subject to $x + 2y \leq 8$

$2x + y \leq 10$

$x, y \geq 0$

10. Minimize $C = 5x + 2y$

subject to
$$\begin{aligned} x + 3y &\ge 15 \\ 2x + y &\ge 20 \\ x, y &\ge 0 \end{aligned}$$

C **11.** Maximize $P = 3x + 4y$

subject to
$$\begin{aligned} x + 2y &\le 12 \\ x + y &\le 7 \\ 2x + y &\le 10 \\ x, y &\ge 0 \end{aligned}$$

12. Minimize $C = 8x + 3y$

subject to
$$\begin{aligned} x + y &\ge 10 \\ 2x + y &\ge 15 \\ x &\ge 3 \\ x, y &\ge 0 \end{aligned}$$

13. Maximize $P = 3x + 2y$

subject to
$$\begin{aligned} 2x + y &\le 22 \\ x + 3y &\le 26 \\ x &\le 10 \\ y &\le 10 \\ x, y &\ge 0 \end{aligned}$$

Applications

14. Electronics. A company uses two machines to solder circuit boards, an oven and a wave soldering machine. A circuit board for a calculator needs 4 minutes in the oven and 2 minutes on the wave machine, while a circuit board for a toaster requires 3 minutes in the oven and 1 minute on the wave machine. (*Source*: Universal Electronics)

(A) How many circuit boards for calculators and toasters can be produced if the oven is available for 5 hours? Express your answer as a linear inequality with appropriate nonnegative restrictions and draw its graph.

(B) How many circuit boards for calculators and toasters can be produced if the wave machine is available for 2 hours? Express your answer as a linear inequality with appropriate nonnegative restrictions and draw its graph.

In Problems 15 and 16, construct a mathematical model in the form of a linear programming problem. (The answers in the back of the book for these application problems include the model.) Then solve the problem by the indicated method.

15. Sail manufacture. South Shore Sail Loft manufactures regular and competition sails. Each regular sail takes 2 hours to cut and 4 hours to sew. Each competition sail takes 3 hours to cut and 10 hours to sew. There are 150 hours available in the cutting department and 380 hours available in the sewing department.

(A) If the Loft makes a profit of \$100 on each regular sail and \$200 on each competition sail, how many sails of each type should the company manufacture to maximize its profit? What is the maximum profit?

(B) An increase in the demand for competition sails causes the profit on a competition sail to rise to \$260. Discuss the effect of this change on the number of sails manufactured and on the maximum profit.

(C) A decrease in the demand for competition sails causes the profit on a competition sail to drop to \$140. Discuss the effect of this change on the number of sails manufactured and on the maximum profit.

16. Animal food. A special diet for laboratory animals is to contain at least 850 units of vitamins, 800 units of minerals, and 1,150 calories. There are two feed mixes available, mix *A* and mix *B*. A gram of mix *A* contains 2 units of vitamins, 2 units of minerals, and 4 calories. A gram of mix *B* contains 5 units of vitamins, 4 units of minerals, and 5 calories.

(A) If mix *A* costs \$0.04 per gram and mix *B* costs \$0.09 per gram, how many grams of each mix should be used to satisfy the requirements of the diet at minimal cost? What is the minimum cost?

(B) If the price of mix *B* decreases to \$0.06 per gram, discuss the effect of this change on the solution in part (A).

(C) If the price of mix *B* increases to \$0.12 per gram, discuss the effect of this change on the solution in part (A).

6 Markov Chains

Introduction

In this chapter, we consider a mathematical model that combines probability and matrices to analyze certain sequences. The model is called a *Markov chain*, after the Russian mathematician Andrei Markov (1856–1922). Recent applications of Markov chains involve a wide variety of topics, including finance, market research, genetics, medicine, demographics, psychology, and political science. Problem 86 in Section 6.1, for example, uses a Markov chain to model a training program for apprentice welders.

In Section 6.1 we introduce the basic properties of Markov chains. In the remaining sections, we discuss the long-term behavior of two different types of Markov chains.

6.1 Properties of Markov Chains

- Introduction
- Transition and State Matrices
- Powers of Transition Matrices
- Application

Introduction

In this section, we explore physical *systems* and their possible *states*. To understand what this means, consider the following examples:

1. A stock listed on the New York Stock Exchange either increases, decreases, or does not change in price each day that the exchange is open. The stock can be thought of as a physical system with three possible states: increase, decrease, or no change.
2. A commuter, relative to a rapid transit system, can be thought of as a physical system with two states, a user or a nonuser.
3. During each congressional election, a voting precinct casts a simple majority vote for a Republican candidate, a Democratic candidate, or a third-party candidate. The precinct, relative to all congressional elections past, present, and future, constitutes a physical system that is in one (and only one) of three states after each election: Republican, Democratic, or other.

If a system evolves from one state to another in such a way that chance elements are involved, then the system's progression through a sequence of states is called a **stochastic process** (*stochos* is the Greek word for "guess"). We will consider a simple example of a stochastic process, and out of it will arise further definitions and methodology.

A toothpaste company markets a product (brand A) that currently has 10% of the toothpaste market. The company hires a market research firm to estimate the percentage of the market that it might acquire in the future if it launches an aggressive sales campaign. The research firm uses test marketing and extensive surveys to predict the effect of the campaign. They find that if a person is using brand A, the probability is .8 that this person will buy it again when he or she runs out of toothpaste. On the other hand, a person using another brand will switch to brand A with a probability of .6 when he or she runs out of toothpaste. So each toothpaste consumer can be considered to be in one of two possible states:

$$A = \text{uses brand } A \qquad \text{or} \qquad A' = \text{uses another brand}$$

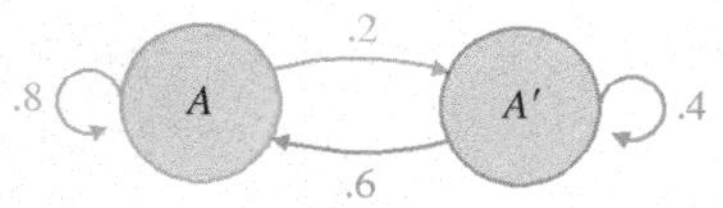

Figure 1 Transition diagram

The probabilities determined by the market research firm can be represented graphically in a **transition diagram** (Fig. 1).

We can also represent this information numerically in a **transition probability matrix**:

$$\text{Current state} \quad \begin{matrix} & \text{Next state} \\ & \begin{matrix} A & A' \end{matrix} \\ \begin{matrix} A \\ A' \end{matrix} & \begin{bmatrix} .8 & .2 \\ .6 & .4 \end{bmatrix} \end{matrix} = P$$

Explore and Discuss 1

(A) Refer to the transition diagram in Figure 1. What is the probability that a person using brand A will switch to another brand when he or she runs out of toothpaste?

(B) Refer to transition probability matrix P. What is the probability that a person who is not using brand A will not switch to brand A when he or she runs out of toothpaste?

(C) In Figure 1, the sum of the probabilities on the arrows leaving each state is 1. Will this be true for any transition diagram? Explain your answer.

(D) In transition probability matrix P, the sum of the probabilities in each row is 1. Will this be true for any transition probability matrix? Explain your answer.

The toothpaste company's 10% share of the market at the beginning of the sales campaign can be represented as an **initial-state distribution matrix**:

$$\begin{matrix} & A & A' \\ S_0 = & [.1 & .9] \end{matrix}$$

If a person is chosen at random, the probability that this person uses brand A (state A) is .1, and the probability that this person does not use brand A (state A') is .9. Thus, S_0 also can be interpreted as an **initial-state probability matrix**.

What are the probabilities of a person being in state A or A' on the first purchase after the start of the sales campaign? Let us look at the probability tree given below.

Note: A_0 represents state A at the beginning of the campaign, A'_1 represents state A' on the first purchase after the campaign, and so on.

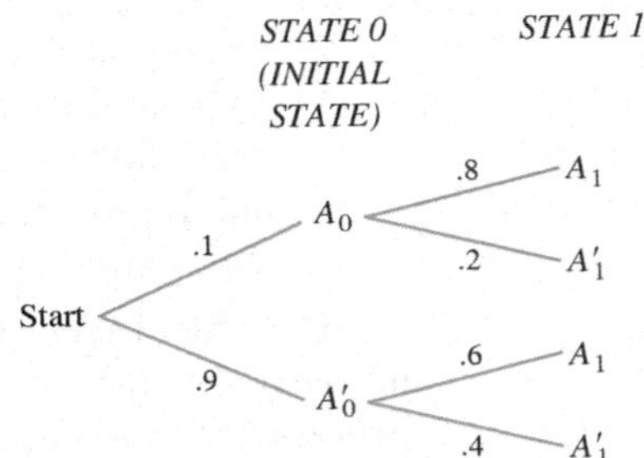

We can read the required probabilities directly from the tree:

$$\begin{aligned} P(A_1) &= P(A_0 \cap A_1) + P(A'_0 \cap A_1) \\ &= (.1)(.8) + (.9)(.6) = .62 \\ P(A'_1) &= P(A_0 \cap A'_1) + P(A'_0 \cap A'_1) \\ &= (.1)(.2) + (.9)(.4) = .38 \end{aligned}$$

Note: $P(A_1) + P(A'_1) = 1$, as expected.

The **first-state matrix** is

$$\begin{matrix} & A & A' \\ S_1 = & [.62 & .38] \end{matrix}$$

This matrix gives us the probabilities of a randomly chosen person being in state A or A' on the first purchase after the start of the campaign. We see that brand A's market share has increased from 10% to 62%.

Now, if you were asked to find the probabilities of a person being in state A or state A' on the tenth purchase after the start of the campaign, you might start to draw additional branches on the probability tree. However, you would soon become discouraged because the number of branches doubles for each successive purchase. By the tenth purchase, there would be $2^{11} = 2{,}048$ branches! Fortunately, we can convert the summing of branch products to matrix multiplication. In particular, if we multiply the initial-state matrix S_0 by the transition matrix P, we obtain the first-state matrix S_1:

$$S_0P = \underbrace{[.1 \quad .9]}_{\text{Initial state}} \underbrace{\overset{\begin{matrix} A & A' \end{matrix}}{\begin{bmatrix} .8 & .2 \\ .6 & .4 \end{bmatrix}}}_{\text{Transition matrix}} = \underbrace{[\underbrace{(.1)(.8) + (.9)(.6)}\quad \underbrace{(.1)(.2) + (.9)(.4)}]}_{\text{Compare with the tree computations above}} = \underbrace{\overset{\begin{matrix} A & A' \end{matrix}}{[.62 \quad .38]}}_{\text{First state}} = S_1$$

As you might guess, we can get the second-state matrix S_2 (for the second purchase) by multiplying the first-state matrix by the transition matrix:

$$S_1P = \overset{\text{First state}}{\begin{matrix} A & A' \\ [.62 & .38] \end{matrix}} \begin{bmatrix} .8 & .2 \\ .6 & .4 \end{bmatrix} = \overset{\text{Second state}}{\begin{matrix} A & A' \\ [.724 & .276] \end{matrix}} = S_2$$

The third-state matrix S_3 is computed in a similar manner:

$$S_2P = \overset{\text{Second state}}{\begin{matrix} A & A' \\ [.724 & .276] \end{matrix}} \begin{bmatrix} .8 & .2 \\ .6 & .4 \end{bmatrix} = \overset{\text{Third state}}{\begin{matrix} A & A' \\ [.7448 & .2552] \end{matrix}} = S_3$$

Examining the values in the first three state matrices, we see that brand A's market share increases after each toothpaste purchase. Will the market share for brand A continue to increase until it approaches 100%, or will it level off at some value less than 100%? These questions are answered in Section 6.2 when we develop techniques for determining the long-run behavior of state matrices.

Transition and State Matrices

The sequence of trials (toothpaste purchases) with the constant transition matrix P is a special kind of stochastic process called a *Markov chain*. In general, a **Markov chain** is a sequence of experiments, trials, or observations such that the transition probability matrix from one state to the next is constant. A Markov chain has no memory. The various matrices associated with a Markov chain are defined in the next box.

DEFINITION Markov Chains

Given a Markov chain with n states, a ***k*th-state matrix** is a matrix of the form

$$S_k = [s_{k1} \quad s_{k2} \quad \cdots \quad s_{kn}]$$

such that no entry is negative and the sum of the entries is 1.

Each entry s_{ki} is the proportion of the population that is in state i after the kth trial, or, equivalently, the probability of a randomly selected element of the population being in state i after the kth trial.

A **transition matrix** is a constant square matrix P of order n such that the entry in the ith row and jth column indicates the probability of the system moving from the ith state to the jth state on the next observation or trial. The sum of the entries in each row must be 1.

CONCEPTUAL INSIGHT

1. Since the entries in a kth-state matrix or transition matrix are probabilities, they must be real numbers between 0 and 1, inclusive.
2. Rearranging the various states and corresponding transition probabilities in a transition matrix will produce a different, but equivalent, transition matrix. For example, both of the following matrices are transition matrices for the toothpaste company discussed earlier:

$$P = \begin{matrix} & \begin{matrix} A & A' \end{matrix} \\ \begin{matrix} A \\ A' \end{matrix} & \begin{bmatrix} .8 & .2 \\ .6 & .4 \end{bmatrix} \end{matrix} \qquad P' = \begin{matrix} & \begin{matrix} A & A' \end{matrix} \\ \begin{matrix} A \\ A' \end{matrix} & \begin{bmatrix} .4 & .6 \\ .2 & .8 \end{bmatrix} \end{matrix}$$

Such rearrangements will affect the form of the matrices used in the solution of a problem but will not affect any of the information obtained from these matrices. In Section 6.3, we encounter situations where it will be helpful to select a transition matrix that has a special form. For now, you can choose any order for the states in a transition matrix.

As we indicated in the preceding discussion, matrix multiplication can be used to compute the various state matrices of a Markov chain:

If S_0 is the initial-state matrix and P is the transition matrix for a Markov chain, then the subsequent state matrices are given by

$$\begin{aligned} S_1 &= S_0P && \textbf{First-state matrix} \\ S_2 &= S_1P && \textbf{Second-state matrix} \\ S_3 &= S_2P && \textbf{Third-state matrix} \\ &\vdots \\ S_k &= S_{k-1}P && \textbf{kth-state matrix} \end{aligned}$$

EXAMPLE 1 **Insurance** An insurance company found that on average, over a period of 10 years, 23% of the drivers in a particular community who were involved in an accident one year were also involved in an accident the following year. They also found that only 11% of the drivers who were not involved in an accident one year were involved in an accident the following year. Use these percentages as approximate empirical probabilities for the following:

(A) Draw a transition diagram.

(B) Find the transition matrix P.

(C) If 5% of the drivers in the community are involved in an accident this year, what is the probability that a driver chosen at random from the community will be involved in an accident next year? Year after next?

SOLUTION

(A)

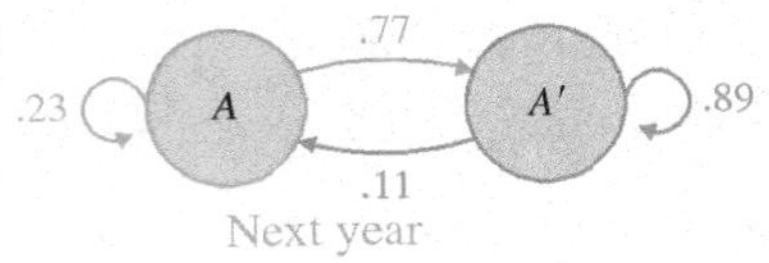

A = accident
A' = no accident

(B)

$$\begin{array}{c} \\ \text{This } A \\ \text{year } A' \end{array}\begin{array}{c} \begin{array}{cc} A & A' \end{array} \\ \begin{bmatrix} .23 & .77 \\ .11 & .89 \end{bmatrix} \end{array} = P \quad \text{Transition matrix}$$

(C) The initial-state matrix S_0 is

$$S_0 = \overset{\begin{array}{cc} A & A' \end{array}}{[.05 \quad .95]} \quad \text{Initial-state matrix}$$

Thus,

$$S_0P = \underset{\substack{\text{This year} \\ \text{(initial state)}}}{\overset{\begin{array}{cc} A & A' \end{array}}{[.05 \quad .95]}} \begin{bmatrix} .23 & .77 \\ .11 & .89 \end{bmatrix} = \underset{\substack{\text{Next year} \\ \text{(first state)}}}{\overset{\begin{array}{cc} A & A' \end{array}}{[.116 \quad .884]}} = S_1$$

$$S_1P = \underset{\substack{\text{Next year} \\ \text{(first state)}}}{\overset{\begin{array}{cc} A & A' \end{array}}{[.116 \quad .884]}} \begin{bmatrix} .23 & .77 \\ .11 & .89 \end{bmatrix} = \underset{\substack{\text{Year after next} \\ \text{(second state)}}}{\overset{\begin{array}{cc} A & A' \end{array}}{[.12392 \quad .87608]}} = S_2$$

The probability that a driver chosen at random from the community will have an accident next year is .116, and the year after next is .12392. That is, it is expected that 11.6% of the drivers in the community will have an accident next year and 12.392% the year after.

Matched Problem 1 An insurance company classifies drivers as low-risk if they are accident-free for one year. Past records indicate that 98% of the drivers in the low-risk category (L) one year will remain in that category the next year, and 78% of the drivers who are not in the low-risk category (L') one year will be in the low-risk category the next year.

(A) Draw a transition diagram.

(B) Find the transition matrix P.

(C) If 90% of the drivers in the community are in the low-risk category this year, what is the probability that a driver chosen at random from the community will be in the low-risk category next year? Year after next?

Powers of Transition Matrices

Next we investigate the powers of a transition matrix.

The state matrices for a Markov chain are defined **recursively**; that is, each state matrix is defined in terms of the preceding state matrix. For example, to find the fourth-state matrix S_4, it is necessary to compute the preceding three state matrices:

$$S_1 = S_0P \qquad S_2 = S_1P \qquad S_3 = S_2P \qquad S_4 = S_3P$$

Is there any way to compute a given state matrix directly without first computing all the preceding state matrices? If we substitute the equation for S_1 into the equation for S_2, substitute this new equation for S_2 into the equation for S_3, and so on, a definite pattern emerges:

$$\begin{aligned} S_1 &= S_0P \\ S_2 &= S_1P = (S_0P)P = S_0P^2 \\ S_3 &= S_2P = (S_0P^2)P = S_0P^3 \\ S_4 &= S_3P = (S_0P^3)P = S_0P^4 \\ &\vdots \end{aligned}$$

In general, it can be shown that the kth-state matrix is given by $S_k = S_0P^k$. We summarize this important result in Theorem 1.

THEOREM 1 Powers of a Transition Matrix

If P is the transition matrix and S_0 is an initial-state matrix for a Markov chain, then the kth-state matrix is given by

$$S_k = S_0P^k$$

The entry in the ith row and jth column of P^k indicates the probability of the system moving from the ith state to the jth state in k observations or trials. The sum of the entries in each row of P^k is 1.

EXAMPLE 2 **Using P^k to Compute S_k** Find P^4 and use it to find S_4 for

$$P = \begin{matrix} & \begin{matrix} A & A' \end{matrix} \\ \begin{matrix} A \\ A' \end{matrix} & \begin{bmatrix} .1 & .9 \\ .6 & .4 \end{bmatrix} \end{matrix} \quad \text{and} \quad S_0 = \begin{matrix} \begin{matrix} A & A' \end{matrix} \\ \begin{bmatrix} .2 & .8 \end{bmatrix} \end{matrix}$$

SOLUTION $P^2 = PP = \begin{bmatrix} .1 & .9 \\ .6 & .4 \end{bmatrix}\begin{bmatrix} .1 & .9 \\ .6 & .4 \end{bmatrix} = \begin{bmatrix} .55 & .45 \\ .3 & .7 \end{bmatrix}$

$$P^4 = P^2P^2 = \begin{bmatrix} .55 & .45 \\ .3 & .7 \end{bmatrix}\begin{bmatrix} .55 & .45 \\ .3 & .7 \end{bmatrix} = \begin{bmatrix} .4375 & .5625 \\ .375 & .625 \end{bmatrix}$$

$$S_4 = S_0P^4 = \begin{bmatrix} .2 & .8 \end{bmatrix}\begin{bmatrix} .4375 & .5625 \\ .375 & .625 \end{bmatrix} = \begin{bmatrix} .3875 & .6125 \end{bmatrix}$$

Matched Problem 2 Find P^4 and use it to find S_4 for

$$P = \begin{matrix} & A & A' \\ A & .8 & .2 \\ A' & .3 & .7 \end{matrix} \quad \text{and} \quad S_0 = \begin{matrix} A & A' \\ [.8 & .2] \end{matrix}$$

If a graphing calculator or a computer is available for computing matrix products and powers of a matrix, finding state matrices for any number of trials becomes a routine calculation.

Application

The next example illustrates the use of Theorem 1 in an application.

EXAMPLE 3 **Student Retention** Part-time students in a university MBA program are considered to be entry-level students until they complete 15 credits successfully. Then they are classified as advanced-level students and can take more advanced courses and work on the thesis required for graduation. Past records indicate that at the end of each year, 10% of the entry-level students (*E*) drop out of the program (*D*) and 30% become advanced-level students (*A*). Also, 10% of the advanced-level students drop out of the program and 40% graduate (*G*) each year. Students that graduate or drop out never return to the program.

(A) Draw a transition diagram. (B) Find the transition matrix *P*.

(C) What is the probability that an entry-level student graduates within 4 years? Drops out within 4 years?

SOLUTION

(A) If 10% of entry-level students drop out and 30% become advanced-level students, then the remaining 60% must continue as entry-level students for another year (see the diagram). Similarly, 50% of advanced-level students must continue as advanced-level students for another year. Since students who drop out never return, all students in state *D* in one year will continue in that state the next year. We indicate this by placing a 1 on the arrow from *D* back to *D*. State *G* is labeled in the same manner.

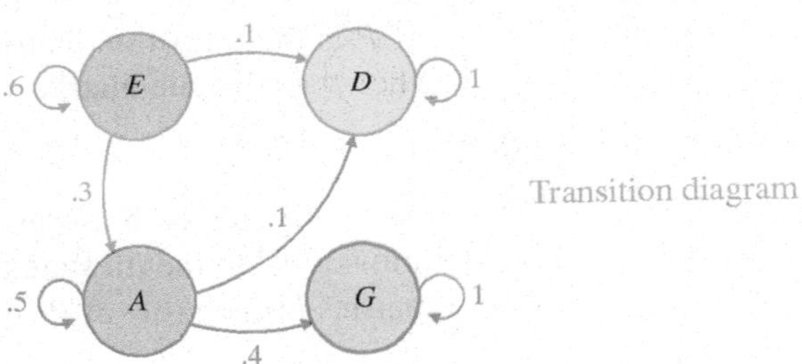

Transition diagram

(B)

$$P = \begin{matrix} & E & D & A & G \\ E & .6 & .1 & .3 & 0 \\ D & 0 & 1 & 0 & 0 \\ A & 0 & .1 & .5 & .4 \\ G & 0 & 0 & 0 & 1 \end{matrix}$$

Transition matrix

(C) The probability that an entry-level student moves from state E to state G within 4 years is the entry in row 1 and column 4 of P^4 (Theorem 1). Hand computation of P^4 requires two multiplications:

$$P^2 = \begin{bmatrix} .6 & .1 & .3 & 0 \\ 0 & 1 & 0 & 0 \\ 0 & .1 & .5 & .4 \\ 0 & 0 & 0 & 1 \end{bmatrix} \begin{bmatrix} .6 & .1 & .3 & 0 \\ 0 & 1 & 0 & 0 \\ 0 & .1 & .5 & .4 \\ 0 & 0 & 0 & 1 \end{bmatrix} = \begin{bmatrix} .36 & .19 & .33 & .12 \\ 0 & 1 & 0 & 0 \\ 0 & .15 & .25 & .6 \\ 0 & 0 & 0 & 1 \end{bmatrix}$$

$$P^4 = P^2P^2 = \begin{bmatrix} .36 & .19 & .33 & .12 \\ 0 & 1 & 0 & 0 \\ 0 & .15 & .25 & .6 \\ 0 & 0 & 0 & 1 \end{bmatrix} \begin{bmatrix} .36 & .19 & .33 & .12 \\ 0 & 1 & 0 & 0 \\ 0 & .15 & .25 & .6 \\ 0 & 0 & 0 & 1 \end{bmatrix}$$

$$= \begin{bmatrix} .1296 & .3079 & .2013 & .3612 \\ 0 & 1 & 0 & 0 \\ 0 & .1875 & .0625 & .75 \\ 0 & 0 & 0 & 1 \end{bmatrix}$$

The probability that an entry-level student has graduated within 4 years is .3612. Similarly, the probability that an entry-level student has dropped out within 4 years is .3079 (the entry in row 1 and column 2 of P^4).

Matched Problem 3 Refer to Example 3. At the end of each year the faculty examines the progress that each advanced-level student has made on the required thesis. Past records indicate that 30% of advanced-level students (A) complete the thesis requirement (C) and 10% are dropped from the program for insufficient progress (D), never to return. The remaining students continue to work on their theses.

(A) Draw a transition diagram.

(B) Find the transition matrix P.

(C) What is the probability that an advanced-level student completes the thesis requirement within 4 years? Is dropped from the program for insufficient progress within 4 years?

Explore and Discuss 2

Refer to Example 3. States D and G are referred to as *absorbing states* because a student who enters either one of these states never leaves it. Absorbing states are discussed in detail in Section 6.3.

(A) How can absorbing states be recognized from a transition diagram? Draw a transition diagram with two states, one that is absorbing and one that is not, to illustrate.

(B) How can absorbing states be recognized from a transition matrix? Write the transition matrix for the diagram you drew in part (A) to illustrate.

Exercises 6.1

Skills Warm-up Exercises

W *In Problems 1–8, find the matrix product, if it is defined.*

1. $\begin{bmatrix} 2 & 5 \\ 4 & 1 \end{bmatrix}\begin{bmatrix} 3 \\ 2 \end{bmatrix}$

2. $\begin{bmatrix} 4 & 5 \end{bmatrix}\begin{bmatrix} 6 & 9 \\ 3 & 7 \end{bmatrix}$

3. $\begin{bmatrix} 3 \\ 2 \end{bmatrix}\begin{bmatrix} 2 & 5 \\ 4 & 1 \end{bmatrix}$

4. $\begin{bmatrix} 6 & 9 \\ 3 & 7 \end{bmatrix}\begin{bmatrix} 4 & 5 \end{bmatrix}$

5. $\begin{bmatrix} 3 & 2 \end{bmatrix}\begin{bmatrix} 2 & 5 \\ 4 & 1 \end{bmatrix}$

6. $\begin{bmatrix} 4 \\ 5 \end{bmatrix}\begin{bmatrix} 6 & 9 \\ 3 & 7 \end{bmatrix}$

7. $\begin{bmatrix} 2 & 5 \\ 4 & 1 \end{bmatrix}\begin{bmatrix} 3 & 2 \end{bmatrix}$

8. $\begin{bmatrix} 6 & 9 \\ 3 & 7 \end{bmatrix}\begin{bmatrix} 4 \\ 5 \end{bmatrix}$

A *In Problems 9–14, use the transition matrix*

$$P = \begin{array}{c} \\ A \\ B \end{array}\begin{array}{c} \begin{array}{cc} A & B \end{array} \\ \begin{bmatrix} .7 & .3 \\ .1 & .9 \end{bmatrix} \end{array}$$

to find S_1 and S_2 for the indicated initial state matrix S_0.

9. $S_0 = [0 \quad 1]$

10. $S_0 = [1 \quad 0]$

11. $S_0 = [.6 \quad .4]$

12. $S_0 = [.2 \quad .8]$

13. $S_0 = [.25 \quad .75]$

14. $S_0 = [.75 \quad .25]$

In Problems 15–20, use the transition diagram

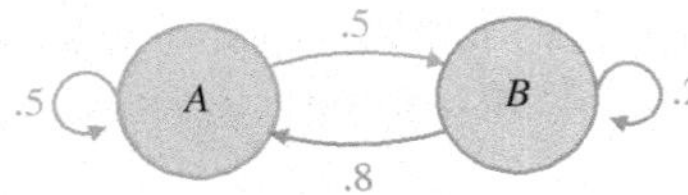

to find S_1 and S_2 for the indicated initial state matrix S_0.

15. $S_0 = [1 \quad 0]$

16. $S_0 = [0 \quad 1]$

17. $S_0 = [.3 \quad .7]$

18. $S_0 = [.9 \quad .1]$

19. $S_0 = [.5 \quad .5]$

20. $S_0 = [.2 \quad .8]$

In Problems 21–26, use the transition matrix

$$P = \begin{array}{c} \\ A \\ B \\ C \end{array}\begin{array}{c} \begin{array}{ccc} A & B & C \end{array} \\ \begin{bmatrix} .2 & .4 & .4 \\ .7 & .2 & .1 \\ .5 & .3 & .2 \end{bmatrix} \end{array}$$

to find S_1 and S_2 for the indicated initial state matrix S_0.

21. $S_0 = [0 \quad 1 \quad 0]$

22. $S_0 = [0 \quad 0 \quad 1]$

23. $S_0 = [.5 \quad 0 \quad .5]$

24. $S_0 = [.5 \quad .5 \quad 0]$

25. $S_0 = [.1 \quad .3 \quad .6]$

26. $S_0 = [.4 \quad .3 \quad .3]$

In Problems 27–32, use the transition diagram

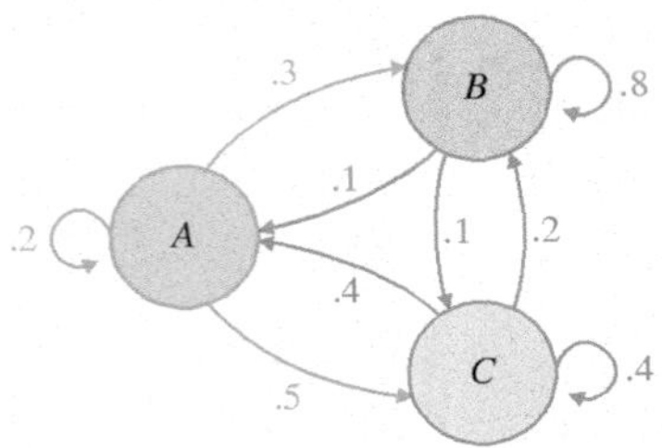

to find S_1 and S_2 for the indicated initial state matrix S_0.

27. $S_0 = [1 \quad 0 \quad 0]$

28. $S_0 = [0 \quad 1 \quad 0]$

29. $S_0 = [0 \quad .4 \quad .6]$

30. $S_0 = [.8 \quad 0 \quad .2]$

31. $S_0 = [.5 \quad .2 \quad .3]$

32. $S_0 = [.2 \quad .7 \quad .1]$

33. Draw the transition diagram that corresponds to the transition matrix of Problem 9.

34. Find the transition matrix that corresponds to the transition diagram of Problem 15.

35. Draw the transition matrix that corresponds to the transition diagram of Problem 27.

36. Find the transition diagram that corresponds to the transition matrix of Problem 21.

In Problems 37–44, could the given matrix be the transition matrix of a Markov chain?

37. $\begin{bmatrix} .3 & .7 \\ 1 & 0 \end{bmatrix}$

38. $\begin{bmatrix} .9 & .1 \\ .4 & .8 \end{bmatrix}$

39. $\begin{bmatrix} .5 & .5 \\ .7 & -.3 \end{bmatrix}$

40. $\begin{bmatrix} 0 & 1 \\ 1 & 0 \end{bmatrix}$

41. $\begin{bmatrix} .1 & .3 & .6 \\ .2 & .4 & .4 \end{bmatrix}$

42. $\begin{bmatrix} .2 & .8 \\ .5 & .5 \\ .9 & .1 \end{bmatrix}$

43. $\begin{bmatrix} .5 & .1 & .4 \\ 0 & .5 & .5 \\ .2 & .1 & .7 \end{bmatrix}$

44. $\begin{bmatrix} .3 & .3 & .4 \\ .7 & .2 & .2 \\ .1 & .8 & .1 \end{bmatrix}$

In Problems 45–50, is there a unique way of filling in the missing probabilities in the transition diagram? If so, complete the transition diagram and write the corresponding transition matrix. If not, explain why.

45.

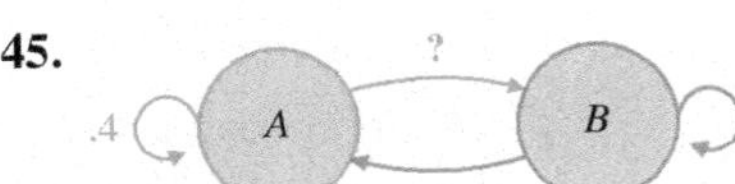

46.

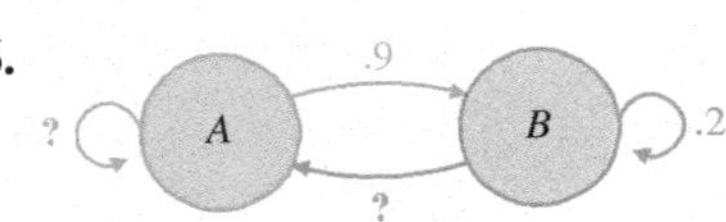

47.

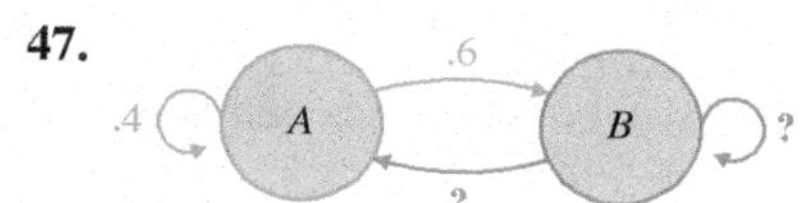

48.

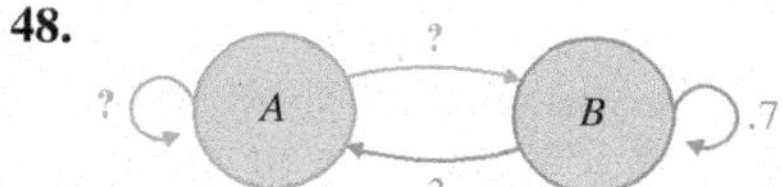

49.

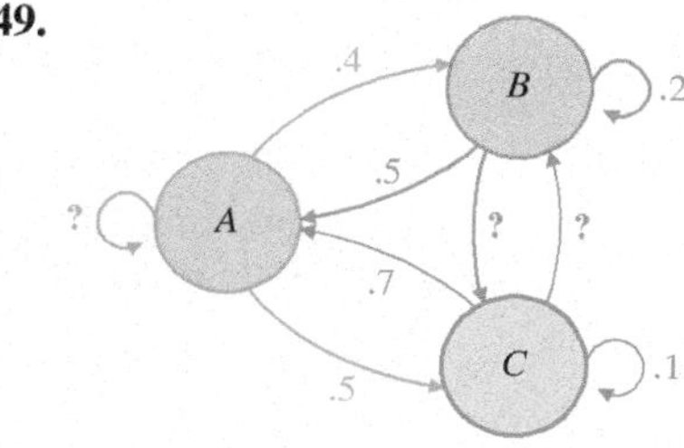

50.

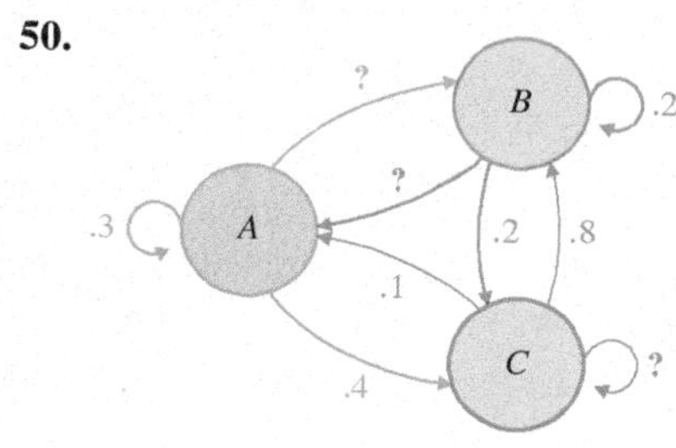

In Problems 51–56, are there unique values of a, b, and c that make P a transition matrix? If so, complete the transition matrix and draw the corresponding transition diagram. If not, explain why.

51. $P = \begin{matrix} & A & B & C \\ A & 0 & .5 & a \\ B & b & 0 & .4 \\ C & .2 & c & .1 \end{matrix}$

52. $P = \begin{matrix} & A & B & C \\ A & a & 0 & .9 \\ B & .2 & .3 & b \\ C & .6 & c & 0 \end{matrix}$

53. $P = \begin{matrix} & A & B & C \\ A & 0 & a & .3 \\ B & 0 & b & 0 \\ C & c & .8 & 0 \end{matrix}$

54. $P = \begin{matrix} & A & B & C \\ A & 0 & 1 & a \\ B & 0 & 0 & b \\ C & c & .5 & 0 \end{matrix}$

55. $P = \begin{matrix} & A & B & C \\ A & .2 & .1 & .7 \\ B & a & .4 & c \\ C & .5 & b & .4 \end{matrix}$

56. $P = \begin{matrix} & A & B & C \\ A & a & .8 & .1 \\ B & .3 & b & .4 \\ C & .6 & .5 & c \end{matrix}$

In Problems 57–60, use the given information to draw the transition diagram and find the transition matrix.

57. A Markov chain has two states, A and B. The probability of going from state A to state B in one trial is .7, and the probability of going from state B to state A in one trial is .9.

58. A Markov chain has two states, A and B. The probability of going from state A to state A in one trial is .6, and the probability of going from state B to state B in one trial is .2.

59. A Markov chain has three states, A, B, and C. The probability of going from state A to state B in one trial is .1, and the probability of going from state A to state C in one trial is .3. The probability of going from state B to state A in one trial is .2, and the probability of going from state B to state C in one trial is .5. The probability of going from state C to state C in one trial is 1.

60. A Markov chain has three states, A, B, and C. The probability of going from state A to state B in one trial is 1. The probability of going from state B to state A in one trial is .5, and the probability of going from state B to state C in one trial is .5. The probability of going from state C to state A in one trial is 1.

Problems 61–70 refer to the following transition matrix P and its powers:

$$P = \begin{matrix} & A & B & C \\ A & .6 & .3 & .1 \\ B & .2 & .5 & .3 \\ C & .1 & .2 & .7 \end{matrix} \qquad P^2 = \begin{matrix} & A & B & C \\ A & .43 & .35 & .22 \\ B & .25 & .37 & .38 \\ C & .17 & .27 & .56 \end{matrix}$$

$$P^3 = \begin{matrix} & A & B & C \\ A & .35 & .348 & .302 \\ B & .262 & .336 & .402 \\ C & .212 & .298 & .49 \end{matrix}$$

61. Find the probability of going from state A to state B in two trials.

62. Find the probability of going from state B to state C in two trials.

63. Find the probability of going from state C to state A in three trials.

64. Find the probability of going from state B to state B in three trials.

65. Find S_2 for $S_0 = [1 \quad 0 \quad 0]$ and explain what it represents.

66. Find S_2 for $S_0 = [0 \quad 1 \quad 0]$ and explain what it represents.

67. Find S_3 for $S_0 = [0 \quad 0 \quad 1]$ and explain what it represents.

68. Find S_3 for $S_0 = [1 \quad 0 \quad 0]$ and explain what it represents.

In Problems 69–72, given the transition matrix P and initial-state matrix S_0, find P^4 and use P^4 to find S_4.

69. $P = \begin{matrix} & A & B \\ A & .1 & .9 \\ B & .6 & .4 \end{matrix}$; $S_0 = [.8 \quad .2]$

70. $P = \begin{matrix} & A & B \\ A & .8 & .2 \\ B & .3 & .7 \end{matrix}$; $S_0 = [.4 \quad .6]$

71. $P = \begin{matrix} & A & B & C \\ A & 0 & .4 & .6 \\ B & 0 & 0 & 1 \\ C & 1 & 0 & 0 \end{matrix}$; $S_0 = [.2 \quad .3 \quad .5]$

72. $P = \begin{matrix} & A & B & C \\ A & 0 & 1 & 0 \\ B & .8 & 0 & .2 \\ C & 1 & 0 & 0 \end{matrix}$; $S_0 = [.4 \quad .2 \quad .4]$

73. A Markov chain with two states has transition matrix P. If the initial-state matrix is $S_0 = [1 \quad 0]$, discuss the relationship between the entries in the kth-state matrix and the entries in the kth power of P.

74. Repeat Problem 73 if the initial-state matrix is $S_0 = [0 \quad 1]$.

C **75.** Given the transition matrix

$$P = \begin{matrix} & A & B & C & D \\ A & .2 & .2 & .3 & .3 \\ B & 0 & 1 & 0 & 0 \\ C & .2 & .2 & .1 & .5 \\ D & 0 & 0 & 0 & 1 \end{matrix}$$

(A) Find P^4.

(B) Find the probability of going from state A to state D in four trials.

(C) Find the probability of going from state C to state B in four trials.

(D) Find the probability of going from state B to state A in four trials.

76. Repeat Problem 75 for the transition matrix

$$P = \begin{matrix} & A & B & C & D \\ A & .5 & .3 & .1 & .1 \\ B & 0 & 1 & 0 & 0 \\ C & 0 & 0 & 1 & 0 \\ D & .1 & .2 & .3 & .4 \end{matrix}$$

A matrix is called a **probability matrix** *if all its entries are real numbers between 0 and 1, inclusive, and the sum of the entries in each row is 1. So transition matrices are square probability matrices and state matrices are probability matrices with one row.*

77. Show that if

$$P = \begin{bmatrix} a & 1 - a \\ 1 - b & b \end{bmatrix}$$

is a probability matrix, then P^2 is a probability matrix.

78. Show that if

$$P = \begin{bmatrix} a & 1 - a \\ 1 - b & b \end{bmatrix} \quad \text{and} \quad S = [c \quad 1 - c]$$

are probability matrices, then SP is a probability matrix.

Applications

79. Scheduling. An outdoor restaurant in a summer resort closes only on rainy days. From past records, it is found that from May through September, when it rains one day, the probability of rain for the next day is .4; when it does not rain one day, the probability of rain for the next day is .06.

(A) Draw a transition diagram.

(B) Write the transition matrix.

(C) If it rains on Thursday, what is the probability that the restaurant will be closed on Saturday? On Sunday?

80. Scheduling. Repeat Problem 79 if the probability of rain following a rainy day is .6 and the probability of rain following a nonrainy day is .1.

81. Advertising. A television advertising campaign is conducted during the football season to promote a well-known brand X shaving cream. For each of several weeks, a survey is made, and it is found that each week, 80% of those using brand X continue to use it and 20% switch to another brand. It is also found that of those not using brand X, 20% switch to brand X while the other 80% continue using another brand.

(A) Draw a transition diagram.

(B) Write the transition matrix.

(C) If 20% of the people are using brand X at the start of the advertising campaign, what percentage will be using it 1 week later? 2 weeks later?

82. Car rental. A car rental agency has facilities at both JFK and LaGuardia airports. Assume that a car rented at either airport must be returned to one or the other airport. If a car is rented at LaGuardia, the probability that it will be returned there is .8; if a car is rented at JFK, the probability that it will be returned there is .7. Assume that the company rents all its 100 cars each day and that each car is rented (and returned) only once a day. If we start with 50 cars at each airport, then

(A) What is the expected distribution on the next day?

(B) What is the expected distribution 2 days later?

83. Homeowner's insurance. In a given city, the market for homeowner's insurance is dominated by two companies: National Property and United Family. Currently, National Property insures 50% of homes in the city, United Family insures 30%, and the remainder are insured by a collection of smaller companies. United Family decides to offer rebates to increase its market share. This has the following effects on insurance purchases for the next several years: each year 25% of National Property's customers switch to United Family and 10% switch to other companies; 10% of United Family's customers switch to National Property and 5% switch to other companies; 15% of the customers of other companies switch to National Property and 35% switch to United Family.

(A) Draw a transition diagram.

(B) Write the transition matrix.

(C) What percentage of homes will be insured by National Property next year? The year after next?

(D) What percentage of homes will be insured by United Family next year? The year after next?

84. Service contracts. A small community has two heating services that offer annual service contracts for home heating: Alpine Heating and Badger Furnaces. Currently, 25% of homeowners have service contracts with Alpine, 30% have service contracts with Badger, and the remainder do not have service contracts. Both companies launch aggressive advertising campaigns to attract new customers, with the following effects on service contract purchases for the next several years: each year 35% of homeowners with no current service contract decide to purchase a contract from Alpine and 40% decide to purchase one from Badger. In addition, 10% of the previous customers at each company decide to switch to the other company, and 5% decide they do not want a service contract.

(A) Draw a transition diagram.

(B) Write the transition matrix.

(C) What percentage of homes will have service contracts with Alpine next year? The year after next?

(D) What percentage of homes will have service contracts with Badger next year? The year after next?

85. Travel agent training. A chain of travel agencies maintains a training program for new travel agents. Initially, all new employees are classified as beginning agents requiring extensive supervision. Every 6 months, the performance of each agent is reviewed. Past records indicate that after each semiannual review, 40% of the beginning agents are promoted to intermediate agents requiring only minimal supervision, 10% are terminated for unsatisfactory performance, and the remainder continue as beginning agents. Furthermore, 30% of the intermediate agents are promoted to qualified travel agents requiring no supervision, 10% are terminated for unsatisfactory performance, and the remainder continue as intermediate agents.

(A) Draw a transition diagram.

(B) Write the transition matrix.

(C) What is the probability that a beginning agent is promoted to qualified agent within 1 year? Within 2 years?

86. Welder training. All welders in a factory begin as apprentices. Every year the performance of each apprentice is reviewed. Past records indicate that after each review, 10% of the apprentices are promoted to professional welder, 20% are terminated for unsatisfactory performance, and the remainder continue as apprentices.

(A) Draw a transition diagram.

(B) Write the transition matrix.

(C) What is the probability that an apprentice is promoted to professional welder within 2 years? Within 4 years?

87. Health plans. A midwestern university offers its employees three choices for health care: a clinic-based health maintenance organization (HMO), a preferred provider organization (PPO), and a traditional fee-for-service program (FFS). Each year, the university designates an open enrollment period during which employees may change from one health plan to another. Prior to the last open enrollment period, 20% of employees were enrolled in the HMO, 25% in the PPO, and the remainder in the FFS. During the open enrollment period, 15% of employees in the HMO switched to the PPO and 5% switched to the FFS, 20% of the employees in the PPO switched to the HMO and 10% to the FFS, and 25% of the employees in the FFS switched to the HMO and 30% switched to the PPO.

(A) Write the transition matrix.

(B) What percentage of employees were enrolled in each health plan after the last open enrollment period?

(C) If this trend continues, what percentage of employees will be enrolled in each plan after the next open enrollment period?

88. Dental insurance. Refer to Problem 87. During the open enrollment period, university employees can switch between two available dental care programs: the low-option plan (LOP) and the high-option plan (HOP). Prior to the last open enrollment period, 40% of employees were enrolled in the LOP and 60% in the HOP. During the open enrollment program, 30% of employees in the LOP switched to the HOP and 10% of employees in the HOP switched to the LOP.

(A) Write the transition matrix.

(B) What percentage of employees were enrolled in each dental plan after the last open enrollment period?

(C) If this trend continues, what percentage of employees will be enrolled in each dental plan after the next open enrollment period?

89. Housing trends. The 2000 census reported that 41.9% of the households in the District of Columbia were homeowners and the remainder were renters. During the next decade, 15.3% of homeowners became renters, and the rest continued to be homeowners. Similarly, 17.4% of renters became homeowners, and the rest continued to rent.

(A) Write the appropriate transition matrix.

(B) According to this transition matrix, what percentage of households were homeowners in 2010?

(C) If the transition matrix remains the same, what percentage of households will be homeowners in 2030?

90. Housing trends. The 2000 census reported that 66.4% of the households in Alaska were homeowners, and the remainder were renters. During the next decade, 37.2% of the homeowners became renters, and the rest continued to be homeowners. Similarly, 71.5% of the renters became homeowners, and the rest continued to rent.

(A) Write the appropriate transition matrix.

(B) According to this transition matrix, what percentage of households were homeowners in 2010?

(C) If the transition matrix remains the same, what percentage of households will be homeowners in 2030?

Answers to Matched Problems

1. (A) 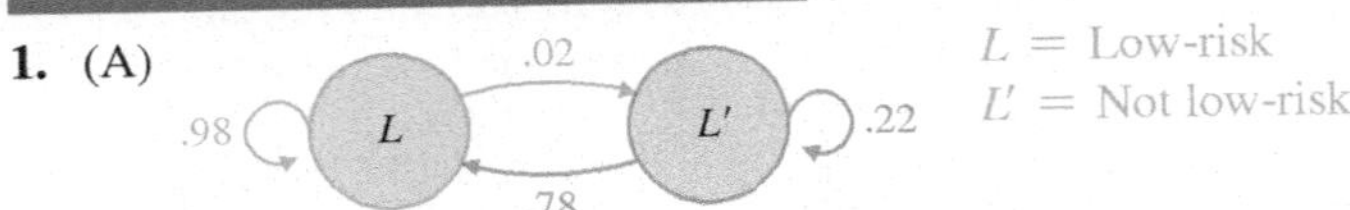

(B)

$$\begin{array}{c} \\ \text{This} \\ \text{year} \end{array} \begin{array}{c} \text{Next year} \\ \begin{array}{cc} & \begin{array}{cc} L & L' \end{array} \\ \begin{array}{c} L \\ L' \end{array} & \begin{bmatrix} .98 & .02 \\ .78 & .22 \end{bmatrix} \end{array} \end{array} = P$$

(C) Next year: .96; year after next: .972

2. $P^4 = \begin{bmatrix} .625 & .375 \\ .5625 & .4375 \end{bmatrix}$; $S_4 = [.6125 \quad .3875]$

3. $S_8 = [.600781 \quad .399219]$

4. (A) 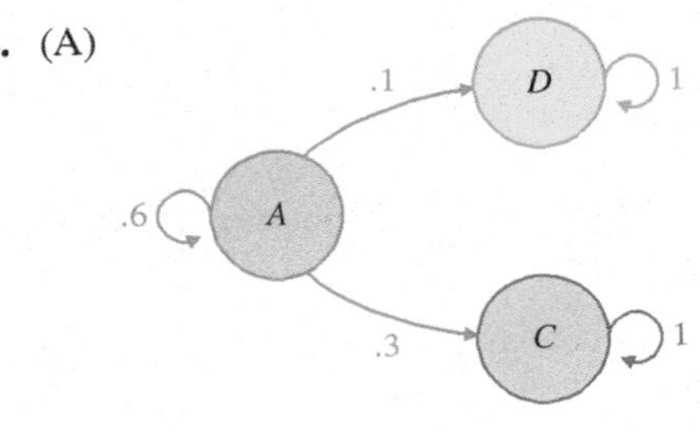

(B) $P = \begin{array}{c} \\ A \\ C \\ D \end{array} \begin{array}{c} \begin{array}{ccc} A & C & D \end{array} \\ \begin{bmatrix} .6 & .3 & .1 \\ 0 & 1 & 0 \\ 0 & 0 & 1 \end{bmatrix} \end{array}$

(C) .6528; .2176

6.2 Regular Markov Chains

- Stationary Matrices
- Regular Markov Chains
- Applications

Given a Markov chain with transition matrix P and initial-state matrix S_0, the entries in the state matrix S_k are the probabilities of being in the corresponding states after k trials. What happens to these probabilities as the number of trials k increases? In this section, we establish conditions on the transition matrix P that enable us to determine the long-run behavior of both the state matrices S_k and the powers of the transition matrix P^k.

Stationary Matrices

We begin by considering a concrete example—the toothpaste company discussed earlier. Recall that the transition matrix was given by

$$P = \begin{array}{c} \\ A \\ A' \end{array} \begin{array}{c} \begin{array}{cc} A & A' \end{array} \\ \begin{bmatrix} .8 & .2 \\ .6 & .4 \end{bmatrix} \end{array} \qquad \begin{array}{l} A = \text{uses brand } A \text{ toothpaste} \\ A' = \text{uses another brand} \end{array}$$

Initially, this company had a 10% share of the toothpaste market. If the probabilities in the transition matrix P remain valid over a long period of time, what will happen to the company's market share? Examining the first several state matrices will give us some insight into this situation (matrix multiplication details are omitted):

$$\begin{aligned} S_0 &= [.1 \quad .9] \\ S_1 = S_0P &= [.62 \quad .38] \\ S_2 = S_1P &= [.724 \quad .276] \\ S_3 = S_2P &= [.7448 \quad .2552] \\ S_4 = S_3P &= [.74896 \quad .25104] \\ S_5 = S_4P &= [.749792 \quad .250208] \\ S_6 = S_5P &= [.7499584 \quad .2500416] \end{aligned}$$

It appears that the state matrices are getting closer and closer to $S = [.75 \quad .25]$ as we proceed to higher states. Let us multiply the matrix S (the matrix that the other state matrices appear to be approaching) by the transition matrix:

$$SP = [.75 \quad .25]\begin{bmatrix} .8 & .2 \\ .6 & .4 \end{bmatrix} = [.75 \quad .25] = S$$

No change occurs! The matrix $[.75 \quad .25]$ is called a **stationary matrix**. If we reach this state or are very close to it, the system is said to be at a steady state; that is, later states either will not change or will not change very much. In terms of this example, this means that in the long run a person will purchase brand A with a probability of .75. In other words, the company can expect to capture 75% of the market, assuming that the transition matrix does not change.

DEFINITION Stationary Matrix for a Markov Chain

The state matrix $S = [s_1 \quad s_2 \quad \ldots \quad s_n]$ is a **stationary matrix** for a Markov chain with transition matrix P if

$$SP = S$$

where $s_i \geq 0$, $i = 1, \ldots, n$, and $s_1 + s_2 + \cdots + s_n = 1$.

Explore and Discuss 1

(A) Suppose that the toothpaste company started with only 5% of the market instead of 10%. Write the initial-state matrix and find the next six state matrices. Discuss the behavior of these state matrices as you proceed to higher states.

(B) Repeat part (A) if the company started with 90% of the toothpaste market.

Regular Markov Chains

Does every Markov chain have a unique stationary matrix? And if a Markov chain has a unique stationary matrix, will the successive state matrices always approach this stationary matrix? Unfortunately, the answer to both these questions is no (see Problems 43–46, Exercises 6.2). However, there is one important type of Markov chain for which both questions always can be answered in the affirmative. These are called *regular Markov chains*.

DEFINITION Regular Markov Chains

A transition matrix P is **regular** if some power of P has only positive entries. A Markov chain is a **regular Markov chain** if its transition matrix is regular.

EXAMPLE 1 **Recognizing Regular Matrices** Which of the following matrices are regular?

(A) $P = \begin{bmatrix} .8 & .2 \\ .6 & .4 \end{bmatrix}$ (B) $P = \begin{bmatrix} 0 & 1 \\ 1 & 0 \end{bmatrix}$ (C) $P = \begin{bmatrix} .5 & .5 & 0 \\ 0 & .5 & .5 \\ 1 & 0 & 0 \end{bmatrix}$

SOLUTION

(A) This is the transition matrix for the toothpaste company. Since all the entries in P are positive, we can immediately conclude that P is regular.

(B) P has two 0 entries, so we must examine higher powers of P:

$$P^2 = \begin{bmatrix} 1 & 0 \\ 0 & 1 \end{bmatrix} \quad P^3 = \begin{bmatrix} 0 & 1 \\ 1 & 0 \end{bmatrix} \quad P^4 = \begin{bmatrix} 1 & 0 \\ 0 & 1 \end{bmatrix} \quad P^5 = \begin{bmatrix} 0 & 1 \\ 1 & 0 \end{bmatrix}$$

Since the powers of P oscillate between P and I, the 2×2 identity, all powers of P will contain 0 entries. Hence, P is not regular.

(C) Again, we examine higher powers of P:

$$P^2 = \begin{bmatrix} .25 & .5 & .25 \\ .5 & .25 & .25 \\ .5 & .5 & 0 \end{bmatrix} \qquad P^3 = \begin{bmatrix} .375 & .375 & .25 \\ .5 & .375 & .125 \\ .25 & .5 & .25 \end{bmatrix}$$

Since all the entries in P^3 are positive, P is regular.

Matched Problem 1 Which of the following matrices are regular?

(A) $P = \begin{bmatrix} .3 & .7 \\ 1 & 0 \end{bmatrix}$ (B) $P = \begin{bmatrix} 1 & 0 \\ 1 & 0 \end{bmatrix}$ (C) $P = \begin{bmatrix} 0 & 1 & 0 \\ .5 & 0 & .5 \\ .5 & 0 & .5 \end{bmatrix}$

The relationships among successive state matrices, powers of the transition matrix, and the stationary matrix for a regular Markov chain are given in Theorem 1. The proof of this theorem is left to more advanced courses.

THEOREM 1 Properties of Regular Markov Chains

Let P be the transition matrix for a regular Markov chain.

(A) There is a unique stationary matrix S that can be found by solving the equation

$$SP = S$$

(B) Given any initial-state matrix S_0, the state matrices S_k approach the stationary matrix S.

(C) The matrices P^k approach a **limiting matrix $\overline{P}$**, where each row of $\overline{P}$ is equal to the stationary matrix S.

EXAMPLE 2 **Finding the Stationary Matrix** The transition matrix for a Markov chain is

$$P = \begin{bmatrix} .7 & .3 \\ .2 & .8 \end{bmatrix}$$

(A) Find the stationary matrix S.

(B) Discuss the long-run behavior of S_k and P^k.

SOLUTION

(A) Since P is regular, the stationary matrix S must exist. To find it, we must solve the equation $SP = S$. Let

$$S = [s_1 \quad s_2]$$

and write

$$[s_1 \quad s_2]\begin{bmatrix} .7 & .3 \\ .2 & .8 \end{bmatrix} = [s_1 \quad s_2]$$

After multiplying the left side, we obtain

$$[(.7s_1 + .2s_2) \quad (.3s_1 + .8s_2)] = [s_1 \quad s_2]$$

which is equivalent to the system

$$\begin{aligned} .7s_1 + .2s_2 &= s_1 \qquad \text{or} \qquad & -.3s_1 + .2s_2 &= 0 \\ .3s_1 + .8s_2 &= s_2 \qquad \text{or} \qquad & .3s_1 - .2s_2 &= 0 \end{aligned} \qquad (1)$$

System (1) is dependent and has an infinite number of solutions. However, we are looking for a solution that is also a state matrix. This gives us another equation that we can add to system (1) to obtain a system with a unique solution.

$$\begin{aligned} -.3s_1 + .2s_2 &= 0 \\ .3s_1 - .2s_2 &= 0 \\ s_1 + s_2 &= 1 \end{aligned} \qquad (2)$$

System (2) can be solved using matrix methods or elimination to obtain

$$s_1 = .4 \qquad \text{and} \qquad s_2 = .6$$

Therefore,

$$S = [.4 \quad .6]$$

is the stationary matrix.

CHECK

$$SP = [.4 \quad .6]\begin{bmatrix} .7 & .3 \\ .2 & .8 \end{bmatrix} = [.4 \quad .6] = S$$

(B) Given any initial-state matrix S_0, Theorem 1 guarantees that the state matrices S_k will approach the stationary matrix S. Furthermore,

$$P^k = \begin{bmatrix} .7 & .3 \\ .2 & .8 \end{bmatrix}^k \quad \text{approaches the limiting matrix} \quad \overline{P} = \begin{bmatrix} .4 & .6 \\ .4 & .6 \end{bmatrix}$$

Matched Problem 2 The transition matrix for a Markov chain is

$$P = \begin{bmatrix} .6 & .4 \\ .1 & .9 \end{bmatrix}$$

Find the stationary matrix S and the limiting matrix $\overline{P}$.

Applications

EXAMPLE 3 **Insurance** Refer to Example 1 in Section 6.1, where we found the following transition matrix for an insurance company:

$$P = \begin{matrix} & \begin{matrix} A & A' \end{matrix} \\ \begin{matrix} A \\ A' \end{matrix} & \begin{bmatrix} .23 & .77 \\ .11 & .89 \end{bmatrix} \end{matrix} \qquad \begin{matrix} A = \text{accident} \\ A' = \text{no accident} \end{matrix}$$

If these probabilities remain valid over a long period of time, what percentage of drivers are expected to have an accident during any given year?

SOLUTION To determine what happens in the long run, we find the stationary matrix by solving the following system:

$$[s_1 \quad s_2]\begin{bmatrix} .23 & .77 \\ .11 & .89 \end{bmatrix} = [s_1 \quad s_2] \qquad \text{and} \qquad s_1 + s_2 = 1$$

which is equivalent to

$$\begin{aligned} .23s_1 + .11s_2 &= s_1 \\ .77s_1 + .89s_2 &= s_2 \\ s_1 + s_2 &= 1 \end{aligned} \qquad \text{or} \qquad \begin{aligned} -.77s_1 + .11s_2 &= 0 \\ .77s_1 - .11s_2 &= 0 \\ s_1 + s_2 &= 1 \end{aligned}$$

Solving this system, we obtain

$$s_1 = .125 \quad \text{and} \quad s_2 = .875$$

The stationary matrix is $[.125 \quad .875]$, which means that in the long run, assuming that the transition matrix does not change, about 12.5% of drivers in the community will have an accident during any given year.

Matched Problem 3 Refer to Matched Problem 1 in Section 6.1, where we found the following transition matrix for an insurance company:

$$P = \begin{matrix} & \begin{matrix} L & L' \end{matrix} \\ \begin{matrix} L \\ L' \end{matrix} & \begin{bmatrix} .98 & .02 \\ .78 & .22 \end{bmatrix} \end{matrix} \qquad \begin{matrix} L = \text{low-risk} \\ L' = \text{not low-risk} \end{matrix}$$

If these probabilities remain valid for a long period of time, what percentage of drivers are expected to be in the low-risk category during any given year?

EXAMPLE 4 **Employee Evaluation** A company rates every employee as below average, average, or above average. Past performance indicates that each year, 10% of the below-average employees will raise their rating to average, and 25% of the average employees will raise their rating to above average. On the other hand, 15% of the average employees will lower their rating to below average, and 15% of the above-average employees will lower their rating to average. Company policy prohibits rating changes from below average to above average, or conversely, in a single year. Over the long run, what percentage of employees will receive below-average ratings? Average ratings? Above-average ratings?

SOLUTION First we find the transition matrix:

$$\text{This year} \quad \begin{matrix} & \begin{matrix} & \text{Next year} & \\ A^- & A & A^+ \end{matrix} \\ \begin{matrix} A^- \\ A \\ A^+ \end{matrix} & \begin{bmatrix} .9 & .1 & 0 \\ .15 & .6 & .25 \\ 0 & .15 & .85 \end{bmatrix} \end{matrix} \qquad \begin{matrix} A^- = \text{below average} \\ A = \text{average} \\ A^+ = \text{above average} \end{matrix}$$

To determine what happens over the long run, we find the stationary matrix by solving the following system:

$$[s_1 \quad s_2 \quad s_3] \begin{bmatrix} .9 & .1 & 0 \\ .15 & .6 & .25 \\ 0 & .15 & .85 \end{bmatrix} = [s_1 \quad s_2 \quad s_3] \quad \text{and} \quad s_1 + s_2 + s_3 = 1$$

which is equivalent to

$$\begin{aligned} .9s_1 + .15s_2 \qquad\qquad &= s_1 \\ .1s_1 + .6s_2 + .15s_3 &= s_2 \\ .25s_2 + .85s_3 &= s_3 \\ s_1 + s_2 + s_3 &= 1 \end{aligned} \quad \text{or} \quad \begin{aligned} -.1s_1 + .15s_2 \qquad\qquad &= 0 \\ .1s_1 - .4s_2 + .15s_3 &= 0 \\ .25s_2 - .15s_3 &= 0 \\ s_1 + s_2 + s_3 &= 1 \end{aligned}$$

Using Gauss–Jordan elimination to solve this system of four equations with three variables, we obtain

$$s_1 = .36 \qquad s_2 = .24 \qquad s_3 = .4$$

In the long run, 36% of employees will be rated as below average, 24% as average, and 40% as above average.

Matched Problem 4 A mail-order company classifies its customers as preferred, standard, or infrequent depending on the number of orders placed in a year. Past records indicate that each year, 5% of preferred customers are reclassified as standard and 12% as infrequent, 5% of standard customers are reclassified as preferred and 5% as infrequent, and 9% of infrequent customers are reclassified as preferred and 10% as standard. Assuming that these percentages remain valid, what percentage of customers are expected to be in each category in the long run?

Exercises 6.2

Skills Warm-up Exercises

In Problems 1–8, without using a calculator, find P^{100}. [Hint: First find P^2.]

1. $\begin{bmatrix} 1 & 0 \\ 0 & 0 \end{bmatrix}$

2. $\begin{bmatrix} 0 & 0 \\ 1 & 0 \end{bmatrix}$

3. $\begin{bmatrix} 1 & 0 \\ 0 & 1 \end{bmatrix}$

4. $\begin{bmatrix} 0 & 1 \\ 1 & 0 \end{bmatrix}$

5. $\begin{bmatrix} 1 & 0 & 0 \\ 0 & 0 & 0 \\ 0 & 0 & 1 \end{bmatrix}$

6. $\begin{bmatrix} 1 & 0 & 0 \\ 0 & 1 & 0 \\ 0 & 0 & 1 \end{bmatrix}$

7. $\begin{bmatrix} 0 & 0 & 1 \\ 0 & 0 & 0 \\ 0 & 0 & 0 \end{bmatrix}$

8. $\begin{bmatrix} 0 & 1 & 1 \\ 0 & 0 & 1 \\ 0 & 0 & 0 \end{bmatrix}$

A *In Problems 9–22, could the given matrix be the transition matrix of a regular Markov chain?*

9. $\begin{bmatrix} .6 & .4 \\ .4 & .6 \end{bmatrix}$

10. $\begin{bmatrix} .3 & .7 \\ .2 & .6 \end{bmatrix}$

11. $\begin{bmatrix} .1 & .9 \\ .5 & .4 \end{bmatrix}$

12. $\begin{bmatrix} .5 & .5 \\ .8 & .2 \end{bmatrix}$

13. $\begin{bmatrix} .4 & .6 \\ 0 & 1 \end{bmatrix}$

14. $\begin{bmatrix} .4 & .6 \\ 1 & 0 \end{bmatrix}$

15. $\begin{bmatrix} 0 & 1 \\ .8 & .2 \end{bmatrix}$

16. $\begin{bmatrix} .3 & .7 \\ .2 & .6 \end{bmatrix}$

17. $\begin{bmatrix} .6 & .4 \\ .1 & .9 \\ .3 & .7 \end{bmatrix}$

18. $\begin{bmatrix} .2 & .5 & .3 \\ .6 & .3 & .1 \end{bmatrix}$

19. $\begin{bmatrix} 0 & 1 & 0 \\ 0 & 0 & 1 \\ .5 & .5 & 0 \end{bmatrix}$

20. $\begin{bmatrix} .2 & 0 & .8 \\ 0 & 0 & 1 \\ .7 & 0 & .3 \end{bmatrix}$

21. $\begin{bmatrix} .1 & .3 & .6 \\ .8 & .1 & .1 \\ 0 & 0 & 1 \end{bmatrix}$

22. $\begin{bmatrix} 0 & 0 & 1 \\ .9 & 0 & .1 \\ 0 & 1 & 0 \end{bmatrix}$

B *For each transition matrix P in Problems 23–30, solve the equation $SP = S$ to find the stationary matrix S and the limiting matrix $\overline{P}$.*

23. $P = \begin{bmatrix} .1 & .9 \\ .6 & .4 \end{bmatrix}$

24. $P = \begin{bmatrix} .8 & .2 \\ .3 & .7 \end{bmatrix}$

25. $P = \begin{bmatrix} .5 & .5 \\ .3 & .7 \end{bmatrix}$

26. $P = \begin{bmatrix} .9 & .1 \\ .7 & .3 \end{bmatrix}$

27. $P = \begin{bmatrix} .5 & .1 & .4 \\ .3 & .7 & 0 \\ 0 & .6 & .4 \end{bmatrix}$

28. $P = \begin{bmatrix} .4 & .1 & .5 \\ .2 & .8 & 0 \\ 0 & .5 & .5 \end{bmatrix}$

29. $P = \begin{bmatrix} .8 & .2 & 0 \\ .5 & .1 & .4 \\ 0 & .6 & .4 \end{bmatrix}$

30. $P = \begin{bmatrix} .2 & .8 & 0 \\ .6 & .1 & .3 \\ 0 & .9 & .1 \end{bmatrix}$

Problems 31–34 refer to the regular Markov chain with transition matrix

$$P = \begin{bmatrix} .5 & .5 \\ .2 & .8 \end{bmatrix}$$

31. For $S = [.2 \quad .5]$, calculate SP. Is S a stationary matrix? Explain.

32. For $S = [.6 \quad 1.5]$, calculate SP. Is S a stationary matrix? Explain.

33. For $S = [0 \quad 0]$, calculate SP. Is S a stationary matrix? Explain.

34. For $S = \begin{bmatrix} \frac{2}{7} & \frac{5}{7} \end{bmatrix}$, calculate SP. Is S a stationary matrix? Explain.

In Problems 35–40, discuss the validity of each statement. If the statement is always true, explain why. If not, give a counterexample.

35. The $n \times n$ identity matrix is the transition matrix for a regular Markov chain.

36. The $n \times n$ matrix in which each entry equals $\frac{1}{n}$ is the transition matrix for a regular Markov chain.

37. If the 2×2 matrix P is the transition matrix for a regular Markov chain, then, at most, one of the entries of P is equal to 0.

38. If the 3×3 matrix P is the transition matrix for a regular Markov chain, then, at most, two of the entries of P are equal to 0.

39. If a transition matrix P for a Markov chain has a stationary matrix S, then P is regular.

40. If P is the transition matrix for a Markov chain, then P has a unique stationary matrix.

C **41.** A red urn contains 2 red marbles and 3 blue marbles, and a blue urn contains 1 red marble and 4 blue marbles. A marble is selected from an urn, the color is noted, and the marble is returned to the urn from which it was drawn. The next marble is drawn from the urn whose color is the same as the marble just drawn. This is a Markov process with two states: draw from the red urn or draw from the blue urn.

(A) Draw a transition diagram for this process.

(B) Write the transition matrix.

(C) Find the stationary matrix and describe the long-run behavior of this process.

42. Repeat Problem 41 if the red urn contains 5 red and 3 blue marbles, and the blue urn contains 1 red and 3 blue marbles.

43. Given the transition matrix

$$P = \begin{bmatrix} 0 & 1 \\ 1 & 0 \end{bmatrix}$$

(A) Discuss the behavior of the state matrices $S_1, S_2, S_3, \ldots$ for the initial-state matrix $S_0 = [.2 \quad .8]$.

(B) Repeat part (A) for $S_0 = [.5 \quad .5]$.

(C) Discuss the behavior of P^k, $k = 2, 3, 4, \ldots$.

(D) Which of the conclusions of Theorem 1 are not valid for this matrix? Why is this not a contradiction?

44. Given the transition matrix

$$P = \begin{bmatrix} 0 & 1 & 0 \\ 0 & 0 & 1 \\ 1 & 0 & 0 \end{bmatrix}$$

(A) Discuss the behavior of the state matrices $S_1, S_2, S_3, \ldots$ for the initial-state matrix $S_0 = [.2 \quad .3 \quad .5]$.

(B) Repeat part (A) for $S_0 = [\frac{1}{3} \quad \frac{1}{3} \quad \frac{1}{3}]$.

(C) Discuss the behavior of P^k, $k = 2, 3, 4, \ldots$.

(D) Which of the conclusions of Theorem 1 are not valid for this matrix? Why is this not a contradiction?

45. The transition matrix for a Markov chain is

$$P = \begin{bmatrix} 1 & 0 & 0 \\ .2 & .2 & .6 \\ 0 & 0 & 1 \end{bmatrix}$$

(A) Show that $R = [1 \quad 0 \quad 0]$ and $S = [0 \quad 0 \quad 1]$ are both stationary matrices for P. Explain why this does not contradict Theorem 1A.

(B) Find another stationary matrix for P. [*Hint*: Consider $T = aR + (1-a)S$, where $0 < a < 1$.]

(C) How many different stationary matrices does P have?

46. The transition matrix for a Markov chain is

$$P = \begin{bmatrix} .7 & 0 & .3 \\ 0 & 1 & 0 \\ .2 & 0 & .8 \end{bmatrix}$$

(A) Show that $R = [.4 \quad 0 \quad .6]$ and $S = [0 \quad 1 \quad 0]$ are both stationary matrices for P. Explain why this does not contradict Theorem 1A.

(B) Find another stationary matrix for P. [*Hint*: Consider $T = aR + (1-a)S$, where $0 < a < 1$.]

(C) How many different stationary matrices does P have?

Applications

47. Transportation. Most railroad cars are owned by individual railroad companies. When a car leaves its home railroad's tracks, it becomes part of a national pool of cars and can be used by other railroads. The rules governing the use of these pooled cars are designed to eventually return the car to the home tracks. A particular railroad found that each month, 11% of its boxcars on the home tracks left to join the national pool, and 29% of its boxcars in the national pool were returned to the home tracks. If these percentages remain valid for a long period of time, what percentage of its boxcars can this railroad expect to have on its home tracks in the long run?

48. Transportation. The railroad in Problem 47 also has a fleet of tank cars. If 14% of the tank cars on the home tracks enter the national pool each month, and 26% of the tank cars in the national pool are returned to the home tracks each month, what percentage of its tank cars can the railroad expect to have on its home tracks in the long run?

49. Labor force. Table 1 gives the percentage of the U.S. female population who were members of the civilian labor force in the indicated years. The following transition matrix P is proposed as a model for the data, where L represents females who are in the labor force and L' represents females who are not in the labor force:

Next decade

$$\begin{array}{cc} & \begin{array}{cc} L & L' \end{array} \\ \text{Current decade} \begin{array}{c} L \\ L' \end{array} & \begin{bmatrix} .92 & .08 \\ .2 & .8 \end{bmatrix} \end{array} = P$$

(A) Let $S_0 = [.433 \quad .567]$, and find S_1, S_2, S_3, and S_4. Compute the matrices exactly and then round entries to three decimal places.

(B) Construct a new table comparing the results from part (A) with the data in Table 1.

(C) According to this transition matrix, what percentage of the U.S. female population will be in the labor force in the long run?

Table 1

Year	Percent
1970	43.3
1980	51.5
1990	57.5
2000	59.8
2010	58.5

50. Home ownership. The U.S. Census Bureau published the home ownership rates given in Table 2.

Table 2

Year	Percent
1996	65.4
2000	67.4
2004	69.0
2008	67.8

The following transition matrix P is proposed as a model for the data, where H represents the households that own their home.

$$\begin{array}{ll} & \text{Four years later} \\ & \quad H \quad\; H' \\ \text{Current year} \begin{array}{c} H \\ H' \end{array} & \begin{bmatrix} .95 & .05 \\ .15 & .85 \end{bmatrix} = P \end{array}$$

(A) Let $S_0 = [.654 \quad .346]$ and find S_1, S_2, and S_3. Compute both matrices exactly and then round entries to three decimal places.

(B) Construct a new table comparing the results from part (A) with the data in Table 2.

(C) According to this transition matrix, what percentage of households will own their home in the long run?

51. Market share. Consumers can choose between three long-distance telephone services: GTT, NCJ, and Dash. Aggressive marketing by all three companies results in a continual shift of customers among the three services. Each year, GTT loses 5% of its customers to NCJ and 20% to Dash, NCJ loses 15% of its customers to GTT and 10% to Dash, and Dash loses 5% of its customers to GTT and 10% to NCJ. Assuming that these percentages remain valid over a long period of time, what is each company's expected market share in the long run?

52. Market share. Consumers in a certain area can choose between three package delivery services: APS, GX, and WWP. Each week, APS loses 10% of its customers to GX and 20% to WWP, GX loses 15% of its customers to APS and 10% to WWP, and WWP loses 5% of its customers to APS and 5% to GX. Assuming that these percentages remain valid over a long period of time, what is each company's expected market share in the long run?

53. Insurance. An auto insurance company classifies its customers in three categories: poor, satisfactory, and preferred. Each year, 40% of those in the poor category are moved to satisfactory, and 20% of those in the satisfactory category are moved to preferred. Also, 20% in the preferred category are moved to the satisfactory category, and 20% in the satisfactory category are moved to the poor category. Customers are never moved from poor to preferred, or conversely, in a single year. Assuming that these percentages remain valid over a long period of time, how many customers are expected in each category in the long run?

54. Insurance. Repeat Problems 53 if 40% of preferred customers are moved to the satisfactory category each year, and all other information remains the same.

55. Genetics. A given plant species has red, pink, or white flowers according to the genotypes RR, RW, and WW, respectively. If each of these genotypes is crossed with a pink-flowering plant (genotype RW), then the transition matrix is

$$\begin{array}{ll} & \text{Next generation} \\ & \quad \textit{Red} \quad \textit{Pink} \quad \textit{White} \\ \text{This generation} \begin{array}{c} \textit{Red} \\ \textit{Pink} \\ \textit{White} \end{array} & \begin{bmatrix} .5 & .5 & 0 \\ .25 & .5 & .25 \\ 0 & .5 & .5 \end{bmatrix} \end{array}$$

Assuming that the plants of each generation are crossed only with pink plants to produce the next generation, show that regardless of the makeup of the first generation, the genotype composition will eventually stabilize at 25% red, 50% pink, and 25% white. (Find the stationary matrix.)

56. Gene mutation. Suppose that a gene in a chromosome is of type A or type B. Assume that the probability that a gene of type A will mutate to type B in one generation is 10^{-4} and that a gene of type B will mutate to type A is 10^{-6}.

(A) What is the transition matrix?

(B) After many generations, what is the probability that the gene will be of type A? Of type B? (Find the stationary matrix.)

57. Rapid transit. A new rapid transit system has just started operating. In the first month of operation, it is found that 25% of commuters are using the system, while 75% still travel by car. The following transition matrix was determined from records of other rapid transit systems:

$$\begin{array}{ll} & \text{Next month} \\ & \textit{Rapid transit} \quad \textit{Car} \\ \text{Current month} \begin{array}{c} \textit{Rapid transit} \\ \textit{Car} \end{array} & \begin{bmatrix} .8 & .2 \\ .3 & .7 \end{bmatrix} \end{array}$$

(A) What is the initial-state matrix?

(B) What percentage of commuters will be using the new system after 1 month? After 2 months?

(C) Find the percentage of commuters using each type of transportation after the new system has been in service for a long time.

58. Politics: filibuster. The Senate is in the middle of a floor debate, and a filibuster is threatened. Senator Hanks, who is still vacillating, has a probability of .1 of changing his mind during the next 5 minutes. If this pattern continues for each 5 minutes that the debate continues and if a 24-hour filibuster takes place before a vote is taken, what is the probability that Senator Hanks will cast a yes vote? A no vote?

(A) Complete the following transition matrix:

$$\begin{array}{ll} & \text{Next 5 minutes} \\ & \begin{array}{cc} \text{Yes} & \text{No} \end{array} \\ \begin{array}{l} \text{Current} \\ \text{5 minutes} \end{array} \begin{array}{l} \text{Yes} \\ \text{No} \end{array} & \begin{bmatrix} .9 & .1 \\ & \end{bmatrix} \end{array}$$

(B) Find the stationary matrix and answer the two questions.

(C) What is the stationary matrix if the probability of Senator Hanks changing his mind (.1) is replaced with an arbitrary probability p?

The population center of the 48 contiguous states of the United States is the point where a flat, rigid map of the contiguous states would balance if the location of each person was represented on the map by a weight of equal measure. In 1790, the population center was 23 miles east of Baltimore, Maryland. By 1990, the center had shifted about 800 miles west and 100 miles south to a point in southeast Missouri. To study this shifting population, the U.S. Census Bureau divides the states into four regions as shown in the figure. Problems 59 and 60 deal with population shifts among these regions.

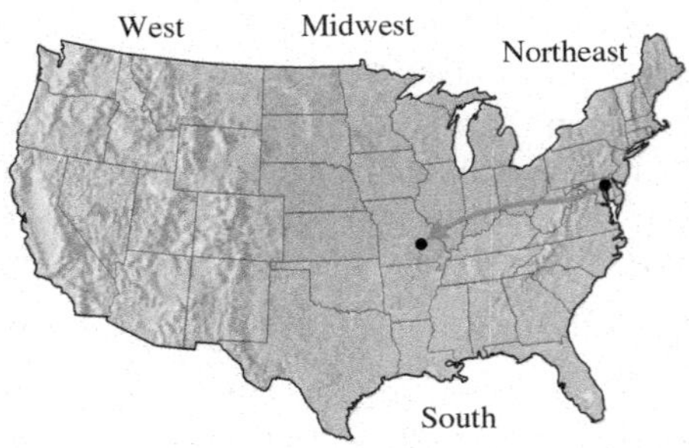

Figure for 59 and 60.: Regions of the United States and the center of population

59. Population shifts. Table 3 gives the percentage of the U.S. population living in the south region during the indicated years.

Table 3

Year	Percent
1970	30.9
1980	33.3
1990	34.4
2000	35.6
2010	37.1

The following transition matrix P is proposed as a model for the data, where S represents the population that lives in the south region:

$$\begin{array}{ll} & \text{Next decade} \\ & \begin{array}{cc} S & S' \end{array} \\ \begin{array}{l} \text{Current} \\ \text{decade} \end{array} \begin{array}{l} S \\ S' \end{array} & \begin{bmatrix} .61 & .39 \\ .21 & .79 \end{bmatrix} = P \end{array}$$

(A) Let $S_0 = [.309 \quad .691]$ and find S_1, S_2, S_3, and S_4. Compute the matrices exactly and then round entries to three decimal places.

(B) Construct a new table comparing the results from part (A) with the data in Table 3.

(C) According to this transition matrix, what percentage of the population will live in the south region in the long run?

60. Population shifts. Table 4 gives the percentage of the U.S. population living in the northeast region during the indicated years.

Table 4

Year	Percent
1970	24.1
1980	21.7
1990	20.4
2000	19.0
2010	17.9

The following transition matrix P is proposed as a model for the data, where N represents the population that lives in the northeast region:

$$\begin{array}{ll} & \text{Next decade} \\ & \begin{array}{cc} N & N' \end{array} \\ \begin{array}{l} \text{Current} \\ \text{decade} \end{array} \begin{array}{l} N \\ N' \end{array} & \begin{bmatrix} .61 & .39 \\ .09 & .91 \end{bmatrix} = P \end{array}$$

(A) Let $S_0 = [.241 \quad .759]$ and find S_1, S_2, S_3, and S_4. Compute the matrices exactly and then round entries to three decimal places.

(B) Construct a new table comparing the results from part (A) with the data in Table 4.

(C) According to this transition matrix, what percentage of the population will live in the northeast region in the long run?

Answers to Matched Problems

1. (A) Regular (B) Not regular (C) Regular

2. $S = [.2 \quad .8]$; $\overline{P} = \begin{bmatrix} .2 & .8 \\ .2 & .8 \end{bmatrix}$

3. 97.5%

4. 28% preferred, 43% standard, 29% infrequent

6.3 Absorbing Markov Chains

- Absorbing States and Absorbing Chains
- Standard Form
- Limiting Matrix
- Graphing Calculator Approximations

In Section 6.2, we saw that the powers of a regular transition matrix always approach a limiting matrix. Not all transition matrices have this property. In this section, we discuss another type of Markov chain, called an *absorbing Markov chain*. Although regular and absorbing Markov chains have some differences, they have one important similarity: the powers of the transition matrix for an absorbing Markov chain also approach a limiting matrix. After introducing basic concepts, we develop methods for finding the limiting matrix and discuss the relationship between the states in the Markov chain and the entries in the limiting matrix.

Absorbing States and Absorbing Chains

A state in a Markov chain is called an **absorbing state** if, once the state is entered, it is impossible to leave.

EXAMPLE 1 **Recognizing Absorbing States** Identify any absorbing states for the following transition matrices:

(A)
$$P = \begin{matrix} & \begin{matrix} A & B & C \end{matrix} \\ \begin{matrix} A \\ B \\ C \end{matrix} & \begin{bmatrix} 1 & 0 & 0 \\ .5 & .5 & 0 \\ 0 & .5 & .5 \end{bmatrix} \end{matrix}$$

(B)
$$P = \begin{matrix} & \begin{matrix} A & B & C \end{matrix} \\ \begin{matrix} A \\ B \\ C \end{matrix} & \begin{bmatrix} 0 & 0 & 1 \\ 0 & 1 & 0 \\ 1 & 0 & 0 \end{bmatrix} \end{matrix}$$

SOLUTION

(A) The probability of going from state A to state A is 1, and the probability of going from state A to either state B or state C is 0. Once state A is entered, it is impossible to leave, so A is an absorbing state. Since the probability of going from state B to state A is nonzero, it is possible to leave B, and B is not an absorbing state. Similarly, the probability of going from state C to state B is nonzero, so C is not an absorbing state.

(B) Reasoning as before, the 1 in row 2 and column 2 indicates that state B is an absorbing state. The probability of going from state A to state C and the probability of going from state C to state A are both nonzero. So A and C are not absorbing states.

Matched Problem 1 Identify any absorbing states for the following transition matrices:

(A)
$$P = \begin{matrix} & \begin{matrix} A & B & C \end{matrix} \\ \begin{matrix} A \\ B \\ C \end{matrix} & \begin{bmatrix} .5 & 0 & .5 \\ 0 & 1 & 0 \\ 0 & .5 & .5 \end{bmatrix} \end{matrix}$$

(B)
$$P = \begin{matrix} & \begin{matrix} A & B & C \end{matrix} \\ \begin{matrix} A \\ B \\ C \end{matrix} & \begin{bmatrix} 0 & 1 & 0 \\ 1 & 0 & 0 \\ 0 & 0 & 1 \end{bmatrix} \end{matrix}$$

The reasoning used to identify absorbing states in Example 1 is generalized in Theorem 1.

THEOREM 1 Absorbing States and Transition Matrices

A state in a Markov chain is **absorbing** if and only if the row of the transition matrix corresponding to the state has a 1 on the main diagonal and 0's elsewhere.

The presence of an absorbing state in a transition matrix does not guarantee that the powers of the matrix approach a limiting matrix nor that the state matrices in the corresponding Markov chain approach a stationary matrix. For example, if we square the matrix P from Example 1B, we obtain

$$P^2 = \begin{bmatrix} 0 & 0 & 1 \\ 0 & 1 & 0 \\ 1 & 0 & 0 \end{bmatrix} \begin{bmatrix} 0 & 0 & 1 \\ 0 & 1 & 0 \\ 1 & 0 & 0 \end{bmatrix} = \begin{bmatrix} 1 & 0 & 0 \\ 0 & 1 & 0 \\ 0 & 0 & 1 \end{bmatrix} = I$$

Since $P^2 = I$, the 3×3 identity matrix, it follows that

$$P^3 = PP^2 = PI = P \quad \text{Since } P^2 = I$$

$$P^4 = PP^3 = PP = I \quad \text{Since } P^3 = P \text{ and } PP = P^2 = I$$

In general, the powers of this transition matrix P oscillate between P and I and do not approach a limiting matrix.

Explore and Discuss 1

(A) For the initial-state matrix $S_0 = [a \quad b \quad c]$, find the first four state matrices, S_1, S_2, S_3, and S_4, in the Markov chain with transition matrix

$$P = \begin{bmatrix} 0 & 0 & 1 \\ 0 & 1 & 0 \\ 1 & 0 & 0 \end{bmatrix}$$

(B) Do the state matrices appear to be approaching a stationary matrix? Discuss.

To ensure that transition matrices for Markov chains with one or more absorbing states have limiting matrices, it is necessary to require the chain to satisfy one additional condition, as stated in the following definition.

DEFINITION Absorbing Markov Chains

A Markov chain is an **absorbing chain** if

1. There is at least one absorbing state; and
2. It is possible to go from each nonabsorbing state to at least one absorbing state in a finite number of steps.

As we saw earlier, absorbing states are identified easily by examining the rows of a transition matrix. It is also possible to use a transition matrix to determine whether a Markov chain is an absorbing chain, but this can be a difficult task, especially if the matrix is large. A transition diagram is often a more appropriate tool for determining whether a Markov chain is absorbing. The next example illustrates this approach for the two matrices discussed in Example 1.

EXAMPLE 2 **Recognizing Absorbing Markov Chains** Use a transition diagram to determine whether P is the transition matrix for an absorbing Markov chain.

(A)
$$P = \begin{matrix} & \begin{matrix} A & B & C \end{matrix} \\ \begin{matrix} A \\ B \\ C \end{matrix} & \begin{bmatrix} 1 & 0 & 0 \\ .5 & .5 & 0 \\ 0 & .5 & .5 \end{bmatrix} \end{matrix}$$

(B)
$$P = \begin{matrix} & \begin{matrix} A & B & C \end{matrix} \\ \begin{matrix} A \\ B \\ C \end{matrix} & \begin{bmatrix} 0 & 0 & 1 \\ 0 & 1 & 0 \\ 1 & 0 & 0 \end{bmatrix} \end{matrix}$$

SOLUTION

(A) From Example 1A, we know that A is the only absorbing state. The second condition in the definition of an absorbing Markov chain is satisfied if we can show that it is possible to go from the nonabsorbing states B and C to the absorbing state A in a finite number of steps. This is easily determined by drawing a transition diagram (Fig. 1). Examining the diagram, we see that it is possible to go from state B to the absorbing state A in one step and from state C to the absorbing state A in two steps. So P is the transition matrix for an absorbing Markov chain.

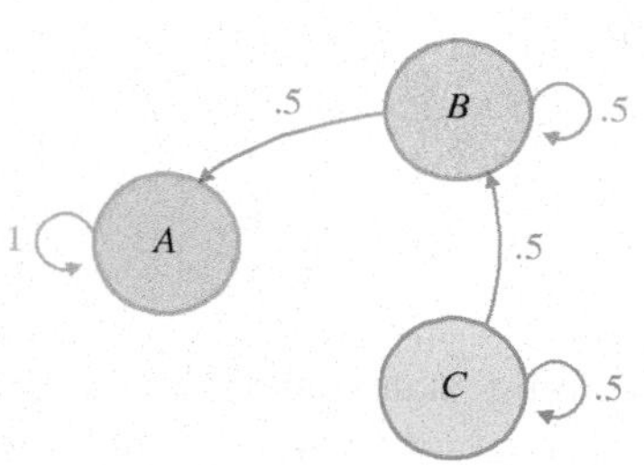

Figure 1

(B) Again, we draw the transition diagram (Fig. 2). From this diagram it is clear that it is impossible to go from either state A or state C to the absorbing state B. So P is not the transition matrix for an absorbing Markov chain.

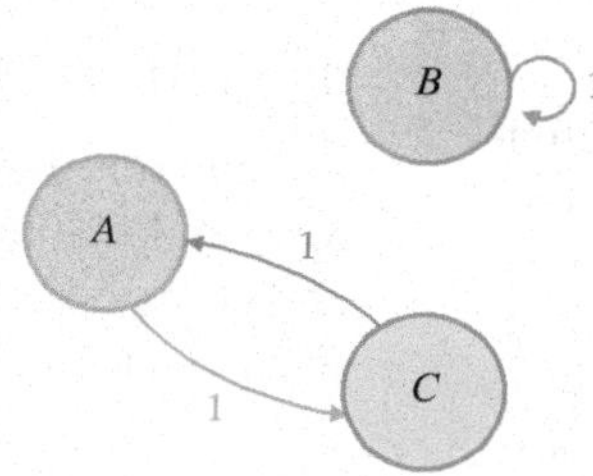

Figure 2

Matched Problem 2 Use a transition diagram to determine whether P is the transition matrix for an absorbing Markov chain.

(A)
$$P = \begin{array}{c} \\ A \\ B \\ C \end{array}\!\!\begin{array}{c} \begin{array}{ccc} A & B & C \end{array} \\ \begin{bmatrix} .5 & 0 & .5 \\ 0 & 1 & 0 \\ 0 & .5 & .5 \end{bmatrix} \end{array}$$

(B)
$$P = \begin{array}{c} \\ A \\ B \\ C \end{array}\!\!\begin{array}{c} \begin{array}{ccc} A & B & C \end{array} \\ \begin{bmatrix} 0 & 1 & 0 \\ 1 & 0 & 0 \\ 0 & 0 & 1 \end{bmatrix} \end{array}$$

Explore and Discuss 2

Determine whether each statement is true or false. Use examples and verbal arguments to support your conclusions.

(A) A Markov chain with two states, one nonabsorbing and one absorbing, is always an absorbing chain.

(B) A Markov chain with two states, both of which are absorbing, is always an absorbing chain.

(C) A Markov chain with three states, one nonabsorbing and two absorbing, is always an absorbing chain.

Standard Form

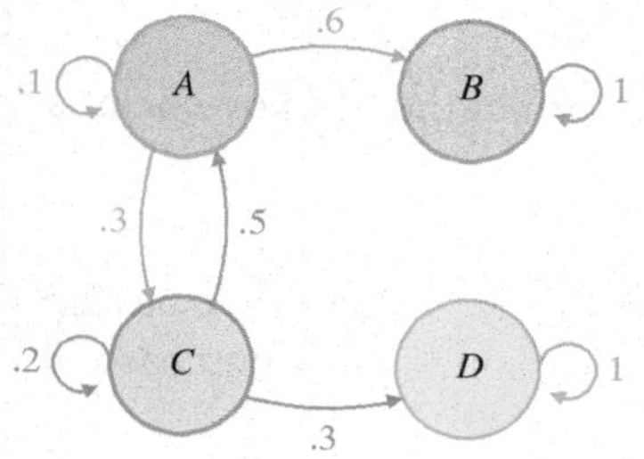

The transition matrix for a Markov chain is not unique. Consider the transition diagram in Figure 3. Since there are $4! = 24$ different ways to arrange the four states in this diagram, there are 24 different ways to write a transition matrix. (Some of these matrices may have identical entries, but all are different when the row and column labels are taken into account.) For example, the following matrices M, N, and P are three different transition matrices for this diagram.

.6 .1 A B 1 .3 .5 .2 C D 1 .3

Figure 3

$$M = \begin{matrix} & \begin{matrix} A & B & C & D \end{matrix} \\ \begin{matrix} A \\ B \\ C \\ D \end{matrix} & \begin{bmatrix} .1 & .6 & .3 & 0 \\ 0 & 1 & 0 & 0 \\ .5 & 0 & .2 & .3 \\ 0 & 0 & 0 & 1 \end{bmatrix} \end{matrix} \quad N = \begin{matrix} & \begin{matrix} D & B & C & A \end{matrix} \\ \begin{matrix} D \\ B \\ C \\ A \end{matrix} & \begin{bmatrix} 1 & 0 & 0 & 0 \\ 0 & 1 & 0 & 0 \\ .3 & 0 & .2 & .5 \\ 0 & .6 & .3 & .1 \end{bmatrix} \end{matrix} \quad P = \begin{matrix} & \begin{matrix} B & D & A & C \end{matrix} \\ \begin{matrix} B \\ D \\ A \\ C \end{matrix} & \begin{bmatrix} 1 & 0 & 0 & 0 \\ 0 & 1 & 0 & 0 \\ .6 & 0 & .1 & .3 \\ 0 & .3 & .5 & .2 \end{bmatrix} \end{matrix} \quad (1)$$

In matrices N and P, notice that all the absorbing states precede all the nonabsorbing states. A transition matrix written in this form is said to be in *standard form*. We will find standard forms very useful in determining limiting matrices for absorbing Markov chains.

Reminder

The identity matrix I in the definition is a square matrix: It has 1's on the principal diagonal and 0's elsewhere (the number of rows in I is the number of absorbing states). The zero matrix 0 is not necessarily square (the number of rows in 0 is the number of absorbing states, and the number of columns is the number of nonabsorbing states).

DEFINITION Standard Forms for Absorbing Markov Chains

A transition matrix for an absorbing Markov chain is in **standard form** if the rows and columns are labeled so that all the absorbing states precede all the nonabsorbing states. (There may be more than one standard form.) Any standard form can always be partitioned into four submatrices:

$$\begin{matrix} & \begin{matrix} A & N \end{matrix} \\ \begin{matrix} A \\ N \end{matrix} & \left[\begin{array}{c|c} I & 0 \\ \hline R & Q \end{array}\right] \end{matrix} \quad \begin{matrix} A = \text{all absorbing states} \\ N = \text{all nonabsorbing states} \end{matrix}$$

where I is an identity matrix and 0 is a zero matrix.

Referring to the matrix P in (1), we see that the submatrices in this standard form are

$$I = \begin{bmatrix} 1 & 0 \\ 0 & 1 \end{bmatrix} \quad 0 = \begin{bmatrix} 0 & 0 \\ 0 & 0 \end{bmatrix} \quad P = \begin{matrix} & \begin{matrix} B & D & A & C \end{matrix} \\ \begin{matrix} B \\ D \\ A \\ C \end{matrix} & \left[\begin{array}{cc|cc} 1 & 0 & 0 & 0 \\ 0 & 1 & 0 & 0 \\ \hline .6 & 0 & .1 & .3 \\ 0 & .3 & .5 & .2 \end{array}\right] \end{matrix}$$

$$R = \begin{bmatrix} .6 & 0 \\ 0 & .3 \end{bmatrix} \quad Q = \begin{bmatrix} .1 & .3 \\ .5 & .2 \end{bmatrix}$$

Limiting Matrix

We will now discuss the long-run behavior of absorbing Markov chains.

EXAMPLE 3 **Real Estate Development** Two competing real estate companies are trying to buy all the farms in a particular area for future housing development. Each year, 20% of the farmers decide to sell to company A, 30% decide to sell to company B, and the rest continue to farm their land. Neither company ever sells any of the farms they purchase.

(A) Draw a transition diagram and determine whether or not the Markov chain is absorbing.

(B) Write a transition matrix that is in standard form.

(C) If neither company owns any farms at the beginning of this competitive buying process, estimate the percentage of farms that each company will purchase in the long run.

(D) If company A buys 50% of the farms before company B enters the competitive buying process, estimate the percentage of farms that each company will purchase in the long run.

SOLUTION

(A)

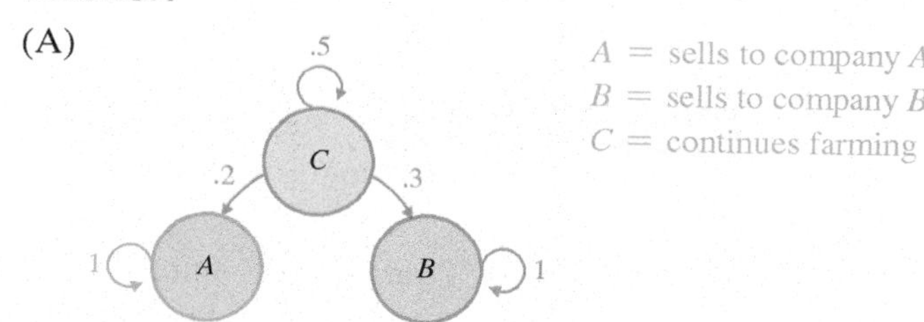

The associated Markov chain is absorbing since there are two absorbing states, A and B. It is possible to go from the nonabsorbing state C to either A or B in one step.

(B) We use the transition diagram to write a transition matrix that is in standard form:

$$P = \begin{matrix} & \begin{matrix} A & B & C \end{matrix} \\ \begin{matrix} A \\ B \\ C \end{matrix} & \begin{bmatrix} 1 & 0 & 0 \\ 0 & 1 & 0 \\ .2 & .3 & .5 \end{bmatrix} \end{matrix} \qquad \text{Standard form}$$

(C) At the beginning of the competitive buying process all the farmers are in state C (own a farm). Thus, $S_0 = [0 \quad 0 \quad 1]$. The successive state matrices are (multiplication details omitted):

$$\begin{aligned}
S_1 &= S_0P = [.2 \quad .3 \quad .5] \\
S_2 &= S_1P = [.3 \quad .45 \quad .25] \\
S_3 &= S_2P = [.35 \quad .525 \quad .125] \\
S_4 &= S_3P = [.375 \quad .5625 \quad .0625] \\
S_5 &= S_4P = [.3875 \quad .58125 \quad .03125] \\
S_6 &= S_5P = [.39375 \quad .590625 \quad .015625] \\
S_7 &= S_6P = [.396875 \quad .5953125 \quad .0078125] \\
S_8 &= S_7P = [.3984375 \quad .59765625 \quad .00390625] \\
S_9 &= S_8P = [.39921875 \quad .598828125 \quad .001953125]
\end{aligned}$$

It appears that these state matrices are approaching the matrix

$$S = \begin{matrix} A & B & C \\ [.4 & .6 & 0] \end{matrix}$$

This indicates that in the long run, company A will acquire approximately 40% of the farms and company B will acquire the remaining 60%.

(D) This time, at the beginning of the competitive buying process 50% of farmers are already in state A and the rest are in state C. So $S_0 = [.5 \quad 0 \quad .5]$. The successive state matrices are (multiplication details omitted):

$$\begin{aligned}
S_1 &= S_0P = [.6 \quad .15 \quad .25] \\
S_2 &= S_1P = [.65 \quad .225 \quad .125] \\
S_3 &= S_2P = [.675 \quad .2625 \quad .0625] \\
S_4 &= S_3P = [.6875 \quad .28125 \quad .03125] \\
S_5 &= S_4P = [.69375 \quad .290625 \quad .015625] \\
S_6 &= S_5P = [.696875 \quad .2953125 \quad .0078125] \\
S_7 &= S_6P = [.6984375 \quad .29765625 \quad .00390625] \\
S_8 &= S_7P = [.69921875 \quad .298828125 \quad .001953125]
\end{aligned}$$

These state matrices approach a matrix different from the one in part (C):

$$S' = \begin{matrix} A & B & C \\ [.7 & .3 & 0] \end{matrix}$$

Because of its head start, company A will now acquire approximately 70% of the farms and company B will acquire the remaining 30%.

Matched Problem 3 Repeat Example 3 if 10% of farmers sell to company A each year, 40% sell to company B, and the remainder continue farming.

Recall from Theorem 1, Section 6.2, that the successive state matrices of a regular Markov chain always approach a stationary matrix. Furthermore, this stationary matrix is unique. That is, changing the initial-state matrix does not change the stationary matrix. The successive state matrices for an absorbing Markov chain also approach a stationary matrix, but this matrix is not unique. To confirm this, consider the transition matrix P and the state matrices S and S' from Example 3:

$$P = \begin{matrix} & \begin{matrix} A & B & C \end{matrix} \\ \begin{matrix} A \\ B \\ C \end{matrix} & \begin{bmatrix} 1 & 0 & 0 \\ 0 & 1 & 0 \\ .2 & .3 & .5 \end{bmatrix} \end{matrix} \qquad S = \begin{matrix} \begin{matrix} A & B & C \end{matrix} \\ [.4 \quad .6 \quad 0] \end{matrix} \qquad S' = \begin{matrix} \begin{matrix} A & B & C \end{matrix} \\ [.7 \quad .3 \quad 0] \end{matrix}$$

It turns out that S and S' are both stationary matrices, as the following multiplications verify:

$$SP = [.4 \quad .6 \quad 0] \begin{bmatrix} 1 & 0 & 0 \\ 0 & 1 & 0 \\ .2 & .3 & .5 \end{bmatrix} = [.4 \quad .6 \quad 0] = S$$

$$S'P = [.7 \quad .3 \quad 0] \begin{bmatrix} 1 & 0 & 0 \\ 0 & 1 & 0 \\ .2 & .3 & .5 \end{bmatrix} = [.7 \quad .3 \quad 0] = S'$$

In fact, this absorbing Markov chain has an infinite number of stationary matrices.

Changing the initial-state matrix for an absorbing Markov chain can cause the successive state matrices to approach a different stationary matrix.

In Section 6.2, we used the unique stationary matrix for a regular Markov chain to find the limiting matrix $\overline{P}$. Since an absorbing Markov chain can have many different stationary matrices, we cannot expect this approach to work for absorbing chains. However, it turns out that transition matrices for absorbing chains do have limiting matrices, and they are not very difficult to find. Theorem 2 gives us the necessary tools. The proof of this theorem is left for more advanced courses.

THEOREM 2 Limiting Matrices for Absorbing Markov Chains

If a standard form P for an absorbing Markov chain is partitioned as

$$P = \left[\begin{array}{c|c} I & 0 \\ \hline R & Q \end{array}\right]$$

then P^k approaches a limiting matrix $\overline{P}$ as k increases, where

$$\overline{P} = \left[\begin{array}{c|c} I & 0 \\ \hline FR & 0 \end{array}\right]$$

The matrix F is given by $F = (I - Q)^{-1}$ and is called the **fundamental matrix** for P.

The identity matrix used to form the fundamental matrix F must be the same size as the matrix Q.

EXAMPLE 4 **Finding the Limiting Matrix**

(A) Find the limiting matrix $\overline{P}$ for the standard form P found in Example 3.

(B) Use $\overline{P}$ to find the limit of the successive state matrices for $S_0 = [0 \quad 0 \quad 1]$.

(C) Use $\overline{P}$ to find the limit of the successive state matrices for $S_0 = [.5 \quad 0 \quad .5]$.

SOLUTION

(A) From Example 3, we have

$$P = \begin{bmatrix} 1 & 0 & 0 \\ 0 & 1 & 0 \\ .2 & .3 & .5 \end{bmatrix} \qquad \left[\begin{array}{c|c} I & 0 \\ \hline R & Q \end{array}\right]$$

where

$$I = \begin{bmatrix} 1 & 0 \\ 0 & 1 \end{bmatrix} \qquad 0 = \begin{bmatrix} 0 \\ 0 \end{bmatrix} \qquad R = [.2 \quad .3] \qquad Q = [.5]$$

If $I = [1]$ is the 1×1 identity matrix, then $I - Q$ is also a 1×1 matrix; $F = (I - Q)^{-1}$ is simply the multiplicative inverse of the single entry in $I - Q$. So

$$F = ([1] - [.5])^{-1} = [.5]^{-1} = [2]$$
$$FR = [2][.2 \quad .3] = [.4 \quad .6]$$

and the limiting matrix is

$$\overline{P} = \begin{matrix} & \begin{matrix} A & B & C \end{matrix} \\ \begin{matrix} A \\ B \\ C \end{matrix} & \begin{bmatrix} 1 & 0 & 0 \\ 0 & 1 & 0 \\ .4 & .6 & 0 \end{bmatrix} \end{matrix} \qquad \left[\begin{array}{c|c} I & 0 \\ \hline FR & 0 \end{array}\right]$$

(B) Since the successive state matrices are given by $S_k = S_0P^k$ (Theorem 1, Section 6.1) and P^k approaches $\overline{P}$, it follows that S_k approaches

$$S_0\overline{P} = [0 \quad 0 \quad 1]\begin{bmatrix} 1 & 0 & 0 \\ 0 & 1 & 0 \\ .4 & .6 & 0 \end{bmatrix} = [.4 \quad .6 \quad 0]$$

which agrees with the results in part (C) of Example 3.

(C) This time, the successive state matrices approach

$$S_0\overline{P} = [.5 \quad 0 \quad .5]\begin{bmatrix} 1 & 0 & 0 \\ 0 & 1 & 0 \\ .4 & .6 & 0 \end{bmatrix} = [.7 \quad .3 \quad 0]$$

which agrees with the results in part (D) of Example 3.

Matched Problem 4 Repeat Example 4 for the standard form P found in Matched Problem 3.

Recall that the limiting matrix for a regular Markov chain contains the long-run probabilities of going from any state to any other state. This is also true for the limiting matrix of an absorbing Markov chain. Let's compare the transition matrix P and its limiting matrix $\overline{P}$ from Example 4:

$$P = \begin{matrix} & A & B & C \\ A & 1 & 0 & 0 \\ B & 0 & 1 & 0 \\ C & .2 & .3 & .5 \end{matrix} \quad \text{approaches} \quad \overline{P} = \begin{matrix} & A & B & C \\ A & 1 & 0 & 0 \\ B & 0 & 1 & 0 \\ C & .4 & .6 & 0 \end{matrix}$$

The rows of P and $\overline{P}$ corresponding to the absorbing states A and B are identical. That is, if the probability of going from state A to state A is 1 at the beginning of the chain, then this probability will remain 1 for all trials in the chain and for the limiting matrix. The entries in the third row of $\overline{P}$ give the long-run probabilities of going from the nonabsorbing state C to states A, B, or C.

The fundamental matrix F provides some additional information about an absorbing chain. Recall from Example 4 that $F = [2]$. It can be shown that the entries in F determine the average number of trials that it takes to go from a given nonabsorbing state to an absorbing state. In the case of Example 4, the single entry 2 in F indicates that it will take an average of 2 years for a farmer to go from state C (owns a farm) to one of the absorbing states (sells the farm). Some will reach an absorbing state in 1 year, and some will take more than 2 years. But the average will be 2 years. These observations are summarized in Theorem 3, which we state without proof.

THEOREM 3 Properties of the Limiting Matrix $\overline{P}$

If P is a transition matrix in standard form for an absorbing Markov chain, F is the fundamental matrix, and $\overline{P}$ is the limiting matrix, then

(A) The entry in row i and column j of $\overline{P}$ is the long-run probability of going from state i to state j. For the nonabsorbing states, these probabilities are also the entries in the matrix FR used to form $\overline{P}$.

(B) The sum of the entries in each row of the fundamental matrix F is the average number of trials it will take to go from each nonabsorbing state to some absorbing state.

(Note that the rows of both F and FR correspond to the nonabsorbing states in the order given in the standard form P).

CONCEPTUAL INSIGHT

1. The zero matrix in the lower right corner of the limiting matrix $\overline{P}$ in Theorem 2 indicates that the long-run probability of going from any nonabsorbing state to any other nonabsorbing state is always 0. That is, in the long run, all elements in an absorbing Markov chain end up in one of the absorbing states.
2. If the transition matrix for an absorbing Markov chain is not in standard form, it is still possible to find a limiting matrix (see Problems 49 and 50, Exercises 6.3). However, it is customary to use standard form when investigating the limiting behavior of an absorbing chain.

Now that we have developed the necessary tools for analyzing the long-run behavior of an absorbing Markov chain, we apply these tools to an earlier application (see Example 4, Section 6.1).

EXAMPLE 5 **Student Retention** The following transition diagram is for part-time students enrolled in a university MBA program:

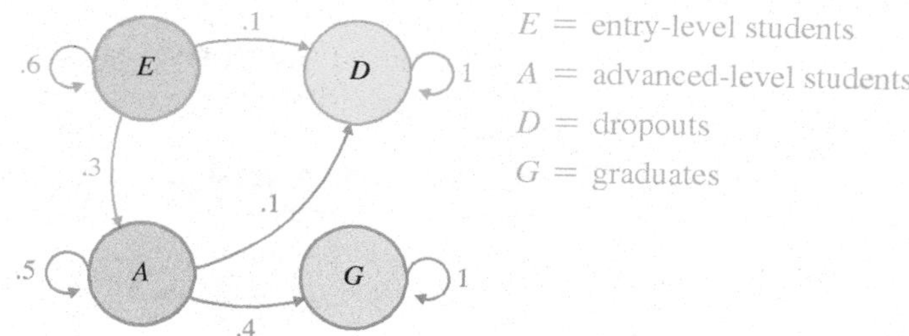

(A) In the long run, what percentage of entry-level students will graduate? What percentage of advanced-level students will not graduate?

(B) What is the average number of years that an entry-level student will remain in this program? An advanced-level student?

SOLUTION

(A) First, notice that this is an absorbing Markov chain with two absorbing states, state D and state G. A standard form for this absorbing chain is

$$P = \begin{array}{c} \\ D \\ G \\ E \\ A \end{array} \begin{array}{c} \begin{array}{cccc} D & G & E & A \end{array} \\ \left[\begin{array}{cc|cc} 1 & 0 & 0 & 0 \\ 0 & 1 & 0 & 0 \\ \hline .1 & 0 & .6 & .3 \\ .1 & .4 & 0 & .5 \end{array}\right] \end{array} \qquad \left[\begin{array}{c|c} I & 0 \\ \hline R & Q \end{array}\right]$$

The submatrices in this partition are

$$I = \begin{bmatrix} 1 & 0 \\ 0 & 1 \end{bmatrix} \quad 0 = \begin{bmatrix} 0 & 0 \\ 0 & 0 \end{bmatrix} \quad R = \begin{bmatrix} .1 & 0 \\ .1 & .4 \end{bmatrix} \quad Q = \begin{bmatrix} .6 & .3 \\ 0 & .5 \end{bmatrix}$$

Therefore,

$$F = (I - Q)^{-1} = \left(\begin{bmatrix} 1 & 0 \\ 0 & 1 \end{bmatrix} - \begin{bmatrix} .6 & .3 \\ 0 & .5 \end{bmatrix}\right)^{-1}$$

$$= \begin{bmatrix} .4 & -.3 \\ 0 & .5 \end{bmatrix}^{-1}$$

$$= \begin{bmatrix} 2.5 & 1.5 \\ 0 & 2 \end{bmatrix}$$

Use row operations to find this matrix inverse.

and

$$FR = \begin{bmatrix} 2.5 & 1.5 \\ 0 & 2 \end{bmatrix}\begin{bmatrix} .1 & 0 \\ .1 & .4 \end{bmatrix} = \begin{bmatrix} .4 & .6 \\ .2 & .8 \end{bmatrix}$$

The limiting matrix is

$$\overline{P} = \begin{array}{c} \\ D \\ G \\ E \\ A \end{array} \begin{array}{c} \begin{array}{cccc} D & G & E & A \end{array} \\ \begin{bmatrix} 1 & 0 & 0 & 0 \\ 0 & 1 & 0 & 0 \\ .4 & .6 & 0 & 0 \\ .2 & .8 & 0 & 0 \end{bmatrix} \end{array} \qquad \left[\begin{array}{c|c} I & 0 \\ \hline FR & 0 \end{array}\right]$$

From this limiting form, we see that in the long run 60% of the entry-level students will graduate and 20% of the advanced-level students will not graduate.

(B) The sum of the first-row entries of the fundamental matrix F is $2.5 + 1.5 = 4$. According to Theorem 3, this indicates that an entry-level student will spend an average of 4 years in the transient states E and A before reaching one of the absorbing states, D or G. The sum of the second-row entries of F is $0 + 2 = 2$. So an advanced-level student spends an average of 2 years in the program before either graduating or dropping out.

Matched Problem 5 Repeat Example 5 for the following transition diagram:

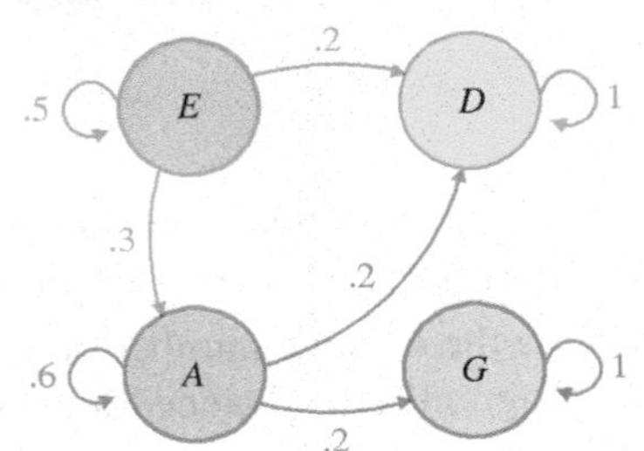

E = entry-level students
A = advanced-level students
D = dropouts
G = graduates

Exercises 6.3

A *In Problems 1–6, identify the absorbing states in the indicated transition matrix.*

1. $P = \begin{array}{c} \\ A \\ B \\ C \end{array}\begin{array}{c} \begin{array}{ccc} A & B & C \end{array} \\ \begin{bmatrix} .6 & .3 & .1 \\ 0 & 1 & 0 \\ 0 & 0 & 1 \end{bmatrix} \end{array}$

2. $P = \begin{array}{c} \\ A \\ B \\ C \end{array}\begin{array}{c} \begin{array}{ccc} A & B & C \end{array} \\ \begin{bmatrix} 0 & 1 & 0 \\ .3 & .2 & .5 \\ 0 & 0 & 1 \end{bmatrix} \end{array}$

3. $P = \begin{array}{c} \\ A \\ B \\ C \end{array}\begin{array}{c} \begin{array}{ccc} A & B & C \end{array} \\ \begin{bmatrix} 0 & 0 & 1 \\ 1 & 0 & 0 \\ 0 & 1 & 0 \end{bmatrix} \end{array}$

4. $P = \begin{array}{c} \\ A \\ B \\ C \end{array}\begin{array}{c} \begin{array}{ccc} A & B & C \end{array} \\ \begin{bmatrix} 1 & 0 & 0 \\ .3 & .4 & .3 \\ 0 & 0 & 1 \end{bmatrix} \end{array}$

5. $P = \begin{array}{c} \\ A \\ B \\ C \\ D \end{array}\begin{array}{c} \begin{array}{cccc} A & B & C & D \end{array} \\ \begin{bmatrix} 1 & 0 & 0 & 0 \\ 0 & 0 & 1 & 0 \\ .1 & .1 & .5 & .3 \\ 0 & 0 & 0 & 1 \end{bmatrix} \end{array}$

6. $P = \begin{array}{c} \\ A \\ B \\ C \\ D \end{array}\begin{array}{c} \begin{array}{cccc} A & B & C & D \end{array} \\ \begin{bmatrix} 0 & 1 & 0 & 0 \\ 1 & 0 & 0 & 0 \\ .1 & .2 & .3 & .4 \\ .7 & .1 & .1 & .1 \end{bmatrix} \end{array}$

In Problems 7–10, identify the absorbing states for each transition diagram, and determine whether or not the diagram represents an absorbing Markov chain.

7.

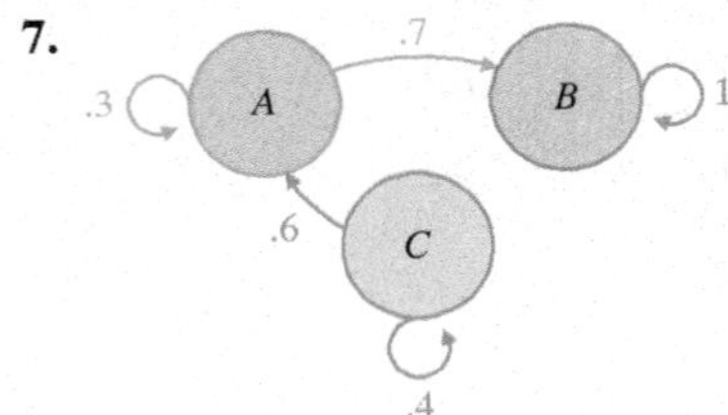

8.

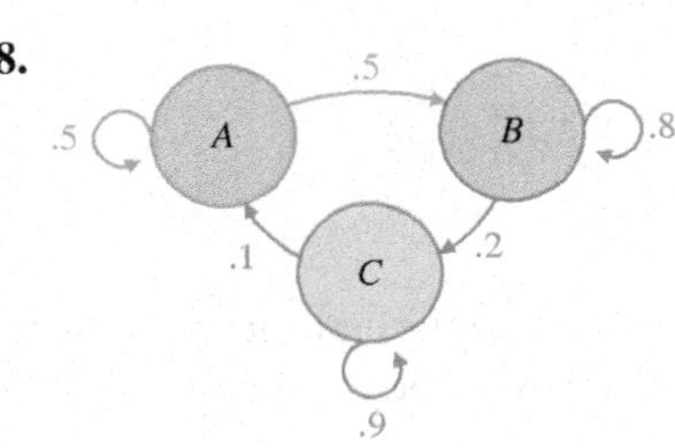

9.

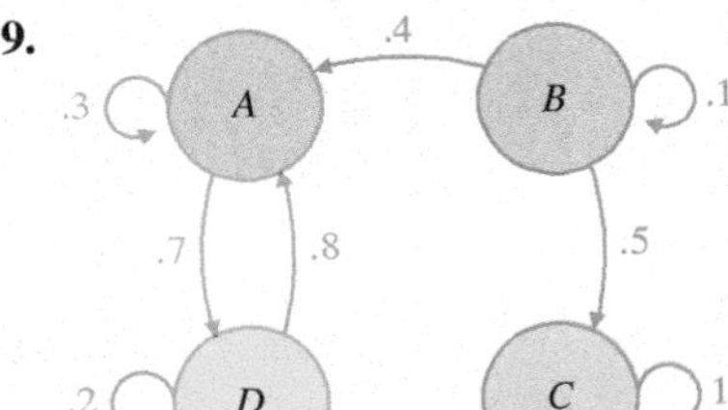

10.

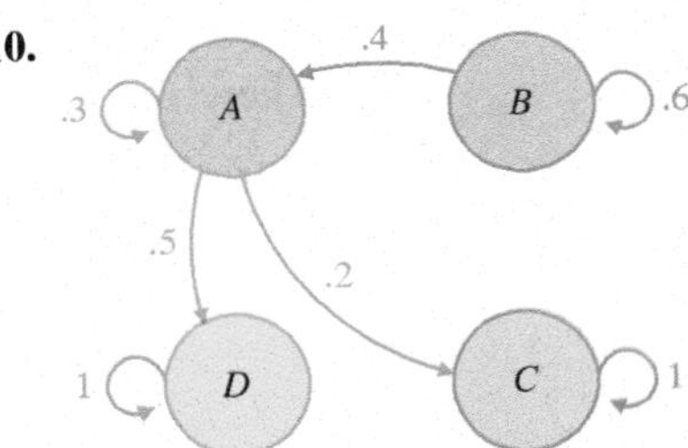

In Problems 11–20, could the given matrix be the transition matrix of an absorbing Markov chain?

11. $\begin{bmatrix} 0 & 1 \\ 1 & 0 \end{bmatrix}$

12. $\begin{bmatrix} 1 & 0 \\ 0 & 1 \end{bmatrix}$

13. $\begin{bmatrix} .3 & .7 \\ 0 & 1 \end{bmatrix}$

14. $\begin{bmatrix} .6 & .4 \\ 1 & 0 \end{bmatrix}$

15. $\begin{bmatrix} 1 & 0 & 0 \\ 0 & 1 & 0 \\ 0 & 0 & 1 \end{bmatrix}$

16. $\begin{bmatrix} 0 & 1 & 0 \\ 0 & 0 & 1 \\ 1 & 0 & 0 \end{bmatrix}$

17. $\begin{bmatrix} .9 & .1 & 0 \\ .1 & .9 & 0 \\ 0 & 0 & 1 \end{bmatrix}$

18. $\begin{bmatrix} .5 & .5 & 0 \\ .4 & .3 & .3 \\ 0 & 0 & 1 \end{bmatrix}$

19. $\begin{bmatrix} .9 & 0 & .1 \\ 0 & 1 & 0 \\ 0 & .2 & .8 \end{bmatrix}$ **20.** $\begin{bmatrix} 1 & 0 & 0 \\ 0 & 0 & 1 \\ 0 & .7 & .3 \end{bmatrix}$

B *In Problems 21–24, find a standard form for the absorbing Markov chain with the indicated transition diagram.*

21.

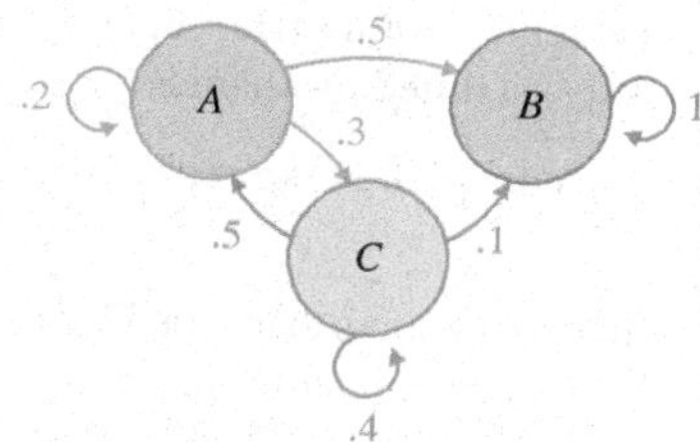

22.

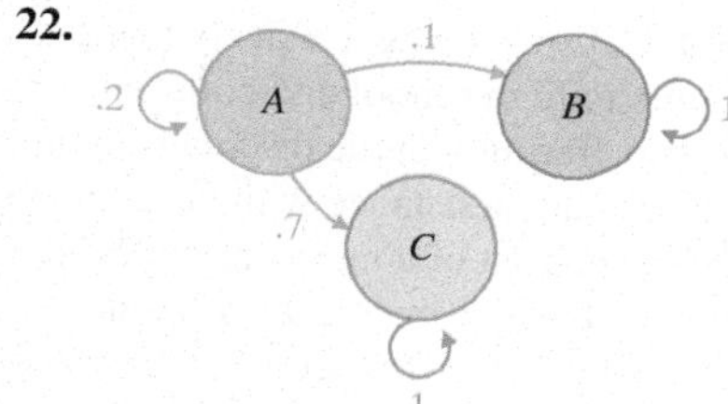

23.

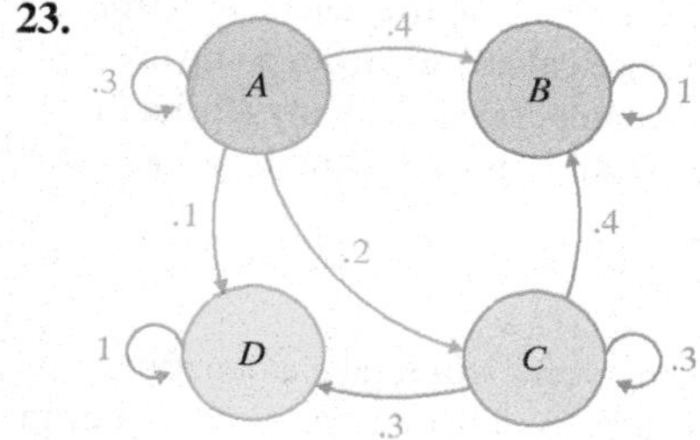

24.

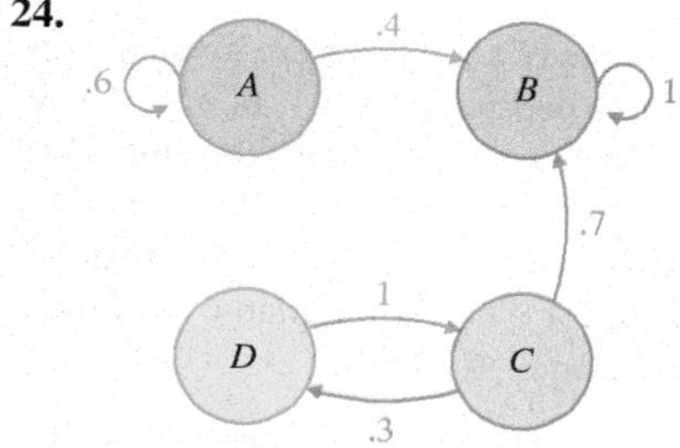

In Problems 25–28, find a standard form for the absorbing Markov chain with the indicated transition matrix.

25. $P = \begin{matrix} & A & B & C \\ A & .2 & .3 & .5 \\ B & 1 & 0 & 0 \\ C & 0 & 0 & 1 \end{matrix}$ **26.** $P = \begin{matrix} & A & B & C \\ A & 0 & 0 & 1 \\ B & 0 & 1 & 0 \\ C & .7 & .2 & .1 \end{matrix}$

27. $P = \begin{matrix} & A & B & C & D \\ A & .1 & .2 & .3 & .4 \\ B & 0 & 1 & 0 & 0 \\ C & .5 & .2 & .2 & .1 \\ D & 0 & 0 & 0 & 1 \end{matrix}$ **28.** $P = \begin{matrix} & A & B & C & D \\ A & 0 & .3 & .3 & .4 \\ B & 0 & 1 & 0 & 0 \\ C & 0 & 0 & 1 & 0 \\ D & .8 & .1 & .1 & 0 \end{matrix}$

In Problems 29–34, find the limiting matrix for the indicated standard form. Find the long-run probability of going from each nonabsorbing state to each absorbing state and the average number of trials needed to go from each nonabsorbing state to an absorbing state.

29. $P = \begin{matrix} & A & B & C \\ A & 1 & 0 & 0 \\ B & 0 & 1 & 0 \\ C & .1 & .4 & .5 \end{matrix}$ **30.** $P = \begin{matrix} & A & B & C \\ A & 1 & 0 & 0 \\ B & 0 & 1 & 0 \\ C & .3 & .2 & .5 \end{matrix}$

31. $P = \begin{matrix} & A & B & C \\ A & 1 & 0 & 0 \\ B & .2 & .6 & .2 \\ C & .4 & .2 & .4 \end{matrix}$ **32.** $P = \begin{matrix} & A & B & C \\ A & 1 & 0 & 0 \\ B & .1 & .6 & .3 \\ C & .2 & .2 & .6 \end{matrix}$

33. $P = \begin{matrix} & A & B & C & D \\ A & 1 & 0 & 0 & 0 \\ B & 0 & 1 & 0 & 0 \\ C & .1 & .2 & .6 & .1 \\ D & .2 & .2 & .3 & .3 \end{matrix}$ **34.** $P = \begin{matrix} & A & B & C & D \\ A & 1 & 0 & 0 & 0 \\ B & 0 & 1 & 0 & 0 \\ C & .1 & .1 & .7 & .1 \\ D & .3 & .1 & .4 & .2 \end{matrix}$

Problems 35–40 refer to the matrices in Problems 29–34. Use the limiting matrix $\overline{P}$ found for each transition matrix P in Problems 29–34 to determine the long-run behavior of the successive state matrices for the indicated initial-state matrices.

35. For matrix P from Problem 29 with
(A) $S_0 = [0 \quad 0 \quad 1]$ (B) $S_0 = [.2 \quad .5 \quad .3]$

36. For matrix P from Problem 30 with
(A) $S_0 = [0 \quad 0 \quad 1]$ (B) $S_0 = [.2 \quad .5 \quad .3]$

37. For matrix P from Problem 31 with
(A) $S_0 = [0 \quad 0 \quad 1]$ (B) $S_0 = [.2 \quad .5 \quad .3]$

38. For matrix P from Problem 32 with
(A) $S_0 = [0 \quad 0 \quad 1]$ (B) $S_0 = [.2 \quad .5 \quad .3]$

39. For matrix P from Problem 33 with
(A) $S_0 = [0 \quad 0 \quad 0 \quad 1]$ (B) $S_0 = [0 \quad 0 \quad 1 \quad 0]$
(C) $S_0 = [0 \quad 0 \quad .4 \quad .6]$ (D) $S_0 = [.1 \quad .2 \quad .3 \quad .4]$

40. For matrix P from Problem 34 with
(A) $S_0 = [0 \quad 0 \quad 0 \quad 1]$ (B) $S_0 = [0 \quad 0 \quad 1 \quad 0]$
(C) $S_0 = [0 \quad 0 \quad .4 \quad .6]$ (D) $S_0 = [.1 \quad .2 \quad .3 \quad .4]$

In Problems 41–48, discuss the validity of each statement. If the statement is always true, explain why. If not, give a counterexample.

41. If a Markov chain has an absorbing state, then it is an absorbing chain.

42. If a Markov chain has exactly two states and at least one absorbing state, then it is an absorbing chain.

43. If a Markov chain has exactly three states, one absorbing and two nonabsorbing, then it is an absorbing chain.

44. If a Markov chain has exactly three states, one nonabsorbing and two absorbing, then it is an absorbing chain.

45. If every state of a Markov chain is an absorbing state, then it is an absorbing chain.

46. If a Markov chain is absorbing, then it has a unique stationary matrix.

47. If a Markov chain is absorbing, then it is regular.

48. If a Markov chain is regular, then it is absorbing.

C **49.** The following matrix P is a nonstandard transition matrix for an absorbing Markov chain:

$$P = \begin{array}{c} \\ A \\ B \\ C \\ D \end{array} \begin{array}{c} \begin{array}{cccc} A & B & C & D \end{array} \\ \begin{bmatrix} .2 & .2 & .6 & 0 \\ 0 & 1 & 0 & 0 \\ .5 & .1 & 0 & .4 \\ 0 & 0 & 0 & 1 \end{bmatrix} \end{array}$$

To find a limiting matrix for P, follow the steps outlined below.

Step 1 Using a transition diagram, rearrange the columns and rows of P to produce a standard form for this chain.

Step 2 Find the limiting matrix for this standard form.

Step 3 Using a transition diagram, reverse the process used in Step 1 to produce a limiting matrix for the original matrix P.

50. Repeat Problem 49 for

$$P = \begin{array}{c} \\ A \\ B \\ C \\ D \end{array} \begin{array}{c} \begin{array}{cccc} A & B & C & D \end{array} \\ \begin{bmatrix} 1 & 0 & 0 & 0 \\ .3 & .6 & 0 & .1 \\ .2 & .3 & .5 & 0 \\ 0 & 0 & 0 & 1 \end{bmatrix} \end{array}$$

Applications

51. Loans. A credit union classifies car loans into one of four categories: the loan has been paid in full (F), the account is in good standing (G) with all payments up to date, the account is in arrears (A) with one or more missing payments, or the account has been classified as a bad debt (B) and sold to a collection agency. Past records indicate that each month 10% of the accounts in good standing pay the loan in full, 80% remain in good standing, and 10% become in arrears. Furthermore, 10% of the accounts in arrears are paid in full, 40% become accounts in good standing, 40% remain in arrears, and 10% are classified as bad debts.

(A) In the long run, what percentage of the accounts in arrears will pay their loan in full?

(B) In the long run, what percentage of the accounts in good standing will become bad debts?

(C) What is the average number of months that an account in arrears will remain in this system before it is either paid in full or classified as a bad debt?

52. Employee training. A chain of car muffler and brake repair shops maintains a training program for its mechanics. All new mechanics begin training in muffler repairs. Every 3 months, the performance of each mechanic is reviewed. Past records indicate that after each quarterly review, 30% of the muffler repair trainees are rated as qualified to repair mufflers and begin training in brake repairs, 20% are terminated for unsatisfactory performance, and the remainder continue as muffler repair trainees. Also, 30% of the brake repair trainees are rated as fully qualified mechanics requiring no further training, 10% are terminated for unsatisfactory performance, and the remainder continue as brake repair trainees.

(A) In the long run, what percentage of muffler repair trainees will become fully qualified mechanics?

(B) In the long run, what percentage of brake repair trainees will be terminated?

(C) What is the average number of quarters that a muffler repair trainee will remain in the training program before being either terminated or promoted to fully qualified mechanic?

53. Marketing. Three electronics firms are aggressively marketing their graphing calculators to high school and college mathematics departments by offering volume discounts, complimentary display equipment, and assistance with curriculum development. Due to the amount of equipment involved and the necessary curriculum changes, once a department decides to use a particular calculator in their courses, they never switch to another brand or stop using calculators. Each year, 6% of the departments decide to use calculators from company A, 3% decide to use calculators from company B, 11% decide to use calculators from company C, and the remainder decide not to use any calculators in their courses.

(A) In the long run, what is the market share of each company?

(B) On average, how many years will it take a department to decide to use calculators from one of these companies in their courses?

54. Pensions. Once a year company employees are given the opportunity to join one of three pension plans: A, B, or C. Once an employee decides to join one of these plans, the employee cannot drop the plan or switch to another plan. Past records indicate that each year 4% of employees elect to join plan A, 14% elect to join plan B, 7% elect to join plan C, and the remainder do not join any plan.

(A) In the long run, what percentage of the employees will elect to join plan A? Plan B? Plan C?

(B) On average, how many years will it take an employee to decide to join a plan?

55. Medicine. After bypass surgery, patients are placed in an intensive care unit (ICU) until their condition stabilizes. Then they are transferred to a cardiac care ward (CCW), where they remain until they are released from the hospital. In a particular metropolitan area, a study of hospital records produced the following data: each day 2% of the patients in the ICU died, 52% were transferred to the CCW, and the remainder stayed in the ICU. Furthermore, each day 4% of the patients in the CCW developed complications and were returned to the ICU, 1% died while in the CCW, 22% were released from the hospital, and the remainder stayed in the CCW.

(A) In the long run, what percentage of the patients in the ICU are released from the hospital?

(B) In the long run, what percentage of the patients in the CCW die without ever being released from the hospital?

(C) What is the average number of days that a patient in the ICU will stay in the hospital?

56. Medicine. The study discussed in Problem 55 also produced the following data for patients who underwent aortic valve replacements: each day 2% of the patients in the ICU died, 60% were transferred to the CCW, and the remainder stayed in the ICU. Furthermore, each day 5% of the patients in the CCW developed complications and were returned to the ICU, 1% died while in the CCW, 19% were released from the hospital, and the remainder stayed in the CCW.

(A) In the long run, what percentage of the patients in the CCW are released from the hospital?

(B) In the long run, what percentage of the patients in the ICU die without ever being released from the hospital?

(C) What is the average number of days a patient in the CCW will stay in the hospital?

57. Psychology. A rat is placed in room F or room B of the maze shown in the figure. The rat wanders from room to room until it enters one of the rooms containing food, L or R. Assume that the rat chooses an exit from a room at random and that once it enters a room with food it never leaves.

(A) What is the long-run probability that a rat placed in room B ends up in room R?

(B) What is the average number of exits that a rat placed in room B will choose until it finds food?

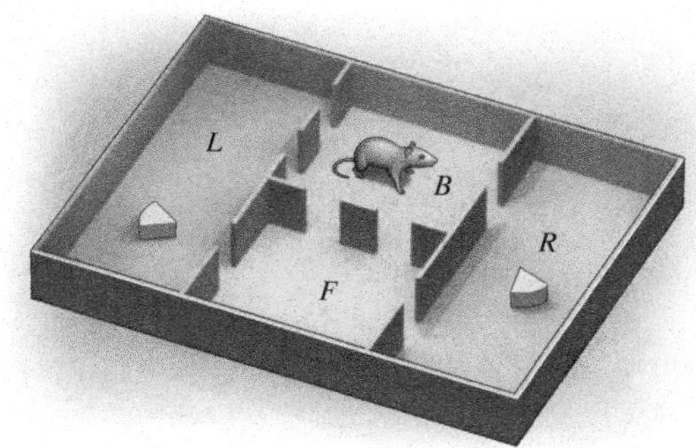

Figure for 67 and 68

58. Psychology. Repeat Problem 57 if the exit from room B to room R is blocked.

Answers to Matched Problems

1. (A) State B is absorbing.
   (B) State C is absorbing.
2. (A) Absorbing Markov chain
   (B) Not an absorbing Markov chain
3. (A)

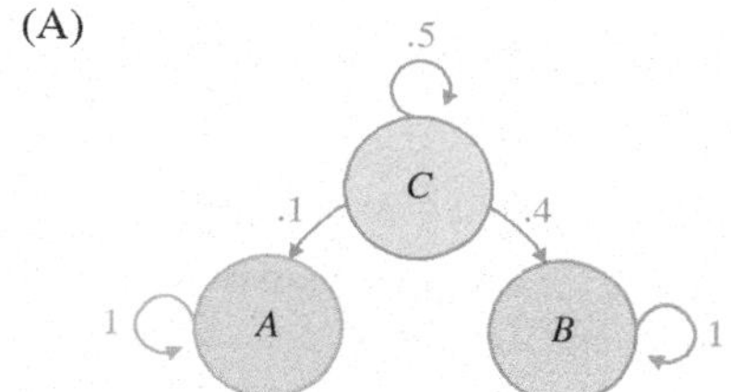

(B)
$$P = \begin{matrix} & \begin{matrix} A & B & C \end{matrix} \\ \begin{matrix} A \\ B \\ C \end{matrix} & \begin{bmatrix} 1 & 0 & 0 \\ 0 & 1 & 0 \\ .1 & .4 & .5 \end{bmatrix} \end{matrix}$$

(C) Company A will purchase 20% of the farms, and company B will purchase 80%.
(D) Company A will purchase 60% of the farms, and company B will purchase 40%.

4. (A)
$$\overline{P} = \begin{matrix} & \begin{matrix} A & B & C \end{matrix} \\ \begin{matrix} A \\ B \\ C \end{matrix} & \begin{bmatrix} 1 & 0 & 0 \\ 0 & 1 & 0 \\ .2 & .8 & 0 \end{bmatrix} \end{matrix}$$

(B) $[.2 \quad .8 \quad 0]$
(C) $[.6 \quad .4 \quad 0]$

5. (A) Thirty percent of entry-level students will graduate; 50% of advanced-level students will not graduate.
   (B) An entry-level student will spend an average of 3.5 years in the program; an advanced-level student will spend an average of 2.5 years in the program.

Chapter 6 Summary and Review

Important Terms, Symbols, and Concepts

6.1 Properties of Markov Chains

EXAMPLES

- The progression of a system through a sequence of states is called a **stochastic process** if chance elements are involved in the transition from one state to the next.
- A **transition diagram** or **transition probability matrix** can be used to represent the probabilities of moving from one state to another. If those probabilities do not change with time, the stochastic process is called a **Markov chain**.

- If a Markov chain has n states, then the entry s_{ki} of the **kth-state matrix**

$$S_k = [s_{k1} \quad s_{k2} \quad \cdots \quad s_{kn}]$$

gives the probability of being in state i after the kth trial. The sum of the entries in S_k is 1. Ex. 1, p. 184 Ex. 2, p. 185

- The entry $p_{i,j}$ of the $n \times n$ **transition matrix** P gives the probability of moving from state i to state j on the next trial. The sum of the entries in each row of P is 1. Ex. 4, p. 186
- If S_0 is an initial-state matrix for a Markov chain, then $S_k = S_0P^k$ (Theorem 1, page 185).

6.2 Regular Markov Chains

- A transition matrix P is **regular** if some power of P has only positive entries. Ex. 1, p. 193
- A Markov chain is a **regular Markov chain** if its transition matrix is regular.
- A state matrix S is **stationary** if $SP = S$. Ex. 2, p. 194
- The state matrices for a regular Markov chain approach a unique stationary matrix S (Theorem 1, page 194). Ex. 3, p. 195
- If P is the transition matrix for a regular Markov chain, then the matrices P^k approach a **limiting matrix** $\overline{P}$, where each row of $\overline{P}$ is equal to the unique stationary matrix S (Theorem 1, page 194). Ex. 4, p. 196

6.3 Absorbing Markov Chains

- A state in a Markov chain is an **absorbing state** if once the state is entered it is impossible to leave. A state is absorbing if and only if its row in the transition matrix has a 1 on the main diagonal and 0's elsewhere. Ex. 1, p. 201
- A Markov chain is an **absorbing Markov chain** if there is at least one absorbing state and it is possible to go from each nonabsorbing state to at least one absorbing state in a finite number of steps. Ex. 2, p. 202
- A transition matrix for an absorbing Markov chain is in **standard form** if the rows and columns are labeled so that all the absorbing states precede all the nonabsorbing states.
- If a standard form P for an absorbing Markov chain is partitioned as Ex. 3, p. 204 Ex. 4, p. 207

$$P = \left[\begin{array}{c|c} I & 0 \\ \hline R & Q \end{array}\right]$$

then P^k approaches a limiting matrix $\overline{P}$ as k increases, where

$$\overline{P} = \left[\begin{array}{c|c} I & 0 \\ \hline FR & 0 \end{array}\right]$$

The matrix $F = (I - Q)^{-1}$, where I is the identity matrix of the same size as Q, is called the **fundamental matrix** for P (Theorem 2, page 206). Ex. 5, p. 209

- The entry in row i and column j of $\overline{P}$ is the long-run probability of going from state i to state j. The sum of the entries in each row of F is the average number of trials that it will take to go from each nonabsorbing state to some absorbing state (Theorem 3, page 208).

Review Exercises

Work through all the problems in this chapter review and check your answers in the back of the book. Answers to all review problems are there along with section numbers in italics to indicate where each type of problem is discussed. Where weaknesses show up, review appropriate sections in the text.

A **1.** Given the transition matrix P and initial-state matrix S_0 shown below, find S_1 and S_2 and explain what each represents:

$$P = \begin{array}{c} \\ A \\ B \end{array}\begin{array}{c} \begin{array}{cc} A & B \end{array} \\ \begin{bmatrix} .6 & .4 \\ .2 & .8 \end{bmatrix} \end{array} \qquad S_0 = [.3 \quad .7]$$

In Problems 2–6, P is a transition matrix for a Markov chain. Identify any absorbing states and classify the chain as regular, absorbing, or neither.

2. $P = \begin{array}{c} \\ A \\ B \end{array}\begin{array}{c} \begin{array}{cc} A & B \end{array} \\ \begin{bmatrix} 1 & 0 \\ .7 & .3 \end{bmatrix} \end{array}$

3. $P = \begin{array}{c} \\ A \\ B \end{array}\begin{array}{c} \begin{array}{cc} A & B \end{array} \\ \begin{bmatrix} 0 & 1 \\ .7 & .3 \end{bmatrix} \end{array}$

4. $P = \begin{array}{c} \\ A \\ B \end{array}\begin{array}{c} \begin{array}{cc} A & B \end{array} \\ \begin{bmatrix} 0 & 1 \\ 1 & 0 \end{bmatrix} \end{array}$

5. $P = \begin{array}{c} \\ A \\ B \\ C \end{array}\begin{array}{c} \begin{array}{ccc} A & B & C \end{array} \\ \begin{bmatrix} .8 & 0 & .2 \\ 0 & 1 & 0 \\ 0 & 0 & 1 \end{bmatrix} \end{array}$

6. $P = \begin{array}{c} \\ A \\ B \\ C \\ D \end{array} \begin{array}{c} \begin{array}{cccc} A & B & C & D \end{array} \\ \begin{bmatrix} 1 & 0 & 0 & 0 \\ 0 & 1 & 0 & 0 \\ 0 & 0 & .3 & .7 \\ 0 & 0 & .6 & .4 \end{bmatrix} \end{array}$

In Problems 7–10, write a transition matrix for the transition diagram indicated, identify any absorbing states, and classify each Markov chain as regular, absorbing, or neither.

7.

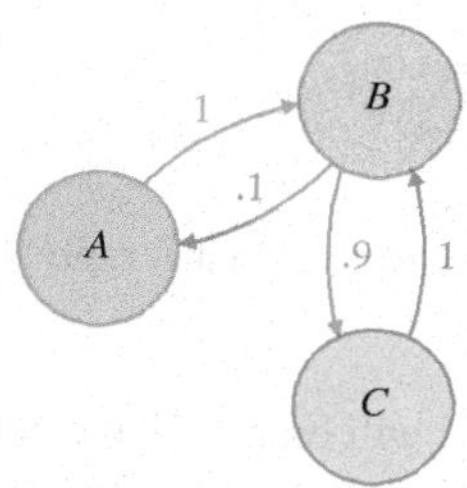

8.

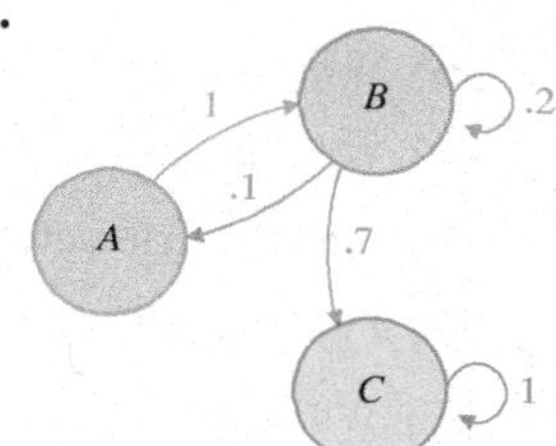

9.

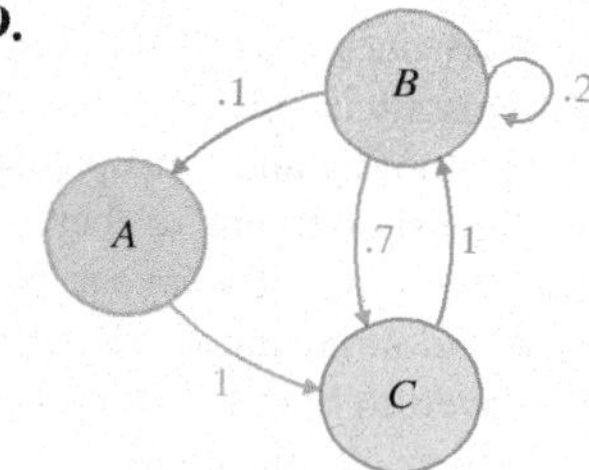

10.

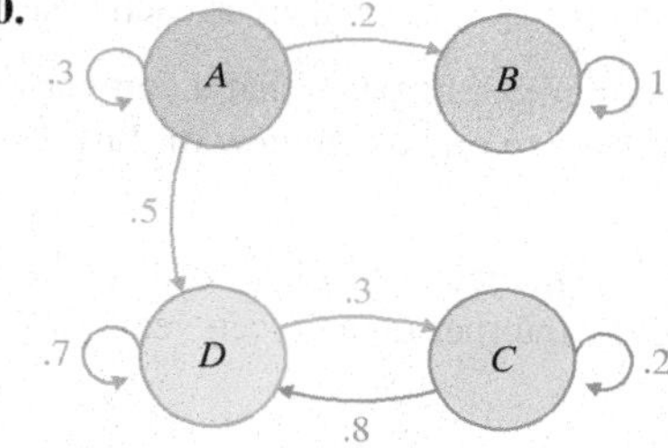

11. A Markov chain has three states, A, B, and C. The probability of going from state A to state B in one trial is .2, the probability of going from state A to state C in one trial is .5, the probability of going from state B to state A in one trial is .8, the probability of going from state B to state C in one trial is .2, the probability of going from state C to state A in one trial is .1, and the probability of going from state C to state B in one trial is .3. Draw a transition diagram and write a transition matrix for this chain.

12. Given the transition matrix

$$P = \begin{array}{c} \\ A \\ B \end{array} \begin{array}{c} \begin{array}{cc} A & B \end{array} \\ \begin{bmatrix} .4 & .6 \\ .9 & .1 \end{bmatrix} \end{array}$$

find the probability of

(A) Going from state A to state B in two trials

(B) Going from state B to state A in three trials

B *In Problems 13 and 14, solve the equation $SP = S$ to find the stationary matrix S and the limiting matrix $\overline{P}$.*

13. $P = \begin{array}{c} \\ A \\ B \end{array} \begin{array}{c} \begin{array}{cc} A & B \end{array} \\ \begin{bmatrix} .4 & .6 \\ .2 & .8 \end{bmatrix} \end{array}$

14. $P = \begin{array}{c} \\ A \\ B \\ C \end{array} \begin{array}{c} \begin{array}{ccc} A & B & C \end{array} \\ \begin{bmatrix} .4 & .6 & 0 \\ .5 & .3 & .2 \\ 0 & .8 & .2 \end{bmatrix} \end{array}$

In Problems 15 and 16, find the limiting matrix for the indicated standard form. Find the long-run probability of going from each nonabsorbing state to each absorbing state and the average number of trials needed to go from each nonabsorbing state to an absorbing state.

15. $P = \begin{array}{c} \\ A \\ B \\ C \end{array} \begin{array}{c} \begin{array}{ccc} A & B & C \end{array} \\ \begin{bmatrix} 1 & 0 & 0 \\ 0 & 1 & 0 \\ .3 & .1 & .6 \end{bmatrix} \end{array}$

16. $P = \begin{array}{c} \\ A \\ B \\ C \\ D \end{array} \begin{array}{c} \begin{array}{cccc} A & B & C & D \end{array} \\ \begin{bmatrix} 1 & 0 & 0 & 0 \\ 0 & 1 & 0 & 0 \\ .1 & .5 & .2 & .2 \\ .1 & .1 & .4 & .4 \end{bmatrix} \end{array}$

In Problems 17–20, use a graphing calculator to approximate the limiting matrix for the indicated transition matrix.

17. Matrix P from Problem 13

18. Matrix P from Problem 14

19. Matrix P from Problem 15

20. Matrix P from Problem 16

21. Find a standard form for the absorbing Markov chain with transition matrix

$$P = \begin{array}{c} \\ A \\ B \\ C \\ D \end{array} \begin{array}{c} \begin{array}{cccc} A & B & C & D \end{array} \\ \begin{bmatrix} .6 & .1 & .2 & .1 \\ 0 & 1 & 0 & 0 \\ .3 & .2 & .3 & .2 \\ 0 & 0 & 0 & 1 \end{bmatrix} \end{array}$$

In Problems 22 and 23, determine the long-run behavior of the successive state matrices for the indicated transition matrix and initial-state matrices.

22. $P = \begin{array}{c} \\ A \\ B \\ C \end{array} \begin{array}{c} \begin{array}{ccc} A & B & C \end{array} \\ \begin{bmatrix} 0 & 1 & 0 \\ 0 & 0 & 1 \\ .2 & .6 & .2 \end{bmatrix} \end{array}$

(A) $S_0 = [0 \quad 0 \quad 1]$

(B) $S_0 = [.5 \quad .3 \quad .2]$

23. $P = \begin{array}{c} \\ A \\ B \\ C \end{array} \begin{array}{c} \begin{array}{ccc} A & B & C \end{array} \\ \begin{bmatrix} 1 & 0 & 0 \\ 0 & 1 & 0 \\ .2 & .6 & .2 \end{bmatrix} \end{array}$

(A) $S_0 = [0 \quad 0 \quad 1]$

(B) $S_0 = [.5 \quad .3 \quad .2]$

24. Let P be a 2×2 transition matrix for a Markov chain. Can P be regular if two of its entries are 0? Explain.

25. Let P be a 3×3 transition matrix for a Markov chain. Can P be regular if three of its entries are 0? If four of its entries are 0? Explain.

C **26.** A red urn contains 2 red marbles, 1 blue marble, and 1 green marble. A blue urn contains 1 red marble, 3 blue marbles, and 1 green marble. A green urn contains 6 red marbles, 3 blue marbles, and 1 green marble. A marble is selected from an urn, the color is noted, and the marble is returned to the urn from which it was drawn. The next marble is drawn from the urn whose color is the same as the marble just drawn. This is a Markov process with three states: draw from the red urn, draw from the blue urn, or draw from the green urn.

(A) Draw a transition diagram for this process.

(B) Write the transition matrix P.

(C) Determine whether this chain is regular, absorbing, or neither.

(D) Find the limiting matrix $\overline{P}$, if it exists, and describe the long-run behavior of this process.

27. Repeat Problem 26 if the blue and green marbles are removed from the red urn.

28. Show that $S = [x \quad y \quad z \quad 0]$, where $0 \le x \le 1$, $0 \le y \le 1$, $0 \le z \le 1$, and $x + y + z = 1$, is a stationary matrix for the transition matrix

$$P = \begin{matrix} & \begin{matrix} A & B & C & D \end{matrix} \\ \begin{matrix} A \\ B \\ C \\ D \end{matrix} & \begin{bmatrix} 1 & 0 & 0 & 0 \\ 0 & 1 & 0 & 0 \\ 0 & 0 & 1 & 0 \\ .1 & .3 & .4 & .2 \end{bmatrix} \end{matrix}$$

Discuss the generalization of this result to any absorbing chain with three absorbing states and one nonabsorbing state.

29. Give an example of a transition matrix for a Markov chain that has no limiting matrix.

30. Give an example of a transition matrix for an absorbing Markov chain that has two different stationary matrices.

31. Give an example of a transition matrix for a regular Markov chain for which $[.3 \quad .1 \quad .6]$ is a stationary matrix.

32. Give an example of a transition matrix for an absorbing Markov chain for which $[.3 \quad .1 \quad .6]$ is a stationary matrix.

33. Explain why an absorbing Markov chain that has more than one state is not regular.

34. Explain why a regular Markov chain that has more than one state is not absorbing.

35. A Markov chain has transition matrix

$$P = \begin{bmatrix} .4 & .6 \\ .2 & .8 \end{bmatrix}$$

For $S = [.3 \quad .9]$, calculate SP. Is S a stationary matrix? Explain.

In Problems 36 and 37, use a graphing calculator to approximate the entries (to three decimal places) of the limiting matrix, if it exists, of the indicated transition matrix.

36. $$P = \begin{matrix} & \begin{matrix} A & B & C & D \end{matrix} \\ \begin{matrix} A \\ B \\ C \\ D \end{matrix} & \begin{bmatrix} .2 & .3 & .1 & .4 \\ 0 & 0 & 1 & 0 \\ 0 & .8 & 0 & .2 \\ 0 & 0 & 1 & 0 \end{bmatrix} \end{matrix}$$

37. $$P = \begin{matrix} & \begin{matrix} A & B & C & D \end{matrix} \\ \begin{matrix} A \\ B \\ C \\ D \end{matrix} & \begin{bmatrix} .1 & 0 & .3 & .6 \\ .2 & .4 & .1 & .3 \\ .3 & .5 & 0 & .2 \\ .9 & .1 & 0 & 0 \end{bmatrix} \end{matrix}$$

Applications

38. Product switching. A company's brand (X) has 20% of the market. A market research firm finds that if a person uses brand X, the probability is .7 that he or she will buy it next time. On the other hand, if a person does not use brand X (represented by X'), the probability is .5 that he or she will switch to brand X next time.

(A) Draw a transition diagram.

(B) Write a transition matrix.

(C) Write the initial-state matrix.

(D) Find the first-state matrix and explain what it represents.

(E) Find the stationary matrix.

(F) What percentage of the market will brand X have in the long run if the transition matrix does not change?

39. Marketing. Recent technological advances have led to the development of three new milling machines: brand A, brand B, and brand C. Due to the extensive retooling and startup costs, once a company converts its machine shop to one of these new machines, it never switches to another brand. Each year, 6% of the machine shops convert to brand A machines, 8% convert to brand B machines, 11% convert to brand C machines, and the remainder continue to use their old machines.

(A) In the long run, what is the market share of each brand?

(B) What is the average number of years that a company waits before converting to one of the new milling machines?

40. Internet. Table 1 gives the percentage of U.S. adults who at least occasionally used the Internet in the given year.

Table 1

Year	Percent
1995	14
2000	49
2005	68
2010	79

Source: Pew Internet & American Life Project Surveys

The following transition matrix P is proposed as a model for the data, where I represents the population of Internet users.

$$\begin{matrix} & & \text{Five years later} \\ & & \begin{matrix} I & I' \end{matrix} \\ \text{Current year} & \begin{matrix} I \\ I' \end{matrix} & \begin{bmatrix} .95 & .05 \\ .40 & .60 \end{bmatrix} \end{matrix} = P$$

(A) Let $S_0 = [.14 \quad .86]$ and find S_1, S_2, and S_3. Compute both matrices exactly and then round entries to two decimal places.

(B) Construct a new table comparing the results from part (A) with the data in Table 1.

(C) According to this transition matrix, what percentage of the adult U.S. population will use the Internet in the long run?

41. Employee training. In order to become a fellow of the Society of Actuaries, a person must pass a series of ten examinations. Passage of the first two preliminary exams is a prerequisite for employment as a trainee in the actuarial department of a large insurance company. Each year, 15% of the trainees complete the next three exams and become associates of the Society of Actuaries, 5% leave the company, never to return, and the remainder continue as trainees. Furthermore, each year, 17% of the associates complete the remaining five exams and become fellows of the Society of Actuaries, 3% leave the company, never to return, and the remainder continue as associates.

(A) In the long run, what percentage of the trainees will become fellows?

(B) In the long run, what percentage of the associates will leave the company?

(C) What is the average number of years that a trainee remains in this program before either becoming a fellow or being discharged?

42. Genetics. A given plant species has red, pink, or white flowers according to the genotypes RR, RW, and WW, respectively. If each of these genotypes is crossed with a red-flowering plant, the transition matrix is

$$\begin{array}{ll} & \quad\text{Next generation} \\ & \begin{array}{ccc} \textit{Red} & \textit{Pin} & \textit{White} \end{array} \\ \text{This generation} \quad \begin{array}{l} \textit{Red} \\ \textit{Pink} \\ \textit{White} \end{array} & \begin{bmatrix} 1 & 0 & 0 \\ .5 & .5 & 0 \\ 0 & 1 & 0 \end{bmatrix} \end{array}$$

If each generation of the plant is crossed only with red plants to produce the next generation, show that eventually all the flowers produced by the plants will be red. (Find the limiting matrix.)

43. Smoking. Table 2 gives the percentage of U.S. adults who were smokers in the given year.

Table 2

Year	Percent
1985	30.1
1995	24.7
2005	20.9
2010	19.3

Source: American Lung Association

The following transition matrix P is proposed as a model for the data, where S represents the population of U.S. adult smokers.

$$\begin{array}{ll} & \quad\text{Five years later} \\ & \quad\; S \qquad S' \\ \text{Current year} \quad \begin{array}{l} S \\ S' \end{array} & \begin{bmatrix} .74 & .26 \\ .03 & .97 \end{bmatrix} = P \end{array}$$

(A) Let $S_0 = [.301 \quad .699]$, and find S_1, S_2, and S_3. Compute the matrices exactly and then round entries to three decimal places.

(B) Construct a new table comparing the results from part (A) with the data in Table 2.

(C) According to this transition matrix, what percentage of the adult U.S. population will be smokers in the long run?

Selected Answers

CHAPTER 1

Exercises 1.1, page 7

1. (a) $\{5, 6, 7\}$ **(b)** $\{1, 2, 3, 4, 5, 7\}$ **(c)** $\{1, 3\}$ **(d)** $\{5, 7\}$ **3. (a)** $\{a, b, c, e, i, o, u\}$ **(b)** $\{a\}$ **(c)** $\varnothing$ **(d)** $\{b, c\}$ **5.** $\varnothing$, $\{1\}$, $\{2\}$, $\{1, 2\}$ **7. (a)** {all freshman college students who like basketball} **(b)** {all college students who do not like basketball} **(c)** {all college students who are neither freshmen nor like basketball} **(d)** {all college students who are either freshmen or like basketball} **9. (a)** $S = \{1999, 2003, 2006, 2010, 2013\}$ **(b)** $T = \{1996, 1997, 1998, 1999, 2003, 2009, 2013\}$ **(c)** $S \cap T = \{1999, 2003, 2013\}$ **(d)** $S \cup T = \{1996, 1997, 1998, 1999, 2003, 2006, 2009, 2010, 2013\}$ **(e)** $S' \cap T = \{1996, 1997, 1998, 2009\}$ **(f)** $S \cap T' = \{2006, 2010\}$ **11.** Between 1996 and 2015, there were only two years in which the Standard and Poor's index increased by 2% or more during the first five days and did not increase by 16% or more for the entire year. **13. (a)** $\{e, f\}$ **(b)** $\{a, b, c, d, e, f\}$ **(c)** $\varnothing$ **(d)** $\{a, b\}$ **(e)** $\varnothing$ **(f)** $\{a, b, d, e, f\}$ **(g)** $\{a, b, c\}$ **(h)** $\{a, b\}$ **(i)** $\{d\}$ **15.** S **17.** U **19.** $\varnothing$ **21.** $L \cup T$ **23.** $L \cap P$ **25.** $P \cap L \cap T$ **27.** S' **29.** $S \cup A \cup D$ **31.** $(A \cap S)' \cap D$ **33.** {students at Mount College who are younger than 35} **35.** {people who are both students and teachers at Mount College} **37.** {people at Mount College who are students or are at most 35} **39.** {people at Mount College who are at least 35} **41.** V' **43.** $V \cap (C \cup S)'$ **45.** $(V \cup C)'$ **47. (a)** $\{B, C, D, E\}$ **(b)** $\{C, D, E, F\}$ **(c)** $\{A, D, E, F\}$ **(d)** $\{A, C, D, E, F\}$ **(e)** $\{A, F\}$ **(f)** $\{D, E\}$ **49.** 8 ways: no toppings; peppers; onions; mushrooms; peppers and onions; peppers and mushrooms; onions and mushrooms; all three toppings **51.** Possible answer: $\{2\}$ **53.** $S \subseteq T$ **55.** True **57.** True **59.** False **61.** True

Exercises 1.2, page 13

1. 6 **3.** 0 **5.** 8 **7.** $S \subseteq T$ **9.** 11 million **11.** 10 **13.** 452

15. **17.** **19.** **21.** **23.** **25.** **27.** **29.** **31.** **33.** **35.** **37.**

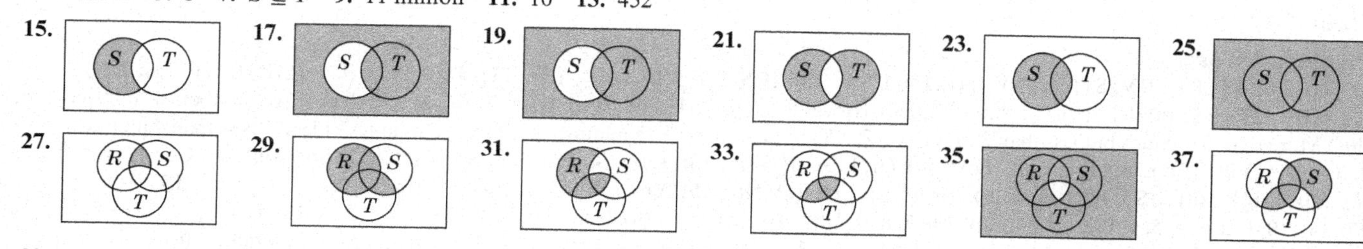

39. $S' \cup T'$ **41.** $S \cap T'$ **43.** U **45.** S' **47.** $R \cap T$ **49.** $R' \cap S \cap T$ **51.** $T \cup (R \cap S')$ **53.** $(R \cap S \cap T) \cup (R' \cap S' \cap T')$ **55.** Everyone who is not a citizen or is both over the age of 18 and employed **57.** Everyone over the age of 18 who is unemployed **59.** Noncitizens who are 5 years of age or older

Exercises 1.3, page 18

1. 11 **3.** 46 **5.** 11 **7.** 75 **9.** 30

11. **13.** **15.** **17.** **19.** **21.** **23.** 25 **25.** 4; 2; 1 **27.** 55 **29.** 5 **31. (a)**

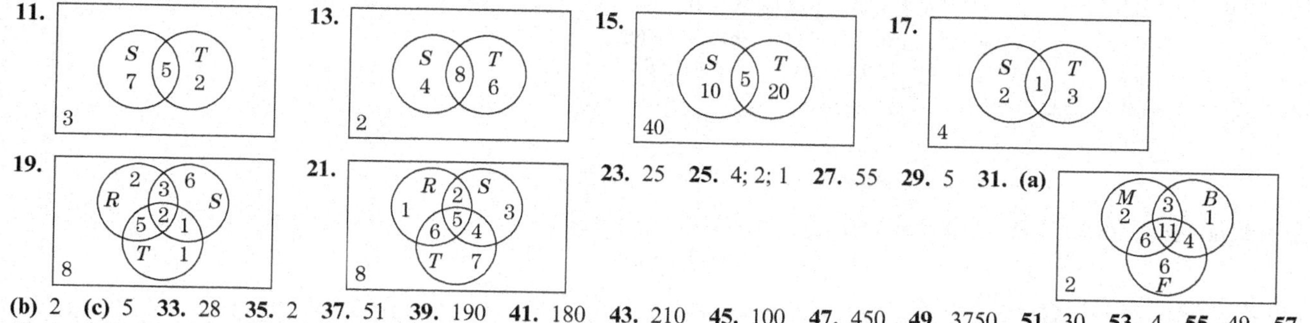

(b) 2 **(c)** 5 **33.** 28 **35.** 2 **37.** 51 **39.** 190 **41.** 180 **43.** 210 **45.** 100 **47.** 450 **49.** 3750 **51.** 30 **53.** 4 **55.** 49 **57.** 29 **59.** 26 **61.** 90 **63.** 6 **65.** 140 **67.** 30 **69.** 30 **71.** 3

Exercises 1.4, page 24

1. $4 \cdot 2 = 8$ **3.** $3 \cdot 2 = 6$ **5.** $44 \cdot 43 \cdot 42 = 79{,}464$ **7.** $20 \cdot 19 \cdot 18 = 6840$ **9.** 30, since $30 \cdot 29 = 870$ **11. (a)** $8 \cdot 7 \cdot 6 \cdot 5 \cdot 4 \cdot 3 \cdot 2 \cdot 1 = 40{,}320$ **(b)** $5 \cdot 4 \cdot 3 \cdot 2 \cdot 1 \cdot 3 \cdot 2 \cdot 1 = 720$ **13.** $4 \cdot 3 \cdot 2 \cdot 1 = 24$ **15.** $2 \cdot 3 = 6$ **17.** $3 \cdot 12 \cdot 10 \cdot 10 \cdot 10 \cdot 10 = 360{,}000$ **19.** $10^9 - 1 = 999{,}999{,}999$ **21.** $8 \cdot 2 \cdot 10 = 160$ **23.** $9 \cdot 10 \cdot 10 \cdot 1 \cdot 1 = 900$ **25.** $26 \cdot 26 \cdot 1 \cdot 1 = 676$ **27.** $15 \cdot 15 = 225$ **29.** $3200 \cdot 2 \cdot 24 \cdot 52 = 7{,}987{,}200$ **31.** Since $26 \cdot 26 \cdot 26 = 17{,}576 < 20{,}000$, two students must have the same initials. **33.** $7 \cdot 5 = 35$ **35.** $5 \cdot 4 = 20$ **37.** $2^6 = 64$ **39.** $2^5 = 32$ **41.** $4^{10} = 1{,}048{,}576$ **43.** $10^5 = 100{,}000$ **45.** $8 \cdot 7 \cdot 6 \cdot 5 \cdot 4 \cdot 3 \cdot 2 \cdot 1 = 40{,}320$; one week **47.** $6 \cdot 7 \cdot 4 = 168$ days or 24 weeks **49.** $5 \cdot 11 \cdot (7 \cdot 2 + 1) \cdot 10 = 8250$ **51.** $2^4 = 16$ **53.** $2 \cdot 38 \cdot 38 = 2888$ **55. (a)** $9 \cdot 8 \cdot 7 \cdot 6 \cdot 5 \cdot 4 \cdot 3 \cdot 2 \cdot 1 = 362{,}880$ **(b)** $8 \cdot 7 \cdot 6 \cdot 5 \cdot 4 \cdot 3 \cdot 2 \cdot 1 \cdot 1 = 40{,}320$ **(c)** $1 \cdot 6 \cdot 5 \cdot 4 \cdot 3 \cdot 2 \cdot 1 \cdot 1 \cdot 1 = 720$ **57.** $\frac{10 \cdot 9}{2} + 10 \cdot 10 = 145$ **59.** $4 \cdot 3 \cdot 3 \cdot 3 \cdot 3 \cdot 3 = 972$ **61.** $7 \cdot 4 \cdot 2^6 = 1792$; $8 \cdot 5 \cdot 3^6 = 29{,}160$ **63.** $2^4 = 16$

Exercises 1.5, page 31
1. 12 **3.** 120 **5.** 120 **7.** 5 **9.** 7 **11.** n **13.** 1 **15.** $\frac{n(n-1)}{2}$ **17.** 720 **19.** 72 **21.** Permutation **23.** Combination **25.** Neither **27.** $4! = 24$ **29.** $C(9, 7) = 36$ **31.** $C(8, 4) = 70$ **33.** $P(65, 5) = 991{,}186{,}560$ **35.** $C(10, 5) = 252$ **37.** $C(100, 3) = 161{,}700$; $C(7, 3) = 35$ **39.** $P(150, 3) = 3{,}307{,}800$ **41.** $C(52, 5) = 2{,}598{,}960$ **43.** $C(13, 5) = 1287$ **45.** $5! = 120$ **47. (a)** $C(10, 4) = 210$ **(b)** $C(10, 6) = 210$ **(c)** Selecting four sweaters to take is equivalent to selecting six sweaters to leave. **49.** $C(8, 2) = 28$ **51.** $C(69, 5) \cdot 26 = 292{,}201{,}338$ **53. (b)** $\frac{C(59, 6)}{C(49, 6)} \approx 3.22$ **55.** Yes; Moe: $C(9, 2) = 36$; Joe: $C(7, 4) = 35$ **57.** $4! \cdot P(4, 3) \cdot P(5, 3) \cdot P(6, 3) \cdot P(7, 3) = 870{,}912{,}000$ **59.** $3! \cdot 3!^3 = 1296$ **61.** 10 **63.** $C(15, 3) + 15 \cdot 14 + 15 = 680$ **65.** $720 - 3! - 5! = 594$ **67. (a)** $C(45, 5) = 1{,}221{,}759$ **(b)** $C(100, 4) = 3{,}921{,}225$ **(c)** Lottery (a) **69.** Yes; the number of ways to shuffle a deck of 52 cards is $52! \approx 8 \times 10^{67}$.

Exercises 1.6, page 40
1. (a) $2^8 = 256$ **(b)** $C(8, 4) = 70$ **3. (a)** $C(7, 5) + C(7, 6) + C(7, 7) = 29$ **(b)** $2^7 - 29 = 99$ **5.** $2 \cdot C(6, 3) = 40$; $2 \cdot C(5, 3) = 20$ **7.** $C(11, 5) \cdot C(6, 5) \cdot 1 = 2772$ **9.** $C(8, 5) = 56$ **11.** $C(7, 2) = 21$ **13.** $C(5, 2) \cdot C(4, 2) = 60$ **15.** $C(6, 2) = 15$ **17. (d)** $56 + 70 = 126$ **19.** $C(8, 3) = 56$ **21.** $C(10, 6) - C(7, 4) = 175$ **23. (a)** $C(12, 5) = 792$ **(b)** $C(7, 5) = 21$ **(c)** $C(7, 2) \cdot C(5, 3) = 210$ **(d)** $C(7, 4) \cdot 5 + 21 = 196$ **25. (a)** $C(10, 3) = 120$ **(b)** $C(8, 3) = 56$ **(c)** $120 - 56 = 64$ **27.** $C(4, 2) \cdot C(6, 2) = 90$ **29.** $C(4, 3) \cdot C(4, 2) = 24$ **31.** $13 \cdot C(4, 3) \cdot 12 \cdot C(4, 2) = 3744$ **33.** $C(7, 5) \cdot 5! \cdot 21 \cdot 20 = 1{,}058{,}400$ **35.** $C(10, 5) \cdot P(21, 5) = 615{,}353{,}760$ **37.** $6! \cdot 7 \cdot 3! = 30{,}240$ **39.** $C(9, 4) = 126$ **41.** $C(26, 22) \cdot C(10, 7) = 1{,}794{,}000$ **43.** $C(12, 6) = 924$ **45.** $C(100, 50)/2^{100} \approx 7.96\%$ **47.** $\frac{C(50, 10) \cdot C(50, 10)}{C(100, 20)} \approx 19.7\%$

CHAPTER 2

Exercises 2.1, page 48
1. (a) {RS, RT, RU, RV, ST, SU, SV, TU, TV, UV} **(b)** {RS, RT, RU, RV} **(c)** {TU, TV, UV} **3. (a)** {HH, HT, TH, TT} **(b)** {HH, HT} **5. (a)** {(I, red), (I, white), (II, red), (II, white)} **(b)** {(I, red), (I, white)} **7. (a)** S = {All positive numbers of minutes} **(b)** "More than 5 minutes but less than 8 minutes"; ∅; "5 minutes or less"; "8 minutes or more"; "5 minutes or less"; "less than 4 minutes"; S **9. (a)** {(Fr, Lib), (Fr, Con), (So, Lib), (So, Con), (Jr, Lib), (Jr, Con), (Sr, Lib), (Sr, Con)} **(b)** {(Fr, Con), (So, Con), (Jr, Con), (Sr, Con)} **(c)** {(Jr, Lib)} **(d)** {(So, Lib), (Jr, Lib), (Sr, Lib)} **11. (a)** No **(b)** Yes **13.** ∅, $\{a\}$, $\{b\}$, $\{c\}$, $\{a, b\}$, $\{a, c\}$, $\{b, c\}$, S **15.** Yes **17. (a)** {0, 1, 2, 3, 4, 5, 6, 7, 8, 9, 10} **(b)** {6, 7, 8, 9, 10} **19. (a)** No **(b)** Yes **(c)** Yes **21.** {0, 1, 2, 3, 4, 5, 6, 7, 8} **23.** (7, 4); 81 **25.** {2, 6, 9, 10}; 25% **27.** {Colonel Mustard, Miss Scarlet, Professor Plum, Mrs. White, Mr. Green, Mrs. Peacock} **(a)** 324 **(b)** "The murder occurred in the library with a gun." **(c)** "Either the murder occurred in the library or it was done with a gun."

Exercises 2.2, page 56
1. Judgmental **3.** Logical
5.

Number of Heads	Probability
0	$\frac{1}{4}$
1	$\frac{1}{2}$
2	$\frac{1}{4}$

7. $\frac{1}{19}$ **9. (a)** $\frac{191}{4487} \approx .04257$ **(b)** $\frac{272}{4487} \approx .06062$ **(c)** $\frac{4215}{4487} \approx .9394$
11. (a) $\frac{3}{13} \approx .2308$ **(b)** $\frac{5}{26} \approx .1923$ **(c)** $\frac{9}{26} \approx .3462$
13. (a) $\frac{1}{9} \approx .1111$ **(b)** $\frac{1}{6} \approx .1667$
15.

Kind of High School	Probability
Public	.820
Private	.172
Home School	.008

17. .64 **19. (a)** .6; .7 **(b)** .4 **(c)** .5 **(d)** .8 **21. (a)**

Number of Colleges Applied To	Probability
1	.10
2	.07
3	.10
4	.13
≥5	.60

(b) .83

23. None. For (a), the probabilities do not add to 1. For (b), $\Pr(s_3) < 0$. For (c), the probabilities do not add to 1. **25.** $\frac{1}{12}$ **27.** .24 **29.** 1 **31.** .9 **33.** .45 **35.** .25 **37. (a)** .7 **(b)** .2 **39.** .6 **41.** 1

Exercises 2.3, page 63

1. **(a)** $\frac{9}{17} \approx .5294$ **(b)** $\frac{8}{17} \approx .4706$ **(c)** $\frac{5}{17} \approx .2941$ **(d)** $\frac{11}{17} \approx .6471$ **3.** **(a)** $\frac{C(5,2)}{C(11,2)} = \frac{2}{11} \approx .1818$ **(b)** $1 - \frac{C(5,2)}{C(11,2)} = \frac{9}{11} \approx .8182$ **5.** **(a)** $\frac{C(6,4) + C(7,4)}{C(13,4)} = \frac{10}{143} \approx .0699$ **(b)** $\frac{C(6,4) + C(6,3) \cdot C(7,1)}{C(13,4)} = \frac{31}{143} \approx .2168$ **7.** $1 - \frac{C(5,3)}{C(7,3)} = \frac{5}{7} \approx .7143$ **9.** $1 - \frac{C(9,3)}{C(13,3)} = \frac{101}{143} \approx .7063$ **11.** $1 - \frac{C(4,3)}{C(10,3)} = \frac{29}{30} \approx .9667$ **13.** $\frac{C(10,7)}{C(22,7)} = \frac{5}{7106} \approx .0007$ **15.** $1 - \frac{C(12,7) + C(12,6) \cdot C(10,1)}{C(22,7)} = \frac{16}{17} \approx .9412$ **17.** $1 - \frac{7 \cdot 6 \cdot 5}{7^3} = \frac{19}{49} \approx .3878$ **19.** $1 - \frac{30 \cdot 29 \cdot 28 \cdot 27}{30^4} = \frac{47}{250} = .188$ **21.** $1 - \frac{P(20,8)}{20^8} \approx .8016$ **23.** $1 - (\frac{364}{365})^{25} \approx .06629$ **25.** $\frac{6 \cdot 5}{6^2} = \frac{5}{6} \approx .8333$ **27.** $\frac{3^4}{6^4} = \frac{1}{16} = .0625$ **29.** $\frac{C(10,4)}{2^{10}} = \frac{105}{512} \approx .2051$ **31.** $1 - \frac{7 \cdot 6 \cdot 5 \cdot 4}{7^4} = \frac{223}{343} \approx .6501$ **33.** **(a)** $\frac{C(3,1) \cdot C(5,2)}{C(8,3)} = \frac{15}{28} \approx .5357$ **(b)** $\frac{C(5,1) \cdot C(3,2)}{C(8,3)} = \frac{15}{56} \approx .2679$ **(c)** $\frac{C(3,1) \cdot 1 \cdot C(3,2)}{C(8,3)} = \frac{9}{56} \approx .1607$ **(d)** $\frac{15}{28} + \frac{15}{56} - \frac{9}{56} = \frac{9}{14} \approx .6429$ **35.** $1 - \frac{4^3}{5^3} = \frac{61}{125} = .488$ **37.** Increase **39.** $\frac{5 \cdot 4 \cdot 3}{5^3} = \frac{12}{25} = .48$ **41.** $\frac{3! \cdot 4 \cdot 2!}{5!} = \frac{2}{5} = .4$ **43.** $\frac{13 \cdot C(4,3) \cdot 12 \cdot C(4,2)}{C(52,5)} = \frac{6}{4165} \approx .0014$ **45.** $\frac{C(13,2) \cdot C(4,2) \cdot C(4,2) \cdot 44}{C(52,5)} = \frac{198}{4165} \approx .0475$ **47.** **(a)** $\frac{4 \cdot C(13,4) \cdot C(13,3) \cdot C(13,3) \cdot C(13,3)}{C(52,13)} \approx .1054$ **(b)** $\frac{C(4,2) \cdot C(13,4) \cdot C(13,4) \cdot 2 \cdot C(13,3) \cdot 1 \cdot C(13,2)}{C(52,13)} \approx .2155$ **49.** $\frac{2}{C(40,6)} = \frac{1}{1{,}919{,}190} \approx .0000005211$ **51.** $\frac{C(5,3) \cdot C(34,2)}{C(39,5)} \approx .0097$ **53.** $1 - \frac{P(100,15)}{100^{15}} \approx .6687$ **55.** $1 - \frac{P(52,5)}{52^5} \approx .1797$; 9 **57.** 253; $1 - (\frac{364}{365})^{253} \approx .5005$ **59.** 48

Exercises 2.4, page 72

1. **(a)** .5 **(b)** .6 **(c)** $\frac{.2}{.6} \approx .3333$ **(d)** $\frac{.2}{.5} = .4$ **3.** **(a)** $\frac{.1}{.4} = \frac{1}{4}$ **(b)** $\frac{.1}{.5} = \frac{1}{5}$ **(c)** $\frac{.4}{.6} = \frac{2}{3}$ **(d)** $\frac{.2}{.6} = \frac{1}{3}$ **5.** **(a)** $\frac{1}{12}$ **(b)** $\frac{\frac{1}{12}}{\frac{5}{12}} = \frac{1}{5}$ **(c)** $\frac{\frac{1}{12}}{\frac{1}{3}} = \frac{1}{4}$ **7.** **(a)** .1 **(b)** .6 **(c)** $\frac{.1}{.3} = \frac{1}{3}$ **(d)** .2 **9.** $\frac{5}{36}/(1 - \frac{1}{6}) = \frac{1}{6}$ **11.** 0 **13.** $\frac{C(7,4)}{C(12,4) - C(5,4)} = \frac{1}{14} \approx .0714$ **15.** $\frac{1}{2}$ **17.** $\frac{.10}{.25} = .4$ **19.** **(a)** $\frac{851}{2898} \approx .2937$ **(b)** $\frac{1201}{2898} \approx .4144$ **(c)** $\frac{522}{851} \approx .6134$ **(d)** $\frac{93}{1697} \approx .0548$ **21.** **(a)** $\frac{228.6}{1291.8} \approx .1770$ **(b)** $\frac{183.2}{1291.8} \approx .1418$ **(c)** $\frac{20.7}{1291.8} \approx .0160$ **(d)** $\frac{20.7}{183.2} \approx .1130$ **(e)** $\frac{20.7}{228.6} \approx .0906$ **23.** $\frac{\frac{1}{3}}{\frac{1}{2}} = \frac{2}{3}$ **25.** $\frac{1}{221} \approx .004525$ **27.** $\frac{1}{2}$ **29.** $.48 \cdot .09 = .0432$ **31.** Three-point shot; .24 vs .29 **33.** Yes **35.** .8 **37.** .6 **39.** .25 **41.** .992 **43.** Not independent **45.** Independent **47.** Not Independent **49.** No **51.** **(a)** $.80 \cdot .75 \cdot .60 = .36$ **(b)** .81 **53.** $.99^5 \cdot .98^5 \cdot .975^3 \approx .7967$ **55.** $.3^4 = .0081$ **57.** **(a)** $1 - .7^4 = .7599$ **(b)** $.7599^{10} \approx .06420$ **(c)** $1 - .9358^{20} = .7347$ **59.** 0 points; $1 - .6 = .4$; $.6 \cdot .4 = .24$; $.6 \cdot .6 = .36$ **63.** $.6 \cdot .4 = .24$; $.4 \cdot .6 = .24$

Exercises 2.5, page 80

1. **3.**

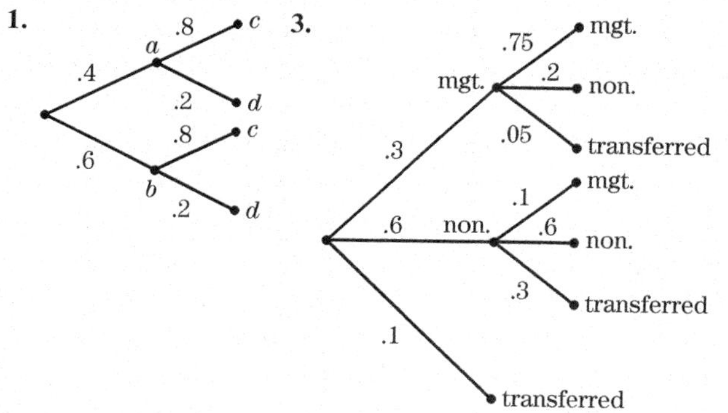

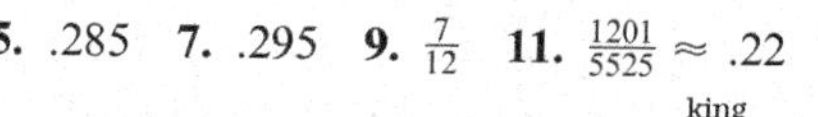

5. .285 **7.** .295 **9.** $\frac{7}{12}$ **11.** $\frac{1201}{5525} \approx .22$

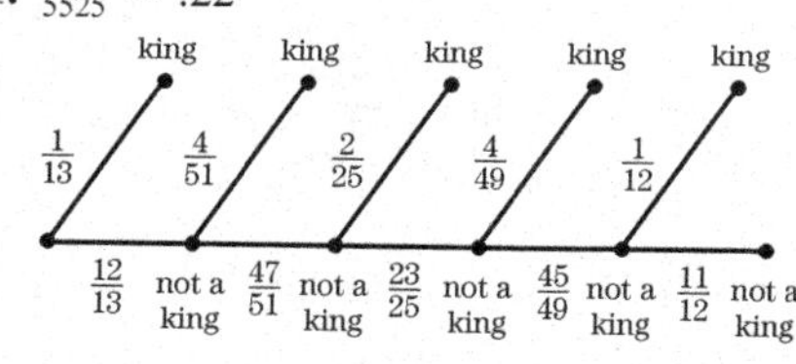

13. .14 **15.** $\frac{16}{17} \approx .9412$ **17.** .8 **19.** $\frac{4}{7}$ **21.** **(a)** .60 **(b)** .75 **23.** .00029997 **25.** $\frac{11}{16}$ **27.** **(a)** $\frac{1}{4}$; $\frac{3}{4}$ **(b)** .7 **29.** $\frac{3}{8}$ **31.** $\frac{25}{26}$ **33.** $\frac{3}{8}$ **35.** **(a)** .99 **(b)** $(.99)^{200} \approx .1340$ **37.** **(a)** $\frac{7}{12}$ **(b)** $\frac{7}{12}$ **(c)** $\frac{25}{36}$ **(d)** Since the red die beats the blue die more than half the time and the blue die beats the green die more than half the time, the red die appears to be the strongest of the three dice and the green die appears to be the weakest. However, paradoxically, the green die beats the red die more than half the time. **39.** True **41.** True **43.** True **45.** .00473 or .473% **47.** $\frac{9}{19} \approx .474$ **49.** .84 or 84%

Exercises 2.6, page 87

1. $\frac{8}{53}$ **3.** $\frac{3}{7}$ **5.** .075 **7.** $\frac{8}{9}$ **9. (a)** .1325 **(b)** $\frac{12}{53} \approx .23$ **11.** $\frac{5}{103} \approx .049$ **13. (a)** .01 **(b)** $\frac{33}{34} \approx .971$ **15.** $\frac{31}{37} \approx .838$ **17.** .3805
19. (a) $\frac{1}{4}$ **(b)** $\frac{13}{17} \approx .765$ **(c)** .130 **21. (a)** $\frac{5}{9}$ **(b)** 11% **23.** $\frac{3}{7}$ **25.** $\frac{8}{9}$ **27.** $\frac{31}{37} \approx .838$ **29.** $\frac{5}{9}$

CHAPTER 3

Exercises 3.1, page 97

1. 71 **3.** 75 **5.** 142 **7.** $E(X) = -0.1$ **9.** \$43.75 **11.** \$0.148 **13.** \$25

15. Probability distribution:

x_i	0	1	2
p_i	$\frac{1}{4}$	$\frac{1}{2}$	$\frac{1}{4}$

$E(X) = 1$

17. Payoff table:

x_i	\$1	−\$1
p_i	$\frac{1}{2}$	$\frac{1}{2}$

$E(X) = 0$; game is fair

19. Payoff table:

x_i	−\$3	−\$2	−\$1	\$0	\$1	\$2
p_i	$\frac{1}{6}$	$\frac{1}{6}$	$\frac{1}{6}$	$\frac{1}{6}$	$\frac{1}{6}$	$\frac{1}{6}$

$E(X) = -50¢$; game is not fair

21. −\$0.50 **23.** −\$0.035; \$0.035 **25.** \$40. Let x = amount you should lose if a 6 turns up. Set up a payoff table; then set the expected value of the game equal to zero and solve for x. **27.** Win \$1 **29.** −\$0.154 **31.** \$2.75 **33.** A_2; \$210

35. Payoff table:

x_i	\$35	−\$1
p_i	$\frac{1}{38}$	$\frac{37}{38}$

$E(X) = -5.26¢$

37. .002 **39.** Payoff table:

x_i	\$499	\$99	\$19	\$4	−\$1
p_i	.0002	.0006	.001	.004	.9942

$E(X) = -80¢$

41. (A)

x_i	0	1	2
p_i	$\frac{7}{15}$	$\frac{7}{15}$	$\frac{1}{15}$

(B) .60

43. (A)

x_i	−\$5	\$195	\$395	\$595
p_i	.985	.0149	.000 059 9	.000 000 06

(B) $E(X) \approx -\$2$

45. \$36.27 **47.** Payoff table:

x_i	\$4,850	−\$150
p_i	.01	.99

$E(X) = -\$100$

49. Site A, with $E(X) = \$3.6$million **51.** 1.54 **53.** −\$1.338

Exercises 3.2, page 103

1. .1323 **3.** $\frac{8}{81} \approx .0988$ **5.** $\frac{15}{128} \approx .1172$ **7.** $\frac{165}{1024} \approx .1611$ **9.** $\frac{1023}{1024} \approx .9990$ **11.** $\frac{1}{1296} \approx .0007716$ **13.** $\frac{85}{648} \approx .1312$
15. $\frac{425}{432} \approx .9838$ **17.** .2220 **19.** .01663 **21.** .08908 **23.** .1478 **25.** .4727 **27. (a)** .375 **(b)** .5 **(c)** .125 **29.** $\Pr(X = 5)$
31. $\binom{40}{10}(.25)^{10}(.75)^{10}$; out of a group of 40 cattle, it is more likely that exactly 10 recover than exactly 9 recover. **33.** The probability that the salesman sells cars to three or four of the customers **35. (a)** .4602 **(b)** .5398 **37.** Since $p = .5$, the probability of k successes and $10 - k$ failures is equal to the probability of $10 - k$ successes and k failures. **39.** 1 **41.** .9821 **43.** .1018 **45.** .3174
47. .1198 **49.** .5781 **51.** .2401, .0756 **53.** 9 **55. (b)** $\binom{3}{0}p^0(1-p)^3$; $\binom{3}{1}p(1-p)^3$

CHAPTER 4

Exercises 4.1, page 114

1. $\xrightarrow{2R_1} \begin{cases} x - 6y = 4 \\ 5x + 4y = 1 \end{cases}$ **3.** $\xrightarrow{R_2 + 5R_1} \begin{cases} x + 2y = 3 \\ 14y = 16 \end{cases}$ **5.** $\xrightarrow{R_3 + (-4)R_1} \begin{cases} x - 2y + z = 0 \\ y - 2z = 4 \\ 9y - z = 5 \end{cases}$ **7.** $\xrightarrow{R_1 + \frac{1}{2}R_2} \left[\begin{array}{cc|c} 1 & 0 & 5 \\ 0 & 1 & 4 \end{array}\right]$

9. $\left[\begin{array}{cc|c} -3 & 4 & -2 \\ 1 & -7 & 8 \end{array}\right]$ **11.** $\left[\begin{array}{ccc|c} 1 & 13 & -2 & 0 \\ 2 & 0 & -1 & 3 \\ 0 & 1 & 0 & 5 \end{array}\right]$ **13.** $\begin{cases} -2y = 3 \\ x + 7y = -4 \end{cases}$ **15.** $\begin{cases} 3x + 2y = -3 \\ y - 6z = 4 \\ -5x - y + 7z = 0 \end{cases}$

17. Multiply the second row of the matrix by $\frac{1}{3}$. **19.** Change the first row of the matrix by adding to it 3 times the second row. **21.** Interchange rows 2 and 3.

23. $\left[\begin{array}{cc|c} 1 & 2 & 0 \\ 0 & 10 & 5 \end{array}\right]$ **25.** $\left[\begin{array}{cc|c} 1 & 2 & 3 \\ 3 & -2 & 0 \end{array}\right]$ **27.** $\left[\begin{array}{cc|c} 1 & 3 & -5 \\ 0 & 1 & 7 \end{array}\right]$ **29.** $R_2 + 2R_1$ **31.** $R_1 + (-2)R_2$ **33.** $R_1 \leftrightarrow R_2$ or $R_1 \leftrightarrow R_3$

35. $R_1 + (-3)R_3$ or $R_2 + (-2)R_3$ **37.** $\left[\begin{array}{ccc|c} 1 & 1 & -1 & 6 \\ 0 & 10 & 2 & 18 \\ 0 & -6 & 5 & -13 \end{array}\right]$ **39.** $x = -1, y = 1$

41. $x = -\frac{8}{7}, y = -\frac{9}{7}, z = -\frac{3}{7}$ **43.** $x = -1, y = 1$ **45.** $x = 1, y = 2, z = -1$ **47.** $x = -2.5, y = 15$ **49.** $x = 1, y = -6, z = 2$ **51.** $x = -1, y = -2, z = 5$ **53.** 30 **55.** d **57.** 150 short sleeve, 200 long sleeve **59.** 190 adults, 85 children **61.** $x = 3.7, y = 3.9, z = 1.9$ **63.** 3 ounces of Brazilian, 6 ounces of Columbian, 7 ounces of Peruvian **65.** \$25,000 in the bond fund, \$50,000 in the health sciences fund, \$25,000 in the real estate fund **67.** $23\frac{1}{3}$ pounds of first type, 85 pounds of second type, $201\frac{2}{3}$ pounds of third type

Exercises 4.2, page 122

1. $\begin{bmatrix} 1 & -2 & 3 \\ 0 & 13 & -8 \end{bmatrix}$ **3.** $\begin{bmatrix} 9 & -1 & 0 & -7 \\ -\frac{1}{2} & \frac{1}{2} & 1 & 3 \\ 5 & -1 & 0 & -3 \end{bmatrix}$ **5.** $\begin{bmatrix} 1 & \frac{3}{2} \\ 0 & -9 \\ 0 & \frac{7}{2} \end{bmatrix}$ **7.** $\begin{bmatrix} 4 & 3 & 0 \\ 1 & 1 & 0 \\ \frac{1}{6} & \frac{1}{2} & 1 \end{bmatrix}$

9. $y =$ any value, $x = 3 + 2y$ **11.** No solution **13.** $x = 1, y = 2$ **15.** No solution **17.** No solution **19.** $z =$ any value, $x = -6 - z, y = 5$ **21.** No solution **23.** No solution **25.** $z =$ any value, $w =$ any value, $x = 2z + w, y = 5 - 3w$ **27.** No solution **29.** Possible answers: $z = 0, x = -13, y = 9; z = 1, x = -8, y = 6; z = 2, x = -3, y = 3$ **31.** Possible answers: $y = 0, x = 23, z = 5; y = 1, x = 16, z = 5; y = 2, x = 9, z = 5$ **33.** Food 3: $z =$ any value between 0 and 100, food 2: $y = 100 - z$, food 1: $x = 300 - z$ **37.** 50 ottomans, 30 sofas, 40 chairs; 5 ottomans, 55 sofas, 35 chairs; 95 ottomans, 5 sofas, 45 chairs **39.** 6 floral squares, the other 90 any mix of solid green and solid blue **41.** No solution if $k \neq -12$; infinitely many if $k = -12$ **43.** None

Exercises 4.3, page 133

1. 2×3 **3.** 1×3, row matrix **5.** 2×2, square matrix **7.** $-4; 0$ **9.** $i = 1, j = 3$

11. $\begin{bmatrix} 9 & 3 \\ 7 & -1 \end{bmatrix}$ **13.** $\begin{bmatrix} 2 & 4 & 2.5 \\ -5.5 & 1 & 1.2 \end{bmatrix}$ **15.** $\begin{bmatrix} 1 & 3 \\ 1 & 2 \\ 4 & -2 \end{bmatrix}$ **17.** $\begin{bmatrix} -7 \\ \frac{1}{6} \end{bmatrix}$ **19.** [11] **21.** [10] **23.** $\begin{bmatrix} 4 & 0 & -\frac{2}{3} \\ -6 & \frac{1}{2} & \frac{1}{3} \end{bmatrix}$

25. $\begin{bmatrix} 3 & 19 \\ 23 & 3 \end{bmatrix}$ **27.** Yes; 3×5 **29.** No **31.** Yes; 3×1 **33.** $\begin{bmatrix} 6 & 17 \\ 6 & 10 \end{bmatrix}$ **35.** $\begin{bmatrix} 21 \\ -4 \\ 8 \end{bmatrix}$

37. $\begin{bmatrix} 5 & 6 \\ 7 & 8 \end{bmatrix}$ **39.** $\begin{bmatrix} .48 & .39 \\ .52 & .61 \end{bmatrix}$ **41.** $\begin{bmatrix} 25 & 17 & 2 \\ 3 & -1 & 2 \\ 1 & 1 & 4 \end{bmatrix}$ **43.** $\begin{bmatrix} \frac{1}{3} & \frac{2}{3} \\ \frac{1}{3} & \frac{2}{3} \end{bmatrix}$ **45.** [30 41] **47.** $\begin{bmatrix} 10 & 0 \\ 0 & 15 \end{bmatrix}$ **49.** $\begin{bmatrix} 0 & 0 \\ 0 & 0 \end{bmatrix}$ **51.** $\begin{bmatrix} 23 & 24 \\ 25 & 26 \end{bmatrix}$

53. $\begin{cases} 2x + 3y = 6 \\ 4x + 5y = 7 \end{cases}$ **55.** $\begin{cases} x + 2y + 3z = 10 \\ 4x + 5y + 6z = 11 \\ 7x + 8y + 9z = 12 \end{cases}$ **57.** $\begin{bmatrix} 3 & 2 \\ 7 & -1 \end{bmatrix}\begin{bmatrix} x \\ y \end{bmatrix} = \begin{bmatrix} -1 \\ 2 \end{bmatrix}$ **59.** $\begin{bmatrix} 1 & -2 & 3 \\ 0 & 1 & 1 \\ 0 & 0 & 1 \end{bmatrix}\begin{bmatrix} x \\ y \\ z \end{bmatrix} = \begin{bmatrix} 5 \\ 6 \\ 2 \end{bmatrix}$

65. (a) $\begin{bmatrix} 340 \\ 265 \end{bmatrix}$ **(b)** Mike's clothes cost \$340; Don's clothes cost \$265. **(c)** $\begin{bmatrix} 25 \\ 18.75 \\ 62.50 \end{bmatrix}$ **(d)** The costs of the three items of clothing after a 25% increase **67. (a)** [2282.50 2322.50 3550.50], total retail value for the white chocolate-covered, milk chocolate-covered, and dark chocolate-covered items **(b)** $\begin{bmatrix} 3138.00 \\ 3337.50 \\ 6772.50 \end{bmatrix}$, total revenue from peanuts, raisins, and espresso beans **(c)** $\begin{bmatrix} 94.50 \\ 351.50 \\ 256.50 \end{bmatrix}$, 10% reduction in the number of pounds sold **69. (a)** I: 2.75, II: 2, III: 1.3 **(b)** A: 74, B: 112, C: 128, D: 64, F: 22 **71.** 10,100 voting Democratic, 7900 voting Republican **73.** Carpenters: \$2000, bricklayers: \$2100, plumbers: \$1200 **75. (a)** [162 150 143], number of units of each nutrient consumed at breakfast **(b)** [186 200 239], number of units of each nutrient consumed at lunch **(c)** [288 300 344], number of units of each nutrient consumed at dinner **(d)** [5 8], total number of ounces of each food that Mikey eats during a day **(e)** [636 650 726], number of units of each nutrient consumed per day **77. (a)** $\begin{bmatrix} 720 \\ 646 \end{bmatrix}$ **(b)** \$720

79. (a)

	Boston cream pie	Carrot cake	
$T =$	30	45	Preparation
	30	50	Baking
	15	10	Finishing

(b) $S = \begin{bmatrix} 20 \\ 8 \end{bmatrix}$ Boston cream pie, Carrot cake; $TS = \begin{bmatrix} 960 \\ 1000 \\ 380 \end{bmatrix}$ Preparation, Baking, Finishing

(c) Total baking time: 1000 minutes, or $16\frac{2}{3}$ hours; total finishing time: 380 minutes, or $6\frac{1}{3}$ hours

81. (a)

	Cutting	Sewing	Finishing	
$T =$	2	3	2	Huge One
	1.5	2	1	Regular Joe

(b) $S = \begin{bmatrix} 32 \\ 24 \end{bmatrix}$ Huge One, Regular Joe

(c) $A = \begin{matrix} \text{Huge One} & \text{Regular Joe} \\ \end{matrix}$ $\begin{bmatrix} 27 & 56 \end{bmatrix}$; $AT = \begin{matrix} \text{Cutting} & \text{Sewing} & \text{Finishing} \end{matrix}$ $\begin{bmatrix} 138 & 193 & 110 \end{bmatrix}$; $AS = \begin{bmatrix} 2208 \end{bmatrix}$ **(d)** 193 hours **(e)** \$2208

85. 4×4 **87.** $\begin{bmatrix} 9257 & 57{,}718 & 89{,}389 \end{bmatrix} \begin{bmatrix} 13.9 \\ 14.9 \\ 14.2 \end{bmatrix}$

Exercises 4.4, page 142

1. $x = 2, y = 0$ **3.** $\begin{bmatrix} 1 & -2 \\ -3 & 7 \end{bmatrix}$ **5.** $\begin{bmatrix} 1 & -1 \\ -\frac{5}{2} & 3 \end{bmatrix}$ **7.** $\begin{bmatrix} 1.6 & -.4 \\ -.6 & 1.4 \end{bmatrix}$

9. $\begin{bmatrix} \frac{1}{3} \end{bmatrix}$ **11.** $x = 4, y = -\frac{1}{2}$ **13.** $x = 32, y = -6$ **15. (a)** $\begin{bmatrix} .8 & .3 \\ .2 & .7 \end{bmatrix} \begin{bmatrix} x \\ y \end{bmatrix} = \begin{bmatrix} m \\ s \end{bmatrix}$ **(b)** $\begin{bmatrix} x \\ y \end{bmatrix} = \begin{bmatrix} 1.4 & -.6 \\ -.4 & 1.6 \end{bmatrix} \begin{bmatrix} m \\ s \end{bmatrix}$ **(c)** 110,000 married; 40,000 single **(d)** 130,000 married; 20,000 single **17. (a)** $\begin{bmatrix} .7 & .1 \\ .3 & .9 \end{bmatrix} \begin{bmatrix} x \\ y \end{bmatrix} = \begin{bmatrix} u \\ v \end{bmatrix}$ **(b)** $\begin{bmatrix} x \\ y \end{bmatrix} = \begin{bmatrix} \frac{3}{2} & -\frac{1}{6} \\ -\frac{1}{2} & \frac{7}{6} \end{bmatrix} \begin{bmatrix} u \\ v \end{bmatrix}$ **(c)** 8500; 4500

19. $x = 9, y = -2, z = -2$ **21.** $x = 21, y = 25, z = 26$ **23.** $x = 1, y = 5, z = -4, w = 9$ **25.** $x = 4, y = -19, z = 2, w = -4$

29. (a) $\begin{bmatrix} 1 & 2 \\ .9 & 0 \end{bmatrix} \begin{bmatrix} x \\ y \end{bmatrix} = \begin{bmatrix} a \\ b \end{bmatrix}$ **(b)** After 1 year: 1,170,000 in group I and 405,000 in group II. After 2 years: 1,980,000 in group I and 1,053,000 in group II. **(c)** 700,000 in group I and 55,000 in group II. **33.** One possible answer is $\begin{bmatrix} 1 & 1 \\ 1 & 1 \end{bmatrix} \begin{bmatrix} x \\ y \end{bmatrix} = \begin{bmatrix} 2 \\ 3 \end{bmatrix}$.

Exercises 4.5, page 146

1. $\begin{bmatrix} -2 & 3 \\ 5 & -7 \end{bmatrix}$ **3.** $\begin{bmatrix} \frac{7}{2} & \frac{3}{2} \\ -2 & -1 \end{bmatrix}$ **5.** No inverse **7.** $\begin{bmatrix} -1 & 2 & -4 \\ 1 & -1 & 3 \\ 0 & 0 & 1 \end{bmatrix}$ **9.** No inverse **11.** $\begin{bmatrix} -5 & 6 & 0 & 0 \\ 1 & -1 & 0 & 0 \\ 0 & 0 & -\frac{1}{46} & \frac{1}{46} \\ 0 & 0 & \frac{25}{46} & -\frac{1}{23} \end{bmatrix}$

13. $x = 2, y = -3, z = 2$ **15.** $x = 2, y = 1, z = 3$ **17.** $x = 4, y = -4, z = 3, w = -1$ **19.** $\begin{bmatrix} -3 & 5 \\ 10 & -16 \end{bmatrix}$

21. $x = 42, y = 21, z = 37$ **23.** $x = 82, y = 17, z = 1$

CHAPTER 5

Exercises 5.1, page 155

1. No **3.** Yes **5.** No **7.** No **9.**

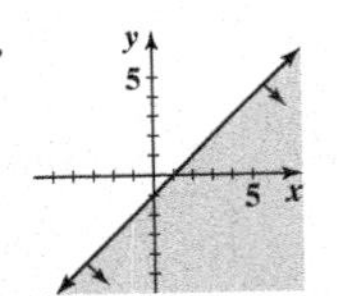

11. **13.**

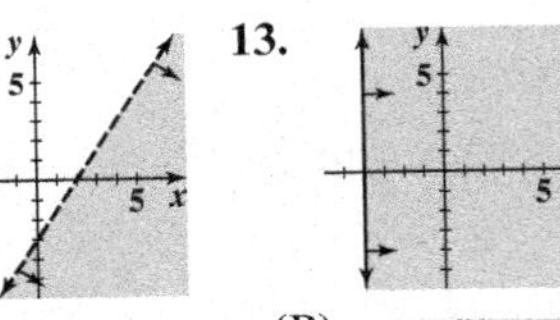

15.

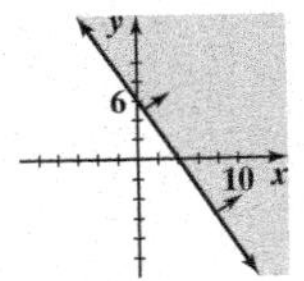

17.

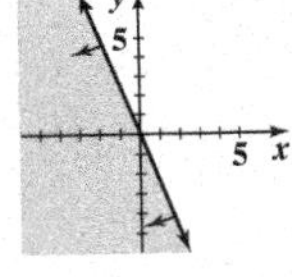

19. (A)

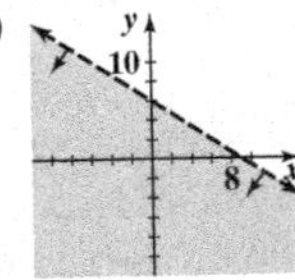

(B)

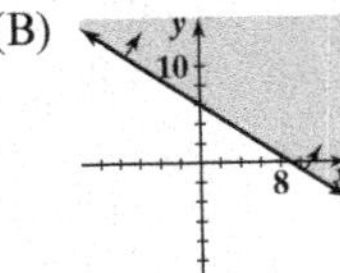

21. (A)

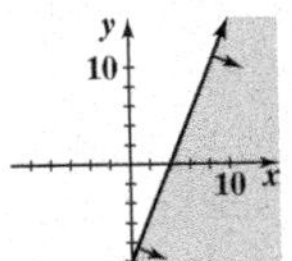

(B)

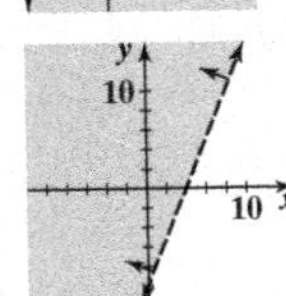

23. Let a = no. of applicants; $a < 10$ **25.** Let h = no. of hours of practice per day; $h \geq 2.5$ **27.** Let p = monthly take-home pay; $p > \$3{,}000$ **29.** Let t = tax rate; $t < 40\%$ **31.** Let e = enrollment; $e \leq 30$ **33.** $2x + 3y = -6$; $2x + 3y \geq -6$ **35.** $y = 3$; $y < 3$ **37.** $4x - 5y = 0$; $4x - 5y \geq 0$ **39.** Let x = enrollment in finite mathematics; let y = enrollment in calculus; $x + y < 300$ **41.** Let x = revenue; y = cost; $x \leq y - 20{,}000$ **43.** Let x = no. of grams of saturated fat; let y = no. of grams of unsaturated fat; $x > 3y$

45.

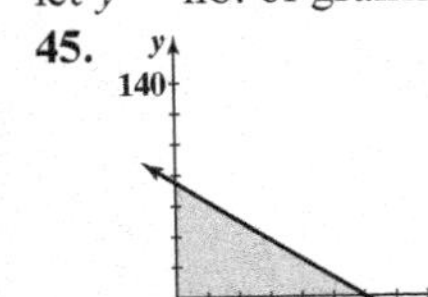

47.

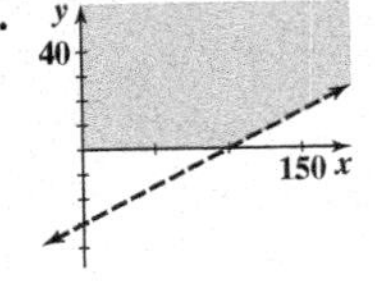

49.

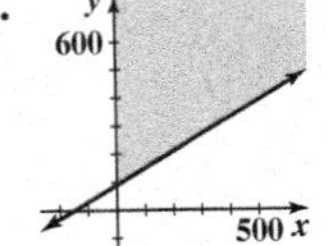

51.

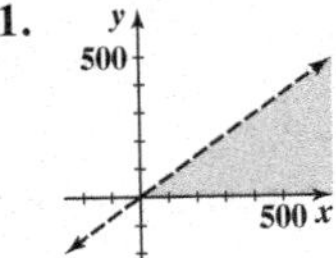

53. The solution set is the empty set and has no graph.

55. Let x = no. of acres planted with corn.
Let y = no. of acres planted with soybeans.
$90x + 70y \leq 11{,}000$, $x \geq 0$, $y \geq 0$

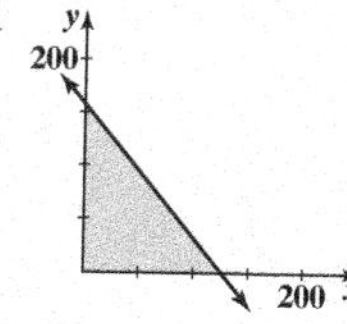

57. Let x = no. of lbs of brand A.
Let y = no. of lbs of brand B.
(A) $0.26x + 0.16y \geq 120$, $x \geq 0$, $y \geq 0$

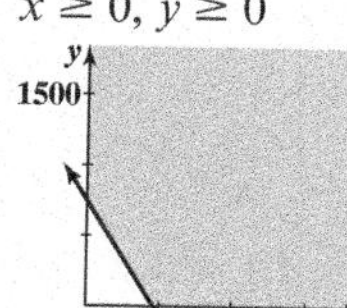

(B) $0.03x + 0.08y \leq 28$, $x \geq 0$, $y \geq 0$

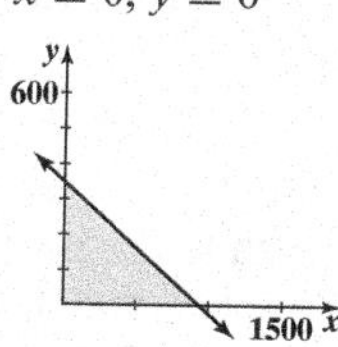

59. Let x = no. of lbs of the standard blend.
Let y = no. of lbs of the deluxe blend.
$0.3x + 0.09y \geq 0.20(x + y)$, $x \geq 0$, $y \geq 0$

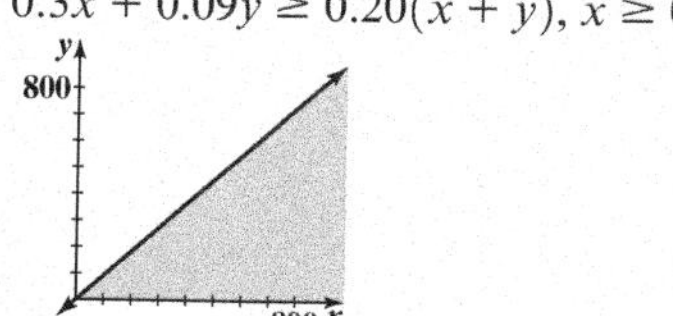

61. Let x = no. of weeks Plant A is operated.
Let y = no. of weeks Plant B is operated.
$10x + 8y \geq 400$, $x \geq 0$, $y \geq 0$

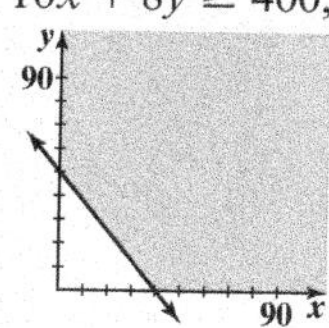

63. Let x = no. of radio spots.
Let y = no. of television spots.
$200x + 800y \leq 10{,}000$, $x \geq 0$, $y \geq 0$

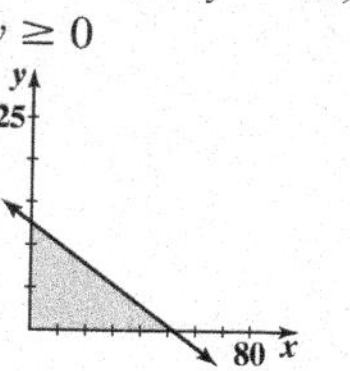

65. Let
x = no. of regular mattresses cut per day.
Let y = no. of king mattresses cut per day
$5x + 6y \leq 3{,}000$, $x \geq 0$, $y \geq 0$

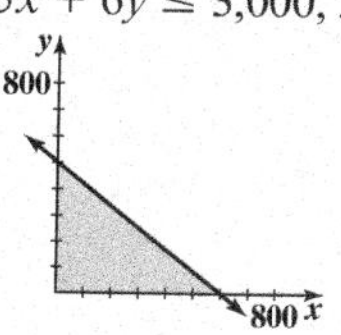

Exercises 5.2, page 161

1. Yes **3.** No **5.** No **7.** Yes **9.** IV **11.** I **13.**

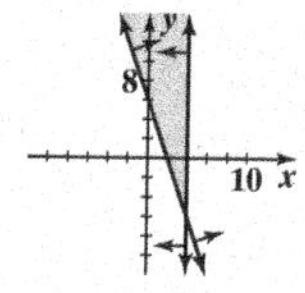

15.

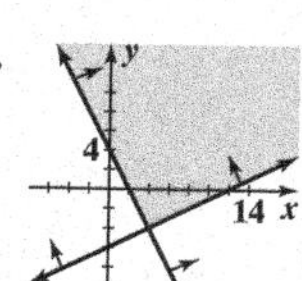

17. IV; (8, 0), (18, 0), (6, 4)
19. I; (0, 16), (6, 4), (18, 0)

21. Bounded **23.** Unbounded **25.** Bounded **27.** Unbounded

29. Bounded

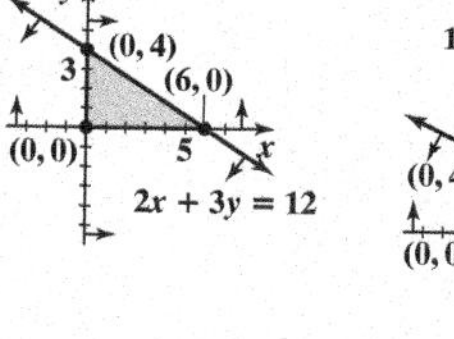

31. Bounded **33.** Unbounded **35.** Bounded **37.** Unbounded

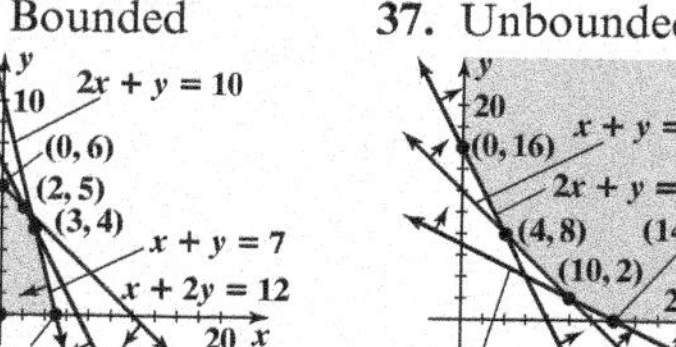

39. Bounded

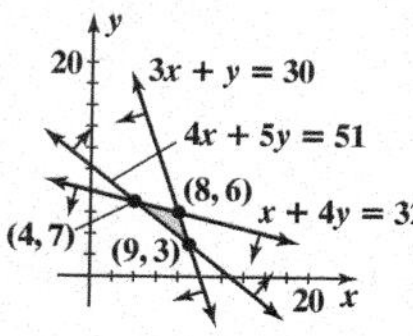

41. Empty **43.** Unbounded **45.** Bounded **47.** Bounded

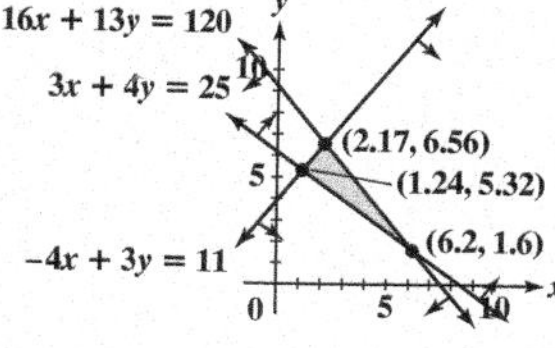

49. (A) $3x + 4y = 36$ and $3x + 2y = 30$ intersect at $(8, 3)$;
$3x + 4y = 36$ and $x = 0$ intersect at $(0, 9)$;
$3x + 4y = 36$ and $y = 0$ intersect at $(12, 0)$;
$3x + 2y = 30$ and $x = 0$ intersect at $(0, 15)$;
$3x + 2y = 30$ and $y = 0$ intersect at $(10, 0)$;
$x = 0$ and $y = 0$ intersect at $(0, 0)$
(B) $(8, 3)$, $(0, 9)$, $(10, 0)$, $(0, 0)$

51. $6x + 4y \le 108$
$x + y \le 24$
$x \ge 0$
$y \ge 0$

53. (A) All production schedules in the feasible region that are on the graph of $50x + 60y = 1{,}100$ will result in a profit of \$1,100. (B) There are many possible choices. For example, producing 5 trick skis and 15 slalom skis will produce a profit of \$1,150. All the production schedules in the feasible region that are on the graph of $50x + 60y = 1{,}150$ will result in a profit of \$1,150.

55. $20x + 10y \ge 460$
$30x + 30y \ge 960$
$5x + 10y \ge 220$
$x \ge 0$
$y \ge 0$

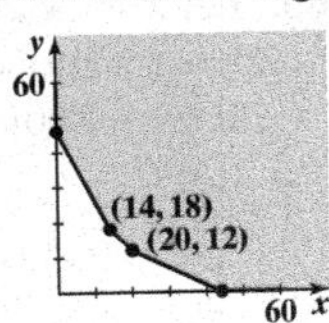

57. $10x + 20y \le 800$
$20x + 10y \le 640$
$x \ge 0$
$y \ge 0$

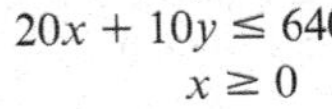

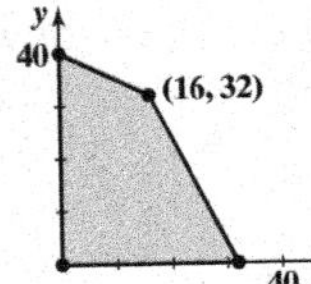

Exercises 5.3, page 172

1. Max $Q = 154$; Min $Q = 0$ **3.** Max $Q = 120$; Min $Q = -60$ **5.** Max $Q = 0$; Min $Q = -32$ **7.** Max $Q = 40$; Min $Q = -48$ **9.** Max $P = 16$ at $x = 7$ and $y = 9$ **11.** Max $P = 84$ at $x = 7$ and $y = 9$, at $x = 0$ and $y = 12$, and at every point on the line segment joining the preceding two points. **13.** Min $C = 32$ at $x = 0$ and $y = 8$ **15.** Min $C = 36$ at $x = 4$ and $y = 3$ **17.** Max $P = 240$ at $x = 24$ and $y = 0$ **19.** Min $C = 90$ at $x = 0$ and $y = 10$ **21.** Max $P = 30$ at $x = 4$ and $y = 2$ **23.** Min $z = 14$ at $x = 4$ and $y = 2$; no max **25.** Max $P = 260$ at $x = 2$ and $y = 5$ **27.** Min $z = 140$ at $x = 14$ and $y = 0$; no max **29.** Min $P = 20$ at $x = 0$ and $y = 2$; Max $P = 150$ at $x = 5$ and $y = 0$ **31.** Feasible region empty; no optimal solutions **33.** Min $P = 140$ at $x = 3$ and $y = 8$; Max $P = 260$ at $x = 8$ and $y = 10$, at $x = 12$ and $y = 2$, or at any point on the line segment from $(8, 10)$ to $(12, 2)$ **35.** Max $P = 26{,}000$ at $x = 400$ and $y = 600$ **37.** Max $P = 5{,}507$ at $x = 6.62$ and $y = 4.25$ **39.** Max $z = 2$ at $x = 4$ and $y = 2$; min z does not exist **41.** $5 < a < 30$ **43.** $a > 30$ **45.** $a = 30$ **47.** $a = 0$

49. (A) Let: x = no. of trick skis
y = no. of slalom skis
Maximize $P = 40x + 30y$
subject to $6x + 4y \le 108$
$x + y \le 24$
$x \ge 0, y \ge 0$
Max profit = \$780 when 6 trick skis and 18 slalom skis are produced.
(B) Max profit decreases to \$720 when 18 trick skis and no slalom skis are produced.
(C) Max profit increases to \$1,080 when no trick skis and 24 slalom skis are produced.

51. (A) Let x = no. of days to operate plant A
y = no. of days to operate plant B
Maximize $C = 1000x + 900y$
subject to $20x + 25y \ge 200$
$60x + 50y \ge 500$
$x \ge 0, y \ge 0$
Plant A: 5 days; Plant B: 4 days; min cost \$8,600
(B) Plant A: 10 days; Plant B: 0 days; min cost \$6,000
(C) Plant A: 0 days; Plant B: 10 days; min cost \$8,000

53. Let x = no. of buses
y = no. of vans
Maximize $C = 1{,}200x + 100y$
subject to $40x + 8y \ge 400$
$3x + y \le 36$
$x \ge 0, y \ge 0$
7 buses, 15 vans; min cost \$9,900

55. Let x = amount invested in the CD
y = amount invested in the mutual fund
Maximize $P = 0.05x + 0.09y$
subject to $x + y \le 60{,}000$
$y \ge 10{,}000$
$x \ge 2y$
$x, y \ge 0$
\$40,000 in the CD and \$20,000 in the mutual fund; max return is \$3,800

57. (A) Let x = no. of gallons produced by the old process
y = no. of gallons produced by the new process
Maximize $P = 60x + 20y$
subject to $20x + 5y \le 16{,}000$
$40x + 20y \le 30{,}000$
$x \ge 0, y \ge 0$
Max P = \$450 when 750 gal are produced using the old process exclusively.
(B) Max P = \$380 when 400 gal are produced using the old process and 700 gal are produced using the new process.
(C) Max P = \$288 when 1,440 gal are produced using the new process exclusively.

59. (A) Let $x =$ no. of bags of brand A
$y =$ no. of bags of brand B
Maximize $N = 8x + 3y$
subject to $4x + 4y \geq 1{,}000$
$2x + y \leq 400$
$x \geq 0, y \geq 0$
150 bags brand A, 100 bags brand B;
Max nitrogen = 1,500 lb
(B) 0 bags brand A, 250 bags brand B;
Min nitrogen = 750 lb

61. Let $x =$ no. of cubic yards of mix A
$y =$ no. of cubic yards of mix B
Minimize $C = 30x + 35y$
subject to $20x + 10y \geq 460$
$30x + 30y \geq 960$
$5x + 10y \geq 220$
$x \geq 0, y \geq 0$
20 yd^3 A, 12 yd^3 B; \$1,020

63. Let $x =$ no. of mice used
$y =$ no. of rats used
Maximize $P = x + y$
subject to $10x + 20y \leq 800$
$20x + 10y \leq 640$
$x \geq 0, y \geq 0$
48; 16 mice, 32 rats

Chapter 5 Review Exercises, page 177

1. *(5.1)*

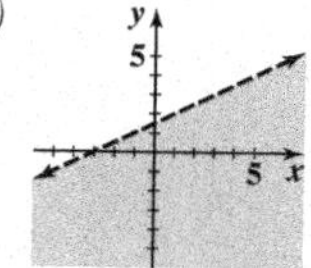

2. *(5.1)*

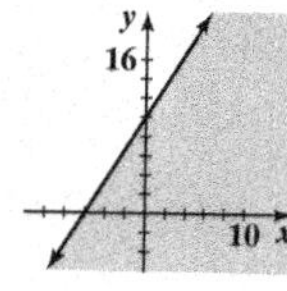

3. Bounded *(5.2)*

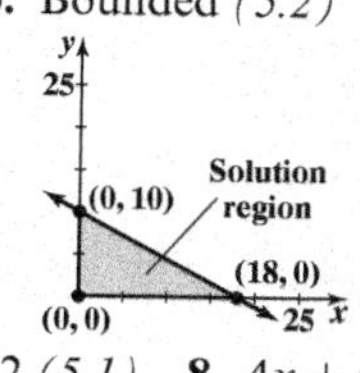

4. Unbounded *(5.2)* **5.** Bounded *(5.2)*

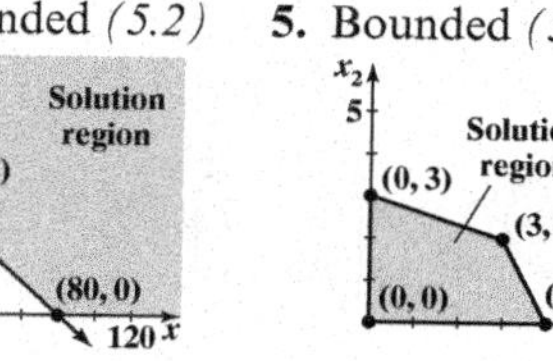

6. Unbounded *(5.2)*

x_2
10
(0, 9)
Solution region
(2, 3)
(8, 0)
10 x_1

7. $2x - 3y = 12$; $2x - 3y \leq 12$ *(5.1)* **8.** $4x + y = 8$; $4x + y \geq 8$ *(5.1)*
9. Max $P = 24$ at $x = 0$ and $y = 4$ *(5.3)* **10.** Min $C = 40$ at $x = 0$ and $y = 20$ *(5.3)* **11.** Max $P = 26$ at $x = 2$ and $y = 5$ *(5.3)* **12.** Min $C = 51$ at $x = 3$ and $y = 9$ *(5.3)* **13.** Max $P = 36$ at $x = 8$ and $y = 6$ *(5.3)*

14. Let $x =$ no. of calculator boards. *(5.1)*
$y =$ no. of toaster boards
(A) $4x + 3y \leq 300, x \geq 0, y \geq 0$

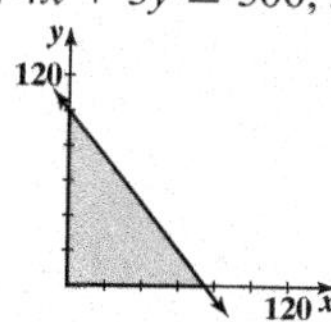

(B) $2x + y \leq 120, x \geq 0, y \geq 0$

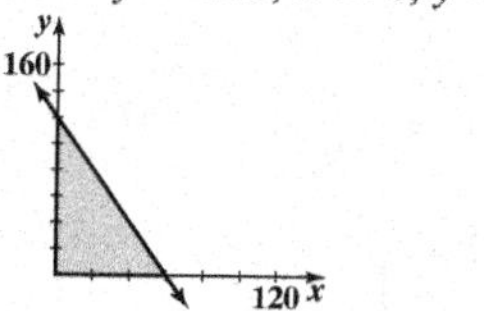

15. (A) Let $x =$ no. of regular sails
$y =$ no. of competition sails
Maximize $P = 100x + 200y$
subject to $2x + 3y \leq 150$
$4x + 10y \leq 380$
$x, y \geq 0$
Max $P =$ \$8,500 when 45 regular and 20 competition sails are produced.
(B) Max profit increases to \$9,880 when 38 competition and no regular sails are produced.
(C) Max profit decreases to \$7,500 when no competition and 75 regular sails are produced. *(5.3)*

16. (A) Let $x =$ no. of grams of mix A
$y =$ no. of grams of mix B
Minimize $C = 0.04x + 0.09y$
subject to $2x + 5y \geq 850$
$2x + 4y \geq 800$
$4x + 5y \geq 1{,}150$
$x, y \geq 0$
Min $C =$ \$16.50 when 300 g mix A and 50 g mix B are used
(B) The minimum cost decreases to \$13.00 when 100 g mix A and 150 g mix B are used
(C) The minimum cost increases to \$17.00 when 425 g mix A and no mix B are used *(5.3)*

CHAPTER 6

Exercises 6.1, page 188

1. $\begin{bmatrix} 16 \\ 14 \end{bmatrix}$ **3.** Not defined **5.** $[14 \quad 17]$ **7.** Not defined **9.** $S_1 = [.1 \quad .9]$; $S_2 = [.16 \quad .84]$ **11.** $S_1 = [.46 \quad .54]$; $S_2 = [.376 \quad .624]$ **13.** $S_1 = [.25 \quad .75]$; $S_2 = [.25 \quad .75]$ **15.** $S_1 = [.5 \quad .5]$; $S_2 = [.65 \quad .35]$ **17.** $S_1 = [.71 \quad .29]$; $S_2 = [.587 \quad .413]$ **19.** $S_1 = [.65 \quad .35]$; $S_2 = [.605 \quad .395]$ **21.** $S_1 = [.7 \quad .2 \quad .1]$; $S_2 = [.33 \quad .35 \quad .32]$ **23.** $S_1 = [.35 \quad .35 \quad .3]$; $S_2 = [.465 \quad .3 \quad .235]$ **25.** $S_1 = [.53 \quad .28 \quad .19]$; $S_2 = [.397 \quad .325 \quad .278]$ **27.** $S_1 = [.2 \quad .3 \quad .5]$; $S_2 = [.27 \quad .4 \quad .33]$ **29.** $S_1 = [.28 \quad .44 \quad .28]$; $S_2 = [.212 \quad .492 \quad .296]$ **31.** $S_1 = [.24 \quad .37 \quad .39]$; $S_2 = [.241 \quad .446 \quad .313]$

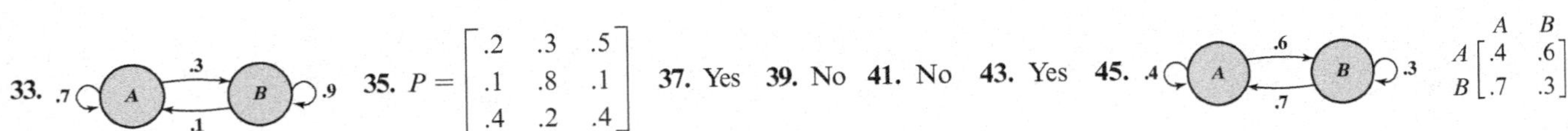

33. (state diagram) **35.** $P = \begin{bmatrix} .2 & .3 & .5 \\ .1 & .8 & .1 \\ .4 & .2 & .4 \end{bmatrix}$ **37.** Yes **39.** No **41.** No **43.** Yes **45.** $\begin{matrix} & A & B \\ A & .4 & .6 \\ B & .7 & .3 \end{matrix}$

47. No **49.** 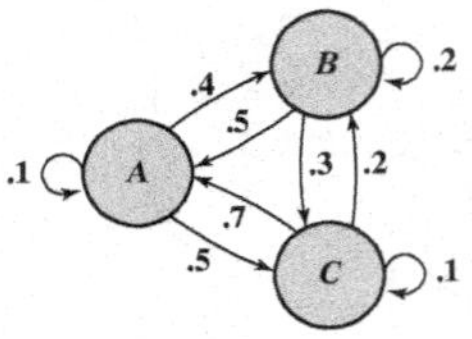 $\begin{matrix} & A & B & C \\ A & .1 & .4 & .5 \\ B & .5 & .2 & .3 \\ C & .7 & .2 & .1 \end{matrix}$ **51.** $a = .5, b = .6, c = .7$ **53.** $a = .7, b = 1, c = .2$ **55.** No

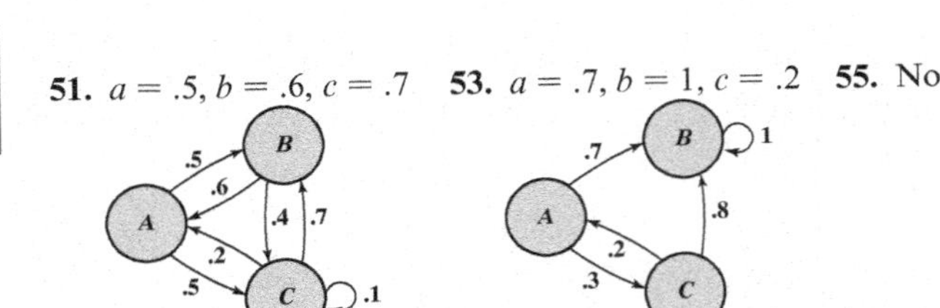

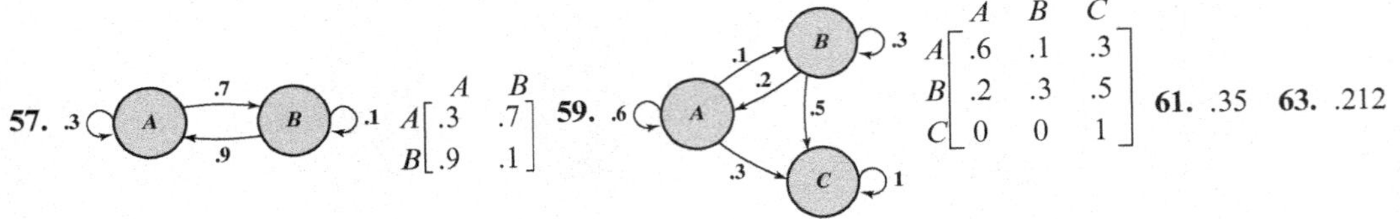

57. $\begin{matrix} & A & B \\ A & .3 & .7 \\ B & .9 & .1 \end{matrix}$ **59.** $\begin{matrix} & A & B & C \\ A & .6 & .1 & .3 \\ B & .2 & .3 & .5 \\ C & 0 & 0 & 1 \end{matrix}$ **61.** .35 **63.** .212

65. $S_2 = \begin{matrix} A & B & C \\ [.43 & .35 & .22] \end{matrix}$; the probabilities of going from state A to states A, B, and C in two trials

67. $S_3 = \begin{matrix} A & B & C \\ [.212 & .298 & .49] \end{matrix}$; the probabilities of going from state C to states A, B, and C in three trials

71. $P^4 = \begin{matrix} & A & B & C \\ A & .36 & .16 & .48 \\ B & .6 & 0 & .4 \\ C & .4 & .24 & .36 \end{matrix}$; $S_4 = \begin{matrix} A & B & C \\ [.452 & .152 & .396] \end{matrix}$

75. (A) $\begin{matrix} & A & B & C & D \\ A & .0154 & .3534 & .0153 & .6159 \\ B & 0 & 1 & 0 & 0 \\ C & .0102 & .2962 & .0103 & .6833 \\ D & 0 & 0 & 0 & 1 \end{matrix}$ (B) .6159 (C) .2962 (D) 0

79. (A) R = rain, R' = no rain (B) $\begin{matrix} & R & R' \\ R & .4 & .6 \\ R' & .06 & .94 \end{matrix}$ (C) Saturday: .196; Sunday: .12664

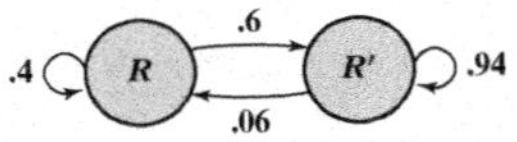

81. (A)

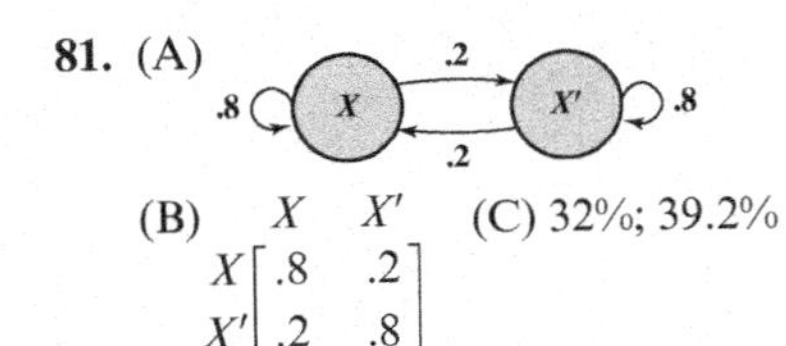

(B) $\begin{matrix} & X & X' \\ X & .8 & .2 \\ X' & .2 & .8 \end{matrix}$ (C) 32%; 39.2%

83. (A) N = National Property, U = United Family, O = other companies

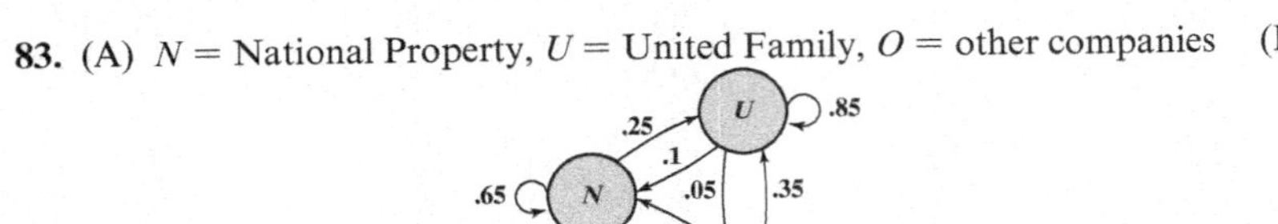

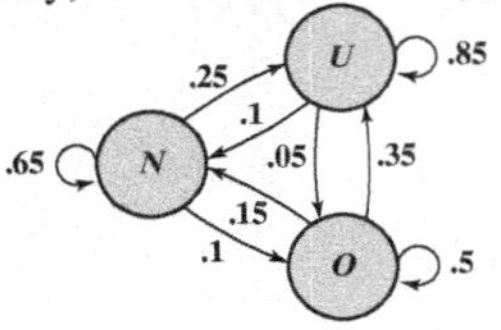

(B) $\begin{matrix} & N & U & O \\ N & .65 & .25 & .1 \\ U & .1 & .85 & .05 \\ C & .15 & .35 & .5 \end{matrix}$ (C) 38.5%; 32% (D) 45%; 53.65%

85. (A) B = beginning agent, I = intermediate agent, T = terminated agent, Q = qualified agent

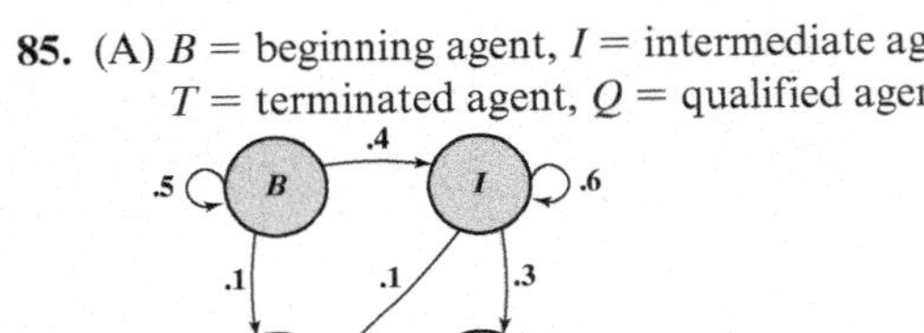

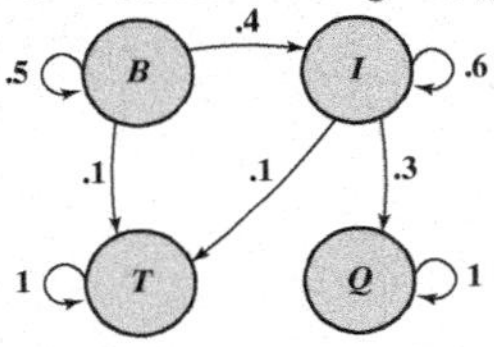

(B) $\begin{matrix} & B & I & T & Q \\ B & .5 & .4 & .1 & 0 \\ I & 0 & .6 & .1 & .3 \\ T & 0 & 0 & 1 & 0 \\ Q & 0 & 0 & 0 & 1 \end{matrix}$ (C) .12; .3612

87. (A) $\begin{array}{c} \\ HMO \\ PPO \\ FFS \end{array}\begin{array}{c} \begin{array}{ccc} HMO & PPO & FFS \end{array} \\ \begin{bmatrix} .8 & .15 & .05 \\ .2 & .7 & .1 \\ .25 & .3 & .45 \end{bmatrix} \end{array}$ (B) HMO: 34.75%; PPO: 37%; FFS: 28.25% (C) HMO: 42.2625%; PPO: 39.5875%; FFS: 18.15% **89.** (A) $\begin{array}{c} \\ H \\ R \end{array}\begin{array}{c} \begin{array}{cc} H & R \end{array} \\ \begin{bmatrix} .847 & .153 \\ .174 & .826 \end{bmatrix} \end{array}$ (B) 45.6% (C) 49.8%

Exercises 6.2, page 197

1. $\begin{bmatrix} 1 & 0 \\ 0 & 0 \end{bmatrix}$ **3.** $\begin{bmatrix} 1 & 0 \\ 0 & 1 \end{bmatrix}$ **5.** $\begin{bmatrix} 1 & 0 & 0 \\ 0 & 0 & 0 \\ 0 & 0 & 1 \end{bmatrix}$ **7.** $\begin{bmatrix} 0 & 0 & 0 \\ 0 & 0 & 0 \\ 0 & 0 & 0 \end{bmatrix}$ **9.** Yes **11.** No **13.** No **15.** Yes **17.** No **19.** Yes **21.** No

23. $S = [.4 \quad .6]$; $\overline{P} = \begin{bmatrix} .4 & .6 \\ .4 & .6 \end{bmatrix}$ **25.** $S = [.375 \quad .625]$; $\overline{P} = \begin{bmatrix} .375 & .625 \\ .375 & .625 \end{bmatrix}$ **27.** $S = [.3 \quad .5 \quad .2]$; $\overline{P} = \begin{bmatrix} .3 & .5 & .2 \\ .3 & .5 & .2 \\ .3 & .5 & .2 \end{bmatrix}$

29. $S = [.6 \quad .24 \quad .16]$; $\overline{P} = \begin{bmatrix} .6 & .24 & .16 \\ .6 & .24 & .16 \\ .6 & .24 & .16 \end{bmatrix}$ **31.** $SP = [.2 \quad .5]$; no, the sum of the entries in S is not 1.

33. $SP = [0 \quad 0]$; no, the sum of the entries in S is not 1 **35.** False **37.** True **39.** False

41. (A) [diagram: Red ⇄ Blue; Red→Red .4, Red→Blue .6, Blue→Red .2, Blue→Blue .8] (B) $\begin{array}{c} \\ Red \\ Blue \end{array}\begin{array}{c} \begin{array}{cc} Red & Blue \end{array} \\ \begin{bmatrix} .4 & .6 \\ .2 & .8 \end{bmatrix} \end{array}$ (C) $[.25 \quad .75]$; in the long run, the red urn will be selected 25% of the time and the blue urn 75% of the time. **43.** (A) The state matrices alternate between $[.2 \quad .8]$ and $[.8 \quad .2]$; so they do not approach any one matrix. (B) The state matrices are all equal to S_0, so S_0 is a stationary matrix. (C) The powers of P alternate between P and I (the 2×2 identity); so they do not approach a limiting matrix. (D) Parts (B) and (C) of Theorem 1 are not valid for this matrix. Since P is not regular, this is not a contradiction. **45.** (A) Since P is not regular, it may have more than one stationary matrix. (B) $[.5 \quad 0 \quad .5]$ is another stationary matrix. (C) P has an infinite number of stationary matrices. **47.** 72.5%

49. (A) $S_1 = [.512 \quad .488]$; $S_2 = [.568 \quad .432]$; $S_3 = [.609 \quad .391]$; $S_4 = [.639 \quad .361]$

(B)

Year	Data (%)	Model (%)
1970	43.3	43.3
1980	51.5	51.2
1990	57.5	56.8
2000	59.8	60.9
2010	58.5	63.9

(C) 71.4%

51. GTT: 25%; NCJ: 25%; Dash: 50% **53.** Poor: 20%; satisfactory: 40%; preferred: 40% **55.** Stationary matrix $= [.25 \quad .50 \quad .25]$ **57.** (A) $[.25 \quad .75]$ (B) 42.5%; 51.25% (C) 60% rapid transit; 40% automobile

59. (A) $S_1 = [.334 \quad .666]$; $S_2 = [.343 \quad .657]$; $S_3 = [.347 \quad .653]$; $S_4 = [.349 \quad .651]$ (B)

Year	Data (%)	Model (%)
1970	30.9	30.9
1980	33.3	33.4
1990	34.4	34.3
2000	35.6	34.7
2010	37.1	34.9

(C) 35%

Exercises 6.3, page 210

1. B, C **3.** No absorbing states **5.** A, D **7.** B is an absorbing state; absorbing chain **9.** C is an absorbing state; not an absorbing chain

11. No **13.** Yes **15.** Yes **17.** No **19.** Yes **21.** $\begin{array}{c} \\ B \\ A \\ C \end{array}\begin{array}{c} \begin{array}{ccc} B & A & C \end{array} \\ \begin{bmatrix} 1 & 0 & 0 \\ .5 & .2 & .3 \\ .1 & .5 & .4 \end{bmatrix} \end{array}$ **23.** $\begin{array}{c} \\ B \\ D \\ A \\ C \end{array}\begin{array}{c} \begin{array}{cccc} B & D & A & C \end{array} \\ \begin{bmatrix} 1 & 0 & 0 & 0 \\ 0 & 1 & 0 & 0 \\ .4 & .1 & .3 & .2 \\ .4 & .3 & 0 & .3 \end{bmatrix} \end{array}$ **25.** $\begin{array}{c} \\ C \\ A \\ B \end{array}\begin{array}{c} \begin{array}{ccc} C & A & B \end{array} \\ \begin{bmatrix} 1 & 0 & 0 \\ .5 & .2 & .3 \\ 0 & 1 & 0 \end{bmatrix} \end{array}$

27. $\begin{array}{c} \\ B \\ D \\ A \\ C \end{array}\begin{array}{c} \begin{array}{cccc} B & D & A & C \end{array} \\ \begin{bmatrix} 1 & 0 & 0 & 0 \\ 0 & 1 & 0 & 0 \\ .2 & .4 & .1 & .3 \\ .2 & .1 & .5 & .2 \end{bmatrix} \end{array}$

29. $\overline{P} = \begin{array}{c} \\ A \\ B \\ C \end{array}\begin{array}{c} \begin{array}{ccc} A & B & C \end{array} \\ \begin{bmatrix} 1 & 0 & 0 \\ 0 & 1 & 0 \\ .2 & .8 & 0 \end{bmatrix} \end{array}$; $P(C \text{ to } A) = .2$; $P(C \text{ to } B) = .8$. It will take an avg. of 2 trials to go from C to either A or B.

31. $\overline{P} = \begin{array}{c} \\ A \\ B \\ C \end{array}\begin{array}{c} \begin{array}{ccc} A & B & C \end{array} \\ \begin{bmatrix} 1 & 0 & 0 \\ 1 & 0 & 0 \\ 1 & 0 & 0 \end{bmatrix} \end{array}$; $P(B \text{ to } A) = 1$; $P(C \text{ to } A) = 1$. It will take an avg. of 4 trials to go from B to A, and an avg. of 3 trials to go from C to A.

33. $\overline{P} = \begin{array}{c} \\ A \\ B \\ C \\ D \end{array}\begin{array}{c} \begin{array}{cccc} A & B & C & D \end{array} \\ \begin{bmatrix} 1 & 0 & 0 & 0 \\ 0 & 1 & 0 & 0 \\ .36 & .64 & 0 & 0 \\ .44 & .56 & 0 & 0 \end{bmatrix} \end{array}$; $P(C \text{ to } A) = .36$; $P(C \text{ to } B) = .64$; $P(D \text{ to } A) = .44$; $P(D \text{ to } B) = .56$. It will take an avg. of 3.2 trials to go from C to either A or B, and an avg. of 2.8 trials to go from D to either A or B.

35. (A) $[.2 \quad .8 \quad 0]$ (B) $[.26 \quad .74 \quad 0]$ **37.** (A) $[1 \quad 0 \quad 0]$ (B) $[1 \quad 0 \quad 0]$ **39.** (A) $[.44 \quad .56 \quad 0 \quad 0]$ (B) $[.36 \quad .64 \quad 0 \quad 0]$ (C) $[.408 \quad .592 \quad 0 \quad 0]$ (D) $[.384 \quad .616 \quad 0 \quad 0]$ **41.** False **43.** False **45.** True **47.** False

49. $\begin{array}{c} \\ A \\ B \\ C \\ D \end{array}\begin{array}{c} \begin{array}{cccc} A & B & C & D \end{array} \\ \begin{bmatrix} 0 & .52 & 0 & .48 \\ 0 & 1 & 0 & 0 \\ 0 & .36 & 0 & .64 \\ 0 & 0 & 0 & 1 \end{bmatrix} \end{array}$

51. (A) 75% (B) 12.5% (C) 7.5 months **53.** (A) Company A: 30%; company B: 15%; company C: 55% (B) 5 yr **55.** (A) 91.52% (B) 4.96% (C) 6.32 days **57.** (A) .375 (B) 1.75 exits

Chapter 6 Review Exercises, page 214

1. $S_1 = \begin{array}{c} \begin{array}{cc} A & B \end{array} \\ [.32 \quad .68] \end{array}$; $S_2 = \begin{array}{c} \begin{array}{cc} A & B \end{array} \\ [.328 \quad .672] \end{array}$. The probability of being in state A after one trial is .32 and after two trials is .328; the probability of being in state B after one trial is .68 and after two trials is .672. *(6.1)* **2.** State A is absorbing; chain is absorbing. *(6.2, 6.3)* **3.** No absorbing states; chain is regular. *(6.2, 6.3)* **4.** No absorbing states; chain is neither. *(6.2, 6.3)* **5.** States B and C are absorbing; chain is absorbing. *(6.2, 6.3)* **6.** States A and B are absorbing; chain is neither. *(6.2, 6.3)*

7. $\begin{array}{c} \\ A \\ B \\ C \end{array}\begin{array}{c} \begin{array}{ccc} A & B & C \end{array} \\ \begin{bmatrix} 0 & 1 & 0 \\ .1 & 0 & .9 \\ 0 & 1 & 0 \end{bmatrix} \end{array}$; No absorbing states; chain is neither. *(6.1, 6.2, 6.3)*

8. $\begin{array}{c} \\ A \\ B \\ C \end{array}\begin{array}{c} \begin{array}{ccc} A & B & C \end{array} \\ \begin{bmatrix} 0 & 1 & 0 \\ .1 & .2 & .7 \\ 0 & 0 & 1 \end{bmatrix} \end{array}$; C is absorbing; chain is absorbing. *(6.1, 6.2, 6.3)*

9. $\begin{array}{c} \\ A \\ B \\ C \end{array}\begin{array}{c} \begin{array}{ccc} A & B & C \end{array} \\ \begin{bmatrix} 0 & 0 & 1 \\ .1 & .2 & .7 \\ 0 & 1 & 0 \end{bmatrix} \end{array}$; No absorbing states; chain is regular. *(6.1, 6.2, 6.3)*

10. $\begin{array}{c} \\ A \\ B \\ C \\ D \end{array}\begin{array}{c} \begin{array}{cccc} A & B & C & D \end{array} \\ \begin{bmatrix} .3 & .2 & 0 & .5 \\ 0 & 1 & 0 & 0 \\ 0 & 0 & .2 & .8 \\ 0 & 0 & .3 & .7 \end{bmatrix} \end{array}$; B is absorbing; chain is neither. *(6.1, 6.2, 6.3)*

11. 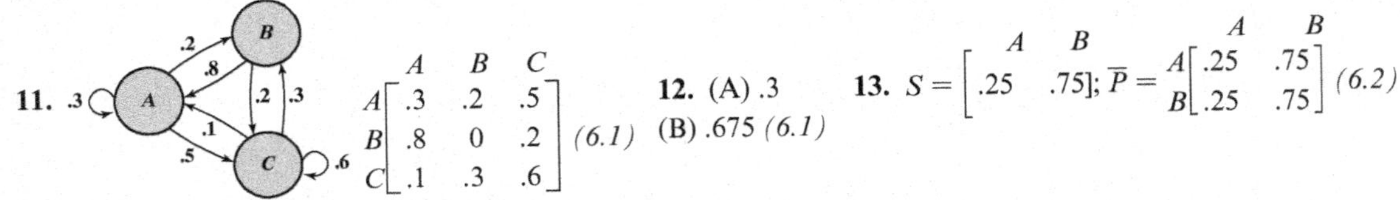

$\begin{array}{c} \\ A \\ B \\ C \end{array}\begin{array}{c} \begin{array}{ccc} A & B & C \end{array} \\ \begin{bmatrix} .3 & .2 & .5 \\ .8 & 0 & .2 \\ .1 & .3 & .6 \end{bmatrix} \end{array}$ *(6.1)*

12. (A) .3 (B) .675 *(6.1)*

13. $S = \begin{array}{c} \begin{array}{cc} A & B \end{array} \\ [.25 \quad .75] \end{array}$; $\overline{P} = \begin{array}{c} \\ A \\ B \end{array}\begin{array}{c} \begin{array}{cc} A & B \end{array} \\ \begin{bmatrix} .25 & .75 \\ .25 & .75 \end{bmatrix} \end{array}$ *(6.2)*

14. $S = \begin{array}{c} \begin{array}{ccc} A & B & C \end{array} \\ [.4 \quad .48 \quad .12] \end{array}$; $\overline{P} = \begin{array}{c} \\ A \\ B \\ C \end{array}\begin{array}{c} \begin{array}{ccc} A & B & C \end{array} \\ \begin{bmatrix} .4 & .48 & .12 \\ .4 & .48 & .12 \\ .4 & .48 & .12 \end{bmatrix} \end{array}$ *(6.2)*

15. $\begin{array}{c} \\ A \\ B \\ C \end{array}\begin{array}{c} \begin{array}{ccc} A & B & C \end{array} \\ \begin{bmatrix} 1 & 0 & 0 \\ 0 & 1 & 0 \\ .75 & .25 & 0 \end{bmatrix} \end{array}$; $P(C \text{ to } A) = .75$; $P(C \text{ to } B) = .25$. It takes an average of 2.5 trials to go from C to an absorbing state. *(6.3)*

16. $\begin{array}{c} \\ A \\ B \\ C \\ D \end{array}\begin{array}{c} \begin{array}{cccc} A & B & C & D \end{array} \\ \begin{bmatrix} 1 & 0 & 0 & 0 \\ 0 & 1 & 0 & 0 \\ .2 & .8 & 0 & 0 \\ .3 & .7 & 0 & 0 \end{bmatrix} \end{array}$; $P(C \text{ to } A) = .2$; $P(C \text{ to } B) = .8$; $P(D \text{ to } A) = .3$; $P(D \text{ to } B) = .7$. It takes an avg. of 2 trials to go from C to an absorbing state and an avg. of 3 trials to go from D to an absorbing state. *(6.3)*

21. $\begin{array}{c} \\ B \\ D \\ A \\ C \end{array}\begin{array}{c} \begin{array}{cccc} B & D & A & C \end{array} \\ \begin{bmatrix} 1 & 0 & 0 & 0 \\ 0 & 1 & 0 & 0 \\ .1 & .1 & .6 & .2 \\ .2 & .2 & .3 & .3 \end{bmatrix} \end{array}$ *(6.3)*

22. (A) $\begin{matrix} A & B & C \\ [.1 & .4 & .5] \end{matrix}$ (B) $\begin{matrix} A & B & C \\ [.1 & .4 & .5] \end{matrix}$ *(6.3)* **23.** (A) $\begin{matrix} A & B & C \\ [.25 & .75 & 0] \end{matrix}$ (B) $\begin{matrix} A & B & C \\ [.55 & .45 & 0] \end{matrix}$ *(6.3)*

24. No. Each row of P would contain a 0 and a 1, but none of the four matrices with this property is regular. *(6.2)* **25.** Yes; for example, $P = \begin{bmatrix} 0 & 0 & 1 \\ 0 & 0 & 1 \\ .2 & .3 & .5 \end{bmatrix}$ is regular. *(6.2)*

26. (A)

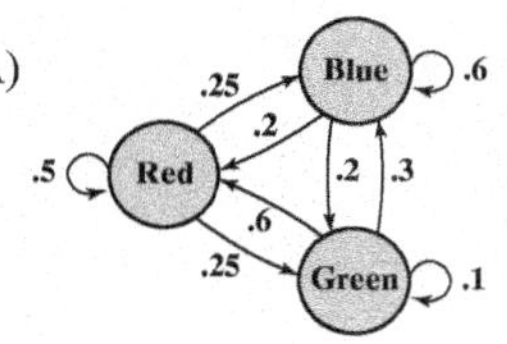

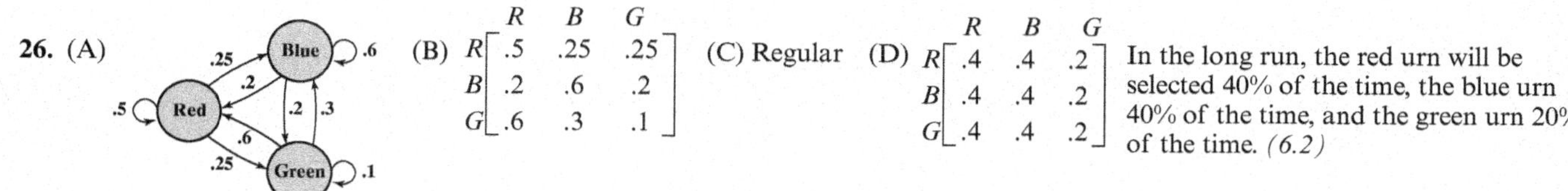

(B) $\begin{matrix} & R & B & G \\ R & .5 & .25 & .25 \\ B & .2 & .6 & .2 \\ G & .6 & .3 & .1 \end{matrix}$ (C) Regular (D) $\begin{matrix} & R & B & G \\ R & .4 & .4 & .2 \\ B & .4 & .4 & .2 \\ G & .4 & .4 & .2 \end{matrix}$ In the long run, the red urn will be selected 40% of the time, the blue urn 40% of the time, and the green urn 20% of the time. *(6.2)*

27. (A)

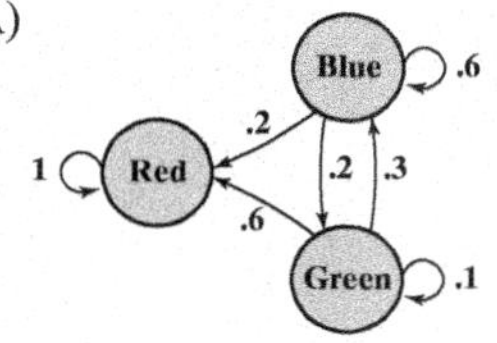

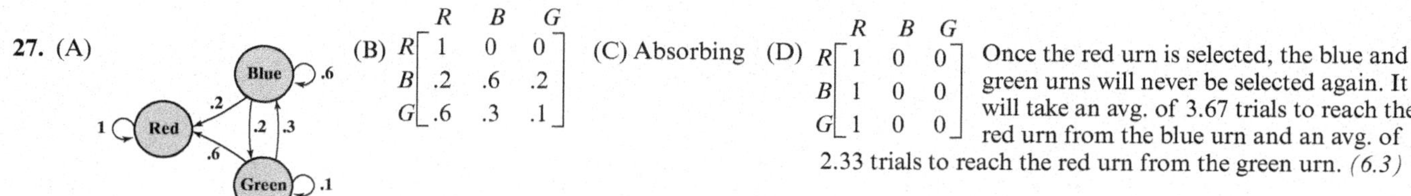

(B) $\begin{matrix} & R & B & G \\ R & 1 & 0 & 0 \\ B & .2 & .6 & .2 \\ G & .6 & .3 & .1 \end{matrix}$ (C) Absorbing (D) $\begin{matrix} & R & B & G \\ R & 1 & 0 & 0 \\ B & 1 & 0 & 0 \\ G & 1 & 0 & 0 \end{matrix}$ Once the red urn is selected, the blue and green urns will never be selected again. It will take an avg. of 3.67 trials to reach the red urn from the blue urn and an avg. of 2.33 trials to reach the red urn from the green urn. *(6.3)*

29. $\begin{bmatrix} 0 & 1 \\ 1 & 0 \end{bmatrix}$ is one example *(6.2)* **30.** $\begin{bmatrix} 1 & 0 \\ 0 & 1 \end{bmatrix}$ is one example *(6.3)* **31.** $\begin{bmatrix} .3 & .1 & .6 \\ .3 & .1 & .6 \\ .3 & .1 & .6 \end{bmatrix}$ is one example *(6.2)*

32. $\begin{bmatrix} 1 & 0 & 0 \\ 0 & 1 & 0 \\ 0 & 0 & 1 \end{bmatrix}$ is one example *(6.3)* **33.** If P is the transition matrix of an absorbing Markov chain with more than one state, then P has a row with 1 on the main diagonal and 0's elsewhere. Every power of P has that same row, so no power of P has all positive entries, and the Markov chain is not regular. *(6.2, 6.3)* **34.** If P is the transition matrix of a regular Markov chain, then some power of P has all positive entries. This is impossible for an absorbing Markov chain with more than one state (see Problem 33), so the Markov chain is not absorbing. *(6.2, 6.3)*

35. $SP = [.3 \quad .9]$; no, the sum of the entries in S is not 1. *(6.1)* **36.** No limiting matrix *(6.2, 6.3* **37.** $P = \begin{matrix} & A & B & C & D \\ A & .392 & .163 & .134 & .311 \\ B & .392 & .163 & .134 & .311 \\ C & .392 & .163 & .134 & .311 \\ D & .392 & .163 & .134 & .311 \end{matrix}$ *(6.2)*

38. (A)

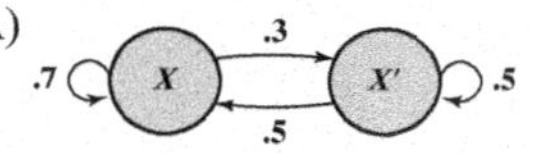

(B) $\begin{matrix} & X & X' \\ X & .7 & .3 \\ X' & .5 & .5 \end{matrix}$ (C) $\begin{matrix} X & X' \\ [.2 & .8] \end{matrix}$ (D) $\begin{matrix} X & X' \\ [.54 & .46] \end{matrix}$; 54% of the consumers will purchase brand X on the next purchase. (E) $\begin{matrix} X & X' \\ [.625 & .375] \end{matrix}$ (F) 62.5% *(6.2)*

39. (A) Brand A: 24%; brand B: 32%; brand C: 44% (B) 4 yr *(6.3)*

40. (A) $S_1 = [.48 \quad .52]$; $S_2 = [.66 \quad .34]$; $S_3 = [.76 \quad .24]$

(B)

Year	Data (%)	Model (%)
1995	14	14
2000	49	48
2005	68	66
2010	79	76

(C) 89% *(6.2)*

41. (A) 63.75% (B) 15% (C) 8.75 yr *(6.3)*

42. $\overline{P} = \begin{matrix} & Red & Pink & White \\ Red & 1 & 0 & 0 \\ Pink & 1 & 0 & 0 \\ White & 1 & 0 & 0 \end{matrix}$ *(6.3)*

43. (A) $S_1 = [.244 \quad .756]$; $S_2 = [.203 \quad .797]$; $S_3 = [.174 \quad .826]$

(B)

Year	Data (%)	Model (%)
1985	30.1	30.1
1995	24.7	24.4
2005	20.9	20.3
2010	19.3	17.4

(C) 10.3% *(6.2)*

Index